Searching for ORDER IN the COMPLEXITY of Evolving Worlds

ACKNOWLEDGMENTS

The SFI Press is supported by William H. Miller and the Miller Omega Program.

◊ ◊ ◊

To produce a mighty book, you must choose a mighty theme. No great and enduring volume can ever be written on the flea, though many there be who have tried it.

—HERMAN MELVILLE
Moby-Dick (1851)

These four volumes are a product of collective intelligence. They have come into existence through the coordinated insights of a global network of complexity scientists. We thank every one of them for their insights and efforts.

We thank our generous Board of Trustees, research foundations, and federal agencies for their support of science, reason, and debate.

We thank our colleagues Kate Joyce, Tim Taylor, Renée Tursi, Ellis Wylie, Katherine Mast, and Bronwynn Woodsworth for reading, commenting, adding to, and improving on the project.

We dedicate these four volumes to the friends and colleagues we have lost during their making: Phil Anderson, Dan Dennett, Herb Gintis, James Hartle, Erica Jen, Richard Lewontin, Dan Lynch, Robert May, Cormac McCarthy, David Padwa, James Pelkey, William Sick, Chuck Stevens, and Douglas White.

David C. Krakauer
Laura Egley Taylor
Sienna Latham
Zato Hebbert

FOUNDATIONAL PAPERS
IN COMPLEXITY SCIENCE

Volume Two

1962–1973

DAVID C. KRAKAUER

editor

THE SANTA FE INSTITUTE PRESS

1399 Hyde Park Road
Santa Fe, New Mexico 87501

Foundational Papers in Complexity Science, Vol. 2
ISBN (PAPERBACK): 978-1-947864-57-3
Library of Congress Control Number: 2024938011

The SFI Press is generously supported by
the Miller Omega Program.

SINCE WE CANNOT EXTRACT BEAUTY from life, let us at least extract beauty from our inability to extract beauty from life. Let us make of our failure a victory, something proud and positive, complete with pillars, majesty and spiritual acquiescence.

—FERNANDO PESSOA.
The Book of Disquiet
translated by Margaret Jull Costa (1991)

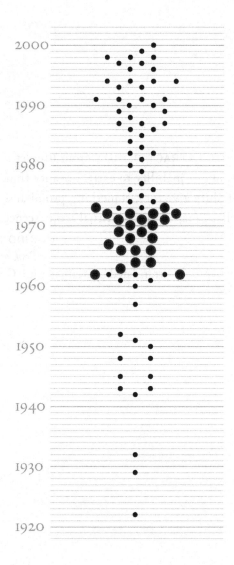

THE PAPERS

Large dots represent papers included in this volume; small dots are the remaining papers in the collection. Dots are positioned from bottom to top according to the year the paper was published. Volume 2 begins with Simon (1962) and ends with Granovetter (1973).

TABLE OF CONTENTS

— Volume Two —

Listed chronologically, with the introduction to each paper
followed by the (☞) annotated paper

VOLUME 2 CONTRIBUTORS

Carl T. Bergstrom *University of Washington*

Tanmoy Bhattacharya *Los Alamos National Laboratory; Santa Fe Institute*

James P. Crutchfield *University of California at Davis; Santa Fe Institute*

Simon DeDeo *Carnegie Mellon University; Santa Fe Institute*

Jennifer A. Dunne *Santa Fe Institute*

J. Doyne Farmer University of Oxford; *Santa Fe Institute*

Walter Fontana *Harvard University*

Neil Gershenfeld *Massachusetts Institute of Technology*

Philipp Honegger *Harvard University*

Sanjay Jain *University of Delhi; Santa Fe Institute*

Erica Jen *Santa Fe Institute*

Timothy A. Kohler *Washington State University; Santa Fe Institute*

Michael Lachmann *Santa Fe Institute*

Manfred D. Laubichler *Arizona State University; Santa Fe Institute*

Simon A. Levin *Princeton University*

Jon Machta *University of Massachusetts Amherst; Santa Fe Institute*

Cristopher Moore *Santa Fe Institute*

Daniel P. Schrag *Harvard University; Santa Fe Institute*

Ricard Solé *Universitat Pompeu Fabra; Santa Fe Institute*

Paul M.B. Vitányi *Santa Fe Institute*

Duncan J. Watts *University of Pennsylvania*

Geoffrey B. West *Santa Fe Institute*

H. Peyton Young *University of Oxford; London School of Economics and Political Science*

HOW TO CITE

When citing *Foundational Papers of Complexity Science* **in full**, please use the following approach:

BIBLIOGRAPHY:

Foundational Papers in Complexity Science. Edited by David C. Krakauer. 4 volumes. Santa Fe, NM: SFI Press, 2024.

LATEX:
```
@book{Krakauer_FP_2024,
      editor = {Krakauer, David C.},
      title = {Foundational Papers in Complexity Science},
      year = {2024},
      publisher = {SFI Press},
      location = {Santa Fe, NM}}
```

When citing a particular **volume** of *Foundational Papers in Complexity Science,* please use the following approach (*volume 1 serves as an example here*):

BIBLIOGRAPHY:

Foundational Papers in Complexity Science. Edited by David C. Krakauer. Volume 1. Santa Fe, NM: SFI Press, 2024.

LATEX:
```
@book{Krakauer_FP_1_2024,
      editor = {Krakauer, David C.},
      title = {Foundational Papers in Complexity Science},
      volume = {1},
      year = {2024},
      publisher = {SFI Press},
      location = {Santa Fe, NM}}
```

When citing a specific **chapter** from this project, please treat the introduction and the annotated paper as a single unit, as follows:

BIBLIOGRAPHY:

Bettencourt, Luís M.A. "Maximum Power as a Physical Principle of Evolution." In *Foundational Papers in Complexity Science.* Edited by David C. Krakauer. Volume 1. Santa Fe, NM: SFI Press, 2024, 1–15.

LATEX:

```
@incollection{Bettencourt_Lotka_2024,
      author = {Bettencourt, Luís M. A.},
      title = {Maximum Power as a Physical Principle of Evolution},
      year = {2024},
      editor = {Krakauer, David C.},
      booktitle = {Foundational Papers in Complexity Science},
      volume = {1},
      publisher = {SFI Press},
      location = {Santa Fe, NM}
      pages = {1—15}}
```

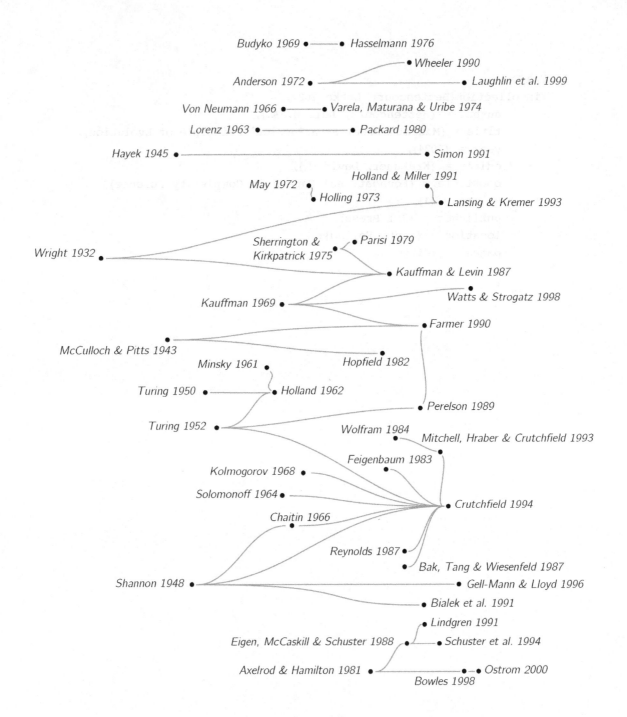

FOUNDATIONAL PAPERS: CITATION CONNECTIVITY

This visualization illustrates citation connections between foundational papers. Only papers that cite or are cited by other foundational papers are included. The papers are arranged left to right according to publication date. The gray connection lines signify that the later paper cites the earlier. *Examples*: Hasselmann 1976 cites Budyko 1969. Both Wheeler 1989 and Laughlin et al. 1999 reference Anderson 1972.

RATIONALE

1. *Foundational Papers in Complexity Science* is a project to discern the unity of an evolving inquiry.

2. After polling members of the extended network of Santa Fe Institute complexity researchers, we selected eighty-nine papers spanning just under a century that chart the formation of the field.

3. These papers—some classics, others cultish—collectively investigate the principles governing open, out-of-equilibrium systems that are self-organizing or selected, in the natural and cultural world.

4. The papers are ordered chronologically to establish patterns of influence and an emerging consensus.

5. Each paper has a unique introduction by a complexity researcher placing its ideas in historical context, and highlighting its perdurable contributions, and the new ideas that it has spawned.

6. Each paper is annotated by a researcher to underscore points where critical insights are made.

7. The year 2000 was established as the cut-off year for the *Foundational Papers*, recognizing that not enough time has elapsed to label subsequent work foundational.

8. These papers are being made available as a print-only four-volume set. The decision in favor of print is based on the prohibitive cost of licensing these papers as online materials.

9. A great deal of effort has gone into making these four volumes as beautiful and practical as possible in order to engage the senses and the mind.

10. *Searching for Order in the Complexity of Evolving Worlds*

—DAVID C. KRAKAUER AND THE SFI PRESS TEAM

BIRTH
June 15, 1916
Milwaukee,
Wisconsin

1920

1930

1933: Chicago World's Fair opens; attractions include the opening of the Museum of Science and Industry.

1938: Chester Barnard publishes The Functions of the Executive.

1940

1950: Claude Shannon publishes "Programming a Computer for Playing Chess."

1950

1956: At the Dartmouth Summer Research Project, Simon, Allen Newell, and Cliff Shaw present "Logic Theorist," a computer program which proves thirty-eight theorems from Principia Mathematica—to a lackluster response.

1960

SIMON 1962
Carnegie-Mellon University, Pittsburgh, Pennsylvania

1970

1978: Simon is awarded the Nobel Prize in Economics.

1980

1993: Carnegie Mellon professor Alex Hills and a team of his students set up the first-ever Wi-Fi network.

1990

1997: IBM's Deep Blue computer beats chess grandmaster and then World Chess Champion Garry Kasparov in a match under tournament conditions.

2000

DEATH
Feb. 9, 2001
Pittsburgh,
Pennsylvania,
complications
after removal of
a cancerous tumor

HERBERT ALEXANDER SIMON

[21]

THE ARCHITECT OF COMPLEXITY

Simon A. Levin, Princeton University

Any paper that elucidates a core concept in any field, especially a developing one, belongs on a list of must-reads for any scholar in that field. Herbert Simon's "The Architecture of Complexity" (1962) checks not one such box but four, interweaving notions of complexity, hierarchy, modularity, and near-decomposability in discussing the evolution and self-organization of complex systems.

Simon wrote his paper just as interest in general systems theory was beginning to accelerate. The Society for General Systems Research, today called the International Society for the Systems Sciences, formally began in 1955 as a truly cross-disciplinary forum, encompassing the physical, biological, and social sciences. Simon was clearly intrigued but cautious, writing, "We might well feel that, while the goal is laudable, systems of such diverse kinds could hardly be expected to have any nontrivial properties in common. Metaphor and analogy can be helpful, or they can be misleading. All depends on whether the similarities the metaphor captures are significant or superficial." He then goes on to extract some truly significant similarities that go well beyond metaphor. The distinction Simon makes is equally relevant today, as scientists move from one discipline to another, at times satisfying themselves with superficiality, at times deriving true progress by demonstrating the insights possible from cross-disciplinary perspectives, and at times exploring the interconnected nature, for example, of biological and social systems.

Simon defining what he means by a complex system, and his definition differs from classical definitions of complexity (Gell-Mann 1995). Simon's complex system is "one made up of a large number of parts that interact in a non-simple way," essentially what John Holland (1995) later referred to as a "complex adaptive system." Simon goes on to

H. A. Simon, "The Architecture of Complexity," *Proceedings of the American Philosophical Society* 106 (6), 467–482 (1962).

Reprinted with permission of the American Philosophical Society.

say that "in such systems, the whole is more than the sum of its parts, not in an ultimate, metaphysical sense, but in the important pragmatic sense that, given the properties of the parts and the laws of their interactions, it is not a trivial matter to infer the properties of the whole." In this, he anticipates by a decade Philip Anderson's (1972) foundational paper, "More Is Different."

One of the substantive sets of generalities about complex systems in general, and complex adaptive systems in particular, is comprised of the principles that make such systems robust to disturbances (Carlson and Doyle 2002; Levin 1999; Levin and Lubchenco 2008). Diversity and heterogeneity are broadly recognized essentials for the adaptive capacity of any system and are, for example, crucial elements of evolutionary theory (Fisher 1930). Redundancy is also crucial to persistence, providing a form of insurance when crucial elements are lost (Ehrlich and Ehrlich 1981). Modularity is the third essential leg of the stool, a topic to which I will return.

Simon turns first to a concept closely related to modularity, that of hierarchy, arguing that hierarchical systems will emerge much more rapidly than "non-hierarchic systems of similar size." Based on this conclusion, he infers that hierarchy itself should be an emergent property of developing systems. "Hierarchy, I shall argue, is one of the central structural themes that the architect of complexity uses." The level of reasoning is not by formal proof but by illustration and conjecture. Obviously this is an intriguing and persuasive line of argument, but one that is open to experimentation and mathematical exploration. Simon points out that his conception of hierarchy is more general than prevalent notions involving top-down control by a "boss," and he further introduces the notion of the span of a system, specifically "the number of sub-systems into which it is partitioned." He does not discuss the idea that systems might exhibit multiple overlapping hierarchies: In our societies, for example, we are labeled both by our familial origins and by our workplaces, and both interact to influence behaviors. Such networks extend further to the international order of nations, and overlapping hierarchies can be key to achieving international agreements (Hannam *et al.* 2015). The complexity of such arrangements was never more in evidence than in the international response to the Russian invasion of Ukraine in 2022.

For Simon, hierarchy and modularity seem inseparable concepts; indeed, they are closely related. But modularity is, I think, a more general concept, and can apply to the distribution of elements at a single level of organization. Simon's arguments regarding modularity are beautifully illustrated by his parable of two watchmakers, Hora and Tempus. One makes watches from beginning to end, never finishing because interruptions force a restart each time. The other completes modules in the process of construction, then stores them for an eventual second step in the hierarchy, assembly. (Thus, in this parable, the notions of modularity and hierarchy are intertwined.) Like one who saves her work in a word-processed manuscript, the second watchmaker never has to retreat farther than to the last module, and watches are completed. Modularity thus protects against loss, and also provides building blocks for future growth (Hartwell *et al.* 1999; Keohane and Ostrom 1994; Ostrom 2009). Modularity more generally provides protection against systemic risk and the contagious spread of disturbances, for example in forest fires, infectious diseases, and market disruptions (Carlson and Doyle 2002; May, Levin, and Sugihara 2008; Mollison and Levin 1995). The loss of modularity through exaggerated interconnectedness in banking systems was a primary factor underlying the market collapse of 2008 (Haldane and May 2011).

Simon concludes by reprising his key work with Albert Ando on the dynamics of near-decomposable systems (Simon and Ando 1961) (Simon and Ando 1961), laying the foundation for the separation of time scales in such systems because intra-cluster dynamics occur on much faster time scales than inter-cluster dynamics. This allows a very powerful algorithmic approach to such systems, and has stimulated work on coarse-graining and aggregation in complex systems (Iwasa, Andreasen, and Levin 1987; Iwasa, Levin, and Andreasen 1989; Li and Rabitz 1991).

Simon writes elegantly and inspirationally, and "The Architecture of Complexity" is rich with insights as relevant today as when the paper was written sixty years ago. ☙

Acknowledgments

I am pleased to acknowledge support under a gift from William H. Miller III to Princeton University, and grants from the National Science Foundation (DMS-1951358) and the Army Research Office (W911NF-19-1-0325).

REFERENCES

Anderson, P. W. 1972. "More Is Different." *Science* 177 (4047): 393–396. https://doi.org/10.1126/science.177.4047.393.

Carlson, J. M., and J. Doyle. 2002. "Complexity and Robustness." *Proceedings of the National Academy of Sciences* 99 (supplement 1): 2538–2545. https://doi.org/10.1073/pnas.012582499.

Ehrlich, P. R., and A. H. Ehrlich. 1981. *Extinction: The Causes and Consequences of the Disappearance of Species.* New York, NY: Random House.

Fisher, R. A. 1930. *The Genetic Theory of Natural Selection.* Oxford, UK: Clarendon Press.

Gell-Mann, M. 1995. "Remarks on Simplicity and Complexity." *Complexity* 1 (1): 16–19. https://doi.org/10.1002/cplx.6130010105.

Haldane, A. G., and R. M. May. 2011. "Systemic Risk in Banking Ecosystems." *Nature* 469:351–355. https://doi.org/10.1038/nature09659.

Hannam, P. M., V. V. Vasconcelos, S. A. Levin, and J. M. Pacheco. 2015. "Incomplete Cooperation and Co-Benefits: Deepending Climate Cooperation with a Proliferation of Small Agreements." *Climactic Change* 144:65–79. https://doi.org/10.1007/s10584-015-1511-2.

Hartwell, L. H., J. J. Hopfield, S. Leibler, and A. W. Murray. 1999. "From Molecular to Modular Cell Biology." *Nature* 402:C47–C52. https://doi.org/10.1038/35011540.

Holland, J. 1995. *Hidden Order: How Adaptation Builds Complexity.* Reading, MA: Addison-Wesley.

Iwasa, Y., V. Andreasen, and S. A. Levin. 1987. "Aggregation in Model Ecosystems: I. Perfect Aggregation." *Ecoogical Modelling* 37 (3–4): 287–302. https://doi.org/10.1016/0304-3800(87)90030-5.

Iwasa, Y., S. A. Levin, and V. Andreasen. 1989. "Aggregation in Model Ecosystems: II. Approximate Aggregation." *Mathematical Medicine and Biology: A Journal of the IMA* 6 (1): 1–23. https://doi.org/10.1093/imammb/6.1.1-a.

Keohane, R., and E. Ostrom. 1994. "Local Commons and Global Interdependence: Heterogeneity and Cooperation in 2 Domains." *Journal of Theoretical Politics* 6 (4): 403–428. https://doi.org/10.1177/0951692894006004001.

Levin, S. A. 1999. *Fragile Dominion: Complexity and the Commons.* Reading, MA: Perseus Books.

Levin, S. A., and J. Lubchenco. 2008. "Resilience, Robustness, and Marine Ecosystem–Based Management." *Bioscience* 58 (1): 27–32. https://doi.org/10.1641/B580107.

Li, G., and H. Rabitz. 1991. "A General Analysis of Lumping." In *Kinetic and Thermodynamic Lumping of Multicomponent Mixtures,* edited by G. Astarita and S. Sandler, 49–62. Amsterdam, Netherlands: Elsevier Science Publishers.

May, R. M., S. A. Levin, and G. Sugihara. 2008. "Ecology for Bankers." *Nature* 451:893–895. https://doi.org/10.1038/451893a.

Mollison, D., and S. A. Levin. 1995. "Spatial Dynamics of Parasitism." In *Ecology of Infectious Diseases in Natural Populations,* edited by B. T. Grenfell and A. P. Dobson, 384–398. Cambridge, UK: Cambridge University Press.

Ostrom, E. 2009. *A Polycentric Approach for Coping with Climate Change.* Working Paper, World Bank Policy Research Working Paper 5095. World Bank.

Paine, R. T. 1980. "Food Webs: Linkage, Interaction Strength, and Community Infrastructure." *Journal of Animal Ecology* 49 (3): 667–685. https://doi.org/10.2307/4220.

Simon, H. A. 1962. "The Architecture of Complexity." *Proceedings of the American Philosophical Society* 106:467–482. https://www.jstor.org/stable/985254.

Simon, H. A., and A. Ando. 1961. "Aggregation of Variables in Dynamic Systems." *Econometrica* 29:111–138. https://doi.org/0012-9682(196104)29:2<111:AOVIDS>2.0.CO;2-Z.

THE ARCHITECTURE OF COMPLEXITY

Herbert A. Simon, Carnegie Institute of Technology

Simon was one of the real pioneers in showing how to elucidate substantive commonalities across systems.

His recognition of the importance of this distinction was what elevated his work above so much justifiably forgotten general systems work.

A number of proposals have been advanced in recent years for the development of "general systems theory" which, abstracting from properties peculiar to physical, biological, or social systems, would be applicable to all of them.[1] We might well feel that, while the goal is laudable, systems of such diverse kinds could hardly be expected to have any nontrivial properties in common. Metaphor and analogy can be helpful, or they can be misleading. All depends on whether the similarities the metaphor captures are significant or superficial.

It may not be entirely vain, however, to search for common properties among diverse kinds of complex systems. The ideas that go by the name of cybernetics constitute, if not a theory, at least a point of view that has been proving fruitful over a wide range of applications.[2] It has been useful to look at the behavior of adaptive systems in terms of the concepts of feedback and homeostasis, and to analyze adaptiveness in terms of the theory of selective information.[3] The ideas of feedback and information provide a frame of reference for viewing a wide range of situations, just as do the ideas of evolution, of relativism, of axiomatic method, and of operationalism.

---

[1] See especially the yearbooks of the Society for General Systems Research. Prominent among the exponents of general systems theory are L. von Bertalanffy, K. Boulding, R. W. Gerard, and J. G. Miller. For a more skeptical view—perhaps too skeptical in the light of the present discussion—see H. A. Simon and A. Newell, Models: Their Uses and Limitations, *in* L. D. White, ed., *The State of the Social Sciences*, 66-83, Chicago, Univ. of Chicago Press, 1956.

[2] N. Wiener, *Cybernetics*, New York, John Wiley & Sons, 1948. For an imaginative forerunner, see A. J. Lotka, *Elements of Mathematical Biology*, New York, Dover Publications, 1951, first published in 1924 as *Elements of Physical Biology*.

[3] C. Shannon and W. Weaver, *The Mathematical Theory of Communication*, Urbana, Univ. of Illinois Press, 1949; W. R. Ashby, *Design for a Brain*, New York, John Wiley & Sons, 1952.

In this paper I should like to report on some things we have been learning about particular kinds of complex systems encountered in the behavioral sciences. The developments I shall discuss arose in the context of specific phenomena, but the theoretical formulations themselves make little reference to details of structure. Instead they refer primarily to the complexity of the systems under view without specifying the exact content of that complexity. Because of their abstractness, the theories may have relevance—application would be too strong a term—to other kinds of complex systems that are observed in the social, biological, and physical sciences.

In recounting these developments, I shall avoid technical detail, which can generally be found elsewhere. I shall describe each theory in the particular context in which it arose. Then, I shall cite some examples of complex systems, from areas of science other than the initial application, to which the theoretical framework appears relevant. In doing so, I shall make reference to areas of knowledge where I am not expert—perhaps not even literate. I feel quite comfortable in doing so before the members of this society, representing as it does the whole span of the scientific and scholarly endeavor. Collectively you will have little difficulty, I am sure, in distinguishing instances based on idle fancy or sheer ignorance from instances that cast some light on the ways in which complexity exhibits itself wherever it is found in nature. I shall leave to you the final judgment of relevance in your respective fields.

I shall not undertake a formal definition of "complex systems."[4] Roughly, by a complex system I mean one made up of a large number of parts that interact in a nonsimple way. In such systems, the whole is more than the sum of the parts, not in an ultimate, metaphysical sense, but in the important pragmatic sense that, given the properties of the parts and the laws of their interaction, it is not a trivial matter to infer the properties of the whole. In the face of complexity, an in-principle reductionist may be at the same time a pragmatic holist.[5]

Appropriately cautious, but we now know this to be true and powerful.

Perhaps thinking about what Holland termed "complex adaptive systems," a special class of complex systems.

"More is different," as Philip Anderson (1972) espoused.

---

[4] W. Weaver, in: "Science and Complexity," *American Scientist* 36: 536, 1948, has distinguished two kinds of complexity, disorganized and organized. We shall be primarily concerned with organized complexity.

[5] See also John R. Platt, "Properties of Large Molecules that Go beyond the Properties of their Chemical Sub-Groups," *Jour. Theoret. Biol.* 1: 342–358, 1961. Since the

The four sections that follow discuss four aspects of complexity. The first offers some comments on the frequency with which complexity takes the form of hierarchy—the complex system being composed of subsystems that, in turn, have their own subsystems, and so on. The second section theorizes about the relation between the structure of a complex system and the time required for it to emerge through evolutionary processes: specifically, it argues that hierarchic systems will evolve far more quickly than non-hierarchic systems of comparable size. The third section explores the dynamic properties of hierarchically-organized systems, and shows how they can be decomposed into subsystems in order to analyze their behavior. The fourth section examines the relation between complex systems and their descriptions.

Thus, the central theme that runs through my remarks is that complexity frequently takes the form of hierarchy, and that hierarchic systems have some common properties that are independent of their specific content. Hierarchy, I shall argue, is one of the central structural schemes that the architect of complexity uses.

Hierarchic Systems

By a *hierarchic system*, or hierarchy, I mean a system that is composed of interrelated subsystems, each of the latter being, in turn, hierarchic in structure until we reach some lowest level of elementary subsystem. In most systems in nature, it is somewhat arbitrary as to where we leave off the partitioning, and what subsystems we take as elementary. Physics makes much use of the concept of "elementary particle" although particles have a disconcerting tendency not to remain elementary very long. Only a couple of generations ago, the atoms themselves were elementary particles; today, to the nuclear physicist they are complex systems. For certain purposes of astronomy, whole stars, or even galaxies, can be regarded as elementary subsystems. In one kind of biological

This is a bold claim, which if true is a deep insight about evolution and self-organization. I'm not sure to what extent it has been tested empirically, though lots of theoretical papers have explored the claim, for example, through digital evolution simulations.

reductionism–holism issue is a major *cause de guerre* between scientists and humanists, perhaps we might even hope that peace could be negotiated between the two cultures along the lines of the compromise just suggested. As I go along, I shall have a little to say about complexity in the arts as well as in the natural sciences. I must emphasize the pragmatism of my holism to distinguish it sharply from the position taken by W. M. Elsasser in *The Physical Foundation of Biology*, New York, Pergamon Press, 1958.

research, a cell may be treated as an elementary subsystem; in another, a protein molecule; in still another, an amino acid residue.

Just why a scientist has a right to treat as elementary a subsystem that is in fact exceedingly complex is one of the questions we shall take up. For the moment, we shall accept the fact that scientists do this all the time, and that if they are careful scientists they usually get away with it.

Etymologically, the word "hierarchy" has had a narrower meaning than I am giving it here. The term has generally been used to refer to a complex system in which each of the subsystems is subordinated by an authority relation to the system it belongs to. More exactly, in a hierarchic formal organization, each system consists of a "boss" and a set of subordinate subsystems. Each of the subsystems has a "boss" who is the immediate subordinate of the boss of the system. We shall want to consider systems in which the relations among subsystems are more complex than in the formal organizational hierarchy just described. We shall want to include systems in which there is no relation of subordination among subsystems. (In fact, even in human organizations, the formal hierarchy exists only on paper; the real flesh-and-blood organization has many inter-part relations other than the lines of formal authority.) For lack of a better term, I shall use hierarchy in the broader sense introduced in the previous paragraphs, to refer to all complex systems analyzable into successive sets of subsystems, and speak of "formal hierarchy" when I want to refer to the more specialized concept.[6]

Here Simon raises the distinction between top-down and bottom-up control.

Social systems in particular, though, can have multiple overlapping hierarchies; individuals, for example, belong to family groups that may be parts of ethnic groups, etc., but also belong to social groups defined by schools or workplaces, etc. Much less theory exists for this. A single biological organism is more strictly hierarchically organized, demonstrating the difference between the roles of selection and self-organization; that is, the importance of the level of selection.

SOCIAL SYSTEMS

I have already given an example of one kind of hierarchy that is frequently encountered in the social sciences: a formal organization. Business firms, governments, universities all have a clearly visible parts-within-parts structure. But formal organizations are not the only, or even the most common, kind of social hierarchy. Almost all societies have elementary units called families, which may be grouped into

---

[6] The mathematical term "partitioning" will not do for what I call here a hierarchy; for the set of subsystems, and the successive subsets in each of these defines the partitioning, independently of any systems of relations among the subsets. By hierarchy I mean the partitioning in conjunction with the relations that hold among its parts.

villages or tribes, and these into larger groupings, and so on. If we make a chart of social interactions, of who talks to whom, the clusters of dense interaction in the chart will identify a rather well-defined hierarchic structure. The groupings in this structure may be defined operationally by some measure of frequency of interaction in this sociometric matrix.

BIOLOGICAL AND PHYSICAL SYSTEMS

The hierarchical structure of biological systems is a familiar fact. Taking the cell as the building block, we find cells organized into tissues, tissues into organs, organs into systems. Moving downward from the cell, well-defined subsystems—for example, nucleus, cell membrane, microsomes, mitochondria, and so on—have been identified in animal cells.

The hierarchic structure of many physical systems is equally clear-cut. I have already mentioned the two main series. At the microscopic level we have elementary particles, atoms, molecules, macromolecules. At the macroscopic level we have satellite systems, planetary systems, galaxies. Matter is distributed throughout space in a strikingly non-uniform fashion. The most nearly random distributions we find, gases, are not random distributions of elementary particles but random distributions of complex systems, i.e. molecules.

A considerable range of structural types is subsumed under the term hierarchy as I have defined it. By this definition, a diamond is hierarchic, for it is a crystal structure of carbon atoms that can be further decomposed into protons, neutrons, and electrons. However, it is a very "flat" hierarchy, in which the number of first-order subsystems belonging to the crystal can be indefinitely large. A volume of molecular gas is a flat hierarchy in the same sense. In ordinary usage, we tend to reserve the word hierarchy for a system that is divided into a *small or moderate number* of subsystems, each of which may be further subdivided. Hence, we do not ordinarily think of or refer to a diamond or a gas as a hierarchic structure. Similarly, a linear polymer is simply a chain, which may be very long, of identical subparts, the monomers. At the molecular level it is a very flat hierarchy.

In discussing formal organizations, the number of subordinates who report directly to a single boss is called his *span of control*. I will speak analogously of the *span* of a system, by which I shall mean the number of subsystems into which it is partitioned. Thus, a hierarchic system is flat at a given level if it has a wide span at that level. A diamond has a wide span at the crystal level, but not at the next level down, the molecular level.

In most of our theory construction in the following sections we shall focus our attention on hierarchies of moderate span, but from time to time I shall comment on the extent to which the theories might or might not be expected to apply to very flat hierarchies.

There is one important difference between the physical and biological hierarchies, on the one hand, and social hierarchies, on the other. Most physical and biological hierarchies are described in spatial terms. We detect the organelles in a cell in the way we detect the raisins in a cake—they are "visibly" differentiated substructures localized spatially in the larger structure. On the other hand, we propose to identify social hierarchies not by observing who lives close to whom but by observing who interacts with whom. These two points of view can be reconciled by defining hierarchy in terms of intensity of interaction, but observing that in most biological and physical systems relatively intense interaction implies relative spatial propinquity. One of the interesting characteristics of nerve cells and telephone wires is that they permit very specific strong interactions at great distances. To the extent that interactions are channeled through specialized communications and transportation systems, spatial propinquity becomes less determinative of structure.

But individuals have multiple interaction networks for different purposes; hence they belong to multiple overlapping hierarchies.

SYMBOLIC SYSTEMS

One very important class of systems has been omitted from my examples thus far: systems of human symbolic production. A book is a hierarchy in the sense in which I am using that term. It is generally divided into chapters, the chapters into sections, the sections into paragraphs, the paragraphs into sentences, the sentences into clauses and phrases, the clauses and phrases into words. We may take the words as our elementary units, or further subdivide them, as the linguist often does, into smaller units. If the book is narrative in character, it may divide into "episodes" instead of sections, but divisions there will be.

Hierarchies in books differ from those in spoken languages. Do we talk in paragraphs? What accounts for the differences?

The hierarchic structure of music, based on such units as movements, parts, themes, phrases, is well known. The hierarchic structure of products of the pictorial arts is more difficult to characterize, but I shall have something to say about it later.

The Evolution of Complex Systems

Let me introduce the topic of evolution with a parable. There once were two watchmakers, named Hora and Tempus, who manufactured very fine watches. Both of them were highly regarded, and the phones in their workshops rang frequently—new customers were constantly calling them. However, Hora prospered, while Tempus became poorer and poorer and finally lost his shop. What was the reason?

The watches the men made consisted of about $1,000$ parts each. Tempus had so constructed his that if he had one partly assembled and had to put it down—to answer the phone say—it immediately fell to pieces and had to be reassembled from the elements. The better the customers liked his watches, the more they phoned him, the more difficult it became for him to find enough uninterrupted time to finish a watch.

The watches that Hora made were no less complex than those of Tempus. But he had designed them so that he could put together subassemblies of about ten elements each. Ten of these subassemblies, again, could be put together into a larger subassembly; and a system of ten of the latter subassemblies constituted the whole watch. Hence, when Hora had to put down a partly assembled watch in order to answer the phone, he lost only a small part of his work, and he assembled his watches in only a fraction of the man-hours it took Tempus.

It is rather easy to make a quantitative analysis of the relative difficulty of the tasks of Tempus and Hora: Suppose the probability that an interruption will occur while a part is being added to an incomplete assembly is p. Then the probability that Tempus can complete a watch he has started without interruption is $(1 - p)^{1000}$—a very small number unless p is .001 or less. Each interruption will cost, on the average, the time to assemble $1/p$ parts (the expected number assembled before interruption). On the other hand, Hora has to complete one hundred eleven sub-assemblies of ten parts each. The probability that he will not be interrupted while completing any one of these is $(1 - p)^{10}$, and each interruption will cost only about the time required to assemble five parts.[7]

Now if p is about .01—that is, there is one chance in a hundred that either watchmaker will be interrupted while adding any one part to an assembly—then a straightforward calculation shows that it will take Tempus, on the average, about four thousand times as long to assemble a watch as Hora.

We arrive at the estimate as follows:

1. Hora must make 111 times as many complete assemblies per watch as Tempus; but,

2. Tempus will lose on the average 20 times as much work for each interrupted assembly as Hora [100 parts, on the average, as against 5]; and,

3. Tempus will complete an assembly only 44 times per million attempts $(.99^{1000} = 44 \times 10^{-6})$, while Hora will complete nine out of ten $(.99^{10} = 9 \times 10^{-1})$. Hence Tempus will have to make 20,000 as many attempts per completed assembly as Hora. $(9 \times 10^{-1})/(44 \times 10^{-6}) = 2 \times 10^4$. Multiplying these three ratios, we get:

$$1/111 \times 100/5 \times .99^{10}/.99^{1000} = 1/111 \times 20 \times 20,000 \sim 4,000.$$

---

[7] The speculations on speed of evolution were first suggested by H. Jacobson's application of information theory to estimating the time required for biological evolution. See his paper, "Information, Reproduction, and the Origin of Life," in *American Scientist* 43: 119-127, January, 1955. From thermodynamic considerations it is possible to estimate the amount of increase in entropy that occurs when a complex system decomposes into its elements. (See, for example, R. B. Setlow and E. C. Pollard, *Molecular Biophysics*, 63–65, Reading, Mass., Addison-Wesley Publishing Co., 1962, and references cited there.) But entropy is the logarithm of a probability, hence information, the negative of entropy, can be interpreted as the logarithm of the reciprocal of the probability—the "improbability," so to speak. The essential idea in Jacobson's model is that the expected time required for the system to reach a particular state is inversely proportional to the probability of the state—hence increases exponentially with the amount of information (negentropy) of the state.

Following this line of argument, but not introducing the notion of levels and stable subassemblies, Jacobson arrived at estimates of the time required for evolution so large as to make the event rather improbable. Our analysis, carried through in the same way, but with attention to the stable intermediate forms, produces very much smaller estimates.

Biological Evolution

There is strong evidence for the evolution of modules in biological evolution. See, for example, Hartwell *et al.* (1999).

What lessons can we draw from our parable for biological evolution? Let us interpret a partially completed subassembly of k elementary parts as the coexistence of k parts in a small volume—ignoring their relative orientations. The model assumes that parts are entering the volume at a constant rate, but that there is a constant probability, p, that the part will be dispersed before another is added, unless the assembly reaches a stable state. These assumptions are not particularly realistic. They undoubtedly underestimate the decrease in probability of achieving the assembly with increase in the size of the assembly. Hence the assumptions understate—probably by a large factor—the relative advantage of a hierarchic structure.

Although we cannot, therefore, take the numerical estimate seriously the lesson for biological evolution is quite clear and direct. The time required for the evolution of a complex form from simple elements depends critically on the numbers and distribution of potential intermediate stable forms. In particular, if there exists a hierarchy of potential stable "subassemblies," with about the same span, s, at each level of the hierarchy, then the time required for a subassembly can be expected to be about the same at each level—that is proportional to $1/(1 - p)^s$. The time required for the assembly of a system of n elements will be proportional to $\log_s n$, that is, to the number of levels in the system. One would say—with more illustrative than literal intent—that the time required for the evolution of multi-celled organisms from single-celled organisms might be of the same order of magnitude as the time required for the evolution of single-celled organisms from macromolecules. The same argument could be applied to the evolution of proteins from amino acids, of molecules from atoms, of atoms from elementary particles.

A whole host of objections to this oversimplified scheme will occur, I am sure, to every working biologist, chemist, and physicist. Before turning to matters I know more about, I shall mention three of these problems, leaving the rest to the attention of the specialists.

First, in spite of the overtones of the watchmaker parable, the theory assumes no teleological mechanism. The complex forms can arise from the simple ones by purely random processes. (I shall propose another model in a moment that shows this clearly.) Direction is provided to the scheme by the stability of the complex forms, once these come into existence. But this is nothing more than survival of the fittest—i.e., of the stable.

Second, not all large systems appear hierarchical. For example, most polymers—e.g., nylon—are simply linear chains of large numbers of identical components, the monomers. However, for present purposes we can simply regard such a structure as a hierarchy with a span of one—the limiting case. For a chain of any length represents a state of relative equilibrium.[8]

Third, the evolution of complex systems from simple elements implies nothing, one way or the other, about the change in entropy of the entire system. If the process absorbs free energy, the complex system will have a smaller entropy than the elements; if it releases free energy, the opposite will be true. The former alternative is the one that holds for most biological systems, and the net inflow of free energy has to be supplied from the sun or some other source if the second law of thermodynamics is not to be violated. For the evolutionary process we are describing, the equilibria of the intermediate states need have only local and not global stability, and they may be stable only in the steady state—that is, as long as there is an external source of free energy that may be drawn upon.[9]

Because organisms are not energetically closed systems, there is no way to deduce the direction, much less the rate, of evolution from classical thermodynamic considerations. All estimates indicate that the amount of entropy, measured in physical units, involved in the formation of a one-celled biological organism is trivially small—about

---

[8] There is a well-developed theory of polymer size, based on models of random assembly. See for example P. J. Flory, *Principles of Polymer Chemistry*, ch. 8, Ithaca, Cornell Univ. Press, 1953. Since *all* subassemblies in the polymerization theory are stable, limitation of molecular growth depends on "poisoning" of terminal groups by impurities or formation of cycles rather than upon disruption of partially-formed chains.

[9] This point has been made many times before, but it cannot be emphasized too strongly. For further discussion, see Setlow and Pollard, *op. cit.*, 49–64; E. Schrödinger, *What is Life?* Cambridge Univ. Press, 1945; and H. Linschitz, "The Information Content of a Bacterial Cell," in H. Questler, ed., *Information Theory in Biology*, 251–262, Urbana, Univ. of Illinois Press, 1953.

-10^{-11} cal/degree.[10] The "improbability" of evolution has nothing to do with this quantity of entropy, which is produced by every bacterial cell every generation. The irrelevance of quantity of information, in this sense, to speed of evolution can also be seen from the fact that exactly as much information is required to "copy" a cell through the reproductive process as to produce the first cell through evolution.

☞

Elinor and Vincent Ostrom's emphasis on polycentricity extends these arguments to social systems.

The effect of the existence of stable intermediate forms exercises a powerful effect on the evolution of complex forms that may be likened to the dramatic effect of catalysts upon reaction rates and steady state distribution of reaction products in open systems.[11] In neither case does the entropy change provide us with a guide to system behavior.

Problem Solving as Natural Selection

Let us turn now to some phenomena that have no obvious connection with biological evolution: human problem-solving processes. Consider, for example, the task of discovering the proof for a difficult theorem. The process can be—and often has been—described as a search through a maze. Starting with the axioms and previously proved theorems, various transformations allowed by the rules of the mathematical systems are attempted, to obtain new expressions. These are modified in turn until, with persistence and good fortune, a sequence or path of transformations is discovered that leads to the goal.

The process usually involves a great deal of trial and error. Various paths are tried; some are abandoned, others are pushed further. Before a solution is found, a great many paths of the maze may be explored. The more difficult and novel the problem, the greater is likely to be the amount of trial and error required to find a solution. At the same time, the trial and error is not completely random or blind; it is, in fact, rather highly selective. The new expressions that are obtained by transforming given ones are examined to see whether they represent progress toward the goal. Indications of progress spur further search

---

[10]See Linschitz, *op. cit.* This quantity, 10^{-11} cal/degree, corresponds to about 10^{13} bits of information.

[11]See H. Kacser, "Some Physico-Chemical Aspects of Biological Organization," Appendix, pp. 191–249 in C. H. Waddington, *The Strategy of the Genes*, London, George Allen & Unwin, 1957.

in the same direction; lack of progress signals the abandonment of a line of search. Problem solving requires *selective* trial and error.[12]

A little reflection reveals that cues signaling progress play the same role in the problem-solving process that stable intermediate forms play in the biological evolutionary process. In fact, we can take over the watchmaker parable and apply it also to problem solving. In problem solving, a partial result that represents recognizable progress toward the goal plays the role of a stable sub-assembly.

Suppose that the task is to open a safe whose lock has ten dials, each with one hundred possible settings, numbered from 0 to 99. How long will it take to open the safe by a blind trial-and-error search for the correct setting? Since there are 100^{10} possible settings, we may expect to examine about one-half of these, on the average, before finding the correct one—that is, fifty billion billion settings. Suppose, however, that the safe is defective, so that a click can be heard when any one dial is turned to the correct setting. Now each dial can be adjusted independently, and does not need to be touched again while the others are being set. The total number of settings that has to be tried is only 10×50, or five hundred. The task of opening the safe has been altered, by the cues the clicks provide, from a practically impossible one to a trivial one.[13]

A considerable amount has been learned in the past five years about the nature of the mazes that represent common human problem-

---

[12]See A. Newell, J. C. Shaw, and H. A. Simon, "Empirical Explorations of the Logic Theory Machine," *Proceedings of the 1957 Western Joint Computer Conference*, February, 1957, New York: Institute of Radio Engineers; "Chess-Playing Programs and the Problem of Complexity," IBM *Journal of Research and Development* 2: 320–335, October, 1958; and for a similar view of problem solving, W. R. Ashby, "Design for an Intelligence Amplifier," 215–233 in C. E. Shannon and J. McCarthy, *Automata Studies*, Princeton, Princeton Univ. Press, 1956.

[13]The clicking safe example was supplied by D. P. Simon. Ashby, *op. cit.*, 230, has called the selectivity involved in situations of this kind "selection by components." The even greater reduction in time produced by hierarchization in the clicking safe example, as compared with the watchmaker's metaphor, is due to the fact that a random *search* for the correct combination is involved in the former case, while in the latter the parts come together in the right order. It is not clear which of these metaphors provides the better model for biological evolution, but we may be sure that the watchmaker's metaphor gives an exceedingly conservative estimate of the savings due to hierarchization. The safe may give an excessively high estimate because it assumes all possible arrangements of the elements to be equally probable.

solving tasks—proving theorems, solving puzzles, playing chess, making investments, balancing assembly lines, to mention a few. All that we have learned about these mazes points to the same conclusion: that human problem solving, from the most blundering to the most insightful, involves nothing more than varying mixtures of trial and error and selectivity. The selectivity derives from various rules of thumb, or heuristics, that suggest which paths should be tried first and which leads are promising. We do not need to postulate processes more sophisticated than those involved in organic evolution to explain how enormous problem mazes are cut down to quite reasonable size.[14]

THE SOURCES OF SELECTIVITY

When we examine the sources from which the problem-solving system, or the evolving system, as the case may be, derives its selectivity, we discover that selectivity can always be equated with some kind of feedback of information from the environment.

Let us consider the case of problem solving first. There are two basic kinds of selectivity. One we have already noted: various paths are tried out, the consequences of following them are noted, and this information is used to guide further search. In the same way, in organic evolution, various complexes come into being, at least evanescently, and those that are stable provide new building blocks for further construction. It is this information about stable configurations, and not free energy or negentropy from the sun, that guides the process of evolution and provides the selectivity that is essential to account for its rapidity.

The second source of selectivity in problem solving is previous experience. We see this particularly clearly when the problem to be solved is similar to one that has been solved before. Then, by simply trying again the paths that led to the earlier solution, or their analogues, trial-and-error search is greatly reduced or altogether eliminated.

What corresponds to this latter kind of information in organic evolution? The closest analogue is reproduction. Once we reach the level of self-reproducing systems, a complex system, when it has once been

---

[14]A. Newell and H. A. Simon, "Computer Simulation of Human Thinking," *Science* 134: 2011–2017, December 22, 1961.

achieved, can be multiplied indefinitely. Reproduction in fact allows the inheritance of acquired characteristics, but at the level of genetic material, of course; i.e., only characteristics acquired by the genes can be inherited. We shall return to the topic of reproduction in the final section of this paper.

ON EMPIRES AND EMPIRE-BUILDING

We have not exhausted the categories of complex systems to which the watchmaker argument can reasonably be applied. Philip assembled his Macedonian empire and gave it to his son, to be later combined with the Persian subassembly and others into Alexander's greater system. On Alexander's death, his empire did not crumble to dust, but fragmented into some of the major subsystems that had composed it.

The watchmaker argument implies that if one would be Alexander, one should be born into a world where large stable political systems already exist. Where this condition was not fulfilled, as on the Scythian and Indian frontiers, Alexander found empire building a slippery business. So too, T. E. Lawrence's organizing of the Arabian revolt against the Turks was limited by the character of his largest stable building blocks, the separate, suspicious desert tribes.

The profession of history places a greater value upon the validated particular fact than upon tendentious generalization. I shall not elaborate upon my fancy, therefore, but will leave it to historians to decide whether anything can be learned for the interpretation of history from an abstract theory of hierarchic complex systems.

CONCLUSION: THE EVOLUTIONARY EXPLANATION OF HIERARCHY

We have shown thus far that complex systems will evolve from simple systems much more rapidly if there are stable intermediate forms than if there are not. The resulting complex forms in the former case will be hierarchic. We have only to turn the argument around to explain the observed predominance of hierarchies among the complex systems nature presents to us. Among possible complex forms, hierarchies are the ones that have the time to evolve. The hypothesis that complexity will be hierarchic makes no distinction among very flat hierarchies, like

Has it really been shown? Simon makes some persuasive arguments as to *why* this should be true, but some simulations and experiments would provide more in the way of proof.

	A1	A2	A3	B1	B2	C1	C2	C3
A1	—	100	—	2	—	—	—	—
A2	100	—	100	1	1	—	—	—
A3	—	100	—	—	2	—	—	—
B1	2	1	—	—	100	2	1	—
B2	—	1	2	100	—	—	1	2
C1	—	—	—	2	—	—	100	—
C2	—	—	—	1	—	100	—	100
C3	—	—	—	—	2	—	100	—

Figure 1. A hypothetical nearly-decomposable system. In terms of the heat-exchange example of the text, A1, A2, and A3 may be interpreted as cubicles in one room, B1 and B2 as cubicles in a second room, and C1, C2, and C3 as cubicles in a third. The matrix entries then are the heat diffusion coefficients between cubicles.

crystals, and tissues, and polymers, and the intermediate forms. Indeed, in the complex systems we encounter in nature, examples of both forms are prominent. A more complete theory than the one we have developed here would presumably have something to say about the determinants of width of span in these systems.

Nearly Decomposable Systems

This is a whole different major contribution of this paper, and of Simon's work with Ando. It anticipates theorems of Tikhonov when multiple time scales are involved, for example, in these modularized systems.

In hierarchic systems, we can distinguish between the interactions *among* subsystems, on the one hand, and the interactions *within* subsystems—i.e., among the parts of those subsystems—on the other. The interactions at the different levels may be, and often will be, of different orders of magnitude. In a formal organization there will generally be more interaction, on the average, between two employees who are members of the same department than between two employees from different departments. In organic substances, intermolecular forces will generally be weaker than molecular forces, and molecular forces than nuclear forces.

In a rare gas, the intermolecular forces will be negligible compared to those binding the molecules—we can treat the individual particles, for many purposes, as if they were independent of each other. We can describe such a system as *decomposable* into the subsystems comprised of the individual particles. As the gas becomes denser, molecular interactions become more significant. But over some range, we can treat the decomposable case as a limit, and as a first approximation. We can use a theory of perfect gases, for example, to describe approximately the behavior of actual gases if they are not too dense. As a second approximation, we may move to a theory of *nearly decomposable* systems, in which the interactions among the subsystems are weak, but not negligible.

At least some kinds of hierarchic systems can be approximated successfully as nearly decomposable systems. The main theoretical findings from the approach can be summed up in two propositions: (*a*) in a nearly decomposable system, the short-run behavior of each of the component subsystems is approximately independent of the short-run behavior of the other components; (*b*) in the long run, the behavior of any one of the components depends in only an aggregate way on the behavior of the other components.

Let me provide a very concrete simple example of a nearly decomposable system.[15] Consider a building whose outside walls provide perfect thermal insulation from the environment. We shall take these walls as the boundary of our system. The building is divided into a large number of rooms, the walls between them being good, but not perfect, insulators. The walls between rooms are the boundaries of our major subsystems. Each room is divided by partitions into a number of cubicles, but the partitions are poor insulators. A thermometer hangs in each cubicle. Suppose that at the time of our first observation

---

[15] This discussion of near-decomposability is based upon H. A. Simon and A. Ando, "Aggregation of Variables in Dynamic Systems," *Econometrica* 29: 111–138, April, 1961. The example is drawn from the same source, 117–118. The theory has been further developed and applied to a variety of economic and political phenomena by Ando and F. M. Fisher. See F. M. Fisher, "On the Cost of Approximate Specification in Simultaneous Equation Estimation," *Econometrica* 29: 139-170, April, 1961, and F. M. Fisher and A. Ando, "Two Theorems on *Ceteris Paribus* in the Analysis of Dynamic Systems," *American Political Science Review* 61: 103–113, March, 1962.

of the system there is a wide variation in temperature from cubicle to cubicle and from room to room—the various cubicles within the building are in a state of thermal disequilibrium. When we take new temperature readings several hours later, what shall we find? There will be very little variation in temperature among the cubicles within each single room, but there may still be large temperature variations *among* rooms. When we take readings again several days later, we find an almost uniform temperature throughout the building; the temperature differences among rooms have virtually disappeared.

We can describe the process of equilibration formally by setting up the usual equations of heat flow. The equations can be represented by the matrix of their coefficients, r_{ij}, where r_{ij} is the rate at which heat flows from the ith cubicle to the jth cubicle per degree difference in their temperatures. If cubicles i and j do not have a common wall, r_{ij} will be zero. If cubicles i and j have a common wall, and are in the same room, r_{ij} will be large. If cubicles i and j are separated by the wall of a room, r_{ij} will be nonzero but small. Hence, by grouping all the cubicles together that are in the same room, we can arrange the matrix of coefficients so that all its large elements lie inside a string of square submatrices along the main diagonal. All the elements outside these diagonal squares will be either zero or small (see figure 1). We may take some small number, ϵ, as the upper bound of the extradiagonal elements. We shall call a matrix having these properties a *nearly decomposable matrix*.

Indeed, most dynamic systems of interest asymptotically collapse toward lower-dimensional manifolds, and ultimately to even lower-dimensional limit point sets, allowing one to separate the dynamics on multiple time scales.

Now it has been proved that a dynamic system that can be described by a nearly decomposable matrix has the properties, stated above, of a nearly decomposable system. In our simple example of heat flow this means that in the short run each room will reach an equilibrium temperature (an average of the initial temperatures of its offices) nearly independently of the others; and that each room will remain approximately in a state of equilibrium over the longer period during which an over-all temperature equilibrium is being established throughout the building. After the intra-room short-run equilibria have been reached, a single thermometer in each room will be adequate to describe the dynamic behavior of the entire system—separate thermometers in each cubicle will be superfluous.

NEAR DECOMPOSABILITY OF SOCIAL SYSTEMS

As a glance at figure 1 shows, near decomposability is a rather strong property for a matrix to possess, and the matrices that have this property will describe very special dynamic systems—vanishingly few systems out of all those that are thinkable. How few they will be depends, of course, on how good an approximation we insist upon. If we demand that epsilon be very small, correspondingly few dynamic systems will fit the definition. But we have already seen that in the natural world nearly decomposable systems are far from rare. On the contrary, systems in which each variable is linked with almost equal strength with almost all other parts of the system are far rarer and less typical.

In economic dynamics, the main variables are the prices and quantities of commodities. It is empirically true that the price of any given commodity and the rate at which it is exchanged depend to a significant extent only on the prices and quantities of a few other commodities, together with a few other aggregate magnitudes, like the average price level or some over-all measure of economic activity. The large linkage coefficients are associated, in general, with the main flows of raw materials and semi-finished products within and between industries. An input-output matrix of the economy, giving the magnitudes of these flows, reveals the nearly decomposable structure of the system—with one qualification. There is a consumption subsystem of the economy that is linked strongly to variables in most of the other subsystems. Hence, we have to modify our notions of decomposability slightly to accommodate the special role of the consumption subsystem in our analysis of the dynamic behavior of the economy.

In the dynamics of social systems, where members of a system communicate with and influence other members, near decomposability is generally very prominent. This is most obvious in formal organizations, where the formal authority relation connects each member of the organization with one immediate superior and with a small number of subordinates. Of course many communications in organizations follow other channels than the lines of formal authority. But most of these channels lead from any particular individual to a very limited number of his superiors, subordinates, and associates. Hence, departmental boundaries play very much the same role as the walls in our heat example.

PHYSICO-CHEMICAL SYSTEMS

In the complex systems familiar in biological chemistry, a similar structure is clearly visible. Take the atomic nuclei in such a system as the elementary parts of the system, and construct a matrix of bond strengths between elements. There will be matrix elements of quite different orders of magnitude. The largest will generally correspond to the covalent bonds, the next to the ionic bonds, the third group to hydrogen bonds, still smaller linkages to van der Waals forces.[16] If we select an epsilon just a little smaller than the magnitude of a covalent bond, the system will decompose into subsystems—the constituent molecules. The smaller linkages will correspond to the intermolecular bonds.

It is well known that high-energy, high-frequency vibrations are associated with the smaller physical subsystems, low-frequency vibrations with the larger systems into which the subsystems are assembled. For example, the radiation frequencies associated with molecular vibrations are much lower than those associated with the vibrations of the planetary electrons of the atoms; the latter, in turn, are lower than those associated with nuclear processes.[17] Molecular systems are nearly decomposable systems, the short-run dynamics relating to the internal structures of the subsystems; the long-run dynamics to the interactions of these subsystems.

---

[16]For a survey of the several classes of molecular and inter-molecular forces, and their dissociation energies see Setlow and Pollard, *op. cit.*, chapter 6. The energies of typical covalent bonds are of the order of 80-100 k cal/mole, of the hydrogen bonds, 10 k cal/mole. Ionic bonds generally lie between these two levels, the bonds due to van der Waals forces are lower in energy.

[17]Typical wave numbers for vibrations associated with various systems (the wave number is the reciprocal of wave length hence proportional to frequency):

steel wire under tension—10^{-10} to 10^{-9} cm^{-1}

molecular rotations—10^0 to 10^2 cm^{-1}

molecular vibrations—10^2 to 10^3 cm^{-1}

planetary electrons—10^4 to 10^5 cm^{-1}

nuclear rotations—10^9 to 10^{10} cm^{-1}

nuclear surface vibrations—10^{11} to 10^{12} cm^{-1}.

A number of the important approximations employed in physics depend for their validity on the near-decomposability of the systems studied. The theory of the thermodynamics of irreversible processes, for example, requires the assumption of macroscopic disequilibrium but microscopic equilibrium,[18] exactly the situation described in our heat-exchange example. Similarly computations in quantum mechanics are often handled by treating weak interactions as producing perturbations on a system of strong interactions.

SOME OBSERVATIONS ON HIERARCHIC SPAN

To understand why the span of hierarchies is sometimes very broad—as in crystals—sometimes narrow, we need to examine more detail of the interactions. In general, the critical consideration is the extent to which interaction between two (or a few) subsystems excludes interaction of these subsystems with the others. Let us examine first some physical examples.

Consider a gas of identical molecules, each of which can form covalent bonds, in certain ways, with others. Let us suppose that we can associate with each atom a specific number of bonds that it is capable of maintaining simultaneously. (This number is obviously related to the number we usually call its valence.) Now suppose that two atoms join, and that we can also associate with the combination a specific number of external bonds it is capable of maintaining. If this number is the same as the number associated with the individual atoms, the bonding process can go on indefinitely—the atoms can form crystals or polymers of indefinite extent. If the number of bonds of which the composite is capable is less than the number associated with each of the parts, then the process of agglomeration must come to a halt.

We need only mention some elementary examples. Ordinary gases show no tendency to agglomerate because the multiple bonding of atoms "uses up" their capacity to interact. While each oxygen atom has a valence of two, the O_2 molecules have a zero valence. Contrariwise, indefinite chains of single-bonded carbon atoms can be built up because

---

[18]S. R. de Groot, *Thermodynamics of Irreversible Processes*, 11–12, New York, Interscience Publishers, 1951.

a chain of any number of such atoms, each with two side groups, has a valence of exactly two.

Now what happens if we have a system of elements that possess both strong and weak interaction capacities, and whose strong bonds are exhaustible through combination? Subsystems will form, until all the capacity for strong interaction is utilized in their construction. Then these subsystems will be linked by the weaker second-order bonds into larger systems. For example, a water molecule has essentially a valence of zero—all the potential covalent bonds are fully occupied by the interaction of hydrogen and oxygen molecules. But the geometry of the molecule creates an electric dipole that permits weak interaction between the water and salts dissolved in it—whence such phenomena as its electrolytic conductivity.[19]

Similarly, it has been observed that, although electrical forces are much stronger than gravitational forces, the latter are far more important than the former for systems on an astronomical scale. The explanation, of course, is that the electrical forces, being bipolar, are all "used up" in the linkages of the smaller subsystems, and that significant net balances of positive or negative charges are not generally found in regions of macroscopic size.

In social as in physical systems there are generally limits on the simultaneous interaction of large numbers of subsystems. In the social case, these limits are related to the fact that a human being is more nearly a serial than a parallel information-processing system. He can carry on only one conversation at a time, and although this does not limit the size of the audience to which a mass communication can be addressed, it does limit the number of people simultaneously involved in most other forms of social interaction. Apart from requirements of direct interaction, most roles impose tasks and responsibilities that are time consuming. One cannot, for example, enact the role of "friend" with large numbers of other people.

It is probably true that in social as in physical systems, the higher frequency dynamics are associated with the subsystems, the lower frequency dynamics with the larger systems. It is generally believed, for

---

[19]See, for example, L. Pauling, *General Chemistry*, ch. 15.

example, that the relevant planning horizon of executives is longer the higher their location in the organizational hierarchy. It is probably also true that both the average duration of an interaction between executives and the average interval between interactions is greater at higher than at lower levels.

SUMMARY: NEAR DECOMPOSABILITY

We have seen that hierarchies have the property of near-decomposability. Intra-component linkages are generally stronger than intercomponent linkages. This fact has the effect of separating the high-frequency dynamics of a hierarchy—involving the internal structure of the components—from the low frequency dynamics—involving interaction among components. We shall turn next to some important consequences of this separation for the description and comprehension of complex systems.

The Description of Complexity

If you ask a person to draw a complex object—e.g., a human face—he will almost always proceed in a hierarchic fashion.[20] First he will outline the face. Then he will add or insert features: eyes, nose, mouth, ears, hair. If asked to elaborate, he will begin to develop details for each of the features—pupils, eyelids, lashes for the eyes, and so on—until he reaches the limits of his anatomical knowledge. His information about the object is arranged hierarchically in memory, like a topical outline.

When information is put in outline form, it is easy to include information about the relations among the major parts and information about the internal relations of parts in each of the suboutlines. Detailed information about the relations of subparts belonging to different parts has no place in the outline and is likely to be lost. The loss of such information and the preservation mainly of information about hierarchic order is a salient characteristic that distinguishes the drawings of a child or someone untrained in representation from the drawing of a trained artist. (I am speaking of an artist who is striving for representation.)

Ecological interaction networks, such as food webs, show similar near-decomposability, in which subsets of species form tightly interacting subsystems that interact only weakly with other subsystems but not exclusively through spatial separation. See, for example, Paine (1980).

---

[20]George A. Miller has collected protocols from subjects who were given the task of drawing faces, and finds that they behave in the manner described here (private communication). See also E. H. Gombrich, *Art and illusion*, 291-296, New York, Pantheon Books, 1960.

NEAR DECOMPOSABILITY AND COMPREHENSIBILITY

From our discussion of the dynamic properties of nearly decomposable systems, we have seen that comparatively little information is lost by representing them as hierarchies. Subparts belonging to different parts only interact in an aggregative fashion—the detail of their interaction can be ignored. In studying the interaction of two large molecules, generally we do not need to consider in detail the interactions of nuclei of the atoms belonging to the one molecule with the nuclei of the atoms belonging to the other. In studying the interaction of two nations, we do not need to study in detail the interactions of each citizen of the first with each citizen of the second.

The fact, then, that many complex systems have a nearly decomposable, hierarchic structure is a major facilitating factor enabling us to understand, to describe, and even to "see" such systems and their parts. Or perhaps the proposition should be put the other way round. If there are important systems in the world that are complex without being hierarchic, they may to a considerable extent escape our observation and our understanding. Analysis of their behavior would involve such detailed knowledge and calculation of the interactions of their elementary parts that it would be beyond our capacities of memory or computation.[21]

I shall not try to settle which is chicken and which is egg: whether we are able to understand the world because it is hierarchic, or whether

---

[21] I believe the fallacy in the central thesis of W. M. Elsasser's *The physical foundation of biology*, mentioned earlier, lies in his ignoring the simplification in description of complex systems that derives from their hierarchic structure. Thus (p. 155): "If we now apply similar arguments to the coupling of enzymatic reactions with the substratum of protein molecules, we see that over a sufficient period of time, the information corresponding to the structural details of these molecules will be communicated to the dynamics of the cell, to higher levels of organization as it were, and may influence such dynamics. While this reasoning is only qualitative, it lends credence to the assumption that in the living organism, unlike the inorganic crystal, the effects of microscopic structure cannot be simply averaged out; as time goes on this influence will pervade the behavior of the cell 'at all levels.'"

But from our discussion of near-decomposability it would appear that those aspects of microstructure that control the slow developmental aspects of organismic dynamics can be separated out from the aspects that control the more rapid cellular metabolic processes. For this reason we should not despair of unravelling the web of causes. See also J. R. Platt's review of Elsasser's book in *Perspectives in Biology and Medicine* 2: 243–245, 1959.

it appears hierarchic because those aspects of it which are not elude our understanding and observation. I have already given some reasons for supposing that the former is at least half the truth—that evolving complexity would tend to be hierarchic—but it may not be the whole truth.

SIMPLE DESCRIPTIONS OF COMPLEX SYSTEMS

One might suppose that the description of a complex system would itself be a complex structure of symbols—and indeed, it may be just that. But there is no conservation law that requires that the description be as cumbersome as the object described. A trivial example will show how a system can be described economically. Suppose the system is a two-dimensional array like this:

$$
\begin{array}{cccccccc}
A & B & M & N & R & S & H & I \\
C & D & O & P & T & U & J & K \\
M & N & A & B & H & I & R & S \\
O & P & C & D & J & K & T & U \\
R & S & H & I & A & B & M & N \\
T & U & J & K & C & D & O & P \\
H & I & R & S & M & N & A & B \\
J & K & T & U & O & P & C & D
\end{array}
$$

Let us call the array $\begin{vmatrix} A & B \\ C & D \end{vmatrix}$ a, the array $\begin{vmatrix} M & N \\ O & P \end{vmatrix}$ m, the array $\begin{vmatrix} R & S \\ T & U \end{vmatrix}$ r, and the array $\begin{vmatrix} H & I \\ J & K \end{vmatrix}$ h. Let us call the array $\begin{vmatrix} a & m \\ m & a \end{vmatrix}$ w, and the array $\begin{vmatrix} r & h \\ h & r \end{vmatrix}$ x. Then the entire array is simply $\begin{vmatrix} w & x \\ x & w \end{vmatrix}$. While the original structure consisted of 64 symbols, it requires only 35 to write down its description:

$$
S = \begin{array}{cc} w & x \\ x & w \end{array}
$$

$$
w = \begin{array}{cc} a & m \\ m & a \end{array}
\qquad\qquad
x = \begin{array}{cc} r & h \\ h & r \end{array}
$$

$$
a = \begin{array}{cc} A & B \\ C & D \end{array}
\quad
m = \begin{array}{cc} M & N \\ O & P \end{array}
\quad
r = \begin{array}{cc} R & S \\ T & U \end{array}
\quad
h = \begin{array}{cc} H & I \\ J & K \end{array}
$$

We achieve the abbreviation by making use of the redundancy in the original structure. Since the pattern $\begin{smallmatrix} A & B \\ C & D \end{smallmatrix}$, for example, occurs four times in the total pattern, it is economical to represent it by the single symbol, a.

If a complex structure is completely unredundant—if no aspect of its structure can be inferred from any other—then it is its own simplest description. We can exhibit it, but we cannot describe it by a simpler structure. The hierarchic structures we have been discussing have a high degree of redundancy, hence can often be described in economical terms. The redundancy takes a number of forms, of which I shall mention three:

1. Hierarchic systems are usually composed of only a few different kinds of subsystems, in various combinations and arrangements. A familiar example is the proteins, their multitudinous variety arising from arrangements of only twenty different amino acids. Similarly, the ninety-odd elements provide all the kinds of building blocks needed for an infinite variety of molecules. Hence, we can construct our description from a restricted alphabet of elementary terms corresponding to the basic set of elementary subsystems from which the complex system is generated.

2. Hierarchic systems are, as we have seen, often nearly decomposable. Hence only aggregative properties of their parts enter into the description of the interactions of those parts. A generalization of the notion of near-decomposability might be called the "empty world hypothesis"—most things are only weakly connected with most other things; for a tolerable description of reality only a tiny fraction of all possible interactions needs to be taken into account. By adopting a descriptive language that allows the absence of something to go unmentioned, a nearly empty world can be described quite concisely. Mother Hubbard did not have to check off the list of possible contents to say that her cupboard was bare.

3. By appropriate "recoding," the redundancy that is present but unobvious in the structure of a complex system can often be made patent. The most common recoding of descriptions of dynamic systems consists in replacing a description of the time path with a description of

a differential law that generates that path. The simplicity, that is, resides in a constant relation between the state of the system at any given time and the state of the system a short time later. Thus, the structure of the sequence, 1 3 5 7 9 11 . . . , is most simply expressed by observing that each member is obtained by adding 2 to the previous one. But this is the sequence that Galileo found to describe the velocity at the end of successive time intervals of a ball rolling down an inclined plane.

It is a familiar proposition that the task of science is to make use of the world's redundancy to describe that world simply. I shall not pursue the general methodological point here, but shall instead take a closer look at two main types of description that seem to be available to us in seeking an understanding of complex systems. I shall call these *state description* and *process description*, respectively.

STATE DESCRIPTIONS AND PROCESS DESCRIPTIONS

"A circle is the locus of all points equidistant from a given point." "To construct a circle, rotate a compass with one arm fixed until the other arm has returned to its starting point." It is implicit in Euclid that if you carry out the process specified in the second sentence, you will produce an object that satisfies the definition of the first. The first sentence is a state description of a circle, the second a process description.

These two modes of apprehending structure are the warp and weft of our experience. Pictures, blueprints, most diagrams, chemical structural formulae are state descriptions. Recipes, differential equations, equations for chemical reactions are process descriptions. The former characterize the world as sensed; they provide the criteria for identifying objects, often by modeling the objects themselves. The latter characterize the world as acted upon; they provide the means for producing or generating objects having the desired characteristics.

The distinction between the world as sensed and the world as acted upon defines the basic condition for the survival of adaptive organisms. The organism must develop correlations between goals in the sensed world and actions in the world of process. When they are made conscious and verbalized, these correlations correspond to what we usually call means-end analysis. Given a desired state of affairs and an existing state of affairs, the task of an adaptive organism is to find the difference between these two states, and then to find the correlating process that will erase the difference.[22]

Thus, problem solving requires continual translation between the state and process descriptions of the same complex reality. Plato, in the *Meno*, argued that all learning is remembering. He could not otherwise explain how we can discover or recognize the answer to a problem unless we already know the answer.[23] Our dual relation to the world is the source and solution of the paradox. We pose a problem by giving the state description of the solution. The task is to discover a sequence of processes that will produce the goal state from an initial state. Translation from the process description to the state description enables us to recognize when we have succeeded. The solution is genuinely new to us—and we do not need Plato's theory of remembering to explain how we recognize it.

There is now a growing body of evidence that the activity called human problem solving is basically a form of means-end analysis that aims at discovering a process description of the path that leads to a desired goal. The general paradigm is: given a blueprint, to find the corresponding recipe. Much of the activity of science is an application of that paradigm: given the description of some natural phenomena, to find the differential equations for processes that will produce the phenomena.

THE DESCRIPTION OF COMPLEXITY IN SELF-REPRODUCING SYSTEMS

The problem of finding relatively simple descriptions for complex systems is of interest not only for an understanding of human knowledge of the world but also for an explanation of how a complex system can reproduce itself. In my discussion of the evolution of complex systems, I touched only briefly on the role of self-reproduction.

Atoms of high atomic weight and complex inorganic molecules are witnesses to the fact that the evolution of complexity does not imply self-reproduction. If evolution of complexity from simplicity is sufficiently

---

[22]See H. A. Simon and A. Newell, "Simulation of Human Thinking," *in* M. Greenberger (ed.), *Management and the Computer of the Future*, 95–114, esp. pp 110 ff., New York, Wiley, 1962.

[23] *The Works of Plato*, B. Jowett, trans., 3: 26–35, New York, Dial Press.

probable, it will occur repeatedly; the statistical equilibrium of the system will find a large fraction of the elementary particles participating in complex systems.

If, however, the existence of a particular complex form increased the probability of the creation of another form just like it, the equilibrium between complexes and components could be greatly altered in favor of the former. If we have a description of an object that is sufficiently clear and complete, we can reproduce the object from the description. Whatever the exact mechanism of reproduction, the description provides us with the necessary information.

Now we have seen that the descriptions of complex systems can take many forms. In particular, we can have state descriptions or we can have process descriptions; blueprints or recipes. Reproductive processes could be built around either of these sources of information. Perhaps the simplest possibility is for the complex system to serve as a description of itself—a template on which a copy can be formed. One of the most plausible current theories, for example, of the reproduction of deoxyribonucleic acid (DNA) proposes that a DNA molecule, in the form of a double helix of matching parts (each essentially a "negative" of the other), unwinds to allow each half of the helix to serve as a template on which a new matching half can form.

On the other hand, our current knowledge of how DNA controls the metabolism of the organism suggests that reproduction by template is only one of the processes involved. According to the prevailing theory, DNA serves as a template both for itself and for the related substance ribonucleic acid (RNA). RNA, in turn, serves as a template for protein. But proteins— according to current knowledge—guide the organism's metabolism not by the template method but by serving as catalysts to govern reaction rates in the cell. While RNA is a blueprint for protein, protein is a recipe for metabolism. [24]

---

[24] C. B. Anfinsen, *The Molecular Basis of Evolution*, chs. 3 and 10, New York, Wiley, 1959, will qualify this sketchy, oversimplified account. For an imaginative discussion of some mechanisms of process description that could govern molecular structure, see H. H. Pattee, "On the Origin of Macromolecular Sequences," *Biophysical Journal* 1: 683–710, 1961.

ONTOGENY RECAPITULATES PHYLOGENY

The DNA in the chromosomes of an organism contains some, and perhaps most, of the information that is needed to determine its development and activity. We have seen that, if current theories are even approximately correct, the information is recorded not as a state description of the organism but as a series of "instructions" for the construction and maintenance of the organism from nutrient materials. I have already used the metaphor of a recipe; I could equally well compare it with a computer program, which is also a sequence of instructions, governing the construction of symbolic structures. Let me spin out some of the consequences of the latter comparison.

If genetic material is a program—viewed in its relation to the organism—it is a program with special and peculiar properties. First, it is a self-reproducing program; we have already considered its possible copying mechanism. Second, it is a program that has developed by Darwinian evolution. On the basis of our watchmaker's argument, we may assert that many of its ancestors were also viable programs—programs for the subassemblies.

Are there any other conjectures we can make about the structure of this program? There is a well-known generalization in biology that is verbally so neat that we would be reluctant to give it up even if the facts did not support it: ontogeny recapitulates phylogeny. The individual organism, in its development, goes through stages that resemble some of its ancestral forms. The fact that the human embryo develops gill bars and then modifies them for other purposes is a familiar particular belonging to the generalization. Biologists today like to emphasize the qualifications of the principle—that ontogeny recapitulates only the grossest aspects of phylogeny, and these only crudely. These qualifications should not make us lose sight of the fact that the generalization does hold in rough approximation—it does summarize a very significant set of facts about the organism's development. How can we interpret these facts?

One way to solve a complex problem is to reduce it to a problem previously solved—to show what steps lead from the earlier solution to a solution of the new problem. If, around the turn of the century, we wanted to instruct a workman to make an automobile, perhaps the simplest way would have been to tell him how to modify a wagon by removing the singletree and adding a motor and transmission. Similarly, a genetic program could be altered in the course of evolution by adding new processes that would modify a simpler form into a more complex one—to construct a gastrula, take a blastula and alter it!

The genetic description of a single cell may, therefore, take a quite different form from the genetic description that assembles cells into a multi-celled organism. Multiplication by cell division would require, as a minimum, a state description (the DNA, say), and a simple "interpretive process"—to use the term from computer language—that copies this description as a part of the larger copying process of cell division. But such a mechanism clearly would not suffice for the differentiation of cells in development. It appears more natural to conceptualize that mechanism as based on a process description, and a somewhat more complex interpretive process that produces the adult organism in a sequence of stages, each new stage in development representing the effect of an operator upon the previous one.

It is harder to conceptualize the interrelation of these two descriptions. Interrelated they must be, for enough has been learned of gene-enzyme mechanisms to show that these play a major role in development as in cell metabolism. The single clue we obtain from our earlier discussion is that the description may itself be hierarchical, or nearly decomposable, in structure, the lower levels governing the fast, "high-frequency" dynamics of the individual cell, the higher level interactions governing the slow, "low-frequency" dynamics of the developing multi-cellular organism.

There are only bits of evidence, apart from the facts of recapitulation, that the genetic program is organized in this way, but such evidence as exists is compatible with this notion.[25] To the extent that we can differentiate

---

[25] There is considerable evidence that successive genes along a chromosome often determine enzymes controlling successive stages of protein syntheses. For a review of some of this evidence, see P. E. Hartman, "Transduction: a Comparative Review," in W. D. McElroy and B. Glass (eds.), *The Chemical Basis of Heredity*, Baltimore, Johns Hopkins Press, 1957, at pp. 442–454. Evidence for differential activity of genes in different tissues and at different stages of development is discussed by J. G. Gall, "Chromosomal Differentiation," in W. D. McElroy and B. Glass (eds.), *The Chemical Basis of Development*, Baltimore, Johns Hopkins Press, 1958, at pp. 103–135. Finally, a model very like that proposed here has been independently, and far more fully, outlined by J. R. Platt, "A 'Book Model' of Genetic Information Transfer in Cells

the genetic information that governs cell metabolism from the genetic information that governs the development of differentiated cells in the multi-cellular organization, we simplify enormously—as we have already seen—our task of theoretical description. But I have perhaps pressed this speculation far enough.

The generalization that in evolving systems whose descriptions are stored in a process language, we might expect ontogeny partially to recapitulate phylogeny has applications outside the realm of biology. It can be applied as readily, for example, to the transmission of knowledge in the educational process. In most subjects, particularly in the rapidly advancing sciences, the progress from elementary to advanced courses is to a considerable extent a progress through the conceptual history of the science itself. Fortunately, the recapitulation is seldom literal—any more than it is in the biological case. We do not teach the phlogiston theory in chemistry in order later to correct it. (I am not sure I could not cite examples in other subjects where we do exactly that.) But curriculum revisions that rid us of the accumulations of the past are infrequent and painful. Nor are they always desirable—partial recapitulation may, in many instances, provide the most expeditious route to advanced knowledge.

SUMMARY: THE DESCRIPTION OF COMPLEXITY

How complex or simple a structure is depends critically upon the way in which we describe it. Most of the complex structures found in the world are enormously redundant, and we can use this redundancy to simplify their description. But to use it, to achieve the simplification, we must find the right representation.

The notion of substituting a process description for a state description of nature has played a central role in the development of modern science. Dynamic laws, expressed in the form of systems of differential or difference equations, have in a large number of cases provided the clue for the simple description of the complex. In the

---

and Tissues," *in* Kasha and Pullman (eds.), *Horizons in Biochemistry*, New York, Academic Press, forthcoming. Of course, this kind of mechanism is not the only one in which development could be controlled by a process description. Induction, in the form envisaged in Spemann's organizer theory, is based on process description, in which metabolites in already formed tissue control the next stages of development.

preceding paragraphs I have tried to show that this characteristic of scientific inquiry is not accidental or superficial. The correlation between state description and process description is basic to the functioning of any adaptive organism, to its capacity for acting purposefully upon its environment. Our present-day understanding of genetic mechanisms suggests that even in describing itself the multicellular organism finds a process description—a genetically encoded program—to be the parsimonious and useful representation.

Conclusion*

Our speculations have carried us over a rather alarming array of topics, but that is the price we must pay if we wish to seek properties common to many sorts of complex systems. My thesis has been that one path to the construction of a nontrivial theory of complex systems is by way of a theory of hierarchy. Empirically, a large proportion of the complex systems we observe in nature exhibit hierarchic structure. On theoretical grounds we could expect complex systems to be hierarchies in a world in which complexity had to evolve from simplicity. In their dynamics, hierarchies have a property, near-decomposability, that greatly simplifies their behavior. Near-decomposability also simplifies the description of a complex system, and makes it easier to understand how the information needed for the development or reproduction of the system can be stored in reasonable compass.

In both science and engineering, the study of "systems" is an increasingly popular activity. Its popularity is more a response to a pressing need for synthesizing and analyzing complexity than it is to any large development of a body of knowledge and technique for dealing with complexity. If this popularity is to be more than a fad,

---

*The ideas in this paper have been the topic of many conversations with my colleague, Allen Newell. George W. Corner suggested important improvements in biological content as well as editorial form. I am also indebted, for valuable comments on the manuscript, to Richard H. Meier, John R. Platt, and Warren Weaver. Some of the conjectures about the nearly decomposable structure of the nucleus-atom-molecule hierarchy were checked against the available quantitative data by Andrew Schoene and William Wise. My work in this area has been supported by a Ford Foundation grant for research in organizations and a Carnegie Corporation grant for research on cognitive processes. To all of the above, my warm thanks, and the usual absolution.

necessity will have to mother invention and provide substance to go with the name. The explorations reviewed here represent one particular direction of search for such substance. ❧

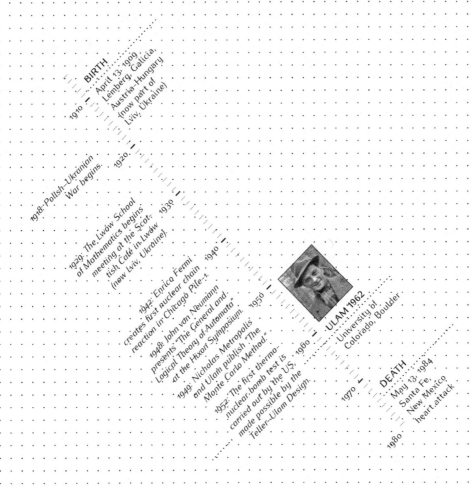

BIRTH
April 13, 1909
Lemberg, Galicia,
Austria-Hungary
(now part of
Lviv, Ukraine)

1910

1918: Polish-Ukrainian
War begins.

1920

1929: The Lwów School
of Mathematics begins
meeting at the Scot-
tish Café in Lwów
(now Lviv, Ukraine).

1930

1942: Enrico Fermi
creates first nuclear chain
reaction in Chicago Pile-1.

1940

1948: John von Neumann
presents "The General and
Logical Theory of Automata"
at the Hixon Symposium.

1949: Nicholas Metropolis
and Ulam publish "The
Monte Carlo Method."

1950

1952: The first thermo-
nuclear bomb test is
carried out by the US,
made possible by the
Teller–Ulam Design.

1960

ULAM 1962
University of
Colorado, Boulder

DEATH
May 13, 1984
Santa Fe,
New Mexico,
heart attack.

1970

1980

STANISŁAW MARCIN ULAM

[22]

CAFÉ ROOTS & FRUITS

Erica Jen, Santa Fe Institute

Stan Ulam's 1962 paper on the mathematics of growth patterns introduced the paradigm of complex behavior emerging in the spatiotemporal evolution of simple discrete dynamical systems, and pioneered the use of computer simulations to explore their analytically recalcitrant features.

The roots of Ulam's work lay in a café known as the Kawiarnia Szkocka (Scottish Café) in the city of Lwów, Poland. From the 1930s up until the German occupation in 1941, it was a gathering place for Polish mathematicians including Hugo Steinhaus, Stefan Banach, Stanisław Mazur, Ulam, Kazimierz Kuratowski, Wacław Sierpiński, Mark Kac, John von Neumann, and many others. As such, it was the birthplace of core mathematical constructs, including functions of real variables, function spaces, the concept of measure, and the foundations of probability theory. Cellular automata (CA), invented by Ulam and von Neumann a decade or so after the forced dispersal of their colleagues and themselves, belong to this lineage as well.

Mathematicians met at the Scottish Café several times a week, often daily, using pencils to scribble problems, conjectures, and solutions on the marble tabletops. Sometime in 1935, Banach's wife supplied a thick notebook with marbled covers for writing up the results of discussions (and preserving them from being scrubbed from tables at night). The notebook was safeguarded by the headwaiter at the café, who would produce it on demand. A total of 193 problems were inscribed in what is now known as The Scottish Book: about a quarter of the problems have yet to be solved (Mauldin 2015).

In the tradition of earlier schools in Göttingen and Paris, most café mathematicians did not make a sharp distinction between mathematics and physics. For example, Banach—the founder of functional analysis—

S. Ulam, "On Some Mathematical Problems Connected with Patterns of Growth in Figures," in *Proceedings of Symposia in Applied Mathematics 14: Mathematical Problems in the Biological Sciences*, ed. R. E. Bellman, 215–224 (1962).

Reprinted by permission of the American Mathematical Society.

lectured and authored a book on mechanics. Nonetheless, pure mathematics was the lifeblood of the Scottish Café: physical reality engaged café *habitués* insofar as it suggested novel mathematical constructs.

Ulam's 1962 work drew on some of the more "eccentric" motifs of the Scottish Café: game theory, infinite matrices, and number theory, among others. The work also represents an early venture into mathematics inspired by biology—in this case, the growth patterns of figures.

Why growth patterns? Ulam relished both playing with simple functions likely to generate surprising behavior and identifying complex behavior with unexpectedly simple explanations. From that perspective, crystal growth was too regular to be interesting; the study of fluid flows, on the other hand, was computationally too time-consuming on serial computers, and not likely to yield to mathematical analysis. Morphogenesis presented diverse examples that Ulam characterized as "intermediate in complexity between inorganic patterns like those of crystals and the more varied intricacies of organic molecules and structures."

Moreover, Ulam believed that the logic of biology could be fundamentally different from that of physics (Ulam 1976). Whereas physical systems were conventionally described by continuum equations (discretized for the purpose of numerical calculations), biological processes such as morphogenesis could be directly modeled as discrete systems (as their cellular structure might suggest). Furthermore biological growth might make use of information processing mechanisms different from standard arithmetical operations. Thus, the study of growth patterns could stimulate new mathematics and exemplify Ulam's credo: "Ask not what mathematics can do for biology, but what biology can do for mathematics" (Ulam 1976).

It was not his first foray into biology. As early as 1930, Ulam and his Scottish Café cohort Mazur had discussed the phenomenon of self-reproduction. Those discussions led Ulam in 1950 to make a critical contribution to von Neumann's objective of building a self-reproducing machine.

At the time, von Neumann was pursuing approaches ranging from a kinematic machine through a neuron model to a 3D robotic factory—none of which was workable. A suggestion from Ulam enabled a breakthrough. Infinite matrices and iterated functions being recurring Scottish Café talking points, Ulam proposed constructing the machine on a 2D lattice of cells with local interaction update rules. Thus CA were born.

The 1962 paper embodies Ulam's vision, as opposed to von Neumann's utilization, of CA. In contrast to von Neumann's self-reproducing machine with some 200,000 cells and twenty-nine possible states per cell, Ulam's automata consist largely of binary-valued cells evolving from a single non-zero initial condition.

Titularly a study of morphogenesis, the work does not purport to provide even a "plausible" mechanism for growth, much less a model with either descriptive or predictive power. The focus is the mathematical questions posed by the evolution of cell arrays with growth-like interaction rules.

The paper contains numerous conjectures and no proofs, and represents a case study in what Ulam called the "heuristics of theory experiments" (Mauldin and Ulam 1987). The crux of the paper is computational simulations of CA which he later described (Feigenbaum 1982) as "manufactur[ing] your own world . . . of hard spheres."

One of Ulam's fortes—on display here—was starting with a simple example and playing with modifications to introduce odd turns. Examples in this paper consider the effects of varying:

(1) spatial geometries;
(2) update rules;
(3) dimensionality; and
(4) the number of states per cell.

The objective was to determine global characteristics such as the limiting density of cells and to describe the dynamics—such as "conflicts" or coalescence or death—of the coherent structures generated in the spatiotemporal evolutions.

To put Ulam's paper in perspective, consider the timeline compiled by Wolfram (2002) cataloging over two millennia of research relating to what we now call "complex systems." The mid-1900s produced numerous prototypical studies, including Turing's model of heterogeneous patterns in embryonic development; von Neumann's self-reproducing system; simulations by Fermi, Pasta, and Ulam that led to soliton theory; design of neural networks by Widrow and Hoff to recognize binary patterns; Alder and Wainwright's simulations of atoms and molecules as colliding hard spheres; iterated maps; and simulations demonstrating "chaotic" behavior in the Lorenz equation, among others.

Ulam's simulations of the emergence of complexity from simple dynamics differ from other work of that era that focuses on the generation of ordered behavior, or behavior resulting from complex rules or features such as aperiodicity or sensitive dependence on initial conditions.

"First" does not mean "most impactful." Ulam's approach—combining originality, intuition, a love of imaginative play and bold conjectures—was not easy to emulate. Certainly the paper offered no algorithmic design principles or easily applicable analytical tools.

Nevertheless, some researchers expanded on Ulam's thesis and succeeded in arousing widespread interest in CA. In the 1970s, Conway's "Game of Life" (Gardner 1970) provided a realization of a universal Turing machine and popularized CA as models of emergence and self-organization. Fredkin and Toffoli (1982) studied the computing ability of reversible CA and their use in modeling of physical laws. Wolfram's (2002) systematic study in the 1980s of 1D CA identified relations among complexity, information, and computation, and established them as prototypical models for the emergence of complexity in natural and computational systems. In the late 1980s Langton (1989) founded the field of artificial life with CA as the logical universe for studies of "life in any of its possible manifestations."

Over time Ulam's study of growth patterns has borne fruit both mathematically and in applications ranging from fluid turbulence through epidemiology and plant morphogenesis to urban planning and environmental design (in all of which areas the paper continues to be cited). Even Ulam might be surprised. ✦

REFERENCES

Alder, B. J., and T. E. Wainwright. 1959. "Studies in Molecular Dynamics." *Journal of Chemical Physics* 31 (2): 459–466. https://doi.org/10.1063/1.1730376.

Butler, J. T., and S. C. Ntafos. 1977. "The Vector String Descriptor as a Tool in the Analysis of Cellular Automata Systems." *Mathematical Biosciences* 35 (1–2): 55–84. https://doi.org/10.1016/0025-5564(77)90086-4.

Cook, M. 2004. "Universality in Elementary Cellular Automata." *Complex Systems* 15 (1): 1–40. https://doi.org/10.25088/ComplexSystems.15.1.1.

Feigenbaum, M. 1982. "Reflections of the Polish Masters: An Interview with Stan Ulam and Mark Kac." *Los Alamos Science* Fall (6): 54–65.

Finkel, L. H., and G. M. Edelman. 1985. "Stanislaw Ulam: The Warmth and Brilliance of an Eclectic Mind." *Letters in Mathematical Physics* 10:243–245. https://doi.org/10.1007/BF00398164.

Fredkin, E., and T. Toffoli. 1982. "Conservative Logic." *International Journal of Theoretical Physics* 21 (3–4): 219–254. https://doi.org/10.1007/BF01857727.

Gardner, M. 1970. "The Fantastic Combinations of John Conway's New Solitaire Game 'Life'." *Scientific American* 223 (4): 120–123. https://doi.org/10.1038/scientificamerican1070-120.

Kawaharada, A. 2014. "Ulam's Cellular Automaton and Rule 150." *Hokaaido Mathematical Journal* 43 (3): 361–383. https://doi.org/10.14492/hokmj/1416837570.

Langton, C. 1989. *Artificial Life.* New York, NY: Routledge.

Mauldin, R. D. 2015. *The Scottish Book: Mathematics from the Scottish Cafe.* 2nd. Basel, Switzerland: Birkhauser.

Mauldin, R. D., and S. Ulam. 1987. "Mathematical Problems and Games." *Advances in Applied Mathematics* 8 (3): 281–344. https://doi.org/10.1016/0196-8858(87)90026-1.

Ulam, S. 1976. *Adventures of a Mathematician.* New York, NY: Charles Scribner's Sons.

Wolfram, S. 2002. *A New Kind of Science.* Champaign, IL: Wolfram Media.

··

ON SOME MATHEMATICAL PROBLEMS CONNECTED WITH PATTERNS OF GROWTH OF FIGURES

··

Stanisław Ulam

1. Introduction

This note will contain a brief discussion of certain properties of figures in two or three dimensional space which are obtained by rather simple recursion relations. Starting from an initial configuration, one defines in successive "generations" additions to the existing figure, representing, as it were, a growth of the initial pattern, in discrete units of time. The basic thing will be a fixed division of the plane (or space) into regular elementary figures. For example, the plane may be divided into squares or else into equilateral triangles (the space into cubes, etc.). An initial configuration will be a finite number of elements of such a subdivision and our induction rule will define successive accretions to the starting configuration.

The simplest patterns observed, for example in crystals, are periodic and the properties of such have been studied mathematically very extensively. The rules which we shall employ will lead to much more complicated and in general nonperiodic structures, whose properties are more difficult to establish, despite the relative simplicity of our recursion relations. The objects defined in that way seem to be, so to say, intermediate in complexity between inorganic patterns like those of crystals and the more varied intricacies of organic molecules and structures. In fact, one of the aims of the present note is to show, by admittedly somewhat artificial examples, an enormous variety of objects which may be obtained by means of rather simple inductive definitions and to throw a sidelight on the question of how much "information" is necessary to describe the seemingly enormously elaborate structures of living objects.

Figure 1.

Much of the work described below was performed in collaboration with Dr. J. Holladay[1] and Robert Schrandt.[2] We have used electronic computing machines at the Los Alamos Scientific Laboratory to produce a great number of such patterns and to survey certain properties of their morphology, both in time and space. Most of the results are empirical in nature, and so far there are very few general properties which can be obtained theoretically.

2.

In the simplest case we have the subdivision of the infinite plane into squares. We start, in the first generation, with a finite number of squares and define now a rule of growth as follows: Given a number of squares in the nth generation, the squares of the $(n + 1)$th generation will be all those which are adjacent to the existing ones but with the following proviso: the squares which are adjacent to more than one square of the nth generation will *not* be taken. For example, starting with one square in the first generation one obtains the following configuration after five generations.

It is obvious that with this rule of growth the figure will continue increasing indefinitely. It will have the original symmetry of the initial

---

[1]Holladay, J. C. and Ulam, S. M., Notices Amer. Math. Soc. 7 (1960), 234.

[2]Schrandt, R. G. and Ulam, S. M., Notices Amer. Math. Soc. 7 (1960), 642.

configuration (1 square) and on the four perpendicular axes all the squares will be present—these are the "stems," from which side branches of variable lengths will grow.

We can consider right away a slightly modified rule of growth. Starting again with a single square and defining the $(n+1)$th generation as before to be squares adjacent to the squares of the nth generation, we modify our exclusion proviso as follows: we will not put into existence any square for the $(n+1)$th generation if another prospective candidate for it would as much as touch at one point the square under consideration. With this second rule we obtain after five generations the figure shown on the next page. With this rule we will again notice immediately that the "stem" will continue indefinitely but now the density of the growing squares will be less than in the previous case. In this case again one can calculate which squares will appear in the plane and which will remain vacant.

A general property of systems growing under the rules (and even somewhat more general ones) is given by a theorem due to J. Holladay. At generations whose index number n is of the form $n = 2^k$, the growth *is cut off* everywhere except on the "stems," i.e., the straight lines issuing from the original point.

The old side-branches will terminate and the only new ones will start growing from the continuation of the stems.

One of the most interesting situations arises when the plane is divided into equilateral triangles and starting from one initial triangle we construct new ones, generation by generation. We can again have the analogue of the first rule, i.e., for the $(n+1)$th generation we consider all triangles adjacent to a triangle of the nth generation. As before we shall not construct those which have two different parents in the nth generation. The system which will grow will have the six-fold symmetry of the original figure. There will appear a rather dense collection of triangles in the plane. The second way is to take the analogue of the second rule of "conflict," i.e., do not construct a triangle in the $(n+1)$th generation if it would so much as touch at one point another prospective child of some other element in the nth generation. (We of course allow two prospective children to touch on their base from two adjacent parents.) This rule will lead to a pattern which has fewer elements and

First experiment: varying the update rule. Butler and Ntafos (1977) proved the existence of a closed-form solution for the patterns generated in a class of 2D "growth-like" CA. For Ulam's example, the limiting density of 1-cells with any finite initial condition is 2/3.

Next experiment: varying the geometry of the underlying spatial array. Subsequent research has shown the critical role played by geometry. A striking example is the modeling of fluid flow as lattice gases. The earliest model (called the "HPP model") was on a square lattice: it lacked rotational invariance, which resulted in the fluid behavior being highly dependent on the direction in which it was measured (producing, for example, square-shaped vortices).

Figure 2.

a smaller density in the plane than the one constructed under the first conflict definition.

One can prove easily that the initial hexagonal symmetry will persist and that the growth will continue indefinitely with the "stems" increasing in each generation by one element, i.e., forming continuous lines. The side branches have variable lengths and get "choked off" at variable times (generations). The author did not manage to prove that there will exist infinitely long side branches. It is possible to demonstrate that there will be arbitrarily long ones. The figure[3] shows a segment of the growing pattern. It represents one-half of a sixty degree section. The other half is obtained by a mirror image. The other sections are obtained by rotation.

For the construction with triangles under the first rule Holladay's cut-off property holds for generations with index of the form 2^k. Under the second rule it was not even possible to prove the value or indeed the existence of a limiting density of the triangles obtained by the construction (relative to all the triangles in the whole plane).

In the division of the plane into regular hexagons and starting with, say, again one element, one can obtain the analogues of the two patterns. Again the analogue of the more liberal construction has the cut-off property. For the more stringent rule it was, so far, impossible to predict the asymptotic properties.

CONTINUED FROM PREVIOUS
A later model (called the "FHP model") changed the geometry to a hexagonal grid with nondeterministic collision and scattering rules. It proved to be largely isotropic, meaning that it no longer exhibited the (unphysical) sensitive dependence on direction, and was able to simulate flows of higher Reynolds numbers.

---

[3]See Example 5 at the end.

3.

The construction of the elements of the $(n+1)$th generation is through a single parentage: each element attempts to generate one new one in the next generation. In the division of the plane into squares, triangles, hexagons, etc., one could adopt a different point of view: in the case of, say triangles, one can consider instead of the areas of the triangles, their vertices only and imagine that each pair of vertices produces a new vertex—namely, the one forming the triangle with the two given vertices as their sides. Actually, the origin of the above-mentioned constructions is due to this point of view:

In a paper, "Quadratic Transformations" (Los Alamos Laboratory Report LA-2305, 1959), P. R. Stein and the writer have considered problems of "binary" reaction systems. Mathematically, these involve the following situation: a great number of elements is given, each element being one of, say, three types. These elements combine in pairs and produce, in the next generation another pair of elements whose types are unique functions of the types of the two parents. The problem is to determine the properties of the composition of the population, as time goes on. If x, y, z denote the proportions of elements of the three types in the nth generation, then the expected value of the numbers of particles of each type in the new generation will be given by a quadratic transformation. For example, the rule could be that an x type and a y type particle together produce an x type, the $(x + x)$ a z type, $(x + z)$ a y type, $(y + y)$ an x type, $(y + z)$ a z type and $(z + z)$ a y type. (Actually there are more than ninety possible and different such rules—we assume, however, that once a rule is chosen it is valid for all time.) The rule above would lead to the new proportions x', y', z' given, as follows:

$$x' = 2xy + y^2,$$
$$y' = z^2 + 2xz,$$
$$z' = y^2 + 2yz.$$

This is a transformation of a part of the plane into itself. We have three variables, but $x + y + z = 1 = x' + y' + z'$. By iterating this transformation one obtains the expected values of the numbers of elements of each type in the subsequent generations. In the above-mentioned study some properties of the iterates of the transformation were established. In particular, in some cases there may be convergence to a stable distribution, in other cases there is a convergence to an oscillating behavior, etc.

These studies concerned a random mating (or collisions) between pairs of elements. The question arose as to the behavior of such systems if the binary production were not a random one but instead subject to some constraints, say due to geometry. A most stringent one seemed to be to imagine, for example, that the elements form the vertices of a division of a plane into regular triangles, each vertex being of one of the three possible "colors." Then consider an initial configuration as given and assume the production of new elements by pairs of vertices forming sides of the triangular division. In the simplest case one can start with one triangle whose three vertices are all different in type. The next generation will be formed then by the three pairs as parents and each side of the given triangle will produce a new vertex whose color is a function of the two colors of the parents. We shall obtain then a second generation and continue in this fashion. It is immediately found, however, that the construction cannot be uniquely continued. After a small number of generations it will appear that two pairs of vertices forming two sides of the configuration will have a single vertex as completing the two triangles to be constructed. Which color to assign to the new vertex? It may be that the two sets of parents will give a conflicting recipe for the color of the new point.

One way out of this dilemma would be not to consider a point for which a conflicting determination of color may be given and leave its position vacant. This recipe extended to points which are doubly determined by two sides of previously constructed triangles gave rise to the study mentioned in the previous paragraphs. Actually the patterns mentioned above could be considered as consisting of points which are of three different kinds (imagining, for example, that the new ones arise in a "molecule" as a result of a double bond, etc.). As it is R. Schrandt and the writer have considered also other recipes for determining the color of points which were given conflicting determinations by the two pairs of parents. One rule (1) was to choose the type not involved in the conflicting determination: since there are three types, if the two determinations for the new points differ, one may choose the third

More twists: Introducing quadratic transformations, probabilistic update rules, and expansion of the set of values per cell.

Finkel and Edelman assert from discussions in the 1970s that Ulam was motivated to make these and other modifications in CA rules by phenomena such as epigenetic interactions in morphogenesis. For example, Ulam developed a model that includes a "rule to change the rules" depending on factors such as the spatial configurations or density of cells with specific values in the automaton. Rules that coevolve in this way with the state of the automata can be used to model processes such as cell induction where groups of cells affect the properties of adjacent groups of cells during cell differentiation, with those properties then influencing future development.

one. Another rule (2) was also considered: to decide, at random with equal probability, which of the two contrasting determinations should be chosen. Still another rule (3) was to choose, in case of such a conflict, a fourth color whose proportion will be denoted by w and such that an x type $+ w$ type produces $x; y + w$ produces y and $z + w$ produces z and $w + w$ produces w in subsequent combinations. This could have an interpretation of representing a molecule of a type which cannot propagate except in combination with itself. We have studied experimentally, on a computing machine, the propagation of such systems. The Rule No. 2 in particular involves sometimes a random determination of points somewhat similar to the study in LA-2305 mentioned above on random mating. Under all these rules, there seems to be a convergence of the number of particles of different types to a steady distribution (in contrast to the behavior given by iteration of the quadratic transformations where in many cases there is an oscillatory limit or even more irregular ergodic asymptotic behavior). In some cases the convergence seems to take place to a fixed point (i.e., a definite value of x, y, z), and under Rule No. 2 to values, numerically not too different from the fixed point of the corresponding quadratic transformation. It has not been possible to *prove* the existence of a limiting distribution but the numerical work strongly indicates it. It should be noted that all the initial configurations were of the simplest possible type, e.g., consisted of one triplet of points. A detailed description of this work will appear in a report by R. Schrandt.

4.

We return now to our discussion of growing patterns where we do not label the new elements by different colors but merely consider, as in paragraph 2, the geometry of the growing figure. The problem arose of considering the properties of growth of such figures with a rule of erasure or "death" of old elements: suppose we fix an integer k arbitrarily and to our recursive definition of construction of new elements add the rule that we erase from the pattern all elements which are k generations old. In particular, suppose $k = 3$ and consider the growth from squares, as in the first rule in paragraph 1, with the additional proviso that after constructing the $(n + 1)$st generation, we shall erase all points of the $(n - 1)$st generation. (The construction allows the configuration to grow back into points of a previous generation of index l where l is less than $n - 1$.) In this construction, starting say with two squares to begin with, one will observe a growth of patterns, then a splitting (due to erasures) and then later recombinations of the pattern. A search was undertaken for initial patterns which in future generations split into figures similar or identical with previous ones, i.e., a reproduction at least for certain values of the index of generation. It was not possible, in general, even in the cases where a growth pattern without erasure could be predicted, to describe the appearance of the apparently moving figures which in general exhibit a very chaotic behavior. In one starting configuration, however, one could predict the future behavior. This configuration consists of two squares touching each other at one point and located diagonally. Under our Rule No. 1 with erasure of the third oldest generation, this pattern is reproduced as four copies of itself in every 2^pth generation ($p = 1, 2, 3 \cdots$), displaced by 2^p units from the original pattern. The same behavior holds for starting patterns of say four squares located diagonally, or 8 points or 16 points, etc.

In case of a triangular subdivision the behavior of growth with a rule of erasure for old elements was also experimentally investigated. The process of growth was considered as follows: given a finite collection of vertices of the triangular subdivision of the plane—some labeled with the index $n - 1$ and others with n—one constructs the points of the $(n + 1)$th generation by adding vertices of the triangles whose sides are labeled either with $n - 1$ and n or n and n—again, however, *not* putting in points which are *doubly* determined. One then erases all points with the index $n - 1$. In case of squares our rules of growth enable the pattern to exist indefinitely, starting with any non-trivial initial condition. This is not always the case for triangles. In particular a starting pattern of two vertices with the same generation terminates after ten generations—that is to say, all possible points of growth are conflicting ones and these are not allowed by our rule of construction. One has to point out here that in the case of the "death" rule which operates by erasure of all elements that are k generations *old* the initial configuration has to specify which elements are of the 1st and which of the 2nd generation. Two vertices,

Ulam points to a variety of "meso-level" dynamics including coalescence, splitting, and (in a followup paper) "fighting" and self-reproduction.

The "very chaotic behavior" he notes has been shown in recent work by Kawaharada to include 1) fractal boundaries of spatial patterns, and 2) embedding within Ulam's 2D CA of the linear "chaotic" elementary CA Rule 150, which was proved by Wolfram and Cook to be capable of universal computation.

Cellular automata—in which the *n*th generation is determined by the *(n-1)*st generation—are mathematically equivalent to recurrence relations defined on, say, the integers.

In the case of 1D CA, Ulam here makes an idiosyncratic choice in defining them as special recurrence relations called "sieves"—examples of which include the algorithms for generating primes or the Fibonacci numbers—modified however to eliminate certain entries based on position in the sequence or on other criteria. (The "lucky number sieve" Ulam constructed in 1956 is an example.) The question then is to study the asymptotic behavior, such as their limiting density on the set of integers, the existence of "twin" entries in the sequence, and other features similar to those of primes.

Ulam enjoyed designing sieves, including probabilistic ones, some of which appear to be mere curiosities and others of which have led to results in ideal theory and commutative algebras.

one labeled 1st and the other 2nd generation, will give rise to a viable pattern.

5.

In three-dimensional space a similar experimental study was made of growth of patterns on a cubical lattice. The rules of growth can be considered in a similar way to the recipes used in two dimensions. Starting with one cube one may construct new ones which are adjacent to it (have a face in common). Again one will not put in new cubes if they have a face in common with more than one cube of the previous generation. The analogue of the first rule gives a system whose density in space tends to 0. This is in contrast to the situation in the plane where a finite density was obtained for this case.

R. Schrandt has investigated on a computer the growth of systems with a rule for erasure of old elements. The case of erasure of elements three generations old was followed. The patterns which appear seem to be characterized by bunches of cubes forming flat groups. These groups are connected by thin threads. Description of these patterns and a few general statements one can make about them will be also contained in Schrandt's report.

These heuristic studies, already in two dimensions, show that the variety of patterns is too great to allow simple characterizations. The writer has attempted to make corresponding definitions in one dimension with the hope that some general properties of sequences defined by analogous recursive rules would be gleaned from them. Suppose we define a sequence of integers as follows: starting with the integers $1, 2$ we construct new ones in sequence by considering sums of two previously defined integers but not including in our collection those integers which can be obtained as a sum of previous ones in more than one way. We never add an integer to itself. The sequence which starts with 1 and 2 will continue as follows: $1, 2, 3, 4, 6, 8, 11, 13, 16, 18, 26, 28, \cdots$. The integer 5 is not in it because it is a sum of two previous ones in two different ways. The next integer which is expressed in one and only one way of the sum of previous ones is 6; 7 has a double representation but 8 is uniquely determined. 11 is the next and so on. Starting with 1 and 3 one obtains the following sequence: $1, 3, 4, 5, 6, 8, 10, 12, 17, 21, \cdots$. Unfortunately, it appears to the writer that even here it is not easy to establish properties of these "unique sum sequences." For example, the question of whether there will be infinitely many twins, i.e., integers in succession differing by two, seems difficult to answer. Even a good estimate of density of these sequences relative to the set of all integers is not easily made.

The aim in presenting these disconnected empirical studies was to point out problems attending the combinatorics of systems which, in an extremely simplified and schematic way, show a growth of figures subject to simple geometrical constraints. It seems obvious that, before one can obtain some general properties in "auxology," a great deal of experimental data have to be surveyed. It was possible to study the effect of many variations in our rules on the computing machines. A scope attached to the machine allows one to survey the resulting patterns visually—their computation takes only a very short time. This work is continuing and perhaps some more general properties of their morphology will be demonstrable. ✸

REFERENCES

Menzel, M. T., Stein P. R., and S. M. Ulam. 1959. *Quadratic Transformations.* Technical report 2305. Los Alamos Laboratory Report.

A current area of CA research is the use of Hausdorff and other fractal dimensions to characterize their spatiotemporal patterns. Ulam came close to anticipating this line of work. Pattern recognition by the brain being a longstanding interest, he did work in the 1970s using Hausdorff dimension of 2D sets as benchmarks to compare possible mechanisms for pattern retrieval and recognition in the presence of noise, transformations, and deformations.

In recent years, the morphology of CA models of biological growth patterns has developed new complexity and structure. CA models of plant morphogenesis, e,g,, incorporate interactions between biochemical and biomechanical signaling that give rise to, and are then acted upon by, the organizational design of the plant. Both computational and experimental evidence point to an extraordinary subtlety and sophistication—the mathematics of such processes could well be bracingly novel.

APPENDIX: EXAMPLES

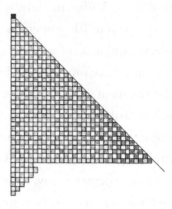

Example 1. Starting with the black square as the first generation, each successive generation consists of those squares that are adjacent to one and only one square of previous generations. In most of these illustrations, only cells in certain directions were drawn. Growth in other directions is the same because of symmetry conditions.

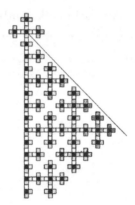

Example 2. "Maltese" crosses. The black cells in this pattern are arranged according to the pattern for Example 1, except that they are more spread out. Here we use the same rule as in Example 1 with the following exception: if a cell would touch some other cell (either already grown or being considered for growth in this generation) on either a corner or a side, it is rejected. However, we made two exceptions to this restriction: (1) if the cell touches some other cell by virtue of having the same parent.

(2) In the following case,
$$\begin{array}{cccccc} & 2^* & & 5^* & & \\ 1 & 2 & 3 & 4 & 5. \\ & 2^* & & 5^* & & \end{array}$$
The two starred elements of the fifth generation are allowed to touch potential, though previously rejected, children of the third generation. This has to be allowed to enable the growth to turn corners. Note that the children of the third generation were rejected only because of the potential children of the starred members of the second generation.

Example 3. This pattern follows the same rule as Example 1, except that triangles are used instead of squares.

Example 4. This pattern follows the same rule as Example 3 with one exception: if a new cell would touch the corner of some old cell (other than a parent), it is rejected.

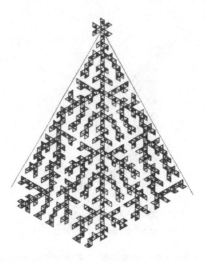

Example 5. This pattern follows the same rule as Example 4 with this exception: if two new cells (other than siblings) would touch each other even on a corner, they are both rejected.

Example 6. This pattern follows the same rule as Example 1, except that hexagons are used instead of squares. The reason it is disconnected is that a triangle of cells is left out. This triangle is the same as that formed in the first few generations for what is drawn plus a mirror image of it.

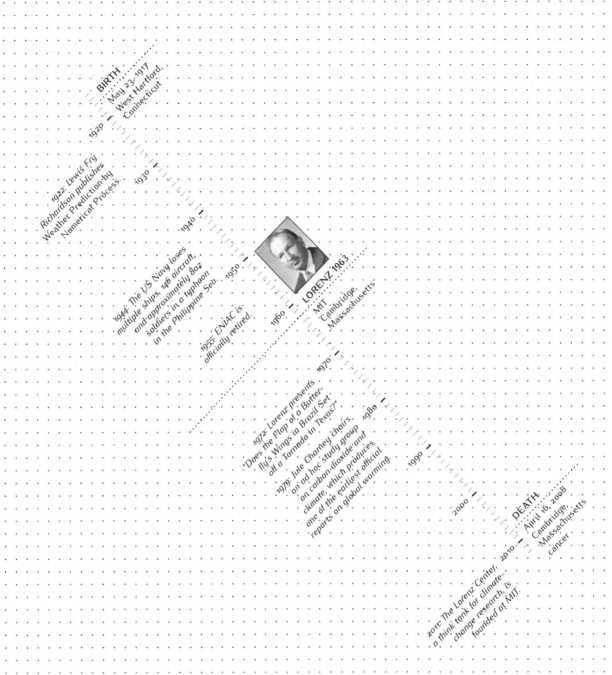

BIRTH
May 23, 1917
West Hartford,
Connecticut

1920

*1922: Lewis Fry
Richardson publishes
Weather Prediction by
Numerical Process.*

1930

1940

*1944: The US Navy loses
multiple ships, 146 aircraft,
and approximately 802
soldiers in a typhoon
in the Philippine Sea.*

1950

*1955: ENIAC is
officially retired.*

LORENZ 1963
MIT
Cambridge,
Massachusetts

1960

1970

*1972: Lorenz presents
"Does the Flap of a Butterfly's Wings in Brazil Set-
off a Tornado in Texas?"*

*1979: Jule Charney chairs
an ad hoc study group
on carbon dioxide and
climate, which produces
one of the earliest official
reports on global warming.*

1980

1990

2000

DEATH
April 16, 2008
Cambridge,
Massachusetts
cancer.

2010

*2011: The Lorenz Center,
a think tank for climate-
change research, is
founded at MIT.*

EDWARD · NORTON · LORENZ

[23]

THE REVOLUTIONARY DISCOVERY
OF CHAOS

J. Doyne Farmer, University of Oxford and Santa Fe Institute

The realization in the late twentieth century that deterministic dynamics can be chaotic fundamentally changed our view of predictability vs. unpredictability. Although pieces of the puzzle were understood in the late nineteenth century, Ed Lorenz's famous 1963 paper brought it all together, explaining the how, why and "so what" of chaos in one fell swoop. In this essay I will explain what chaos is, why this paper was a key original contribution, why it triggered a revolution, how chaos fits into the broader framework of complex systems, and its practical and philosophical implications.

As most readers will know, chaos implies fundamental limits to prediction, but it is more than that: Chaos is a remarkable example of endogenous motion, that is, motion that spontaneously emerges in an otherwise static environment. It is also an example of an unsolvable phenomenon, the dynamical systems analog of Gödel's proof or Turing's halting problem. In fact, chaos is a double-edged sword: In some circumstances, the realization that chaos underpins random-looking phenomena leads to vastly improved predictions (Farmer and Sidorowich 1987).

Many phenomena in nature and social science are chaotic. Fluid turbulence and weather are the most famous examples, but there are many others. Celestial mechanics is the canonical example of predictability, but, nonetheless, chaos places a fundamental limit on predicting motion in the solar system of about 20 million years. The first experimental system to be definitively shown to be chaotic was a chemical oscillator, in which the chemical composition fluctuates irregularly in time—a phenomenon that was believed to be theoretically impossible until past the middle of the twentieth century. Chaos

E. N. Lorenz, "Deterministic Nonperiodic Flow," *Journal of the Atmospheric Sciences* 20 (2), 130–141 (1963).

Reprinted with permission of the American Meteorological Society; published 1963 by the American Meteorological Society.

735

explains why populations of species can change spontaneously and unpredictably. Though this is controversial, many (like me) believe that business cycles are due at least in part to chaotic dynamics. At a more theoretical level, the ergodic hypothesis, which underpins all of statistical mechanics, depends on chaotic behavior at the microscopic level. And there are important implications for free will.

To explain why Lorenz's paper was so revolutionary, we need to revisit the mindset of mathematical scientists pre-chaos. The conundrum posed by Newton's laws is poetically summarized by (Laplace 1814):

> *We may regard the present state of the universe as the effect of its past and the cause of its future. An intellect which at a certain moment would know all forces that set nature in motion, and all positions of all items of which nature is composed, if this intellect were also vast enough to submit these data to analysis, it would embrace in a single formula the movements of the greatest bodies of the universe and those of the tiniest atom; for such an intellect nothing would be uncertain and the future just like the past would be the present to it.*

The laws of Newtonian mechanics are deterministic, and so are the laws of quantum mechanics, even if the precision of measurements is limited. So why is much of nature so unpredictable? Pre-chaos, everyone assumed that the only limit to predictability was feasibility. No "intellect" (later called Laplace's demon) could ever know the positions and velocities of all the items of which nature is composed. But chaos shows that, even if there were such an intellect, the reason the future is not just like the past is because the future is inherently unpredictable. Even though Newton's laws are deterministic, chaotic dynamics are too complex—closed-form solutions are impossible, so there is no formula like the one that Laplace imagined.

The chaotic attractor that Lorenz found has many remarkable properties:

1. *It is an attractor.* Its three variables have well-defined maxima and minima. Initial conditions on the attractor remain on the attractor.

Initial conditions in its basin of attraction all end up on the attractor. It is globally stable, meaning that perturbations to motion on the attractor return to the attractor.

2. *The attractor is a fractal*, meaning that any point on the attractor is arbitrarily close to points that are not on the attractor. (A ball of any finite radius centered on any point on the attractor always contains points that are outside the attractor.) As explained below, one can think of the attractor as a two-dimensional sheet that has been folded an infinite number of times.

3. *Motion is irregular*, meaning that it cannot be decomposed into oscillations with rationally related frequencies. If one listens to the motion by converting it into sound, the sound is noisy, with a roar like wind in a storm. (In contrast, a fixed point attractor makes no sound, and a periodic limit cycle attractor makes a pure tone, like someone whistling).

4. *Motion on the attractor is locally unstable*, meaning that two nearby initial conditions diverge from each other on average at an exponential rate, so that they eventually become far apart.

5. *Motion on the attractor destroys information*, meaning that the information in the initial condition is eventually lost.

6. *Motion on the attractor is mixing*, meaning that the points in any small disc on the attractor eventually end up scattered all over the attractor.

7. *Motion is endogenous*, meaning that it occurs spontaneously, without any external driving. It seems to come from nowhere. Think of a cascading waterfall: Everything in the environment is fixed, yet the water moves as if it has a will of its own.

8. *Prediction of the motion along a trajectory requires ongoing computation.* The trajectories of the system cannot be solved in closed form, meaning that there is no simple formula for the position of a trajectory at time t that one can simply plug into. The solution

requires computation, and a trajectory of length $T > 1$ requires T times as much computation as a trajectory of length 1.

9. *There are only three variables*, so the motion can be visualized as the motion of a point in a three-dimensional space. The equations of the dynamical system are very simple, yet they generate remarkably complex motion.

The fact that there are only three variables makes it possible to analyze the motion visually. Each point (x,y,z) in the state space can be thought of as having an arrow attached to it that states where the system will go at the next instant. (This way of visualizing dynamical systems is due to Henri Poincaré). Because there are only three variables, Lorenz was able to visualize the attractor and understand what caused the chaos that he observed. In fact, Lorenz was already aware in the late fifties that there were equations that generated irregular motion, but they had many variables and were too complicated to analyze. Then in 1961 he had a discussion with his meteorology colleague Barry Saltzman, who was studying a set of equations that were an approximation for the motion of water in a vessel that is steadily heated from below. He had found a dynamical system with seven variables that made irregular oscillations. Lorenz began experimenting with this system on his Royal McBee LGP-30 computer (a loud desk-sized box that the meteorology department at MIT purchased for him in 1961) and realized that four of the seven variables eventually reached constant values. He removed these four variables from Saltzman's equations and found that the remaining three variables still made irregular oscillations.

He then did a series of numerical simulations and tests that allowed him to understand what caused the chaos. Here is a highly simplified version: Imagine a set of parallel trajectories forming a two-dimensional sheet in a three dimensional space. Now imagine stretching one end of the sheet, so that the trajectories separate (at an exponential rate). Now fold the sheet over onto itself and repeat an infinite number of times. The action is much like kneading bread dough, which is why the motion is mixing, locally unstable and destroys information. For more detailed explanations with better graphics, see Abraham and Shaw (1985) or Crutchfield *et al.* (1986).

Lorenz's system is a little more complicated—the description above is for an even simpler set of equations with only one nonlinear term, discovered by Otto Rössler. Lorenz's system is like two interlocking sheets, hence the resemblance to a butterfly, but the basic mechanism is the same.

Lorenz's popular book *The Essence of Chaos* (1993) contains a nice history of the discoveries of chaos preceding his work. He begins the story with the discovery of Neptune, which is much too faint to be seen with the naked eye. Its existence was inferred from the fact that the orbit of Uranus behaved unpredictably. By assuming that the unpredictability must come from another yet undiscovered planet, it was possible to tell astronomers where to point their telescopes, and Neptune was found.

You may be wondering how it was possible to predict the motion of a planet like Uranus, which is strongly influenced by Jupiter and Saturn, not to mention Neptune, in 1846. This was done by a series of approximations. If only Jupiter orbited the sun in our solar system, using Newton's laws it would be possible to predict Jupiter's trajectory exactly. Given this, if we assume that Saturn has no effect on Jupiter, it is possible to approximately predict the motion of Saturn. But then, once this is done, if we now assume that Jupiter doesn't affect Saturn, it is possible to approximately predict how Saturn will affect Jupiter. This can then be used to get a better approximation of Saturn's motion, and the process can be repeated until the desired accuracy is achieved. This of course required a lot of pencils and sheets of paper . . .

Poincaré became interested in this problem, and to make a long story short, he made a series of fundamental breakthroughs in dynamical systems theory that allowed him to show why a solution to the three-body problem (not to mention the n-body problem) was unlikely to be found (see Poincaré 1893).

A couple of decades later, Poincaré wrote a popular book, *Science et Méthod*, that reflects on the causes of chance and uncertainty. There he uses the term sensitive dependence on initial conditions to describe situations where a very small change can have a very large effect. His examples include a ball balanced on the peak of a cone, which can roll off in any direction, or the game of *rouge et noir* (roulette), where a tiny difference in the way the ball is thrown can result in a different number. But he doesn't connect this to his work on the three-body problem.

Lorenz studied mathematics at Dartmouth and then at Harvard, where he came under the influence of Garrett Birkhoff, the first American mathematician to be taken seriously on the international stage. Although Birkhoff was very familiar with the work of Poincaré, Lorenz was apparently not familiar with Poincaré's work on celestial mechanics. During World War II Lorenz switched to meteorology, and after the war he got a PhD in that subject from MIT.

In addition to Poincaré, there were several other precursors to Lorenz's discovery of chaos, including Cartwright and Littlewood (1945), Stein and Ulam (1962), and Ueda (1991, but really 1961). All of these papers are important, but none of them put together all the elements of chaos and fully realized its significance. Poincaré's pathbreaking work on the three-body problem was of monumental importance, but its main focus was on the impossibility of closed-form solutions rather than fundamental limits to predictability. Chaos in dynamical systems where energy is conserved is very different than in dissipative systems. In conservative systems there are no attractors and no endogenous motion. Similarly, Cartwright and Littlewood and Ueda's work was on driven nonlinear oscillators, so, again, no endogenous motion. Lorenz's work, in contrast, was the result of a decade-long quest to understand why there seemed to be limits to the predictability of the weather. Lorenz's analysis stands out for its clarity, simplicity, and completeness. Because Lorenz's 1963 paper was published in a meteorology journal, it didn't get much attention until the mathematics community discovered it in 1971. It became the canonical source for the discovery of chaos and now has more than 28,000 citations.

To put the impact of Lorenz's paper in context, when I was a graduate student in the late 1970s, I gave many talks about chaos in physics and math departments. Mathematicians often responded, "How do you know this is not just numerical error?" In physics departments, the old guard developing the theory of turbulence were reluctant to give up their "it's complicated" explanation, expressing skepticism about the idea that chaos was of fundamental importance.

Chaos supports the foundations of statistical mechanics. The fundamental postulate of statistical mechanics is that, on the microscopic scale, things are as random as they can be subject to constraints such as conservation of energy. The ergodic hypothesis asserts that this is true. Although it has been around for more than 150 years, it remains to be proved. We now know that chaos is the source of the needed randomness, but energy-conserving chaos has complicated structure and does not necessarily uniformly fill the entire state space. This suggests that, strictly speaking, the ergodic hypothesis is probably not true. But it is likely a good approximation.

Chaos shows us how dynamical systems (such as Newton's laws) can transform information. The binary shift map is the simplest example. It is a mapping of the interval into itself, consisting of multiplication by two mod one. The dynamical system can be visualized as two parallel line segments of slope 2, one connecting $(0,0)$ to $(½, 1)$ and the other connecting $(½, 0)$ to $(1, 1)$. If we represent a number between 0 and 1 in base 2, for example 0.1101001101, the shift map converts it successively to 0.101001101?, 0.01001101??, 0.1001101???, and so on, until we are left entirely with question marks. In other words, it converts microscopic information into macroscopic information and then throws it away. Chaos destroys information. This is why chaotic systems do not have closed-form solutions, and why their solution requires ongoing computation—because it is necessary to replace the information that is lost, it is impossible to compute the answer for all time.

Chaos is an emergent property. The only way to know whether it is present in a dynamical system is to solve it numerically. Chaos can emerge suddenly, as if from nowhere, under small perturbations in parameters. It is ultimately less interesting and much easier to understand than its information-creating cousins, self-organizing systems. Nonetheless, it is a stepping stone to complex systems: After we became aware that dynamics can destroy information, we realized it can create it, too (even if this requires an understanding of what information is relevant and what isn't). Chaos was the first example where the connection between information and dynamics became clear (Shaw 1981).

To understand the analogy between chaos and the halting problem, let's think about computation in terms of trajectories in the space of logical propositions. When a program yields a unique answer, this is like convergence to a fixed-point attractor.

But now consider the Cretan paradox: Epimenides the Cretan says, "all Cretans are liars," but Epimenides is himself a Cretan; therefore he is himself a liar. But if he is a liar, what he says is untrue, and consequently, the Cretans are veracious; but Epimenides is a Cretan, and therefore what he says is true . . . ad infinitum. To a dynamical-systems person, this suggests an attractor that is a periodic orbit of period 2. Similarly, programs that do not halt and do not settle into periodic orbits are analogous to chaotic attractors.

Randomness is necessary for many things. For example, evolution involves a trade-off between exploration and adaptation, and exploration requires randomness. Serendipity plays an important role in creativity and design –for example, when he got stuck, Mozart used a method based on rolling dice to suggest musical phrases. Strictly speaking, the only "fundamental" source of randomness is quantum measurement, but in most real-world applications, randomness is caused by chaos (or at least sensitive dependence on initial conditions) rather than quantum mechanics. And even here, some believe that we may eventually discover that the uncertainty in quantum measurement is due to chaos (Palmer 2022).

To return to Laplace, without chaos, nothing would be uncertain and the future, just like the past, would be the present to it. In these circumstances there would be no free will—everything would be determined, the future would be obvious, and the laws of physics would leave us without choices. But in the real, chaotic world, the actions of humans are unpredictable. At the very least we can have the illusion of free will, even if our actions are determined by a combination of our genes and past experience. Lorenz's closing comment on this topic is amusing:

> We must then wholeheartedly believe in free will. If free will is a reality, we shall have made the correct choice. If it is not, we shall still not have made an incorrect choice, because we shall not have made any choice at all, not having a free will to do so.

I will close by asserting without proof that, without chaos, the world would be extraordinarily boring: life and thought would be impossible without it. ✒

Postscript

As a graduate student I had the good fortune to work for Ed Lorenz as a summer intern. He was a gentle, soft-spoken, shy person who gracefully combined intelligence, humility, and intellectual honesty, and who could climb a mountain remarkably quickly. He is one of my intellectual heroes and one of the great scientists of the twentieth century.

REFERENCES

Abraham, R., and C. Shaw. 1985. *Dynamics: The Geometry of Behavior: Part III.* Santa Cruz, CA: Ariel Press.

Cartwright, M. L., and J. E. Littlewood. 1945. "On Non-Linear Differential Equations of the Second Order: I. The Equation $\ddot{y} -k(1 - y^2)\dot{y} + y = b\lambda k\cos(t + a), k$ Large." *Journal of the London Mathematical Society* s1-20 (3): 180–189. https://doi.org/10.1112/jlms/s1-20.3.180.

Crutchfield, J. P., J. D. Farmer, N. H. Packard, and R. S. Shaw. 1986. "Chaos." *Scientific American* 255 (6): 46–57. https://doi.org/10.1038/scientificamerican1286-46.

Farmer, J. D., and J. J. Sidorowich. 1987. "Predicting Chaotic Time Series." *Physical Review Letters* 59 (8): 845. https://doi.org/10.1103/PhysRevLett.59.845.

Feigenbaum, M. J. 1978. "Quantitative Universality for a Class of Nonlinear Transformations." *Journal of Statistical Physics* 19:25–52. https://doi.org/10.1007/BF01020332.

Laplace, P.-S. 1814. *A Philosophical Essay on Probabilities.* Paris, France: V Courcier.

Lorenz, E. N. 1993. *The Essence of Chaos.* London, UK: UCL Press Ltd.

Metropolis, N., M. L. Stein, and P. R. Stein. 1973. "On Finite Limit Sets for Transformations on the Unit Interval." *Journal of Combinatorial Theory, Series A* 15 (1): 25–44. https://doi.org/10.1016/0097-3165(73)90033-2.

Palmer, T. N. 2022. *The Primacy of Doubt: From Climate Change to Quantum Physics, How the Science of Uncertainty Can Help Predict and Understand Our Chaotic World.* Oxford, UK: Oxford University Press.

Poincaré. 1893. *Les Méthodes Nouvelles de la Mécanique Céleste.* Paris, France: Gauthiers-Villar.

Shaw, R. 1981. "Strange Attractors, Chaotic Behavior, and Information Flow." *Zeitschrift für Naturforschung A* 36 (1): 80–112. https://doi.org/10.1515/zna-1981-0115.

Stein, P. R., and S. M. Ulam. 1962. *Non-Linear Transformation Studies on Electronic Computers.* Technical report LADC-5688. Los Alamos, NM: Los Alamos Scientific Laboratory.

Ueda, Y. 1991. "Survey of Regular and Chaotic Phenomena in the Forced Duffing Oscillator." (Ueda first discovered chaotic behavior in 1961.) *Chaos, Solitons & Fractals* 1 (3): 199–231. https://doi.org/10.1016/0960-0779(91)90032-5.

DETERMINISTIC NONPERIODIC FLOW

Edward N. Lorenz, Massachusetts Institute of Technology

Lorenz originally titled this paper "Deterministic Turbulence," but the editor of the journal felt that the behavior he described did not satisfy all the criteria associated with turbulence. At the time it was assumed that turbulence required random perturbations, so, to most readers, either title would have seemed like an oxymoron.

Abstract

Finite systems of deterministic ordinary nonlinear differential equations may be designed to represent forced dissipative hydrodynamic flow. Solutions of these equations can be identified with trajectories in phase space. For those systems with bounded solutions, it is found that nonperiodic solutions are ordinarily unstable with respect to small modifications, so that slightly differing initial states can evolve into considerably different states. Systems with bounded solutions are shown to possess bounded numerical solutions.

A simple system representing cellular convection is solved numerically. All of the solutions are found to be unstable, and almost all of them are nonperiodic.

The feasibility of very-long-range weather prediction is examined in the light of these results.[1]

1. Introduction

Certain hydrodynamical systems exhibit steady-state flow patterns, while others oscillate in a regular periodic fashion. Still others vary in an irregular, seemingly haphazard manner, and, even when observed for long periods of time, do not appear to repeat their previous history.

These modes of behavior may all be observed in the familiar rotating-basin experiments, described by Fultz *et al.* (1959) and Hide (1958). In these experiments, a cylindrical vessel containing water is rotated about its axis, and is heated near its rim and cooled near its center in a steady symmetrical fashion. Under certain conditions the resulting flow is as symmetric and steady as the heating which gives rise to it. Under different conditions a system of regularly spaced waves develops, and progresses at a uniform speed without changing its shape. Under

---

[1] The research reported in this work has been sponsored by the Geophysics Research Directorate of the Air Force Cambridge Research Center, under Contract No. AF 19(604)-4969.

still different conditions an irregular flow pattern forms, and moves and changes its shape in an irregular nonperiodic manner.

Lack of periodicity is very common in natural systems, and is one of the distinguishing features of turbulent flow. Because instantaneous turbulent flow patterns are so irregular, attention is often confined to the statistics of turbulence, which, in contrast to the details of turbulence, often behave in a regular well-organized manner. The short-range weather forecaster, however, is forced willy-nilly to predict the details of the large-scale turbulent eddies—the cyclones and anticyclones—which continually arrange themselves into new patterns.

Thus there are occasions when more than the statistics of irregular flow are of very real concern.

In this study we shall work with systems of deterministic equations which are idealizations of hydrodynamical systems. We shall be interested principally in nonperiodic solutions, i.e., solutions which never repeat their past history exactly, and where all approximate repetitions are of finite duration. Thus we shall be involved with the ultimate behavior of the solutions, as opposed to the transient behavior associated with arbitrary initial conditions.

A closed hydrodynamical system of finite mass may ostensibly be treated mathematically as a finite collection of molecules—usually a very large finite collection—in which case the governing laws are expressible as a finite set of ordinary differential equations. These equations are generally highly intractable, and the set of molecules is usually approximated by a continuous distribution of mass. The governing laws are then expressed as a set of partial differential equations, containing such quantities as velocity, density, and pressure as dependent variables.

It is sometimes possible to obtain particular solutions of these equations analytically, especially when the solutions are periodic or invariant with time, and, indeed, much work has been devoted to obtaining such solutions by one scheme or another. Ordinarily, however, nonperiodic solutions cannot readily be determined except by numerical procedures. Such procedures involve replacing the continuous variables by a new finite set of functions of time, which may perhaps be the values of the continuous variables at a chosen grid of points, or the coefficients in the expansions of these variables in series

Lorenz was a meteorologist, and this drove his quest for a fundamental understanding of the underlying reason for "irregular, haphazard" behavior. He was a good subjective weather forecaster. While I was his intern, I was illegally camped on the mesa that the National Center for Atmospheric Research sits on and hid my tent during the day. Every day I would stop by Ed's office and ask him whether I needed to set my tent up. He would stare out over the Great Plains and answer either "yep," "nope," or "can't tell." He was never wrong.

By "we shall be involved with the ultimate behavior of the solutions," Lorenz means, in modern terms: We will study the attractors of the motion.

of orthogonal functions. The governing laws then become a finite set of ordinary differential equations again, although a far simpler set than the one which governs individual molecular motions.

In any real hydrodynamical system, viscous dissipation is always occurring, unless the system is moving as a solid, and thermal dissipation is always occurring, unless the system is at constant temperature. For certain purposes many systems may be treated as conservative systems, in which the total energy, or some other quantity, does not vary with time. In seeking the ultimate behavior of a system, the use of conservative equations is unsatisfactory, since the ultimate value of any conservative quantity would then have to equal the arbitrarily chosen initial value. This difficulty may be obviated by including the dissipative processes, thereby making the equations nonconservative, and also including external mechanical or thermal forcing, thus preventing the system from ultimately reaching a state of rest. If the system is to be deterministic, the forcing functions, if not constant with time, must themselves vary according to some deterministic rule.

In this work, then, we shall deal specifically with finite systems of deterministic ordinary differential equations, designed to represent forced dissipative hydrodynamical systems. We shall study the properties of nonperiodic solutions of these equations.

It is not obvious that such solutions can exist at all. Indeed, in dissipative systems governed by finite sets of *linear* equations, a constant forcing leads ultimately to a constant response, while a periodic forcing leads to a periodic response. Hence, nonperiodic flow has sometimes been regarded as the result of nonperiodic or random forcing.

The reasoning leading to these conclusions is not applicable when the governing equations are nonlinear. If the equations contain terms representing advection—the transport of some property of a fluid by the motion of the fluid itself—a constant forcing can lead to a variable response. In the rotating-basin experiments already mentioned, both periodic and nonperiodic flow result from thermal forcing which, within the limits of experimental control, is constant. Exact periodic solutions of simplified systems of equations, representing dissipative flow with constant thermal forcing, have been obtained analytically by the writer

In part due to the limited availability of computers in 1963, most mathematical scientists were constrained by equations they could solve in closed form This meant that they mainly worked with linear equations, and their intuition derived from this experience. Linear equations cannot support chaos. Lorenz, in contrast, had a computer in his office. Lorenz's remark "It is not obvious that such solutions can exist at all" was a typical understatement. Prior to his work, most mathematical scientists were highly skeptical that such behavior was possible.

This phrase succinctly summarizes the remarkable emergent property of nonlinear dynamics to generate motion where none is imposed externally.

(Lorenz 1962a). The writer (Lorenz 1962b) has also found nonperiodic solutions of similar systems of equations by numerical means.

2. Phase Space

Consider a system whose state may be described by M variables $X_1, \cdots, X_M$. Let the system be governed by the set of equations

$$dX_i/dt = F_i(X_i, \cdots, X_M), \quad i = 1, \cdots, M, \tag{1}$$

where time t is the single independent variable, and the functions F_i possess continuous first partial derivatives. Such a system may be studied by means of *phase space*—an M-dimensional Euclidean space Γ whose coordinates are $X_1, \cdots, X_M$. Each *point* in phase space represents a possible instantaneous state of the system. A state which is varying in accordance with 1 is represented by a moving *particle* in phase space, traveling along a *trajectory* in phase space. For completeness, the position of a stationary particle, representing a steady state, is included as a trajectory.

Phase space has been a useful concept in treating finite systems, and has been used by such mathematicians as Gibbs (1902) in his development of statistical mechanics, Poincaré (1881) in his treatment of the solutions of differential equations, and Birkhoff (1927) in his treatise on dynamical systems.

From the theory of differential equations (e.g., Ford 1933, ch. 6), it follows, since the partial derivatives $\partial F_i/\partial X_j$ are continuous, that if t_0 is any time, and if $X_{10}, \cdots, X_{M0}$ is any point in Γ, equations 1 possess a unique solution

$$X_i = f_i(X_{10}, \cdots, X_{M0}, t), \quad i = 1, \cdots, M, \tag{2}$$

valid throughout some time interval containing t_0, and satisfying the condition

$$f_i(X_{10}, \cdots, X_{M0}, t_0) = X_{i0}, \quad i = 1, \cdots, M. \tag{3}$$

The functions f_i are continuous in $X_{10}, \cdots, X_{M0}$ and t. Hence there is a unique trajectory through each point of Γ. Two or more trajectories may, however, approach the same point or the same curve asymptotically as $t \to \infty$ or as $t \to -\infty$. Moreover, since the functions f_i are continuous, the passage of time defines a continuous deformation of any region of Γ into another region.

In the familiar case of a conservative system, where some positive definite quantity Q, which may represent some form of energy, is invariant with time, each trajectory is confined to one or another of the surfaces of constant Q. These surfaces may take the form of closed concentric shells.

If, on the other hand, there is dissipation and forcing, and if, whenever Q equals or exceeds some fixed value Q_1, the dissipation acts to diminish Q more rapidly then the forcing can increase Q, then $(-dQ/dt)$ has a positive lower bound where $Q \geq Q_1$, and each trajectory must ultimately become trapped in the region where $Q < Q_1$. Trajectories representing forced dissipative flow may therefore differ considerably from those representing conservative flow.

Forced dissipative systems of this sort are typified by the system

$$dX_i/dt = \sum_{j,k} a_{ijk} X_j X_k - \sum_j b_{ij} X_j + c_i, \qquad (4)$$

where $\sum a_{ijk} X_j X_k$ vanishes identically, $\sum b_{ij} X_i X_j$ is positive definite, and $c_1, \cdots, c_M$ are constants. If

$$Q = \frac{1}{2} \sum_i X_i{}^2, \qquad (5)$$

and if $e_1, \cdots, e_M$ are the roots of the equations

$$\sum_j (b_{ij} + b_{ji}) e_j = c_i, \qquad (6)$$

it follows from 4 that

$$dQ/dt = \sum_{i,j} b_{ij} e_i e_j - \sum_{i,j} b_{ij} (X_i - e_i)(X_j - e_j). \qquad (7)$$

The right side of 7 vanishes only on the surface of an ellipsoid E, and is positive only in the interior of E. The surfaces of constant Q are concentric spheres. If S denotes a particular one of these spheres whose interior R contains the ellipsoid E, it is evident that each trajectory eventually becomes trapped within R.

At the time mathematical scientists were in general much more familiar with the conservative dynamical systems of physics, whose properties are very different than those of dissipative systems. Conservative systems can display chaos, but they do not have attractors and they do not spontaneously generate endogenous motion.

The terms central and non-central didn't stick. Instead, a point would now either be said to be on an attractor, in which case it remains on the attractor, or in its basin of attraction, in which case its trajectory is on the attractor in the limit $t \to \infty$.

The definitions of stability and types of motion are reflective of the fact that Lorenz had to set the stage with concepts that would be taken for granted now.

3. The Instability of Nonperiodic Flow

In this section we shall establish one of the most important properties of deterministic nonperiodic flow, namely, its instability with respect to modifications of small amplitude. We shall find it convenient to do this by identifying the solutions of the governing equations with trajectories in phase space. We shall use such symbols as $P(t)$ (variable argument) to denote trajectories, and such symbols as P or $P(t_0)$ (no argument or constant argument) to denote points, the latter symbol denoting the specific point through which $P(t)$ passes at time t_0.

We shall deal with a phase space Γ in which a unique trajectory passes through each point, and where the passage of time defines a continuous deformation of any region of Γ into another region, so that if the points $P_1(t_0), P_2(t_0), \cdots$ approach $P_0(t_0)$ as a limit, the points $P_1(t_0 + \tau), P_2(t_0 + \tau), \cdots$ must approach $P_0(t_0 + \tau)$ as a limit. We shall furthermore require that the trajectories be uniformly bounded as $t \to \infty$; that is, there must be a bounded region R, such that every trajectory ultimately remains with R. Our procedure is influenced by the work of Birkhoff (1927) on dynamical systems, but differs in that Birkhoff was concerned mainly with conservative systems. A rather detailed treatment of dynamical systems has been given by Nemytskii and Stepanov (1960), and rigorous proofs of some of the theorems which we shall present are to be found in that source.

We shall first classify the trajectories in three different manners, namely, according to the absence or presence of transient properties, according to the stability or instability of the trajectories with respect to small modifications, and according to the presence or absence of periodic behavior.

Since any trajectory $P(t)$ is bounded, it must possess at least one *limit point* P_0, a point which it approaches arbitrarily closely arbitrarily often. More precisely, P_0 is a limit point of $P(t)$ if for any $\epsilon > 0$ and any time t_1 there exists a time $t_2(\epsilon, t_1) > t_1$ such that $|P(t_2) - P_0| < \epsilon$. Here absolute-value signs denote distance in phase space. Because Γ is continuously deformed as t varies, every point on the trajectory through P_0 is also a limit point of $P(t)$, and the set of limit points of $P(t)$ forms a trajectory, or a set of trajectories, called the *limiting trajectories* of $P(t)$. A limiting trajectory is obviously contained within R in its entirety.

If a trajectory is contained among its own limiting trajectories, it will be called *central*; otherwise it will be called *noncentral*. A central trajectory passes arbitrarily closely arbitrarily often to any point through which it has previously passed, and, in this sense at least, separate sufficiently long segments of a central trajectory are statistically similar. A noncentral trajectory remains a certain distance away from any point through which it has previously passed. It must approach its entire set of limit points asymptotically, although it need not approach any particular limiting trajectory asymptotically. Its instantaneous distance from its closest limit point is therefore a transient quantity, which becomes arbitrarily small as $t \to \infty$.

A trajectory $P(t)$ will be called *stable at a point* $P(t_1)$ if any other trajectory passing sufficiently close to $P(t_1)$ at time t_1 remains close to $P(t)$ as $t \to \infty$; i.e., $P(t)$ is stable at $P(t_1)$ if for any $\epsilon > 0$ there exists a $\delta(\epsilon, t_1) > 0$ such that if $|P_1(t_1) - P(t_1)| < \delta$ and $t_2 > t_1$, $|P_1(t_2) - P(t_2)| < \epsilon$. Otherwise $P(t)$ will be called *unstable* at $P(t_1)$. Because Γ is continuously deformed as t varies, a trajectory which is stable at one point is stable at every point, and will be called a *stable* trajectory. A trajectory unstable at one point is unstable at every point, and will be called an *unstable* trajectory. In the special case that $P(t)$ is confined to one point, this definition of stability coincides with the familiar concept of stability of steady flow.

A stable trajectory $P(t)$ will be called uniformly stable if the distance within which a neighboring trajectory must approach a point $P(t_1)$, in order to be certain of remaining close to $P(t)$ as $t \to \infty$, itself possesses a positive lower bound as $t_1 \to \infty$; i.e., $P(t)$ is uniformly stable if for any $\epsilon > 0$ there exists a $\delta(\epsilon) > 0$ and a time $t_0(\epsilon)$ such that if $t_1 > t_0$ and $|P_1(t_1) - P(t_1)| < \delta$ and $t_2 > t_1$, $|P_1(t_2) - P(t_2)| < \epsilon$. A limiting trajectory $P_0(t)$ of a uniformly stable trajectory $P(t)$ must be uniformly stable itself, since all trajectories passing sufficiently close to $P_0(t)$ must pass arbitrarily close to some point of $P(t)$ and so must remain close to $P(t)$, and hence to $P_0(t)$, as $t \to \infty$.

Since each point lies on a unique trajectory, any trajectory passing through a point through which it has previously passed must continue to repeat its past behavior, and so must be *periodic*. A trajectory $P(t)$ will be called *quasi-periodic* if for some arbitrarily large time interval τ, $P(t + \tau)$ ultimately remains arbitrarily close to $P(t)$, i.e., $P(t)$ is quasi-periodic if for any $\epsilon > 0$ and for any time interval τ_0, there exists a $\tau(\epsilon, \tau_0) > \tau_0$ and a time $t_1(\epsilon, \tau_0)$ such that if $t_2 > t_1$, $|P(t_2 + \tau) - P(t_2)| < \epsilon$. Periodic trajectories are special cases of quasi-periodic trajectories.

A trajectory which is not quasi-periodic will be called *nonperiodic*. If $P(t)$ is nonperiodic, $P(t_1 + \tau)$ may be arbitrarily close to $P(t_1)$ for some time t_1 and some arbitrarily large time interval τ, but, if this is so, $P(t + \tau)$ cannot remain arbitrarily close to $P(t)$ as $t \to \infty$. Nonperiodic trajectories are of course representations of deterministic nonperiodic flow, and form the principal subject of this paper.

Periodic trajectories are obviously central. Quasi-periodic central trajectories include multiple periodic trajectories with incommensurable periods, while quasi-periodic noncentral trajectories include those which approach periodic trajectories asymptotically. Nonperiodic trajectories may be central or noncentral.

We can now establish the theorem that a trajectory with a stable limiting trajectory is quasi-periodic. For if $P_0(t)$ is a limiting trajectory of $P(t)$, two distinct points $P(t_1)$ and $P(t_1 + \tau)$, with τ arbitrarily large, may be found arbitrary close to any point $P_0(t_0)$. Since $P_0(t)$ is stable, $P(t)$ and $P(t + \tau)$ must remain arbitrarily close to $P_0(t + t_0 - t_1)$, and hence to each other, as $t \to \infty$, and $P(t)$ is quasi-periodic.

It follows immediately that a stable central trajectory is quasi-periodic, or, equivalently, that a nonperiodic central trajectory is unstable.

The result has far-reaching consequences when the system being considered is an observable nonperiodic system whose future state we may desire to predict. It implies that two states differing by imperceptible amounts may eventually evolve into two considerably different states. If, then, there is any error whatever in observing the present state—and in any real system such errors seem inevitable—an acceptable prediction of an instantaneous state in the distant future may well be impossible.

This defines what is now called "chaos" in clear and simple terms.

As for noncentral trajectories, it follows that a uniformly stable noncentral trajectory is quasi-periodic, or, equivalently, a nonperiodic noncentral trajectory is not uniformly stable. The possibility of a nonperiodic noncentral trajectory which is stable but not uniformly stable still exists. To the writer, at least, such trajectories, although possible on paper, do not seem characteristic of real hydrodynamical phenomena. Any claim that atmospheric flow, for example, is represented by a trajectory of this sort would lead to the improbable conclusion that we ought to master long-range forecasting as soon as possible, because, the longer we wait, the more difficult our task will become.

In summary, we have shown that, subject to the conditions of uniqueness, continuity, and boundedness prescribed at the beginning of this section, a central trajectory, which in a certain sense is free of transient properties, is unstable if it is nonperiodic. A noncentral trajectory, which is characterized by transient properties, is not uniformly stable if it is nonperiodic, and, if it is stable at all, its very stability is one of its transient properties, which tends to die out as time progresses. In view of the impossibility of measuring initial conditions precisely, and thereby distinguishing between a central trajectory and a nearby noncentral trajectory, all nonperiodic trajectories are effectively unstable from the point of view of practical prediction.

Here Lorenz has shown that nonperiodic implies instability, which is not obvious. (Back then it was not obvious that a trajectory could be nonperiodic).

4. Numerical Integration of Nonconservative Systems

The theorems of the last section can be of importance only if nonperiodic solutions of equations of the type considered actually exist. Since statistically stationary nonperiodic functions of time are not easily described analytically, particular nonperiodic solutions can probably be found most readily by numerical procedures. In this section we shall examine a numerical-integration procedure which is especially applicable to systems of equations of the form 4. In a later section we shall use this procedure to determine a nonperiodic solution of a simple set of equations.

Nowadays no one would ever write such a section. Instead they would just say, "I used the Runge–Kutta algorithm for numerical integration of differential equations."

To solve 1 numerically we may choose an initial time t_0 and a time increment Δt, and let

$$X_{i,n} = X_i(t_0 + n\Delta t). \tag{8}$$

We then introduce the auxiliary approximations

$$X_{i(n+1)} = X_{i,n} + F_i(P_n)\Delta t, \tag{9}$$

$$X_{i((n+2))} = X_{i(n+1)} + F_i(P_{(n+1)})\Delta t, \tag{10}$$

where P_n and $P_{(n+1)}$ are the points whose coordinates are

$$(X_{1,n}, \cdots, X_{M,n}) \quad \text{and} \quad (X_{1(n+1)}, \cdots, X_{M(n+1)}).$$

The simplest numerical procedure for obtaining approximate solutions of 1 is the forward-difference procedure,

$$X_{i,n+1} = X_{i(n+1)}. \tag{11}$$

In many instances better approximations to the solutions of 1 may be obtained by a centered-difference procedure

$$X_{i,n+1} = X_{i,n-1} + 2F_i(P_n)\Delta t. \tag{12}$$

This procedure is unsuitable, however, when the deterministic nature of 1 is a matter of concern, since the values of $X_{1,n}, \cdots, X_{M,n}$ do not uniquely determine the values of $X_{1,n+1}, \cdots, X_{M,n+1}$.

A procedure which largely overcomes the disadvantages of both the forward-difference and centered-difference procedures is the double-approximation procedure, defined by the relation

$$X_{i,n+1} = X_{i,n} + \frac{1}{2}[F_i(P_n) + F_i(P_{(n+1)})]\Delta t. \tag{13}$$

Here the coefficient of Δt is an approximation to the time derivative of X_i at time $t_0 + (n + \frac{1}{2})\Delta t$. From 9 and 10, it follows that 13 may be rewritten

$$X_{i,n+1} = \frac{1}{2}(X_{i,n} + X_{i((n+2))}). \tag{14}$$

A convenient scheme for automatic computation is the successive evaluation of $X_{i(n+1)}$, $X_{i((n+2))}$, and $X_{i,n+1}$ according to 9, 10 and 14. We have used this procedure in all the computations described in this study.

In phase space a numerical solution of 1 must be represented by a jumping particle rather than a continuously moving particle. Moreover, if a digital computer is instructed to represent each number in its memory by a preassigned fixed number of bits, only certain discrete points in phase space will ever be occupied. If the numerical solution is bounded, repetitions must eventually occur, so that, strictly speaking, every numerical solution is periodic. In practice this consideration may be disregarded, if the number of different possible states is far greater than the number of iterations ever likely to be performed. The necessity for repetition could be avoided altogether by the somewhat uneconomical procedure of letting the precision of computation increase as n increases.

Consider now numerical solutions of equations 4, obtained by the forward-difference procedure 11. For such solutions,

$$Q_{n+1} = Q_n + (dQ/dt)_n \Delta t + \frac{1}{2} \sum_i F_{i^2}(P_n) \Delta t^2. \qquad (15)$$

Let S' be any surface of constant Q whose interior R' contains the ellipsoid E where dQ/dt vanishes, and let S be any surface of constant Q whose interior R contains S'.

Since $\sum F_{i^2}$ and dQ/dt both possess upper bounds in R', we may choose Δt so small that P_{n+1} lies in R if P_n lies in R'. Likewise, since $\sum F_{i^2}$ possesses an upper bound and dQ/dt possesses a *negative* upper bound in $R\text{-}R'$, we may choose Δt so small that $Q_{n+1} < Q_n$ if P_n lies in $R - R'$. Hence Δt may be chosen so small that any jumping particle which has entered R remains trapped within R, and the numerical solution does not blow up. A blow-up may still occur, however, if initially the particle is exterior to R.

Consider now the double-approximation procedure 14. The previous arguments imply not only that $P_{(n+1)}$ lies within R if P_n lies within R, but also that $P_{((n+2))}$ lies within R if $P_{(n+1)}$ lies within R. Since the region R is convex, it follows that P_{n+1}, as given by 14, lies within R if P_n lies within R. Hence if Δt is chosen so small that the forward-difference procedure does not blow up, the double-approximation procedure also does not blow up.

We note in passing that if we apply the forward-difference procedure to a conservative system where $dQ/dt = 0$ everywhere,

$$Q_{n+1} = Q_n + \frac{1}{2} \sum_i F_{i^2}(P_n) \Delta t^2. \qquad (16)$$

In this case, for any fixed choice of Δt the numerical solution ultimately goes to infinity, unless it is asymptotically approaching a steady state. A similar result holds when the double-approximation procedure 14 is applied to a conservative system.

5. The Convection Equations of Saltzman

In this section we shall introduce a system of three ordinary differential equations whose solutions afford the simplest example of deterministic nonperiodic flow of which the writer is aware. The system is a simplification of one derived by Saltzman (1962) to study finite-amplitude convection. Although our present interest is in the nonperiodic nature of its solutions, rather than in its contributions to the convection problem, we shall describe its physical background briefly.

Rayleigh (1916) studied the flow occurring in a layer of fluid of uniform depth H, when the temperature difference between the upper and lower surfaces is maintained at a constant value ΔT. Such a system possesses a steady-state solution in which there is no motion, and the temperature varies linearly with depth. If this solution is unstable, convection should develop.

In the case where all motions are parallel to the $x - z$-plane, and no variations in the direction of the y-axis occur, the governing equations may be written (see Saltzman 1962)

$$\frac{\partial}{\partial t}\nabla^2\psi = -\frac{\partial(\psi, \nabla^2\psi)}{\partial(x, z)} + \nu\nabla^4\psi + g\alpha\frac{\partial\theta}{\partial x}, \qquad (17)$$

$$\frac{\partial}{\partial t}\theta = -\frac{\partial(\psi, \theta)}{\partial(x, z)} + \frac{\Delta T}{H}\frac{\partial\psi}{\partial x} + \kappa\nabla^2\theta. \qquad (18)$$

Here ψ is a stream function for the two-dimensional motion, θ is the departure of temperature from that occurring in the state of no convection, and the constants g, α, ν, and κ denote, respectively, the acceleration of gravity, the coefficient of thermal expansion, the kinematic viscosity, and the thermal conductivity. The problem is most tractable when both the upper and lower boundaries are taken to be free, in which case ψ and $\Delta^2\psi$ vanish at both boundaries.

Rayleigh found that fields of motion of the form

$$\psi = \psi_0 \sin(\pi a H^{-1}x)\sin(\pi H^{-1}z), \qquad (19)$$

$$\theta = \theta_0 \cos(\pi a H^{-1}x)\sin(\pi H^{-1}z), \qquad (20)$$

would develop if the quantity

$$R_a = g\alpha H^3\Delta T\nu^{-1}\kappa^{-1}, \qquad (21)$$

One of the compelling things about this paper is that it is based on a real physical example. While only a crude approximation, it is suggestive. Lorenz's earlier nonperiodic equations described a more complicated system, and couldn't be reduced to such a simple set of equations.

now called the *Rayleigh number*, exceeded a critical value

$$R_c = \pi^4 a^{-2} (1 + a^2)^3. \qquad (22)$$

The minimum value of R_c, namely $27\pi^4/4$, occurs when $a^2 = \frac{1}{2}$.

Saltzman (1962) derived a set of ordinary differential equations by expanding ψ and θ in double Fourier series in x and z, with functions of t alone for coefficients, and substituting these series into 17 and 18. He arranged the right-hand sides of the resulting equations in double-Fourier-series form, by replacing products of trigonometric functions of x (or z) by sums of trigonometric functions, and then equated coefficients of similar functions of x and z. He then reduced the resulting infinite system to a finite system by omitting reference to all but a specified finite set of functions of t, in the manner proposed by the writer (1960).

He then obtained time-dependent solutions by numerical integration. In certain cases all except three of the dependent variables eventually tended to zero, and these three variables underwent irregular, apparently nonperiodic fluctuations.

These same solutions would have been obtained if the series had at the start been truncated to include a total of three terms. Accordingly, in this study we shall let

$$a(1 + a^2)^{-1} \kappa^{-1} \psi = X \sqrt{2} \sin(\pi a H^{-1} x) \sin(\pi H^{-1} z), \qquad (23)$$

$$\pi R_c^{-1} R_a \Delta T^{-1} \theta = Y \sqrt{2} \cos(\pi a H^{-1} x) \sin(\pi H^{-1} z) - Z \sin(2\pi H^{-1} z), \qquad (24)$$

where X, Y, and Z are functions of time alone. When expressions 23 and 24 are substituted into 17 and 18, and trigonometric terms other than those occurring in 23 and 24 are omitted, we obtain the equations

$$X^{\cdot} = \quad -\sigma X + \sigma Y, \qquad (25)$$

$$Y^{\cdot} = -XZ + rX - Y, \qquad (26)$$

$$Z^{\cdot} = \quad XY \qquad\qquad - bZ. \qquad (27)$$

Here a dot denotes a derivative with respect to the dimensionless time $\tau = \pi^2 H^{-2}(1 + a^2)\kappa t$, while $\sigma = \kappa^{-1}\nu$ is the *Prandtl number*, $r = R_c^{-1}R_a$, and $b = 4(1 + a^2)^{-1}$. Except for multiplicative constants, our variables X,

These equations are linear except for the terms XZ and XY. They are very simple!

Y, and Z are the same as Saltzman's variables A, D, and G. Equations 25, 26, and 27 are the convection equations whose solutions we shall study.

In these equations X is proportional to the intensity of the convective motion, while Y is proportional to the temperature difference between the ascending and descending currents, similar signs of X and Y denoting that warm fluid is rising and cold fluid is descending. The variable Z is proportional to the distortion of the vertical temperature profile from linearity, a positive value indicating that the strongest gradients occur near the boundaries.

Equations 25–27 may give realistic results when the Rayleigh number is slightly supercritical, but their solutions cannot be expected to resemble those of 17 and 18 when strong convection occurs, in view of the extreme truncation.

6. Applications of Linear Theory

Although equations 25–27, as they stand, do not have the form of 4, a number of linear transformations will convert them to this form. One of the simplest of these is the transformation

$$X' = X, \quad Y' = Y, \quad Z' = Z - r - \sigma. \tag{28}$$

Solutions of 25–27 therefore remain bounded within a region R as $\tau \to \infty$, and the general results of Sections 2, 3 and 4 apply to these equations.

The stability of a solution $X(\tau)$, $Y(\tau)$, $Z(\tau)$ may be formally investigated by considering the behavior of small superposed perturbations $x_0(\tau)$, $y_0(\tau)$, $z_0(\tau)$. Such perturbations are temporarily governed by the linearized equations

$$\begin{bmatrix} x_0 \\ y_0 \\ z_0 \end{bmatrix}^{\cdot} = \begin{bmatrix} -\sigma & \sigma & 0 \\ (r - Z) & -1 & -X \\ Y & X & -b \end{bmatrix} \begin{bmatrix} x_0 \\ y_0 \\ z_0 \end{bmatrix} \tag{29}$$

Since the coefficients in 29 vary with time, unless the basic state X, Y, Z is a steady-state solution of 25–27, a general solution of 29 is not feasible. However, the variation of the volume V_0 of a small region in phase space, as each point in the region is displaced in accordance with 25–27, is determined by the diagonal sum of the matrix of coefficients; specifically

$$V_0^{\cdot} = -(\sigma + b + 1)V_0. \tag{30}$$

This is perhaps most readily seen by visualizing the motion in phase space as the flow of a fluid, whose divergence is

$$\frac{\partial X^{\cdot}}{\partial X} + \frac{\partial Y^{\cdot}}{\partial Y} + \frac{\partial Z^{\cdot}}{\partial Z} = -(\sigma + b + 1). \tag{31}$$

Hence each small volume shrinks to zero as $\tau \to \infty$, at a rate independent of X, Y, and Z. This does not imply that each small volume shrinks to a point; it may simply become flattened into a surface. It follows that the volume of the region initially enclosed by the surface S shrinks to zero at this same rate, so that all trajectories ultimately become confined to a specific subspace having zero volume. This subspace contains all those trajectories which lie entirely within R, and so contains all central trajectories.

The fact that volumes tend to shrink over time means that this is a dissipative dynamical system, i.e., one in which kinetic energy is converted to heat.

Equations 25–27 possess the steady-state solution $X = Y = Z = 0$, representing the state of no convection. With this basic solution, the characteristic equation of the matrix in 29 is

$$[\lambda + b][\lambda^2 + (\sigma + 1)\lambda + \sigma(1 - r)] = 0. \tag{32}$$

This equation has three real roots when $r > 0$; all are negative when $r < 1$, but one is positive when $r > 1$. The criterion for the onset of convection is therefore $r = 1$, or $R_a = R_c$, in agreement with Rayleigh's result.

When $r > 1$, equations 25–27 possess two additional steady-state solutions $X = Y = \pm\sqrt{b(r - 1)}$, $Z = r - 1$. For either of these solutions, the characteristic equation of the matrix in 29 is

$$\lambda^3 + (\sigma + b + 1)\lambda^2 + (r + \sigma)b\lambda + 2\sigma b(r - 1) = 0. \tag{33}$$

This equation possesses one real negative root and two complex conjugate roots when $r > 1$; the complex conjugate roots are pure imaginary if the product of the coefficients of λ^2 and λ equals the constant term, or

$$r = \sigma(\sigma + b + 3)(\sigma - b - 1)^{-1}. \tag{34}$$

This is the critical value of r for the instability of steady convection. Thus if $\sigma < b + 1$, no positive value of r satisfies 34, and steady convection is always stable, but if $\sigma > b + 1$, steady convection is unstable for sufficiently high Rayleigh numbers. This result of course applies only to idealized convection governed by 25–27, and not to the solutions of the partial differential equations 17 and 18.

The presence of complex roots of 34 shows that if unstable steady convection is disturbed, the motion will oscillate in intensity. What happens when the disturbances become large is not revealed by linear theory. To investigate finite-amplitude convection, and to study the subspace to which trajectories are ultimately confined, we turn to numerical integration.

7. Numerical Integration of the Convection Equations

To obtain numerical solutions of the convection equations, we must choose numerical values for the constants. Following Saltzman (1962), we shall let $\sigma = 10$ and $a^2 = \frac{1}{2}$, so that $b = 8/3$. The critical Rayleigh number for instability of steady convection then occurs when $r = 470/19 = 24.74$.

We shall choose the slightly supercritical value $r = 28$. The states of steady convection are then represented by the points $(6\sqrt{2}, 6\sqrt{2}, 27)$ and $(-6\sqrt{2}, -6\sqrt{2}, 27)$ in phase space, while the state of no convection corresponds to the origin $(0, 0, 0)$.

We have used the double-approximation procedure for numerical integration, defined by 9, 10, and 14. The value $\Delta\tau = 0.01$ has been chosen for the dimensionless time increment. The computations have been performed on a Royal McBee LGP-30 electronic computing machine. Approximately one second per iteration, aside from output time, is required.

The figure shown took about four days' worth of computer time to generate! This could now be done in much less than a millisecond.

For initial conditions we have chosen a slight departure from the state of no convection, namely $(0, 1, 0)$. Table 1 has been prepared by the computer. It gives the values of N (the number of iterations), X, Y, and Z at every fifth iteration for the first 160 iterations. In the printed output (but not in the computations) the values of X, Y, and Z are multiplied by ten, and then only those figures to the left of the decimal point are printed. Thus the states of steady convection would

N	X	Y	Z
0000	0000	0010	0000
0005	0004	0012	0000
0010	0009	0020	0000
0015	0016	0036	0002
0020	0030	0066	0007
0025	0054	0115	0024
0030	0093	0192	0074
0035	0150	0268	0201
0040	0195	0234	0397
0045	0174	0055	0483
0050	0097	−0067	0415
0055	0025	−0093	0340
0060	−0020	−0089	0298
0065	−0046	−0084	0275
0070	−0061	−0083	0262
0075	−0070	−0086	0256
0080	−0077	−0091	0255
0085	−0084	−0095	0258
0090	−0089	−0098	0266
0095	−0093	−0098	0275
0100	−0094	−0093	0283
0105	−0092	−0086	0297
0110	−0088	−0079	0286
0115	−0083	−0073	0281
0120	−0078	−0070	0273
0125	−0075	−0071	0264
0130	−0074	−0075	0257
0135	−0076	−0080	0252
0140	−0079	−0087	0251
0145	−0083	−0093	0254
0150	−0088	−0098	0262
0155	−0092	−0099	0271
0160	−0094	−0096	0281

Table 1. Numerical solution of the convection equations. Values X, Y, Z are given at every fifth iteration N, for the first 160 iterations.

N	X	Y	Z	N	X	Y	Z
0045	0174	0055	0483	3029	0117	0075	0352
0107	−0091	−0083	0287	3098	0123	0076	0365
0168	−0092	−0084	0288	3171	0134	0082	0383
0230	−0092	−0084	0289	3268	0155	0069	0435
0292	−0092	−0083	0290	3333	−0114	−0079	0342
0354	−0093	−0083	0292	3400	−0117	−0077	0350
0416	−0093	−0083	0293	3468	−0125	−0083	0361
0478	−0094	−0082	0295	3541	−0129	−0073	0378
0540	−0094	−0082	0296	3625	−0146	−0074	0413
0602	−0095	−0082	0298	3695	0127	0079	0370
0664	−0096	−0083	0300	3772	0136	0072	0394
0726	−0097	−0083	0302	3853	−0144	−0077	0407
0789	−0097	−0081	0304	3926	0129	0072	0380
0851	−0099	−0083	0307	4014	0148	0068	0421
0914	−0100	−0081	0309	4082	−0120	−0074	0359
0977	−0100	−0080	0312	4153	−0129	−0078	0375
1040	−0102	−0080	0315	4233	−0144	−0082	0404
1103	−0104	−0081	0319	4307	0135	0081	0385
1167	−0105	−0079	0323	4417	−0162	−0069	0450
1231	−0107	−0079	0328	4480	0106	0081	0324
1295	−0111	−0082	0333	4544	0109	0082	0329
1361	−0111	−0077	0339	4609	0110	0080	0334
1427	−0116	−0079	0347	4675	0112	0076	0341
1495	−0120	−0077	0357	4741	0118	0081	0349
1566	−0125	−0072	0371	4810	0120	0074	0360
1643	−0139	−0077	0396	4881	0130	0081	0376
1722	0140	0075	0401	4963	0141	0068	0406
1798	−0135	−0072	0391	5035	−0133	−0081	0381
1882	0146	0074	0413	5124	−0151	−0076	0422
1952	−0127	−0078	0370	5192	0119	0075	0358
2029	−0135	−0070	0393	5262	0129	0083	0372
2110	0146	0083	0408	5340	0140	0079	0397
2183	−0128	−0070	0379	5419	−0137	−0067	0399
2268	−0144	−0066	0415	5495	0140	0081	0394
2337	0126	0079	0368	5576	−0141	−0072	0405
2412	0137	0081	0389	5649	0135	0082	0384
2501	−0153	−0080	0423	5752	0160	0074	0443
2569	0119	0076	0357	5816	−0110	−0081	0332
2639	0129	0082	0371	5881	−0113	−0082	0339
2717	0136	0070	0395	5948	−0114	−0075	0346
2796	−0143	−0079	0402				
2871	0134	0076	0388				
2962	−0152	−0072	0426				

Table 2. Numerical solution of the convection equations. Values of X, Y, Z are given at every iteration N for which Z possesses a relative maximum, for the first 6,000 iterations.

appear as $0084, 0084, 0270$ and $-0084, -0084, 0270$, while the state of no convection would appear as $0000, 0000, 0000$.

The initial instability of the state of rest is evident. All three variables grow rapidly, as the sinking cold fluid is replaced by even colder fluid from above, and the rising warm fluid by warmer fluid from below, so that by step 35 the strength of the convection far exceeds that of steady convection. Then Y diminishes as the warm fluid is carried over the top of the convective cells, so that by step 50, when X and Y have opposite signs, warm fluid is descending and cold fluid is ascending. The motion thereupon ceases and reverses its direction, as indicated by the negative values of X following step 60. By step 85 the system has reached a state not far from that of steady convection. Between steps 85 and 150 it executes a complete oscillation in its intensity, the slight amplification being almost indetectable.

The subsequent behavior of the system is illustrated in Fig. 1, which shows the behavior of Y for the first 3000 iterations. After reaching its early peak near step 35 and then approaching equilibrium near step 85, it undergoes systematic amplified oscillations until near step 1650. At this point a critical state is reached, and thereafter Y changes sign at seemingly irregular intervals, reaching sometimes one, sometimes two, and sometimes three or more extremes of one sign before changing sign again.

Fig. 2 shows the projections on the $X - Y$- and $Y - Z$-planes in phase space of the portion of the trajectory corresponding to iterations 1400–1900. The states of steady convection are denoted by C and C'. The first portion of the trajectory spirals outward from the vicinity of C', as the oscillations about the state of steady convection, which have been occurring since step 85, continue to grow. Eventually, near step 1650, it crosses the $X - Z$-plane, and is then deflected toward the neighborhood of C. It temporarily spirals about C, but crosses the $X - Z$-plane after one circuit, and returns to the neighborhood of C', where it soon joins the spiral over which it has previously traveled. Thereafter it crosses from one spiral to the other at irregular intervals.

Fig. 3, in which the coordinates are Y and Z, is based upon the printed values of X, Y, and Z at every fifth iteration for the first 6000 iterations. These values determine X as a smooth single-valued function of Y and Z over much of the range of Y and Z; they determine X as one of two smooth

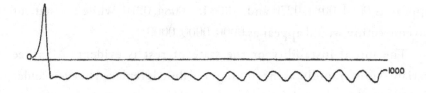

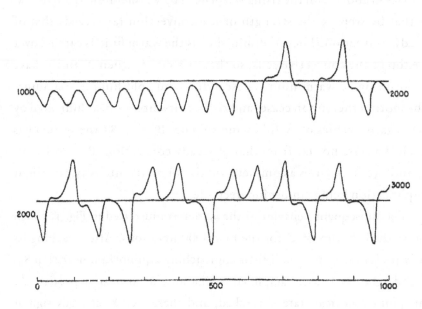

Up until about time 2000, the amplitude of the oscillations increases in time, indicating that the motion is transient. After that it is close to being on the attractor—close enough that it would be difficult to say that it wasn't.

Figure 1. Numerical solution of the convection equations. Graph of Y as a function of time for the first 1000 iterations (upper curve), second 1000 iterations (middle curve), and third 1000 iterations (lower curve).

single-valued functions over the remainder of the range. In Fig. 3 the thin solid lines are isopleths of X, and where two values of X exist, the dashed lines are isopleths of the lower value. Thus, within the limits of accuracy of the printed values, the trajectory is confined to a pair of surfaces which appear to merge in the lower portion of Fig. 3. The spiral about C lies in the upper surface, while the spiral about C' lies in the lower surface. Thus it is possible for the trajectory to pass back and forth from one spiral to the other without intersecting itself.

Additional numerical solutions indicate that other trajectories, originating at points well removed from these surfaces, soon meet these surfaces. The surfaces therefore appear to be composed of all points lying on limiting trajectories.

Because the origin represents a steady state, no trajectory can pass

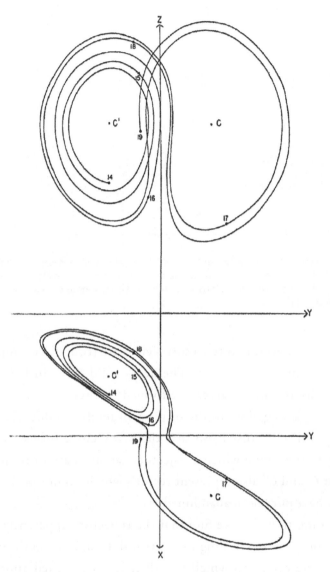

Figure 2. Numerical solution of the convection equations. Projections on the $X - Y$-plane and the $Y - Z$-plane in phase space of the segment of the trajectory extending from iteration 1400 to iteration 1900. Numerals "14," "15," etc., denote positions at iterations 1400, 1500, etc. States of steady convection are denoted by C and C'.

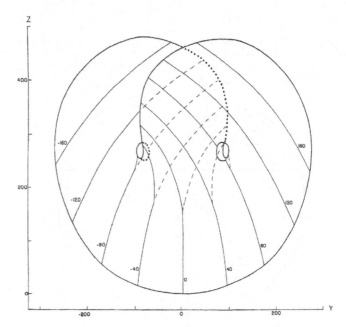

"Isopleth" means curves along which the value of X is constant. This figure shows how the attractor can approximately be thought of as two sheets folding into each other.

Figure 3. Isopleths of X as a function of Y and Z (thin solid curves), and isopleths of the lower of two values of X, where two values occur (dashed curves), for approximate surfaces formed by all points on limiting trajectories. Heavy solid curve, and extensions as dotted curves, indicate natural boundaries of surfaces.

through it. However, two trajectories emanate from it, i.e., approach it asymptotically as $\tau \rightarrow -\infty$. The heavy solid curve in Fig. 3, and its extensions as dotted curves, are formed by these two trajectories. Trajectories passing close to the origin will tend to follow the heavy curve, but will not cross it, so that the heavy curve forms a natural boundary to the region which a trajectory can ultimately occupy. The holes near C and C' also represent regions which cannot be occupied after they have once been abandoned.

Returning to Fig. 2, we find that the trajectory apparently leaves one spiral only after exceeding some critical distance from the center. Moreover, the extent to which this distance is exceeded appears to determine the point at which the next spiral is entered; this in turn seems to determine the number of circuits to be executed before changing spirals again.

It therefore seems that some single feature of a given circuit should predict the same feature of the following circuit. A suitable feature of this sort is the maximum value of Z, which occurs when a circuit is nearly completed. Table 2 has again been prepared by the computer, and shows the values of X, Y, and Z at only those iterations N for which Z has a relative maximum. The succession of circuits about C and C' is indicated by the succession of positive and negative values of X and Y. Evidently X and Y change signs following a maximum which exceeds some critical value printed as about 385.

Fig. 4 has been prepared from Table 2. The abscissa is M_n, the value of the nth maximum of Z, while the ordinate is M_{n+1}, the value of the following maximum. Each point represents a pair of successive values of Z taken from Table 2. Within the limits of the round-off in tabulating Z, there is a precise two-to-one relation between M_n and M_{n+1}. The initial maximum $M_1 = 483$ is shown as if it had followed a maximum $M_0 = 385$, since maxima near 385 are followed by close approaches to the origin, and then by exceptionally large maxima.

It follows that an investigator, unaware of the nature of the governing equations, could formulate an empirical prediction scheme from the "data" pictured in Figs. 2 and 4. From the value of the most recent maximum of Z, values at future maxima may be obtained by repeated applications of Fig. 4. Values of X, Y, and Z between maxima of Z may be found from Fig. 2, by interpolating between neighboring curves. Of course, the accuracy of predictions made by this method is limited by the exactness of Figs. 2 and 4, and, as we shall see, by the accuracy with which the initial values of X, Y, and Z are observed.

Some of the implications of Fig. 4 are revealed by considering an idealized two-to-one correspondence between successive members of sequences $M_0, M_1, \ldots$, consisting of numbers between zero and one. These sequences satisfy the relations

$$
\begin{aligned}
M_{n+1} = 2M_n & \qquad \text{if} \quad M_n < \frac{1}{2} \\
M_{n+1} \text{ is undefined} & \qquad \text{if} \quad M_n = \frac{1}{2} \qquad\qquad (35) \\
M_{n+1} = 2 - 2M_n & \qquad \text{if} \quad M_n > \frac{1}{2}.
\end{aligned}
$$

The correspondence defined by 35 is shown in Fig. ??, which is an idealization of Fig. 4. It follows from repeated applications of 35 that in any particular sequence,

$$M_n = m_n \pm 2^n M_0, \tag{36}$$

where m_n is an even integer.

Consider first a sequence where $M_0 = u/2^p$, where u is odd. In this case $M_{p-1} = \frac{1}{2}$, and the sequence terminates. These sequences form a denumerable set, and correspond to the trajectories which score direct hits upon the state of no convection.

Next consider a sequence where $M_0 = u/2^p v$, where u and v are relatively prime odd numbers. Then if $k > 0$, $M_{p+1+k} = u_k/v$, where u_k and v are relatively prime and u_k is even. Since for any v the number of proper fractions u_k/v is finite, repetitions must occur, and the sequence is periodic. These sequences also form a denumerable set, and correspond to periodic trajectories.

The periodic sequences having a given number of distinct values, or phases, are readily tabulated. In particular there are a single one-phase, a single two-phase, and two three-phase sequences, namely

$$2/3, \cdots ,$$
$$2/5, 4/5, \cdots ,$$
$$2/7, 4/7, 6/7, \cdots ,$$
$$2/9, 4/9, 8/9, \cdots .$$

The two three-phase sequences differ qualitatively in that the former possesses two numbers, and the latter only one number, exceeding $\frac{1}{2}$. Thus the trajectory corresponding to the former makes two circuits about C, followed by one about C' (or vice versa). The trajectory corresponding to the latter makes three circuits about C, followed by three about C', so that actually only Z varies in three phases, while X and Y vary in six.

Now consider a sequence where M_0 is not a rational fraction. In this case 36 shows that M_{n+k} cannot equal M_n if $k > 0$, so that no repetitions occur. These sequences, which form a nondenumerable set, may conceivably approach periodic sequences asymptotically and be quasi-periodic, or they may be nonperiodic.

Finally, consider two sequences $M_0, M_1, \cdots$ and $M'_0, M'_1, \cdots$, where $M'_0 = M_{0+\epsilon}$. Then for a given k, if ϵ is sufficiently small, $M'_k =$

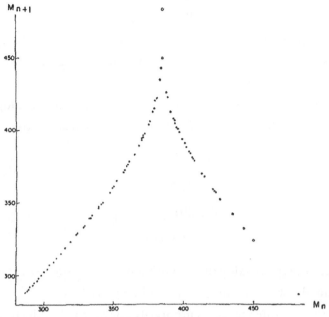

Figure 4. Corresponding values of relative maximum of Z (abscissa) and subsequent relative maximum of Z (ordinate) occurring during the first 6000 iterations.

Here, if we fill in between the points shown, Lorenz has reduced the system to a one-dimensional discrete dynamical system mapping the interval into itself. The fact that the slopes are on average greater than 1 implies that nearby points will separate, which implies local instability—the interval is stretched and folded.

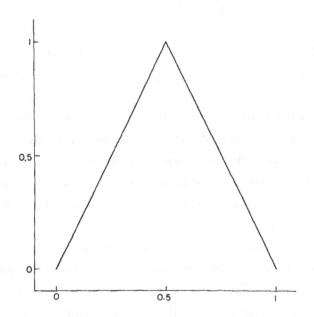

Figure 5. The function $M_{n+1} = 2M_n$ if $M_n < \frac{1}{2}$, $M_{n+1} = 2 - 2M_n$ if $M_n > \frac{1}{2}$, serving as an idealization of the locus of points in Fig. 4.

This idealization is now called the tent map. It is very similar to the binary shift map I described in the introduction.

$M_k \pm 2^k \epsilon$. All sequences are therefore unstable with respect to small modifications. In particular, all periodic sequences are unstable, and no other sequences can approach them asymptotically. All sequences except a set of measure zero are therefore nonperiodic, and correspond to nonperiodic trajectories.

Returning to Fig. 4, we see that periodic sequences analogous to those tabulated above can be found. They are given approximately by

$$398, \cdots ,$$
$$377, 410, \cdots ,$$
$$369, 391, 414, \cdots ,$$
$$362, 380, 419, \cdots .$$

The trajectories possessing these or other periodic sequences of maxima are presumably periodic or quasiperiodic themselves.

The above sequences are temporarily approached in the numerical solution by sequences beginning at iterations 5340, 4881, 3625, and 3926. Since the numerical solution eventually departs from each of these sequences, each is presumably unstable.

More generally, if $M'_n = M_n + \epsilon$, and if ϵ is sufficiently small, $M'_{n+k} = M_{n+k} + \Lambda\epsilon$, where Λ is the product of the slopes of the curve in Fig. 4 at the points whose abscissas are $M_n, \cdots , M_{n+k-1}$. Since the curve apparently has a slope whose magnitude exceeds unity everywhere, all sequences of maxima, and hence all trajectories, are unstable. In particular, the periodic trajectories, whose sequences of maxima form a denumerable set, are unstable, and only exceptional trajectories, having the same sequences of maxima, can approach them asymptotically. The remaining trajectories, whose sequences of maxima form a nondenumerable set, therefore represent deterministic nonperiodic flow.

These conclusions have been based upon a finite segment of a numerically determined solution. They cannot be regarded as mathematically proven, even though the evidence for them is strong. One apparent contradiction requires further examination.

It is difficult to reconcile the merging of two surfaces, one containing each spiral, with the inability of two trajectories to merge.

☞

The punchline! In fact, the unstable periodic trajectories form a kind of skeleton representing the structure of the chaos. The way in which these trajectories disappear as the height of the tent changes was extensively (independently) studied by Metropolis, Stein, and Stein (1973), who show that this sequence is universal for any unimodal mapping of the interval into itself. This inspired the famous paper on the universality of period doubling by Feigenbaum (1978).

It is not difficult, however, to explain the *apparent* merging of the surfaces. At two times τ_0 and τ_1, the volumes occupied by a specified set of particles satisfy the relation

$$V_0(\tau_1) = e^{-(\sigma+b+1)(\tau_1-\tau_0)}V_0(\tau_0), \qquad (37)$$

according to 30. A typical circuit about C or C' requires about 70 iterations, so that, for such a circuit, $\tau_2 = \tau_1 + 0.7$, and, since $\sigma + b + 1 = 41/3$,

$$V_0(\tau_1) = 0.00007V_0(\tau_0). \qquad (38)$$

Two particles separated from each other in a suitable direction can therefore come together very rapidly, and appear to merge.

It would seem, then, that the two surfaces merely appear to merge, and remain distinct surfaces. Following these surfaces along a path parallel to a trajectory, and circling C or C', we see that each surface is really a pair of surfaces, so that, where they appear to merge, there are really four surfaces. Continuing this process for another circuit, we see that there are really eight surfaces, etc., and we finally conclude that there is an infinite complex of surfaces, each extremely close to one or the other of two merging surfaces.

The infinite set of values at which a line parallel to the X-axis intersects these surfaces may be likened to the set of all numbers between zero and one whose decimal expansions (or some other expansions besides binary) contain only zeros and ones. This set is plainly nondenumerable, in view of its correspondence to the set of all numbers between zero and one, expressed in binary. Nevertheless it forms a set of measure zero. The sequence of ones and zeros corresponding to a particular surface contains a history of the trajectories lying in that surface, a one or zero immediately to the right of the decimal point indicating that the last circuit was about C or C', respectively, a one or zero in second place giving the same information about the next to the last circuit, etc. Repeating decimal expansions represent periodic or quasi-periodic trajectories, and, since they define rational fractions, they form a denumerable set.

If one first visualizes this infinite complex of surfaces, it should not be difficult to picture nonperiodic deterministic trajectories embedded in these surfaces.

Conclusion

Certain mechanically or thermally forced nonconservative hydrodynamical systems may exhibit either periodic or irregular behavior when there is no obviously related periodicity or irregularity in the forcing process. Both periodic and nonperiodic flow are observed in some experimental models when the forcing process is held constant, within the limits of experimental control. Some finite systems of ordinary differential equations designed to represent these hydrodynamical systems possess periodic analytic solutions when the forcing is strictly constant. Other such systems have yielded nonperiodic numerical solutions.

A finite system of ordinary differential equations representing forced dissipative flow often has the property that all of its solutions are ultimately confined within the same bounds. We have studied in detail the properties of solutions of systems of this sort. Our principal results concern the instability of nonperiodic solutions. A nonperiodic solution with no transient component must be unstable, in the sense that solutions temporarily approximating it do not continue to do so. A nonperiodic solution with a transient component is sometimes stable, but in this case its stability is one of its transient properties, which tends to die out.

To verify the existence of deterministic nonperiodic flow, we have obtained numerical solutions of a system of three ordinary differential equations designed to represent a convective process. These equations possess three steady-state solutions and a denumerably infinite set of periodic solutions. All solutions, and in particular the periodic solutions, are found to be unstable. The remaining solutions therefore cannot in general approach the periodic solutions asymptotically, and so are nonperiodic.

When our results concerning the instability of nonperiodic flow are applied to the atmosphere, which is ostensibly nonperiodic, they indicate that prediction of the sufficiently distant future is impossible by any method, unless the present conditions are known exactly. In view of the inevitable inaccuracy and incompleteness of weather observations, precise very-long-range forecasting would seem to be non-existent.

There remains the question as to whether our results really apply to the atmosphere. One does not usually regard the atmosphere as either deterministic or finite, and the lack of periodicity is not a mathematical certainty, since the atmosphere has not been observed forever.

The foundation of our principal result is the eventual necessity for any bounded system of finite dimensionality to come arbitrarily close to acquiring a state which it has previously assumed. If the system is stable, its future development will then remain arbitrarily close to its past history, and it will be quasi-periodic.

In the case of the atmosphere, the crucial point is then whether analogues must have occurred since the state of the atmosphere was first observed. By analogues, we mean specifically two or more states of the atmosphere, together with its environment, which resemble each other so closely that the differences may be ascribed to errors in observation. Thus, to be analogues, two states must be closely alike in regions where observations are accurate and plentiful, while they need not be at all alike in regions where there are no observations at all, whether these be regions of the atmosphere or the environment. If, however, some unobserved features are implicit in a succession of observed states, two successions of states must be nearly alike in order to be analogues.

If it is true that two analogues have occurred since atmospheric observation first began, it follows, since the atmosphere has not been observed to be periodic, that the successions of states following these analogues must eventually have differed, and no forecasting scheme could have given correct results both times. If, instead, analogues have not occurred during this period, some accurate very-long-range prediction scheme, using observations at present available, may exist. But, if it does exist, the atmosphere will acquire a quasi-periodic behavior, never to be lost, once an analogue occurs. This quasi-periodic behavior need not be established, though, even if very-long-range forecasting is feasible, if the variety of possible atmospheric states is so immense that analogues need never occur. It should be noted that these conclusions do not depend upon whether or not the atmosphere is deterministic.

There remains the very important question as to how long is "very-long-range." Our results do not give the answer for the atmosphere;

To provide context, this was one of the key approaches to weather forecasting prior to 1980 or so. Under the method of analogues, a forecaster searches through a library of past weather maps to find a weather map that provides a good match, then uses the weather maps on subsequent days to make a prediction of the future.

conceivably it could be a few days or a few centuries. In an idealized system, whether it be the simple convective model described here, or a complicated system designed to resemble the atmosphere as closely as possible, the answer may be obtained by comparing pairs of numerical solutions having nearly identical initial conditions. In the case of the real atmosphere, if all other methods fail, we can wait for an analogue. ✦

Acknowledgments

The writer is indebted to Dr. Barry Saltzman for bringing to his attention the existence of nonperiodic solutions of the convection equations. Special thanks are due to Miss Ellen Fetter for handling the many numerical computations and preparing the graphical presentations of the numerical material.

Note the reference to Poincaré below. However, Lorenz is referring to a different paper that the one where Poincaré shows that solutions to the three-body problem are problematic.

REFERENCES

Birkhoff, G. O. 1927. *Dynamical Systems.* New York, NY: American Mathematical Society.

Ford, L. R. 1933. *Differential Equations.* 264. New York, NY: McGraw-Hill.

Fultz, D., R. R. Long, G. V. Owens, W. Bohan, R. Kaylor, and J. Weil. 1959. "Studies of Thermal Convection in a Rotating Cylinder with Some Implications for Large-Scale Atmospheric Motions." In *Studies of Thermal Convection in a Rotating Cylinder with Some Implications for Large-Scale Atmospheric Motions,* 4:104. Boston, MA: American Meteorological Society.

Gibbs, J. W. 1902. *Elementary Principles in Statistical Mechanics.* 207. New York, NY: Scribner.

Hide, R. 1958. "An Experimental Study of Thermal Convection in a Rotating Liquid." *Philosophical Transactions of the Royal Society of London Series A* 250:441–478.

Lorenz, E. N. 1960. "Maximum Simplification of the Dynamic Equations." *Tellus* 12:243–254.

———. 1962a. "Simplified Dynamic Equations Applied to the Rotating-Basin Experiments." *Journal of Atmospheric Sciences* 19:39–51.

———. 1962b. "The Statistical Prediction of Solutions of Dynamic Equations." In *Proceedings of the International Symposium on Numerical Weather Prediction in Tokyo November 7–13, 1960,* 629–635. New York, NY: Meteorological Society of Japan.

Poincaré, H. 1881. "Mémoire sur Les Courbes Définies par une Équation Différentielle (I)" [in French]. *Journal de Mathématiques Pures et Appliquées* 7:375–422.

Rayleigh, Lord. 1916. "On Convection Currents in a Horizontal Layer of Fluid, when the Higher Temperature is on the Under Side." *Philosophical Magazine,* 6th ser., 32 (192): 529–546.

Saltzman, B. 1962. "Finite Amplitude Free Convection as an Initial Value Problem—I." *Journal of the Atmospheric Sciences* 19:329–341.

BIRTH
Nov. 4, 1927
San Francisco,
California

*1929: Kurt Gödel
presents the proof
of his completeness
theorem in 1929 as
part of his dissertation.*

1930

1940

*1953: Cambridge
University begins the
world's first computer
science program.*

1950

COBHAM 1964
IBM Research
Labs, (York-
town Heights,
New York).

*1956: Automata Studies
is published and includes
work by Claude Shannon,
Marvin Minsky, Ross
Ashby, John von Neumann,
and John McCarthy.*

1960

*1965: Jack Edmonds
publishes "Paths,
Trees, and Flowers."*

*1971: The first floppy disks
are sold with compat-
ible IBM products.*

1970

*1984: Cobham designs
Playbridge, a bridge-
playing program that was
the most sophisticated
of its kind to date.*

1980

1990

2000

DEATH
June 28, 2011
Middletown,
Connecticut,
cause unknown

2010

ALAN·BELMONT·COBHAM

[24]

EASY VS. HARD: THE DAWN OF COMPUTATIONAL COMPLEXITY

Cristopher Moore, Santa Fe Institute

The triumphs of Kurt Gödel, Alan Turing, and Alonzo Church in the 1930s showed that some problems are infinitely hard. There are mathematical truths with no finite proof, no matter how long that proof can be. There are problems that no computer program can solve, no matter how long we let it run. These undecidability and uncomputability results placed fundamental limits on our ability—or any system's ability—to prove and compute, and they reverberated throughout logic, mathematics, and the nascent field of computer science.

After the Second World War, as computing became more of a practical reality, the question was not "Can this problem ever be solved?" but "Can we solve it in a reasonable amount of time?" As computers became more powerful and capable of solving larger problems, it became more and more important to understand how the difficulty of these problems scales. If a problem twice as large takes just twice as long to solve, then larger and larger problems will quickly come within reach as our computers get faster.

Mathematically, let $f(n)$ be the amount of computation we need to solve problems of size n: solving equations in n variables, navigating a city with n locations, or analyzing a network with n nodes. If $f(n) = n^2$, then $f(2n) = 4f(n)$. If $f(n) = n^3$, then $f(2n) = 8f(n)$. This kind of growth is called *polynomial*, also known as a power law. With this kind of scaling, the amount of computation we need grows with n, but not too badly.

On the other hand, suppose $f(n) = 2^n$, that is, $\overbrace{2 \times 2 \times \cdots \times 2}^{n \text{ times}}$. In that case, $f(n+1) = 2f(n)$. Whenever we add a new variable, location, or node to the problem, changing n to $n+1$, it becomes twice as hard.

A. Cobham, "The Intrinsic Computational Difficulty of Functions," in *Proceedings of the 1964 International Congress on Logic, Methodology, and Philosophy of Science*, ed. Y. Bar-Hillel, North-Holland Publishing Company, 24–30 (1965).

Reproduced with permission of Cambridge University Press and the Journal of Symbolic Logic.

Its difficulty increases exponentially: if $n = 1000$, then $f(n) = 2^{1000}$, or roughly 1 followed by 301 zeroes. The complexity of the problem is finite but astronomical, and large problems will remain forever out of reach.

This motivated the first, and still the most significant, distinction in computational complexity theory: between polynomial and exponential time. In a groundbreaking paper contemporary with Alan Cobham's called "Paths, Trees, and Flowers," Jack Edmonds presented an efficient algorithm for a problem in graph theory. In a valuable digression he discussed what "efficient" means:

> There is an obvious finite algorithm, but that algorithm increases in difficulty exponentially with the size of the graph. . . . For practical purposes the difference between algebraic [i.e., polynomial] and exponential order is often more crucial that the difference between finite and non-finite.

The distinction between polynomial and exponential often hinges on whether we have an insight into the structure of the problem. An insight can give us an algorithmic shortcut, leading us quickly and surely to a solution. Without such an insight, we may simply have to search a vast landscape of possible solutions, taking exponential time.

But phrasing it this way—whether "we" have an insight—makes computational complexity sound like a subjective matter of our own cleverness or lack of it. Certainly many problems that seem hard at first turn out to be easy. But perhaps some problems have no shortcut, and no way to avoid an exponential search. As we will see when we discuss Richard Karp's foundational paper on NP-completeness, there is strong evidence that this is true for many problems.

Cobham was among the first to argue that problems have an *intrinsic* complexity—an objective fact about their structure, not a subjective one about whether or not we have found a clever algorithm. His initial question puts this in a beautiful and accessible way: Is multiplication harder than addition? We all learned methods for these problems in grade school. To add two five-digit numbers takes just five steps:

$$
\begin{array}{r}
3\ 1\ 4\ 1\ 5 \\
+\ 1\ 2\ 3\ 2\ 1 \\
\hline
4\ 3\ 7\ 3\ 6
\end{array}
$$

where each step consists of adding a single pair of digits (maybe with a little carrying). More generally, we can add n-digit numbers in n steps, so the complexity of addition is linear.

The traditional method to multiply two five-digit numbers, on the other hand, takes considerably more work:

$$
\begin{array}{r}
3\ 1\ 4\ 1\ 5 \\
\times\ 1\ 2\ 3\ 2\ 1 \\
\hline
3\ 1\ 4\ 1\ 5 \\
6\ 2\ 8\ 3\ 0 \\
9\ 4\ 2\ 4\ 5 \\
6\ 2\ 8\ 3\ 0 \\
3\ 1\ 4\ 1\ 5 \\
\hline
3\ 8\ 7\ 0\ 6\ 4\ 2\ 1\ 5
\end{array}
$$

Here we performed $5 \times 5 = 25$ single-digit multiplications, or n^2 steps for n-digit numbers. Adding up those products to get the final answer takes about n^2 more steps, for a total of $2n^2$. But we don't care about this factor of 2 in front, just like we don't care about how fast your computer is. What matters is that the complexity of this algorithm scales as n^2.

Thus the complexity of multiplication appears to be quadratic rather than linear, that is, n^2 rather than n. But is this a property of multiplication itself or just of our method? What if this is not the best algorithm? What is the true complexity of this problem?

The challenge is that an algorithm for a problem only places an upper bound on its complexity. The grade-school method shows that the intrinsic complexity of multiplication is at most n^2. But to pin down its complexity, we need a lower bound as well. That is, we need to show that this is the best we can do: that no possible algorithm can multiply n-digit numbers in anything less than n^2 time. How in the world can we do that? It seems hard to improve on the traditional method, but it also seems hard to exclude all possible alternate strategies.

Cobham identifies this question and makes several points that remain vital to the foundations of computation. First, he points out that the details of our computing hardware don't matter. A Turing machine reads and writes symbols on a "tape" like the whirring magnetic reels of yore, while a modern computer has multiple processors that can leap in a single bound to any location in their memory. But while the Turing machine might be slower, since it has to spin its tape to the location it wants to read, this can't make the difference between polynomial and exponential time. At most it will change the time from one polynomial to another, say, from n^2 to n^3.

Thus the class P of problems that can be solved in polynomial time, which Cobham calls $\mathcal{L}$, is robust to our choice of computational model: It is independent of the substrate. Computers can simulate each other, so what one can do in polynomial time, they all can. While of course we can imagine exotic computers that can solve vast problems in a single step, Cobham argues that this equivalence holds for any *real* computer, that is, any device that we could actually build in our universe. This is an early statement of what we now call the strong physical Church–Turing thesis.[1]

Cobham points out that the class P is robust to many ways of combining simpler functions to make more complicated ones. One polynomial-time function can call upon another, or use another in a loop, while keeping the total running time polynomial. He phrases these facts in the ancient language of recursive function theory, but in modern programming we call these subroutines and for-loops.

Cobham also discusses computational resources other than time, such as memory (for a Turing machine, the length of its tape). In modern computer science, we use multiple measures of complexity, such as the number of processors, how much they communicate with each other, how much energy they use, and even how much randomness we need. Each of these resources gives us a different way to measure the

---

[1] The possible exception is quantum computation. Peter Shor discovered in 1994 that quantum computers can factor integers (and thus break RSA public-key encryption) in polynomial time. We think these problems require exponential time on a classical computer—but since there might be faster *classical* algorithms than the ones we know about, we can't be sure.

complexity of a problem. As he says, no one measure reflects all the types of complexity we encounter.

For computational complexity theorists, all these questions are not about computers, or programming, or any of the technologies that enlighten and burden our lives. They are about the fundamental mathematical structure of problem-solving, of proof, and of search. And while the computational power of a system is not the only way to think about its complexity, it remains one of the major lenses we can use to perceive complexity, simplicity, and everything in between.

Finally, a wonderful postscript: It turns out that the grade-school method of multiplication is not the best possible. In 1962, Karatsuba and Ofman gave an algorithm that multiplies n-digit numbers in time $n^{1.585}$ instead of n^2. It was published in a Soviet journal, and Cobham seems not to have been aware of it. A series of improvements culminated in a beautiful algorithm that uses Fourier analysis and takes nearly linear time, although with a large constant in front that makes it impractical for small problems. Thus multiplication turns out to be, intrinsically, just a little more complex than addition. ✝

REFERENCES

Agrawal, M., N. Kayal, and N. Saxena. 2004. "Primes is in P." *Annals of Mathematics* 160 (2): 781–793. https://doi.org/10.4007/annals.2004.160.781.

Edmonds, J. 1965. "Paths, Trees, and Flowers." *Canadian Journal of Mathematics* 17:449–467. https://doi.org/10.4153/CJM-1965-045-4.

Karatsuba, A., and Y. Ofman. 1962. "Multiplication of Many-Digital Numbers by Automatic Computers." Translation in the academic journal *Physics-Doklady* 7 (1963), pp. 595–596, *Proceedings of the USSR Academy of Sciences* 145:293–294.

Shor, P. W. 1994. "Algorithms for Quantum Computation: Discrete Logarithms and Factoring." In *SFCS '94: Proceedings of the 35th Annual Symposium on Foundations of Computer Science,* 124–134. USA: IEEE Computer Society. https://doi.org/10.1109/sfcs.1994.365700.

THE INTRINSIC COMPUTATIONAL DIFFICULTY OF FUNCTIONS

Alan Cobham, IBM Research Center

The subject of my talk is perhaps most directly indicated by simply asking two questions: first, is it harder to multiply than to add? and second, why? I grant I have put the first of these questions rather loosely; nevertheless, I think the answer, ought to be: *yes*. It is the second, which asks for a justification of this answer which provides the challenge.

The difficulty does not stem from the fact that the first question has been imprecisely formulated. There seems to be no substantial problem in showing that using the standard algorithms it is in general harder— in the sense that it takes more time or more scratch paper—to multiply two decimal numbers than to add them. But this does not answer the question, which is concerned with the computational difficulty of these two operations without reference to specific computational methods; in other words, with properties intrinsic to the functions themselves and not with properties of particular related algorithms. Thus to complete the argument, I would have to show that there is no algorithm for multiplication computationally as simple as that for addition, and this proves something of a stumbling block. Of course, as I have implied, I feel this must be the case and that multiplication is in this absolute sense harder than addition, but I am forced to admit that at present my reasons for feeling so are of an essentially extra-mathematical character.

Questions of this sort belong to a field which I think we might well call *metanumerical-analysis*. The name seems appropriate not only because it is suggestive of the subject matter, namely, the methodology of computation, but also because the relationship of the field to computation is closely analogous to that of metamathematics to mathematics. In metamathematics, we encounter problems concerned with specific proof systems; e.g., the existence of proofs having a

To show that the grade-school algorithm is the best we can do, we have to reason about all possible alternatives. This is much harder than exhibiting a single algorithm. In computational complexity, upper bounds are easy but lower bounds are hard, since we never know if our current method is the best possible. This is why many questions in computational complexity remain open, including the P vs. NP problem (see Karp's paper below in this volume).

certain form, or the adequacy of a system in a given context. We also encounter problems concerned with provability but independently of any particular proof system; e.g., the undecidability of mathematical theories. So in metanumerical-analysis we encounter problems related to specific computational systems or categories of computing machines as well as problems such as those mentioned above which, though concerned with computation, arc independent of any particular method of computation. It is this latter segment of metanumerical-analysis I would like to look at more closely.

Let me begin by stating two of the very few results which fall squarely within this area (others appear in Hartmanis and Stearns 1963; Myhill 1960; Radin 1960). Both are drawn from Ritchie's work on predictably computable functions (Ritchie 1963), the first being an almost immediate generalization of one part of that work, the second an incomplete rendering of another part. These relate, perhaps not in the most happy fashion, the computational complexity of a function with its location in the Grzegorczyk hierarchy (Grzegorczyk 1953). Recall that this hierarchy is composed of a sequence of classes:

$$\mathscr{E}^0 \subset \mathscr{E}^1 \subset \mathscr{E}^2 \subset \dots,$$

each properly contained in the next, and having as union the class of all primitive recursive functions. $\mathscr{E}^2$ can be characterized as the smallest class containing the successor and multiplication functions, and closed under the operations of explicit transformation, composition, and limited recursion. The classes $\mathscr{E}^3$ (which is the familiar class of Kalmar elementary functions) and $\mathscr{E}^4$ have similar characterizations, with exponentiation and the function $x^{x^{\cdot^{\cdot^{x}}}} \Big\} y$ respectively, replacing multiplication in the characterization of $\mathscr{E}^2$. The higher classes can be characterized inductively in like manner.

With each single-tape Turing machine Z which computes a function of one variable we may associate two functions, σ_z and τ_z. Assuming some standard encoding of natural numbers—we might take decimal notation to be specific—we define $\sigma_z(n)$, where n is a natural number, to be the numbers of steps (instruction executions) in the computation

This theorem defines a hierarchy of complexity classes where each one contains functions that the previous class cannot compute. However, it is quite crude: each class is enormously more powerful than the one before it, and already $\mathscr{E}^4$ contains absurdly large functions. We can now draw much finer distinctions (see below).

on Z starting with n encoded on its tape, and define $\tau_z(n)$ to be the number of distinct tape squares scanned during the course of this computation. Restricting attention to functions of one variable, we have the following.

Theorem: For each $k \geq 3$ the following five statements are equivalent:

1. $f \varepsilon \mathscr{E}^k$;
2. there exists a Turing machine Z which computes f and such that $\sigma_z \varepsilon \mathscr{E}^k$;
3. there exists a Turing machine Z which computes f and a function $g \varepsilon \mathscr{E}^k$ such that, for all n, $\sigma_z(n) \leqq g(n)$;

4–5. Same as 2–3 with τ_z in place of σ_z.

This theorem has an immediate generalization to functions of several variables. From it we can infer that (in effect, but not quite precisely) if one function is simpler to compute than another, in the very strong sense that for any value of the argument the computation can be done in fewer steps or with less tape, then that function lies no higher than the other in the Grzegorczyk hierarchy. We cannot conclude the converse however: that if one function lies lower than another, it is necessarily simpler to compute. As a matter of fact, it appears that a function in the lower part of the hierarchy may actually be *on average* harder to compute than one higher up, though, of course it cannot be harder for all values of the argument.

A word is needed as to why I have included a theorem involving Turing machines in a discussion which I said was going to be about method-independent aspects of computation. The fact is the theorem remains correct even if one considers far wider classes of computing machines. In particular, it holds for Turing machines with more than one tape or with multi-dimensional tapes providing the cells of the latter are arranged in reasonably orderly fashion. It also holds if the set of possible instructions is extended to include, e.g., erasure of an entire tape or resetting of a scanning head to its initial position (although I doubt such operations should be considered *steps* since it does not appear that they can be executed in a bounded amount of time).

Computational complexity theory usually demands that an algorithm work in every case, and therefore in the worst case. In many contexts this is too strict. We don't expect our brain to quickly understand every possible image or sentence, and we don't blame ourselves if we get confused by a few diabolical examples. For some problems, hard examples exist but are rare, making the problem easy on average; for others, such as cryptography, even average problems are hard.

The hardware doesn't matter: computational complexity is largely free of its substrate. Each step of a Turing machine can be expressed with simple mathematics, and any variant of a Turing machine can easily encode and simulate any other. The physical Church–Turing thesis states that the same is true for any device we could build in our universe.

The reason for such general applicability can be found on examination of the proof of this theorem. There we find that the fact that we are dealing with a particular class of Turing machines is quite incidental: it is the form of their arithmetization which counts. The geometry and basic operations of a Turing machine are of a sort which admit an arithmetization in which the functions which describe the step-by-step course of a computation on it are of a very simple nature, lying, in particular, well within the class $\mathscr{E}^2$. This is all that is needed to obtain the preceding theorem (as well as the one which follows). Now the class $\mathscr{E}^2$ is so rich in functions that it is almost inconceivable to me that there could exist *real* computers not having mathematical models whose arithmetization could be carried out in such a way that these associated functions would fall within it. Thus I suspect this theorem does indeed say something about the absolute computational properties of functions, and so fits properly in the discussion.

The five equivalences of the preceding theorem do not hold for $k <$ 3. Ritchie has obtained a hierarchy which decomposes the range between $\mathscr{E}^2$ and $\mathscr{E}^3$ into classes of functions of varying degrees of computational difficulty; however, rather than go into this, I would like now to turn to the problem of classifying the functions within $\mathscr{E}^2$, where many of the functions most frequently encountered in computational work, addition and multiplication in particular, are located. First, concerning $\mathscr{E}^2$ itself, we have (Ritchie 1963) the following.

Theorem: A function f belongs to $\mathscr{E}^2$ if and only if there exists a Turing machine Z which computes f and constants c_1 and c_2 such that $\tau_z(n) \leqq c_1 l(n) + c_2$, for all n.

Here $l(n)$ is the length of n, that is, the number of digits in its decimal representation. Machines which compute in the fashion described are equivalent to those which Myhill has called linear bounded automata (Myhill 1960). Since merely writing n requires $l(n)$ tape squares, we must have $c_1 \geqq 1$. As a matter of fact, if we consider machines with arbitrarily large alphabets, then c_1 need only be enough larger than this to permit writing of the answer on the tape; e.g., if $f(n) = n^2$ we can take $c_1 = 2$; if $f(n) \leqq n$ for all n we can take $c_1 = 1$. In other words, if we have enough space to write the larger of the value and the argument of a function in $\mathscr{E}^2$ then we have enough space to carry out the entire computation. Consequently, the function τ is not a suitable tool for making fine distinctions concerning the computational difficulty of functions within $\mathscr{E}^2$. We might attempt to redefine what we mean by the amount of tape used during a computation by distinguishing between those locations used for writing input and output and those used in the actual computation. But the artificiality of such a seemingly ad hoc distinction would seem to be trending away from our goal of obtaining a natural analysis independent of the method or type of machine used in the computation.

This may be a good point to mention that, although I have so far been tacitly equating computational difficulty with time and storage requirements, I don't mean to commit myself to either of these measures. It may turn out that some measure related to the physical notion of work will lead to the most satisfactory analysis; or we may ultimately find that no single measure adequately reflects our intuitive concept of difficulty. In any case, for the present, I see no harm in restricting the discussion somewhat and having discarded τ as a tool for reasons just stated, confining further attention to the analysis of computation time.

This leaves us some latitude for differentiating among functions in $\mathscr{E}^2$. The closest analog of the foregoing theorem concerning σ, rather than τ, that I know of states that for any f in $\mathscr{E}^2$ there exists a Turing machine Z which computes it and such that σ_z is bounded by a polynomial in its argument f itself must also be bounded by a polynomial in its argument, but I don't know whether these two conditions in turn imply that f is in $\mathscr{E}^2$.

To obtain some idea as to how we might go about the further classification of relatively simple functions, we might take a look at how we ordinarily set about computing some of the more common of them. Suppose, for example, that m and n are two numbers given in decimal notation with one written above the other and their right ends aligned. Then to add m and n we start at the right and proceed digit-by-digit to the left writing down the sum. No matter how large m and n, this process terminates with the answer after a number of steps equal at most to one greater than the larger of $l(m)$ and $l(n)$. Thus the process of adding m

Besides time and memory, we can ask how much parallel processing, communication, energy, or randomness we need to solve a problem. Yet other measures of complexity focus on the length of the program, or the thermodynamic work it takes to create an object. Which measure of complexity matters depends on which resource is limited, and on what kind of natural or artificial process we are trying to understand.

and n can be carried out in a number of steps which is bounded by a linear polynomial in $l(m)$ and $l(n)$. Similarly, we can multiply m and n in a number of steps bounded by a quadratic polynomial in $l(m)$ and $l(n)$. So, too, the number of steps involved in the extraction of square roots, calculation of quotients, etc., can be bounded by polynomials in the lengths of the numbers involved, and this seems to be a property of simple functions in general. This suggests that we consider the class, which I will call $\mathcal{L}$, of all functions having this property.

For several reasons the class $\mathcal{L}$ seems a natural one to consider. For one thing, if we formalize the above definition relative to various general classes of computing machines we seem always to end up with the same well-defined class of functions. Thus we can give a mathematical characterization of $\mathcal{L}$ having some confidence that it characterizes correctly our informally defined class. This class then turns out to have several natural closure properties, being closed in particular under explicit transformation, composition, and limited recursion on notation (digit-by-digit recursion). To be more explicit concerning the latter operation, which incidentally seems quite appropriate to computational work, we say that a function f is defined from functions $g, h_0, \ldots, h_9$, and k by limited recursion on notation (assuming decimal notation) if

$$f(x, 0) = g(x)$$
$$f(x, s_i(y)) = h_i(\mathbf{x}, y, f(\mathbf{x}, y)) \quad (i = 0, \ldots, 9; \; i \neq 0 \text{ if } y = 0)$$
$$f(\mathbf{x}, y) \leqq k(\mathbf{x}, y),$$

where s_i is the generalized successor: $s_i(y) = 10y + i$. $\mathcal{L}$ is in fact the smallest class closed under these operations and containing the functions s_i and $x^{l(y)}$. It is closely related to, perhaps identical with, the class of what Bennett has called the extended rudimentary functions (Bennett 1962). Since $\mathcal{L}$ contains $x^{l(y)}$, which cannot, by the second of the theorems mentioned earlier, belong to $\mathcal{E}^2$, $\mathcal{L}$ is not a subclass of $\mathcal{E}^2$. On the other hand, I strongly suspect that the function $f(n) =$ the nth prime, which is known to be in $\mathcal{E}^2$, does not belong to $\mathcal{L}$. If this is the case then $\mathcal{E}^2$ and $\mathcal{L}$ are incomparable and we have the unsurprising result that the categorization of the simpler functions as to computational difficulty yields divergent classifications according

Polynomial time (Cobham's $\mathcal{L}$, now called P) is extremely robust to our model of computation. For almost any device we can imagine, the boundary between polynomial and exponential time is the same. The one exception seems to be quantum computers, which can solve some problems in polynomial time—like factoring large integers—that classical computers, to the best of our knowledge, cannot. (Note that P is defined as what classical computers can do in polynomial time.)

Polynomial-time functions can be combined and composed in many ways. In modern terms, they can call each other recursively, or use each other in for-loops.

The fastest algorithm is often not the one that uses the least memory, and vice versa. Different strategies are optimal for different resources.

to the criterion of difficulty selected—in this case time and storage requirements. Concerning functions which are relatively simple under both criteria, that is, those in both $\mathscr{E}^2$ and $\mathscr{L}$, I can only offer further conjecture, namely that $\mathscr{E}^2 \cap \mathscr{L}$ is a subclass of the constructive arithmetic functions, probably even a proper subclass. (The function $f(n) = 1$ or 0, according as n is or is not prime, is constructive arithmetic but seemingly not in $\mathscr{L}$.)

An attempt to construct a natural computational hierarchy within $\mathscr{L}$ now brings out quite sharply one of the basic problems entailed in the study of absolute or intrinsic computational properties of functions. Suppose we start out in the obvious way and define, for each k, a subclass $\mathscr{L}^k$ of $\mathscr{L}$ consisting of all functions which can be computed in such a way that the number of steps in the computation is bounded by a polynomial of degree k in the lengths of the arguments. So defined, the classes $\mathscr{L}^k$ form an increasing sequence whose union is $\mathscr{L}$. Clearly, almost as a matter of definition, the analog of the theorem concerning the Grzegorczyk hierarchy I mentioned earlier will hold for this hierarchy: a function in the upper part of the hierarchy cannot be simpler to compute for every argument than one further down.

If we are to make any application of this theorem, we need a precise, mathematical characterization of the classes $\mathscr{L}^k$. Unlike the foregoing situation, however, we find that it makes a definite difference what class of computational methods and devices we consider in our attempt to formalize the definition. Thus, if we restrict attention to single-tape Turing machines, we find that addition does not belong to $\mathscr{L}^1$, whereas it does if we permit our machines to have several tapes. Similarly, multiplication gets into $\mathscr{L}^2$ only if we permit multi-tape machines. This certainly does not mean that there is no reasonable formalization of the classes of this hierarchy, but it does suggest that there may be some difficulty both in finding this formalization and, once found, in convincing oneself that it correctly captures all relevant aspects of the intuitive model.

The problem is reminiscent of, and obviously closely related to, that of the formalization of the notion of effectiveness. But the emphasis is different in that the physical aspects of the computation process are here of predominant concern. The question of what may legitimately

This problem remained open for many years. Then, in 2002, Manindra Agrawal, Neeraj Kayal, and Nitin Saxena found a polynomial-time algorithm that tells whether an n-digit number is prime, showing that $f(n)$ is in P after all. Note that this is different from factoring an integer into its prime factors—this is not yet known to be in P, but it might be.

Hartmanis and Stearns proved this hierarchy theorem using a clever Cantor-like argument. When $f(n)$ grows more slowly than $g(n)$, there are functions we can compute in $g(n)$ time but not $f(n)$ time. The same is true of memory. If our time or memory is n, n^2, n^3, and so on, each level of this hierarchy is more powerful than the one below—but that doesn't mean we can tell to which level a given problem belongs.

The details of our hardware don't make a difference between polynomial and exponential time, but they can influence linear and quadratic time (n vs. n^2). For instance, a machine with RAM can store and retrieve information more efficiently than a Turing machine can. If we want to solve problems as quickly as possible, architecture matters.

be considered to constitute a step of a computation is quite unlike that of what constitutes an effective operation. I did not dwell particularly on what I consider to be the properties of legitimate step when I was discussing the classification of functions outside of $\mathscr{E}^2$ because, as I pointed out, one could admit all sorts of questionable operations as steps and, so long as they could be represented by functions in $\mathscr{E}^2$, the results obtained would remain unaltered. Quite similar remarks can be made concerning permissible geometric arrangements of the working area of a computation, and even concerning the types of notation used for representing natural numbers. If, however, we are to make fine distinctions, say between functions in $\mathscr{L}^1$ and functions in $\mathscr{L}^2$, then we must have an equally fine analysis of all phases of the computational process. It is no longer a problem of finding convincing arguments that every conceivable computing method can be arithmetized within $\mathscr{E}^2$ but rather of finding convincing arguments that these can somehow be arithmetized within whatever presumably more restricted class we settle upon as a formalization for $\mathscr{L}^1$. Of course, at the same time, we must be prepared to argue that we haven't taken too broad a class for $\mathscr{L}^1$, and thus admitted to it functions not in actuality computable in a number of steps linearly bounded by the lengths of its arguments. I think this is one of the fundamental problems of metanumerical-analysis and one whose resolution may well call for considerable patience and discrimination, but until it, and several related problems, have received more intensive treatment, I doubt we can find any really satisfying proof that multiplication is indeed harder than addition.

It turns out that we can multiply n-digit numbers in much less than n^2 time, at least when n is large. Thus the gap between multiplication and addition is not nearly as wide as the grade-school methods would suggest. However, as Cobham anticipates, proving that some problems are hard—that they resist all algorithmic strategies and all possible shortcuts—remains one of the deepest sources of open questions in computational complexity.

REFERENCES

Bennett, J. H. 1962. "On Spectra." PhD diss., Princeton University.

Grzegorczyk, A. 1953. *Some Classes of Recursive Functions.* Warsaw, Poland: Instytut Matematyczny Polskiej Akademi Nauk.

Hartmanis, J., and R. E. Stearns. 1963. "On the Computational Complexity of Algorithms." *American Mathematiical Society* 376 (2): 59–79.

Myhill, J. 1960. *Linear Bounded Automata*. Wright–Patterson Air Force Base, Ohio: Wright Air Development Division, Air Research / Technology Command, United States Air Force.

Radin, M. O. 1960. *Degree of Difficulty of Computing a Function and a Partial Ordering of Recursive Sets.* Technical report Report No. 2. Jerusalem, Israel: Hebrew University, April.

Ritchie, R. W. 1963. "Classes of Predictably Computable Functions." *Transactions of the American Mathematical Society* 106:139–173.

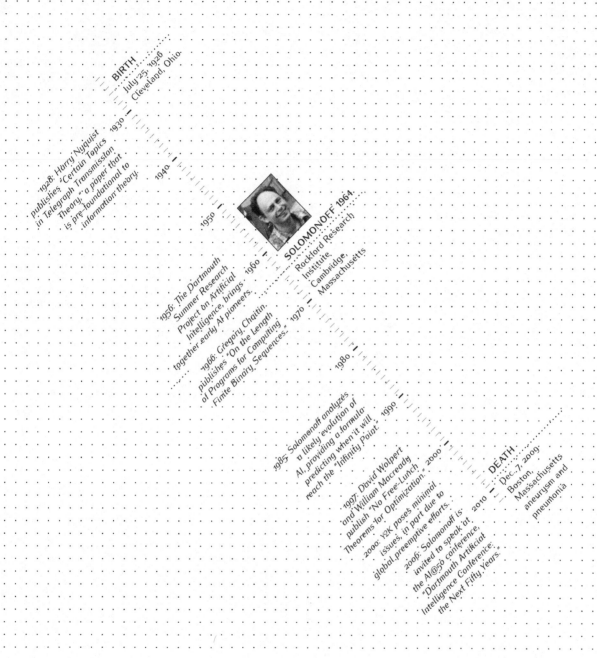

BIRTH
July 25, 1926.
Cleveland, Ohio.

1928: Harry Nyquist publishes "Certain Topics in Telegraph Transmission Theory," a paper that is pre-foundational to information theory.

1930

1940

1950

1956: The Dartmouth Summer Research Project on Artificial Intelligence, brings together early AI pioneers.

1960

SOLOMONOFF 1964.
Rockford Research Institute, Cambridge, Massachusetts.

1966: Gregory Chaitin publishes "On the Length of Programs for Computing Finite Binary Sequences."

1970

1980

1985: Solomonoff analyzes a likely evolution of AI, providing a formula predicting when it will reach the "Infinity Point."

1990

1997: David Wolpert and William Macready publish "No Free-Lunch Theorems for Optimization."

2000: Y2K poses minimal issues, in part due to global preemptive efforts.

2000

2006: Solomonoff is invited to speak at the AI@50 conference, "Dartmouth Artificial Intelligence Conference: the Next Fifty Years."

2010

DEATH.
Dec. 7, 2009.
Boston, Massachusetts. aneurysm and pneumonia.

RAYMOND J. SOLOMONOFF

[25]

A GENERAL SYSTEM FOR MACHINE LEARNING

Paul M. B. Vitányi, CWI and University of Amsterdam

Ray J. Solomonoff (1926–2009), founding father of algorithmic information theory, was born in Cleveland, Ohio in the United States. Algorithmic information theory (Li and Vitányi 2019) deals with the shortest effective description length of objects and is commonly designated by the term "Kolmogorov complexity."

The latter notion was a side product of his approach to induction. His crucial results concerning prediction, in 1960 and later, partially resolve the old philosophical problem of how to obtain a valid prior distribution in Bayes's rule by showing that a single "universal" distribution can be used instead of any computable prior with almost the same resulting predictions. This may be viewed as a central problem of artificial intelligence, machine learning, and statistical inference—with the caveat that the universal distribution is incomputable. Solomonoff's theory has led to feasible induction and prediction procedures (Fine 1973). His contributions to science together with biographical remarks are outlined in Gács and Vitányi (2011) and Li and Vitányi (2019), while his scientific autobiography up to 1997 can be found in Solomonoff (1997).[1]

In 1956, Solomonoff attended the Dartmouth Summer Study Group on Artificial Intelligence at Dartmouth College in Hanover, New Hampshire, organized by Marvin Minsky, John McCarthy, Claude Shannon, and Nathaniel Rochester—the meeting gave that AI its name. Solomonoff stayed on to spend the whole summer there, writing a memo on inductive inference. McCarthy had proposed that every mathematical problem could be translated into the form: "Given a machine and a desired output, find an input from which the machine

R. J. Solomonoff, "A Formal Theory of Inductive Inference, Part I," in *Information and Control* 7 (1): 1–22 (1964).

Reprinted from *Information and Control*, with permission from Elsevier.

---

[1] See also Ray Solomonoff's Home Page: http://raysolomonoff.com.

computes that output." Solomonoff suggested that there was a class of problems for which this was not true: "Given an initial segment of a sequence, predict its continuation." McCarthy responded that if one saw a machine producing the initial segment, and then continuing past that point, would one not think that the continuation was a reasonable extrapolation? With that the idea got stuck, and the participants left it.

Solomonoff (1960) based his first approach on Turing machines with markers that delimit the input. This led to awkward convergence problems with which he tried to deal in an *ad hoc* manner. The young Leonid A. Levin at the State University of Moscow[2] learned from his thesis advisor Andrey N. Kolmogorov about Solomonoff's work. He added a reference to it, but had a hard time digesting the informalities, only later coming to appreciate the wealth of ideas in Solomonoff (1960, 1964). Solomonoff's publications apparently received little attention until Kolmogorov started to refer to them from 1968 onward.

Solomonoff's 1960 paper already contains in veiled form suggestions about randomness of finite strings, incomputability of Kolmogorov complexity, computability of approximations to the Kolmogorov complexity, and resource-bounded Kolmogorov complexity. With respect to induction, after its publication Solomonoff welcomed Levin's new formalism with one exception: it bothered him that the universal *a priori* probability for prediction is a semimeasure (a generalization of a probability measure obtained by relaxing the additivity requirement to super-additivity). He continued to advocate for a normalization operation in a long technical argument with Levin and the logician Robert Solovay.

Solomonoff's ultimate goal in AI, as pursued in many subsequent papers,[3] was a general system for machine learning. The goal is not so much to acquire knowledge itself but rather to determine how learning is performed by machines. The idea is as follows: The machine starts out, like a human infant, with a set of primitive concepts. We then give it a simple problem, which it solves using these primitive concepts. In solving the first problem, it acquires new concepts that help it solve the

---

[2]Levin developed his own mathematical framework, which became the source of a beautiful theory of randomness, in (Zvonkin and Levin 1970).

[3]See https://raysolomonoff.com/publications/ and R.J. Solomonoff, Wikipedia, accessed June 13, 2022.

more difficult second problem, and so on. A suitable training sequence of problems of increasing difficulty brings the machine to a high level of problem-solving skill. The principal activity of the present research is the design of training sequences of this kind.

Initially, the machine will learn two types of problems.

(i) Function inversion: the P and NP problems of computer science like theorem proving, solutions to equations, graph coloring, and the like.

(ii) Time-limited optimization, like inductive inference of different types, surface reconstruction, image restoration, and so on.

Some Technical Details

"Probability" is used in the sense of the probability assigned by the best probabilistic model we can find in the available time for the given data. The following outline is taken from Gács and Vitányi (2011).

(1) Initially, the system has a small number of problem-solving techniques. We call the set of these PST. It also has a simple general conditional probability distribution (GCPD) $P^t : PST \times \mathscr{P} \to [0, 1]$ defined by $P^t(pst|p)$ where p is an element of the problem set $\mathscr{P}$ and $pst \in PST$. In this way, $P^t(pst|p)$ is defined to be the probability that problem p is solved by technique pst within time t. The conceptual jump size (CJS) of problem p is related to the minimum of $t/P^t(pst|p)$ over t, pst.

(2) For $i = 1, 2, \ldots$, do: given problem p_i (the ith problem) the system uses the current PST and P^t to solve p_i. Here we initially use a small upper bound T and consider only those t such that $t \leq T$. We spend at most time $\Sigma t(pst, p_i, T) = P^t(pst|p_i)T$ on problem p using solution method pst. If we find a solution, then we stop. In total we spend at most $\Sigma t(pst, pi, T) \leq T$ time, where the sum is taken over the elements of PST. If we don't find a solution, then we double T. This process continues until p_i is solved. Note that if this process terminates with final T_f, then the total time spent is at most $2T_f$. Also, if $t \leq T_f$ (which means that p_i is solved in

time t by some method in PST), then the solution time is at most $2 \cdot t(pst, p_i, T_f)/P^t(pst|pi)$.

As above, Solomonoff calls $t(pst, p_i, T_f)/P^t(pst|p_i)$ the conceptual jump size of problem p_i. Note that $t(pst, p_i, T_f)/P^t(pst|p_i) \approx \min t/P^t(pst|p) : pst \in PST, p \in P$.

Next the system uses the update algorithm which replaces $PST \leftarrow PST_0$ where PST_0 equals PST with some additions and deletions. Also $\mathscr{P} \leftarrow \mathscr{P}_0$ where $\mathscr{P}_0$ equals $\mathscr{P}$ with some additions and deletions, and $P^t \leftarrow P_0^t$ where P_0^t is now a new GCPD over the new PST and the new set $\mathscr{P}$. Here we leave open how the updates to PST, $\mathscr{P}$, and P^t are done.

In the initial PST we include Levin's universal search (Lsearch). This means that if $P^t(Lsearch|p) = 1$ and $|p| = n$ and the fastest algorithm solves p in time $f(n)$ then $t \approx 2^{K(p)} f(n)$ where $K(p)$ is the length of a shortest effective description of p in a prefix code (such that no end-of-description marker is required). For feasibility, initially we require a problem p with very low $K(p)$ in our training sequence. Said differently, we initially require problems to have small conceptual jump size. At the start, the problems in $\mathscr{P}$ have Lsearch probability $2^{-K(p)}$. But in the update phase this probability distribution is modified. Suppose we solve p_i in the ith trial using Lsearch. Then, in the update phase we update p's probability in Lsearch to a much greater probability.

Also, the update algorithms may perhaps be similar to inductive inference problems of the type the machine regularly solves. Hence, the updates may be equivalent to the solving of particular problems.

(3) A *training sequence* is $(Q_1, A_1), (Q_2, A_2), \ldots$ is a sequence of questions and answers to problems of increasing difficulty. Here the Qs are questions and the corresponding As are (correct) answers. We have to design such a training sequence (or more of them) to train and evolve the system to have greater capabilities. For every i, given $(Q_1, A_1), \ldots, (Q_i, A_i)$ the system tries to find a function F_i such that $F_i(Q_j) = A_j$ for all $1 \leq j \leq i$. (In the context of the above, Q is a problem and A is its correct answer. So the system has

to solve Q and obtain the answer A. This results in a function F so that $F(Q) = A$.)

A problem p should be "factored" in subproblems $p_1, p_2, \ldots, p_n$ and each of these in other subproblems, etc. "Factoring" here is the inverse of "chunking." The problem p is solved by the solutions to $p_1, \ldots, p_n$. The final subproblems should be simple enough to be solved by simple Lsearch. Altogether, this looks like a network of (sub)problems with the main problem to be solved on top and below it layers of subproblems. This way, the teacher can derive the training sequence giving the question-answer pairs of the subproblems at the lower layers first.

Solomonoff's inference method has spawned an elaborate theory of modeling in statistics, statistical inference, and prediction in both static and reactive unknown environments, based on universal distributions with arbitrary loss bounds (rather than just the logarithmic loss) using extensions and variations of the proof method, inspiring information theorists such as Thomas M. Cover (1974). Examples include the direction pioneered by Marcus Hutter (2005) and related work on prediction and Kolmogorov complexity, using various loss bounds, going by the name of predictive complexity, in a time-limited setting, introduced by Vladimir G. Vovk (1989). Solomonoff's work has led to a novel approach in statistics leading to applicable inference procedures such as the minimal description length principle (Grünwald 2007). Jorma J. Rissanen, credited with the latter, relates that his invention is based on Solomonoff's work with the idea of applying it to classical statistical inference (Rissanen 1983, 1989, 2007). ❦

REFERENCES

Carnap, R. 1950. *Logical Foundations of Probability.* Chicago, IL: University of Chicago Press.

Cover, T. M. 1974. *Universal Gambling Schemes and the Complexity Measures of Kolmogorov and Chaitin.* Technical report 12. Stanford University Department of Statistics.

Fine, T. L. 1973. *Theories of Probability: An Examination of Foundations.* New York, NY: Academic Press.

Gács, P., and P. M. B. Vitányi. 2011. "Raymond J. Solomonoff 1926–2009." *IEEE Information Theory Society Newsletter* 61 (1): 11–16. https://www.itsoc.org/sites/default/files/2021-03/nits-NL_0311-Web.pdf.

Grünwald, P. D. 2007. *The Minimum Description Length Principle.* Cambridge, MA: MIT Press.

Hutter, M. 2005. *Universal Artificial Intelligence: Sequential Decisions Based on Algorithmic Probability.* Berlin, Germany: Springer-Verlag.

Li, M., and P. M. B. Vitányi. 2019. *Introduction to Kolmogorov Complexity and Its Applications.* 4th. New York, NY: Springer.

Rissanen, J. J. 1983. "A Universal Prior for Integers and Estimation by Minimal Description Length." *Annals of Statistics* 11 (2): 416–431. https://doi.org/10.1214/aos/1176346150.

———. 1989. *Stochastic Complexity in Statistical Inquiry.* London, UK: World Scientific Publishing.

———. 2007. *Information and Complexity in Statistical Modeling.* New York, NY: Springer.

Solomonoff, R. J. 1960. *A Preliminary Report on a General Theory of Inductive Inference.* Technical report V-131. Zator Company, Cambridge, MA.

———. 1964. "A Formal Theory of Inductive Inference, Part I." *Information and Control* 7 (1): 1–22. https://doi.org/10.1016/S0019-9958(64)90223-2.

———. 1997. "The Discovery of Algorithmic Probability." *Journal of Computer and System Sciences* 55 (1): 73–88. https://doi.org/10.1006/jcss.1997.1500.

Vovk, V. G. 1989. "Prediction of Stochastic Sequences." *Problems of Information Transmission* 25 (4): 285–296.

Zvonkin, A. K., and L. A. Levin. 1970. "The Complexity of Finite Objects and the Development of the Concepts of Information and Randomness by Means of the Theory of Algorithms." *Russian Mathematical Surveys* 25 (6): 83–124. https://doi.org/10.1070/RM1970v025n06ABEH001269.

A FORMAL THEORY OF INDUCTIVE INFERENCE. PART I

R. J. Solomonoff, Rockford Research Institute, Inc.

1. Summary

In Part I, four ostensibly different theoretical models of induction are presented, in which the problem dealt with is the extrapolation of a very long sequence of symbols—presumably containing all of the information to be used in the induction. Almost all, if not all problems in induction can be put in this form.

Some strong heuristic arguments have been obtained for the equivalence of the last three models. One of these models is equivalent to a Bayes formulation, in which a priori probabilities are assigned to sequences of symbols on the basis of the lengths of inputs to a universal Turing machine that are required to produce the sequence of interest as output.

Though it seems likely, it is not certain whether the first of the four models is equivalent to the other three.

Few rigorous results are presented. Informal investigations are made of the properties of these models. There are discussions of their consistency and meaningfulness, of their degree of independence of the exact nature of the Turing machine used, and of the accuracy of their predictions in comparison to those of other induction methods.

In Part II these models are applied to the solution of three problems—prediction of the Bernoulli sequence, extrapolation of a certain kind of Markov chain, and the use of phrase structure grammars for induction.

Though some approximations are used, the first of these problems is treated most rigorously. The result is Laplace's rule of succession.

The solution to the second problem uses less certain approximations, but the properties of the solution that are discussed, are fairly independent of these approximations.

In this context, a string of 0s and 1s is finite, and a sequence is usually infinite. Every letter of a finite alphabet can be coded in 0s and 1s in the usual manner.

We are primarily interested in the first three models incorporating the induction method and most extensively treated. See Li and Vitányi (2019) for further reading.

Laplace's rule of succession: If we repeat an experiment that we know can result in a success or failure n times independently and get s successes and $n - s$ failures, then the probability that the next repetition will succeed is $(s + 1) = (n + 2)$.

The third application, using phrase structure grammars, is least exact of the three. First a formal solution is presented. Though it appears to have certain deficiencies, it is hoped that presentation of this admittedly inadequate model will suggest acceptable improvements in it. This formal solution is then applied in an approximate way to the determination of the "optimum" phrase structure grammar for a given set of strings. The results that are obtained are plausible, but subject to the uncertainties of the approximation used.

2. Introduction and General Discussion: The Nature of the Problem

The problem dealt with will be the extrapolation of a long sequence of symbols—these symbols being drawn from some finite alphabet. More specifically, given a long sequence, represented by T, what is the probability that it will be followed by the subsequence represented by a? In the language of Carnap (1950), we want $c(a, T)$, the degree of confirmation of the hypothesis that a will follow, given the evidence that T has just occurred. This corresponds to Carnap's probability$_1$.

The author feels that all problems in inductive inference, whether they involve continuous or discrete data, or both, can be expressed in the form of the extrapolation of a long sequence of symbols. Although many examples have been investigated to lend credence to this hypothesis, this point is not essential to the present paper, which is limited to the problem of extrapolation of sequences of discrete symbols. In all cases being considered, the known sequence of symbols is very long, and contains all of the information that is to be used in the extrapolation.

Several methods will be presented for obtaining formal solutions to this problem. By a formal solution is meant a mathematical equation that in some sense expresses the probability desired as a function of the sequences involved. It will not, in general, be practical to evaluate the probability directly from this equation. In most cases, there is some question as to whether it is even possible *in theory* to perform the indicated evaluation. In all cases, however, the equations will suggest approximations, and the approximations that have been investigated give predictions that seem both qualitatively and quantitatively reasonable.

Solomonoff obtained a bachelor of philosophy and master's of science in physics at the University of Chicago. He was already interested in problems of inductive inference and exchanged viewpoints with the resident philosopher of science Rudolf Carnap (1950), who taught an influential course in probability theory.

In 1956 Solomonoff presented a paper at the IEEE Symposium on Information Theory, describing a program to learn arithmetic formulas from examples unsupervised. Noam Chomsky (1956) gave a talk at the same meeting, which started Solomonoff thinking anew about formal machines in induction. In 1958 he joined Zator Company, a small research outfit in Cambridge, MA, which had been founded by Calvin Mooers and employed visitors including Marvin Minsky.

The "solutions" that are proposed involve Bayes' Theorem. A priori probabilities are assigned to strings of symbols by examining the manner in which these strings might be produced by a universal Turing machine. Strings with short and/or numerous "descriptions" (a "description" of a string being an input to the machine that yields that string as output) are assigned high a priori probabilities. Strings with long, and/or few descriptions are assigned small a priori probabilities.

Four ostensibly different models of this general nature are presented in Sections 3.1, 3.2, 3.3 and 3.4 respectively.

It should be noted that in these sections, no theorems or rigorous proofs are presented.

Each of the models is described in some detail. Statements are made about various properties of these models. In few cases have any *rigorous* proofs been constructed for these statements, but in all cases, they represent the author's strong opinions—based for the most part on plausibility arguments and numerous specific examples. The text will sometimes give these arguments and examples.

Occasionally, the phrase, "it can be shown that," will introduce a statement for which either a rigorous proof or a *very* convincing "plausibility argument" has been found. In such cases, the demonstration will not be presented.

These models all lead to somewhat different expressions for the probabilities of various possible extrapolations of a given sequence. Although it is not demonstrated in the present text, it can be made very plausible that the last three methods are equivalent. Whether the first method is equivalent to the other three is not, at the present time, certain, though the author is inclined to think that it is.

These alternate formulations of a general theory make it easier to understand the operation and application of the theory in a variety of types of problems.

That these kinds of models might be valid is suggested by "Occam's razor," one interpretation of which is that the more "simple" or "economical" of several hypotheses is the more likely. Turing machines are then used to explicate the concepts of "simplicity" or "economy"—the most "simple" hypothesis being that with the shortest "description."

Bayes' theorem is $P(A|B) = P(B|A)P(A)/P(B)$ with A a hypothesis, B the evidence. In the rule $P(B)$ is the prior probability that B happens (without any conditionals), $P(A)$ is the prior probability that hypothesis A is true (without any conditionals), $P(B|A)$ is the probability that evidence B arises given that hypothesis A is true, and $P(A|B)$ is the posterior probability that hypothesis A is true given that evidence B happened. The rule is straightforward computationally provided we know the prior probabilities which give us $P(A)$; $P(B)$ while $P(B|A)$ can be computed (we assume that hypothesis A gives a procedure to assess the probability of evidence B).

Most instructive are methods 1 and 2. They lead most clearly to what is now called Solomonoff induction.

Occam's razor says that with competing theories or explanations, the simpler one, for example a model with fewer parameters, is to be preferred. The idea is frequently attributed to English Franciscan friar William of Ockham (circa 1287–1347). There have been many disagreements over what is meant by "simpler." Solomonoff here chooses the objective meaning of "having a shorter binary effective description."

The principle of indifference states that in the absence of any relevant evidence, the probability should be distributed equally among all the possible outcomes under consideration.

Instead of Huffman coding, which effectively reduces the length of strings, we use the Kolmogorov complexity which is the shortest effective description length and we denote the Kolmogorov complexity of an object x by $C(x)$. Usually x is for us a binary string. This is no real restriction since all appropriate objects can be coded as binary strings.

We will come back to this question of the optimality of this method in section 3.2. For now we can say that the modern version is in the long run better than other methods and provably so.

Another suggested point of support is the principle of indifference. If all inputs to a Turing machine that are of a given fixed length, are assigned "indifferently equal a priori" likelihoods, then the probability distribution on the output strings is equivalent to that imposed by the third model described, i.e., that of Section 3.3.

Huffman coding gives a third rationale for these models. If we start out with an ensemble of long strings of a certain type, and we know the probability of each of these strings, then Huffman coding will enable us to code these strings, "minimally," so that on the average, the codes for the most probable strings are as short as possible.

More briefly, given the probability distribution on the strings, Huffman tells us how to code them minimally. The presently proposed inductive inference methods can in a sense be regarded as an inversion of Huffman coding, in that we first obtain the minimal code for a string, and from this code, we obtain the probability of that string.

The question of the "validity" of these inductive inference methods is a difficult one. In general, it is impossible to prove that any proposed inductive inference method is "correct." It is possible to show that one is "incorrect" by proving it to be internally inconsistent, or showing that it gives results that are grossly at odds with our intuitive evaluations.

The strongest evidence that we can obtain for the validity of a proposed induction method, is that it yields results that are in accord with intuitive evaluations in many different kinds of situations in which we have strong intuitive ideas.

The internal consistency and meaningfulness of the proposed methods are discussed in the sections following 3.1.1. The author feels that the proposed systems are consistent and meaningful, but at the present time, this feeling is supported only by heuristic reasoning and several nonrigorous demonstrations.

Evidence for the validity of the methods is principally in the form of applications to specific problems. Some of these have been worked out in Part II. Although the results of these applications appear to be strongly in accord with intuitive evaluations of the problems treated, several approximations are used in going from the basic inference methods to the final solutions. For this reason, the "correctness" of these apparent solutions makes a rather imperfect corroboration of the basic inference methods.

The extrapolation problems dealt with in the present paper are a Bernoulli sequence, and two types of sequences generated by progressively more complex formal grammars.

Success has been obtained in applying the basic methods to problems in continuous prediction such as fitting curves to empirical data, and it is expected that the results of this work will appear in forthcoming papers.

2.1 An Evaluation of the Validity of the Methods Proposed

There are four types of evidence presented for the validity of the proposed models.

First, there is the general intuitive basis, involving such things as Occam's razor, the principle of indifference, and the inversion of Huffman codes. This type of evidence is of much less importance than the *second* kind—the application of the methods to specific problems and comparison of the results with intuitive evaluations. The *third* type is given in section 3.4, in which it is made plausible that for a certain "goodness" criterion, and a very large body of data, the model is at least as good as any other that may be proposed. Any proposed general inductive inference system must at *least* satisfy this condition.

The *fourth* type of evidence is the discussion of the consistency and meaningfulness of the methods in the sections following 3.1.1.

Of most importance is the second type of evidence, which is presented in Part II. In evaluating a method of induction, we apply it to problems in which we have strong intuitive ideas about what the solutions are, or about certain properties of the solutions. The degree of correlation between our intuitive beliefs and the results obtained through the theory, will largely determine our degree of confidence in the theory. If this correlation is high in many problems of diverse nature in which we have strong intuitive feelings, we will begin to trust the theory in cases in which our intuitive feelings are weaker.

The first application of the present approach is made in section 4.1 of Part II. Prediction of the next element of a Bernoulli sequence is shown to obtain Laplace's rule of succession. Though this particular result is by no means universally accepted, it is not an unreasonable one.

The second application, in section 4.2, treats a type of sequence in which there are certain kinds of intersymbol constraints, and the results seem to be very reasonable.

The third application, in section 4.3, deals with extrapolation through the use of context-free phrase structure grammars. Little work has been done in this field, and we have few intuitive ideas about what the results should be. However, some of the properties of the results are investigated and are found to be intuitively reasonable.

Another application, which is not dealt with in the present paper, is the fitting of curves to empirical data. The results obtained thus far agree with results obtained by classical methods.

3. Several Inductive Inference Systems

Sections 3.1, 3.2, 3.3 and 3.4 will describe in some detail four ostensibly different systems for extrapolating a long sequence of symbols.

It has been made plausible that the last three methods are essentially the same, but it is not certain as to whether the first one is the same as the others.

Section 3 will define more exactly the concepts "description" and "universal machine."

Section 3.1 describes an induction system in which an a priori probability is assigned to a sequence on the basis of a weighted sum of all possible descriptions of that sequence with all possible continuations of it. The weight assigned to a description of length N is 2^{-N}. Several criticisms of this model are discussed—among them, the meaningfulness of the formulation and the degree of dependence upon just what Turing machine was used.

The probability of a binary string of length n is 2^{-n}, assuming the string is flipped by n throws of a fair coin.

Section 3.2 describes a model of induction that attempts to explain in a uniform way, all of the data that we receive from the universe around us. A new type of universal machine, more like an ordinary digital computer is introduced. It is a kind of 3-tape Turing machine, and some of its properties are discussed. A comparison is made between the induction models being presented, and induction that is based on the explicit formulation of scientific laws.

Section 3.3 is a model in which the a priori probability assigned to a string is proportional to the number of descriptions that it has of a given fixed length. This model may be viewed as a more exact formulation of "The principle of insufficient reason."

Section 3.4 is a model whose predictions are a weighted sum of the predictions of all describable probability evaluation methods. The weights are assigned to a method on the basis of both its past success and its a priori probability.

It is then made plausible that this "summation" method under certain conditions, is at least as "good" as any of its component methods for a stated "goodness" criterion.

The methods described will all use universal Turing machines or approximations to such machines to detect regularities in the known part of the sequence. These regularities will then be used for extrapolation.

Critical in the concepts of induction considered here is the "description" of a "corpus" or body of data with respect to a given machine.

Suppose that we have a general purpose digital computer M_1 with a very large memory. Later we shall consider Turing machines—essentially computers having infinitely expandable memories.

Any finite string of 0's and 1's is an acceptable input to M_1. The output of M_1 (when it has an output) will be a (usually different) string of symbols, usually in an alphabet other than the binary. If the input string S to machine M_1 gives output string T, we shall write

$$M_1(S) = T$$

Under these conditions, we shall say that "S is a description of T with respect to machine M_1." $M_1(S)$ will be considered to be meaningless if M_1 never stops when it is given the input S.

Next, the concept of "universal machine" will be defined. A "universal machine" is a subclass of universal Turing machines that can simulate any other computing machine in a certain way.

More exactly, suppose M_2 is an arbitrary computing machine, and $M_2(x)$ is the output of M_2, for input string x. Then if M_1 is a "universal

This is a standard way, but it ignores the implied proportionality between the sum of the methods and the best method in the summation.

The regularities in a string are accounted for in the Kolmogorov complexity of that string. Note that these regularities should be effective.

Solomonoff means here an "optimal" universal Turing machine. The idea is that the set of all Turing machines can be computationally enumerated. If $T_1, T_2, \ldots$ is such an enumeration, a Turing machine U is optimally universal if $U(p, i) = T_i(p)$ for all integers i and strings p. To show that there are universal Turing machines that are universal but not optimally so, consider a Turing machine V such that $V(pp, i) = T_i(p)$ for all integers i and strings p and it does not halt otherwise.

machine," there exists some string, α (which is a function of M_1 and M_2, but not of x), such that for any string, x,

$$M_1(\widehat{\alpha x}) = M_2(x)$$

α may be viewed as the "translation instructions" from M_1 to M_2. Here the notation $\widehat{\alpha x}$ indicates the concatenation of string α and string x.

It is possible to devise a complete theory of inductive inference using Bayes' theorem, if we are able to assign an a priori probability to every conceivable sequence of symbols. In accord with this approach, it is felt that sequences should be given high a priori probabilities if they have short descriptions and/or many different descriptions. The methods of Sections 3.1, 3.2, 3.3 and 3.4 may be regarded as more exact formulations of these two ideas; they give, in effect, a relative weighting for these two aspects of the descriptions of a sequence.

In general, any regularity in a corpus may be utilized to write a shorter description of that corpus. Remaining regularities in the descriptions can, in turn, be used to write even shorter descriptions, etc.

The simplest example of a description that will be given is in section 4.1. Here, a Bernoulli sequence is described.

It is seen that any "regularities" (i.e., deviations of the relative frequencies of various symbols from the average), result in shorter and/or more numerous descriptions.

On a direct intuitive level, the high a priori probability assigned to a sequence with a short description corresponds to one possible interpretation of "Occam's Razor." The assignment of high a priori probabilities to sequences with many descriptions corresponds to a feeling that if an occurrence has many possible causes, then it is more likely.

3.1 INDUCTIVE INFERENCE SYSTEM USING ALL POSSIBLE DESCRIPTIONS AND ALL POSSIBLE CONTINUATIONS OF THE CORPUS

The first method to be discussed will assign a probability to any possible continuation of a known finite string of symbols.

Suppose T is a very long sequence of symbols in some known alphabet, A.

A, the "output alphabet," contains just r different symbols.

In the original Kolmogorov complexity $C(x)$ of a string x, this string x is assumed to be in between endmarkers. But in real programs the program tells itself where it ends, for example by having an end-of-program instruction. If we design Turing machines only with programs that tell where they end, the scan of the program stops at the end of this program. With these restrictions the shortest so-called self-delimiting program has a length that is called the "prefix" Kolmogorov complexity K. For every string x we have $C(x) \leq K(x) \leq C(x) + 2\log C(x) + 1$. The prefix complexity was introduced by Leonid Levin (1974). It turns out that the number of prefix descriptions (prefix programs) of a given length is restricted, and if a string has many long prefix descriptions it also has a shorter one.

T is the corpus that we will extrapolate, and *must contain all of the information that we want to use in the induction.*

M_1 is a universal machine with output alphabet A, and a binary input alphabet.

a is a finite sequence of symbols of alphabet A, and is therefore a possible immediate continuation of sequence T. We want to find the probability of this possible continuation.

$P(a, T, M_1)$ might be called "the probability with respect to M_1, that a will follow T."

What we wish to call P is not of very much importance. P will be *defined* by Eq. (1), and we will then investigate the properties of the quantity defined. It will later appear that this quantity has most (if not all) of the qualities desired in an explication of Carnap's probability $_1$ (Carnap, 1950) and so we have chosen to refer to P as a "probability." The reader may find it distasteful to refer to P as "probability" until it has been proven to have all of the necessary properties—in which case he might for the time being mentally read "probability$_x$" whenever P is referred to.

$C_{n,k}$ is a sequence of n symbols in the *output* alphabet of the universal machine M_1. There are r different symbols, so there are r^n different sequences of this type. $C_{n,k}$ is the kth such sequence. k may have any value from 1 to r^n.

$TaC_{n,k}$ is the same as $\widehat{Ta}\widehat{C_{n,k}}$.

$\left(S_{TaC_{n,k}}\right)_i$ is the ith description of $TaC_{n,k}$ with respect to machine M_1. The descriptions can be made in order of length, but the exact ordering method is not critical.

$N_{\left(S_{TaCn,k}\right)_i}$ is the number of bits in $\left(S_{TaC_{n,k}}\right)_i$.

$$P(a, T, M_1) \equiv \lim_{\epsilon \to 0} \lim_{n \to \infty} \frac{\sum_{k=1}^{r^n} \sum_{i=1}^{\infty} [(1-\epsilon)/2]^{N_{\left(S_{Ta C_{n,k}}\right)_i}}}{\sum_{k=1}^{r^{n+1}} \sum_{i=1}^{\infty} [(1-\epsilon)/2]^{N_{\left(S_{TC_{n+1,k}}\right)_i}}} \quad (1)$$

To get some understanding of this rather complex definition we will first consider only the numerator of the right side of Eq. (1). The denominator is a normalization factor; without it, the equation gives something like the relative probability of the continuation a, as

Here Solomonoff seems to refer to the fact that the summed "probabilities" are possibly less than 1. That is, he is talking about a semiprobability or discrete semimeasure.

The modern version of Solomonoff's inductive procedure in equation (1) can be written in the terms of Zvonkin and Levin (1970) as (using the same notation for clarity) $P(a, T, M_1) = \mathbf{m}(a|T) = \mathbf{m}(Ta) = \mathbf{m}(T)$, where M_1 is the optimal universal prefix Turing machine used to define the universal semiprobability $\mathbf{m}$, a is without loss of generality 0 or 1 (elements of a finite alphabet can be coded in 0s and 1s in the standard way), and T is a string of 0s and 1s. The proof relies just on the fact that $\mathbf{m}(x)$ dominates multiplicatively all computable probabilities (even all lower semicomputable semiprobabilities). It generalizes therefore to any family of probabilities that has a dominating probability—in particular, to any countable family of probabilities. This way we get rid of the $(1-\epsilon)$ terms, the limits, and so on.

In Section 3.2 we will use many programs rather than a single program, and this formulation is generally adopted as it was by Solomonoff.

compared with other possible continuations. Next, set ϵ to zero, and let n also equal zero. This gives the very approximate expression

$$\sum_{t=1}^{\infty} \left(\frac{1}{2}\right)^{N_{(s_{Ta})_i}} \tag{2}$$

It becomes clear at this point that if the sequence Ta has a short description (i.e., for some i, $N_{(s_{Ta})_i}$ is small), then expression (2) will hold a lot of weight for that description. Furthermore, if there are many such short descriptions of Ta, then expression (2) will be given much additional weight.

Unfortunately, it can be shown that the number of descriptions of length m of Ta (or any other sequence) is at least proportional to 2^m for large enough m. This causes expression 2 to diverge, and so the $1 - \epsilon$ factor of Eq. (1) is inserted, giving

$$\lim_{\epsilon \to 0} \sum_{i=1}^{\infty} \left(\frac{1 - \epsilon}{2}\right)^{N_{(s_{Ta})_i}} \tag{3}$$

For nonzero ϵ, the effect is to give negligible weight to descriptions whose lengths are many times greater than $1/\epsilon$.

In the method of Section 3.2, this convergence is obtained in a somewhat different manner.

Another way in which Eq. (1) differs from expression (3) is that Eq. (1) considers that the partial sequence Ta might have been the beginning of any number of longer sequences that start with Ta. By including all possible continuations of Ta — i.e., $C_{n,k}$, we give the sequence Ta a larger probability if it is capable of being the beginning of a *longer* sequence that is of high probability. An example is the coding of the sequence $D \equiv abcdabcdabcdabcdab$ which can be dealt with using the methods of Section 4.2.

This is one of the heuristics used to partially approximate $C(D)$ of the string D.

If described in a direct way, the sequence D has a rather lengthy description. If, however, we first define the subsequence $abcd$ to be represented by the intermediate symbol α, we can write D as $B\alpha\alpha\alpha ab$, B being a subsequence that defines α to be $abcd$. It is reasonably likely that the sequence D has the continuation $cdabcd$ . . . . Though the sequence $B\alpha\alpha\alpha ab$ is much shorter than the original D, the description of the sequence Dcd is $B\alpha\alpha\alpha\alpha$, which is even shorter.

The sequences like $B\alpha\alpha\alpha ab$ are to be considered as "intermediate codes" for D. The method by which they are represented as a single positive integer—or a sequence of 0's and 1's—is dealt with in Sections 4.1.1 and 4.2.2. It will become clear that the intermediate sequence $B\alpha\alpha\alpha\alpha$ has a far shorter code than $B\alpha\alpha\alpha ab$, since in the latter case, the symbols a and b have not been used much in the intermediate code, and therefore are effectively represented by relatively long expressions in the final code.

It must be stressed that while the above reasoning gives some of the reasons for the choice of Eq. (1) as a reasonable definition of probability, these arguments are meant to be heuristic only. The final decision as to whether Eq. (1) is a good definition or not rests to a rather small extent upon the heuristic reasoning that gave rise to it, and almost entirely upon the results of investigations of the properties of this definition. Investigations of this type are presented in Part II.

The author feels that Eq. (1) is likely to be correct or almost correct, but that the methods of working the problems of Sections 4.1 to 4.3 are *more* likely to be correct than Eq. (1). If Eq. (1) is found to be meaningless, inconsistent, or somehow gives results that are intuitively unreasonable, then Eq. (1) should be modified in ways that do not destroy the validity of the methods used in Sections 4.1 to 4.3.

3.1.1. Criticisms and Questions About Eq. (1)

There are several questions that immediately come to mind when equation 1 is proposed as an explication of probability.

3.1.1.1. The terms of the summation do not include descriptions that are "meaningless," i.e., inputs to the universal machine M_1, for which the machine does not stop. Turing (1937) has shown that it is impossible to devise a Turing machine that will always be able to tell, in a finite time, whether an arbitrary string will be "meaningful" for another particular universal Turing machine. This raises the question of whether the right side of Eq. (1) defines anything at all.

3.1.1.2. It has not been shown rigorously that the limit of the right side of Eq. (1) exists, as ϵ, n, and i approach their respective limits.

This is why **m** is incomputable and just lower semi-computable. However, the expression is not meaningless but just ineffective.

This may be a valid point with respect to the original equation (1).

This is partially true, but different optimal universal machines cause the probabilities to alter by just a constant multiplicative factor.

3.1.1.3. It would seem that the value of $P(a, T, M_1)$ would be critically dependent upon just what universal machine, M_1, was used. Is there any particular M_1 that we can use that is better than any other?

3.1.2. Replies to Criticisms of Eq. (1)

3.1.2.1. It is clear that many of the individual terms of Eq. (1) are not "effectively computable" in the sense of Turing (1937). It is very reasonable to conjecture that the entire right side of Eq. (1) is not "effectively computable." This does *not* mean, however, that we cannot use Eq. (1) as the heuristic basis of various approximations. If an approximation to Eq. (1) is found that yields intuitively reasonable probability values and *is* effectively computable, we would probably adopt such an approximation as a better explication of probability$_1$ than Eq. (1).

This amounts to time-limited versions.

One approach to such an approximation can be made by first considering as "meaningful" input to the universal machine, only those that complete their output in less than τ operations. With such a limitation, each of the terms of Eq. (1) is "effectively computable." The summations on i and k both become finite summations. If we let τ approach infinity and then let ϵ approach zero we will have some sort of approximation to Eq. (1).

At the present rudimentary state of development of the theory, different approximations to Eq. (1) are used for different types of problems. It is hoped that further work in this field may yield a unified, useful approximation to Eq. (1).

3.1.2.2. Though the existence of the limits designated on the right side of Eq. (1) has not yet been proved, various approximations to this equation have been made which tacitly assume the existence of these limits. Some of these approximations are described in Sections 4.1 to 4.3.

3.1.2.3. It is likely that Eq. (1) is fairly independent of just what universal machine is used, if T is sufficiently long, and contains enough redundance, and M_1 is "fairly good" at expressing the regularities of T. Although a proof is not available, an outline of the heuristic reasoning behind this statement will give clues as to the meanings of the terms used and the degree of validity to be expected of the statement itself.

Suppose we have a very long sequence T, containing m symbols, and we have two universal machines, M_1 and M_2. We will try to show that

$$P(a, T, M_1) \approx P(a, T, M_2) \qquad (4)$$

Let $N_{(s_T, 1)}$ and $N_{(s_T, 2)}$ represent the lengths of the shortest codes for T, with respect to M_1 and M_2 respectively.

Let α_1 be M_2's simulation instructions for M_1.

Let α_2 be M_1's simulation instructions for M_2.

Then for all strings, x,

$$M_1(x) = M_2(\widehat{\alpha_1 x})$$

and

$$M_2(x) = M_1(\widehat{\alpha_2 x}).$$

Let N_{α_1} and N_{α_2} be the number of bits in α_1 and α_2, respectively. Then

$$N_{(s_T, 1)} \leqq N_{(s_T, 2)} + N_{\alpha_2} \qquad (5)$$

and

$$N_{(s_T, 2)} \leqq N_{(s_T, 1)} + N_{\alpha_1} \qquad (6)$$

To explain Eq. (5), note that M_1 can always code anything by using M_2's code, prefixed by α_2. Thus M_1's shortest code cannot be more than N_{α_2} longer than M_2's shortest code for the same sequence. A similar argument holds for Eq. (6).

Suppose that M_1 is basically more efficient in coding T. Then if m, the number of symbols in T, is sufficiently large, it is plausible to hypothesize that M_2's shortest code will indeed be obtained by simulating M_1 and using M_1's shortest code. It is necessary to assume that m is very large, because any slight advantage between M_1's and M_2's coding methods is accentuated in coding a long sequence. One might suppose that for values of m that are not too large, the difference between the code lengths are roughly proportional to m. When m becomes large enough so that the difference is about N_{α_1}, then the

These intuitive or heuristic arguments are subsumed under the formalization of Kolmogorov complexity.

difference remains constant, because M_2 is forming its minimal code by simulating M_1.

If M_2's shortest codes are all N_{α_1} bits longer than M_1's shortest codes, it is clear that the largest terms of $P(a, T, M_1)$ in Eq. (1) (i.e., the terms due to the shortest codes) will all be $2^{N_{\alpha_1}}$ times as large as the corresponding terms in a corresponding expression for $P(a, T, M_2)$. Since these terms occur in both numerator and denominator, this factor will approximately cancel out with the result that $P(a, T, M_1)$ and $P(a, T, M_2)$ are approximately equal.

Though the weak points in the above heuristic arguments are many, the reasoning is strong to the extent that

1. M_1 is appreciably more efficient than M_2 in coding regularities of the type that occur in T.

2. M_2 is "close" to M_1 in the sense that N_{α_1} is "small".

3. m is sufficiently large so that M_1's shortest code for T is much longer than N_{α_1}.

In using $P(a, T, M_1)$ it would seem best to select an M_1 that is fairly efficient in coding the sequences in which we will be interested. The LISP list processing language in which recursive definitions are easily implimented, or any of the other computer languages that have been devised for convenience in dealing with material in certain large areas of science (Green, Jr. 1961) might be used as the basis of simulation of M_1.

3.1.3. A Method of Applying Eq. (1)

In many situations in which induction is to be applied, the sequence T is not constant, but grows in time. The problem is to make many inferences at different times, each based upon the entire sequence up to that time. Instead of having to recode the entire sequence each time to obtain the desired inference, it is possible to summarize the previous work by modifying the machine M_1 suitably and concern one's self only with the coding of the new data. More exactly, suppose that T is our original sequence, and we have made some inferences based on T alone. Later, we are given the subsequence D, which is part of the continuation of T, and are

Here the previously scanned information is incorporated in the universal Turing machine.

asked to make inferences based on $\widehat{TD}$. Then there always exists a universal machine, M_2 such that

$$P\left(a, \widehat{TD}, M_1\right) = P\left(a, D, M_2\right)$$

for any conceivable subsequence a. In general, the nature of M_2 will depend upon both T and M_1.

M_2 can be viewed as a summary of the inductive data of T, with respect to M_1.

Though it has been possible to prove that at least one M_2 exists satisfying the requirements described, the M_2 thereby obtained makes the problem of finding short codes for $\widehat{Da}$ just as difficult as the problem of finding short codes for $\widehat{T\ Da}$. It is clear that the M_2 obtained in this way does not summarize, in any *useful* way, the information contained in the sequence T. It is felt, however, that if suitable approximations to Eq. (1) are used, it is indeed possible to have M_2 summarize in a useful manner the information contained in T. A trivial example occurs if the only regularity in T is contained in the frequencies of its various symbols. If M_2 contains a listing of the number of occurrences of each of the symbols of T, it will then contain a summary of T in a form that is adequate for most additions of new data on the continuation of T.

It is possible, however, that data that *seems* to summarize the regularities of T, does not do so, in view of new data. For example, if we had "summarized" T by the frequencies of its various symbols, we would not be able to notice the exact repetition of the entire sequence T, if it occurred later.

3.2 SYSTEM IN THE FORM OF A MODEL TO ACCOUNT FOR ALL REGULARITIES IN THE OBSERVED UNIVERSE

Suppose that all of the sensory observations of a human being since his birth were coded in some sort of uniform digital notation and written down as a long sequence of symbols. Then a model that accounts in an *optimum* manner for the creation of this string, including the interaction of the man with his environment, can be formed by supposing that the string was created as the output of a universal machine of random input.

Again, this refers to a shortest program of which the length is the Kolmogorov complexity of the string encoding the sensory observations and so on.

Here "random input" means that the input sequence is a Markov chain with the probability of each symbol being a function of only previous symbols in the finite past. The input alphabet may be any finite alphabet.

In the simplest case, the input will be a binary sequence with equal probabilities for zero and one. This situation appears, at first glance, to be identical to Eq. (1), with this equation being used for Bayes' inference, given equal a priori probabilities to all possible input sequences of the same length.

There is, however, an important difference in that the present case deals with infinitely long inputs, while Eq. (1) deals with *finite* inputs only. The meaningfulness of "a legal output" of the machine with infinitely long inputs must then be defined. In Eq. (1), any finite input leading to a nonterminating output is effectively given a priori probability zero. For an infinitely long input, however, the output is often nonterminating.

In the present case, we shall regard an input as "meaningful" if every symbol of the output takes only a finite number of operations to compute it. It is easiest to give this a more rigorous meaning in machines that have separate tapes for infinite input, infinite output and infinitely expandable memory. In such a 3-tape machine we can stipulate that an output symbol, once written, can never be erased, and so we need ask that for each output symbol not more than a finite time elapse before that symbol is written.

There appears to be a difference between the present method and that of Section 3.1, in that the present method only considers part of the future of the sequence to be extrapolated—it does *not* consider its extension into the infinite future, as does Section 3.1.

To compare the method of the present section with that of Eq. (1), first consider the following definitions, which are to be used in the *present section only*.

M_2 is a 3-tape machine with unidirectional output and input tapes.

T is a possible output sequence containing just m symbols.

S is a possible input sequence.

Then we shall say that "S is a code of T (with respect to M_2)," if the subsequence composed of the first m symbols of $M_2(S)$ is identical to T.

We shall say that "S is a minimal code of T" if (a) S is a code of T and (b) if the last symbol of S is removed then the resultant sequence is no longer a code of T.

Here Solomonoff tries to define infinite sequences and (semi)measures on the set of infinite sequences, a task which is done mathematically correctly elsewhere (see Zvonkin and Levin 1970 and Li and Vitányi 2019).

Since every minimal code of T is directly representable as a positive integer, these minimal codes can be linearly ordered.

Let $N(T, i)$ be the number of bits in the ith minimal code of T.

Then using the model previously described in the present section, and a simple application of Bayes' theorem, it is found that the probability that the sequence T will be followed by the subsequence a, is

$$P'(a, T, M_2) \equiv \frac{\sum_{i=1}^{\infty} 2^{-N(Ta,i)}}{\sum_{i=1}^{\infty} 2^{-N(T,i)}} \tag{7}$$

The apparent simplicity of Eq. 7 over Eq. 1 is due to two factors: first, Eq. (7) has a very simple automatic device for considering possible continuations of Ta. This device is built into the definition of the "minimal codes of Ta." Second, there are no problems of convergence, since the sums of both numerator or denominator are bounded by unity. This makes the $1 - \epsilon$ factor of Eq. (1) unnecessary.

It should be noted that M_2 of Eq. (7) is somewhat different from M_1 of Eq. (1). If $T = M_2(S)$ then if we adjoin more symbols to the right of S, as $\widehat{S\alpha}$, then $\widehat{S\alpha}$ will still be "a code of T," and $M_2(\widehat{S\alpha})$ will consist of the string $\widehat{Tb}$, where b is a finite, infinite or null string.

This condition if *not* true of M_1, which is an unconstrained universal machine. If $M_1(S) = T$, then little, if anything, can be said about $M_1(\widehat{S\alpha})$. $M_1(\widehat{S\alpha})$ could be longer or shorter than T; it may even be the null sequence. These properties of M_1 make it difficult to define "a minimal code of T (with respect to M_1)," in the sense that it was defined for M_2.

At the beginning of the present section, it was mentioned that the present model would account for the sequence of interest, in "an optimum manner."

By "optimum manner" it is meant that the model we are discussing is at *least* as good as any other model of the universe in accounting for the sequence in question. Other models may devise mechanistic explanations of the sequence in terms of the known laws of science, or they may devise empirical mechanisms that optimumly approximate the behavior and observations of the man within certain limits. Most of the models that we use to explain the universe around us are based upon laws and informal stochastic relations that are the result of induction using much data that we or others have observed. The induction methods used in the present paper

Equation (7) presages the currently used $\mathbf{M}(Ta) = \mathbf{M}(T)$ with the (continuous) universal distribution $\mathbf{M}$. Restrict consideration to sources $x_1 x_2 \ldots$ producing infinite sequences (over a binary alphabet. Let $\mu(x)$ denote the semimeasure (or semiprobability continuous analog) of the set of all infinite sequences starting with x. For a letter $b \in 0, 1$ denote $\mu(b|x) = \mu(xb)/\mu(x)$. We use the so-called universal semimeasure $\mathbf{M}$. A semimeasure is a measure where the equalities are relaxed to less-than inequalities (hence a semiprobability on a discrete set is a discrete semimeasure but not the other way around since we now deal with continuous sets). Let $\mathcal{M}$ be a set of semimeasures on all infinite binary sequences. A semimeasure μ_0 is universal (or maximal) for $\mathbf{M}$ if $\mu_0 \in \mathbf{M}$, and for all $\mu \in \mathbf{M}$, there exists a constant $c > 0$ such that for all $x \in 0, 1^*$, we have $\mu_0(x) \geq c\mu(x)$. We call a semimeasure μ lower semicomputable if there is a computable function ϕ such that for every binary string x and every integer k (i) $\phi(x, k+1) \geq \phi(x, k)$ and (ii) $\lim_{k \to \infty} \phi(x, k) = \mu x$. It can be shown that there is a universal lower semi-computable continuous semimeasure. We denote the reference by $\mathbf{M}$. To give a feeling for $\mathbf{M}$ it can be shown that for every binary string x we have $C(x) \leq -\log \mathbf{M}(x) \leq K(x)$ where $C(x)$ is the Kolmogorov complexity of x and $K(x)$ satisfies $C(x) \leq K(x) \leq C(x) + 2\log C(x)$.

We turn next to how good this type of induction or prediction really is. Consider the set of all computable distributions (measures) or probabilities of the set of infinite binary sequences. Choose a probability P of this set. The following result says that the formula $\mathbf{M}(b|x_1 \ldots x_n)$, gets closer and closer to the conditional probability $P(b|x_1 \ldots x_n)$ as n grows closer, for example in a mean square sense (and then also with P-probability 1). This is better than any classical predictive strategy can do. More explicitly, the value $S_n = \sum\limits_{x:|x|n-1} \sum\limits_{b \in \{0,1\}}$ $P(x)(\mathbf{M}(b|x) - P(b|x))^2$ is the expected error of the squared probability of the nth prediction if we use the universal $\mathbf{M}$ instead of the unknown P. Solomonoff showed $\Sigma_{n=1}^{\infty} S_n < \infty$. (The bound is essentially the complexity $K(P)$ of P so it is relatively small for simple distributions P. There is no bound when P is not even computable.) Hence the expected squared error can be said to degrade faster than $1 = n$ (provided the expectation is "smooth"). The set of all computable distributions is very wide indeed and presumably contains all that we are realistically interested in. A caveat is that $\mathbf{M}$ is just lower semicomputable, and thus we have to approximate it by a computable process.

are meant to bypass the explicit formulation of scientific laws, and use the data of the past directly to make inductive inferences about specific future events.

It should be noted, then, that if the present model of the universe is to compete with other models of the universe that use scientific laws, then the sequence used in the present model must contain enough data of the sort that gave rise to the induction of these scientific laws.

The laws of science that have been discovered can be viewed as summaries of large amounts of empirical data about the universe. In the present context, each such law can be transformed into a method of compactly coding the empirical data that gave rise to that law.

Instead of including the raw data in our induction sequence, it is possible, using a suitable formalism, to write the laws based on this data into the sequence and obtain similar results in induction. Using the raw data will, however, give predictions that are at least as good, and usually better, than using the summaries of the data. This is because these summaries of the data are almost always imperfect and lose much information through this imperfection.

It may, at this point, seem gratuitous to claim that the proposed model is optimum with respect to all other conceivable models, many of which have not yet been discovered. It would seem to be impossible to compare the present model with the undiscovered models of the future, and thus claim optimality. We will, however, give in Section 3.4 a model of induction, apparently equivalent to the present one, in which all possible induction models are formally considered. The predictions of each possible induction model are used in a weighted sum to obtain predictions that are at least as "good" (in a certain stated sense) as any of the component induction models.

3.2.1 The concept of stochastic languages (Solomonoff 1959) suggests another way of looking at the induction model of Section 3.2. A stochastic language is an assignment of probability values to all finite strings of some finite alphabet. Though a specific type of stochastic language is dealt with in Section 4.3, we can characterize the most general possible stochastic language through the use of a 3-tape universal machine, with binary input, and an output in the alphabet of the desired language.

Let D be an arbitrary finite binary sequence, let M_1 be such a 3-tape universal machine, and let R_i be a random infinite binary sequence, with equal probability for zero or one.

$M_1\left(\widehat{DR_i}\right)$ will define a probability distribution on all possible output strings. This distribution will then constitute a stochastic language. The string D, can be considered to be a description of this language with respect to M_1.

The independence of the induction methods of the present paper upon the exact nature of the Turing machine used can be put in a particularly compact form using this concept. If $[\alpha_j]$ is the set of "translation instructions" from M_1 to all other possible universal machines, M_j, then we may say that the stochastic language defined by $M_1\left(\widehat{\alpha_j R_i}\right)$ is fairly independent of α_j for very long sentences, and for α_j within a rather large class.

3.3 SYSTEM USING A UNIVERSAL MACHINE WITH ALL POSSIBLE INPUT STRINGS OF A FIXED LENGTH

Consider a very long string T of m symbols drawn from an alphabet of r different symbols. We shall first obtain a method for assigning a priori probabilities to all strings longer than T. On this basis we can use Bayes' theorem to obtain a probability distribution for various possible continuations of T. As before, it is desirable that T contain much redundance, and that it contain all of the information that we expect to use, either directly or indirectly, in our induction.

Choose some large number, R, such that

$$2^R \gg r^m \qquad (8)$$

In this way, binary strings of length R can be expected to contain more "information" than the string T. In the following development, we shall allow R to approach infinity.

Suppose M to be a universal machine with binary input alphabet, and an output alphabet that is the same as that of T. We shall consider M to be either of the ordinary type, M_1, described in Section 3.1, or the 3-tape type, M_2, described in Section 3.2. In the present case, it has been proved that these two machine types give equivalent results.

Consider all binary strings of length R. Say N_R of them are meaningful inputs to M—i.e., they cause M to stop eventually. Of these N_R meaningful inputs to M, say N_T of them result in outputs whose first m symbols are, respectively, identical to the m symbols of T. Then the a priori probability assigned to T will be

$$N_T/N_R \qquad (9)$$

This ratio will become more exact as R approaches infinity, but will usually be good enough if R satisfies Eq. (8).

It can be proved that the present inductive inference model is identical to that of Section 3.2, if M is a machine of either type M_1 or of type M_2.

Although it has not been rigorously proved, it seems likely, at the present time, that the methods of the present section give results identical to those of Section 3.1.

An equation that follows from Eq. (9) that is, however, similar to Eq. (1), is

$$P''(a, T, M_1) \equiv \lim_{\epsilon \to 0} \frac{\sum_{n=1}^{\infty} \sum_{k=1}^{r^n} \sum_{i=1}^{\infty} [(1-\epsilon)/2]^{N(S_{Ta}C_{n,k})_i}}{\sum_{n=1}^{\infty} \sum_{k=1}^{r^{n+1}} \sum_{i=1}^{\infty} [(1-\epsilon)/2]^{N(S_{TC_{n+1,k}})_i}} \qquad (10)$$

A corresponding expression for the probability that the subsequence a (rather than any other subsequence) will follow T, that is based on Eq. (9), is

$$P'''(a, T, M_1) \equiv \lim_{R \to \infty} \frac{N_{Ta}}{N_R} \cdot \left(\frac{N_T}{N_R}\right)^{-1} = \lim_{R \to \infty} \frac{N_{Ta}}{N_T} \qquad (11)$$

The formulation of the induction system as a universal machine with input strings of fixed length has an interesting interpretation in terms of "the principle of insufficient reason." If we consider the input sequence to be the "cause" of the observed output sequence, and we consider all input sequences of a given length to be equiprobable (since we have no a priori reason to prefer one rather than any other) then we obtain the present model of induction.

3.4 A SYSTEM EMPLOYING ALL POSSIBLE PROBABILITY EVALUATION METHODS

An inductive inference system will be described that makes probability evaluations by using a weighted mean of the evaluations given by all possible probability evaluation methods. The weight given to any particular evaluation method depends upon two factors. The first factor is the success that method would have had in predicting the now known sequence. The second is the a priori probability of that probability evaluation method. It is approximately measured by the minimum number of bits required to describe that method.

3.4.1. A More Detailed Description of the System

Consider the extrapolation of a long string, T, containing m symbols, drawn from an alphabet, A, containing r different symbols, $b_i(i = 1, 2, \cdots, r)$.

This is the idea of summing over all induction methods and giving weights to the individual items. We assume that all these induction methods are countable (otherwise they cannot be summed) and such that an individual item is a constant fraction of the sum.

A "probability evaluation method" (which we will henceforth designate as "a PEM") is a method of assigning a priori probability values to any sequence of symbols in A. From these probability assignments it is then possible, using Bayes' theorem, to find the probability of any specified continuation of a known sequence.

A normalized PEM (which we will henceforth designate as a "NPEM") is one in which the sum of the probabilities of all possible continuations of a sequence is equal to the probability of that sequence. More exactly, let $P_i(B)$ be the a priori probability assigned to string B by a certain PEM, Q_i.

If, for all strings, a,

$$\sum_{j=1}^{r} P_i\left(\widehat{ab_j}\right) = P_i(a)$$

and

$$\sum_{j=1}^{r} P_i\left(b_j\right) = 1$$

then Q_i is a NPEM.

To compute with respect to Q_i the probability that string T will have the continuation a, we can use Bayes' theorem to obtain the value

$$P_i(\widehat{Ta})/P_i(T) \tag{12}$$

If Q_i is a NPEM, we shall define D_i, to be "a binary description of Q_i, with respect to machine M_2," if for all strings, a, $M_2(\widehat{D_i\Delta a})$ is an infinite string giving the binary expansion of $P_i(a)$. The symbols of D_i are to be drawn from a binary alphabet, and Δ is a special symbol that is used to tell M_2 where D_i ends and a begins.

In order that it be meaningful for M_2 to have an infinite output sequence, we will specify that M_2 be a 3-tape universal machine of the type that was discussed in Section 3.2.

Consider all binary strings of length R. For a given large value of R, a certain fraction of these strings will be binary descriptions with respect to M_2, of the NPEM, Q_i. We will assume (and this assumption can be made plausible) that this fraction approaches a limit, f_i, as R approaches infinity.

The inductive inference system that shall be proposed is

$$P''''(a, T, M_2) \equiv \frac{\sum_{i=1}^{\infty} f_i P_i(\widehat{Ta})}{\sum_{i=1}^{\infty} f_i P_i(T)} \qquad (13)$$

Here, the summations in numerator and denominator range over all possible NPEM's, Q_i.

Though it is not difficult to show that P'''' defines a NPEM, this NPEM is not "effectively computable" (in the sense of Turing 1937) and so it does not include itself in the summations of equation 13.

3.4.2 A Comparison of the Present System with Other PEM's

An important characteristic of Eq. (13) is illustrated, if we write it in the form

Here we conclude that the largest fraction becomes the more important one.

$$P''''(a, T, M_2) \equiv \sum_{i=1}^{\infty} \left[\frac{P_i(\widehat{Ta})}{P_i(T)} \cdot \frac{f_i P_i(T)}{\sum_{j=1}^{\infty} f_j P_j(T)} \right] \qquad (14)$$

Here, $P_i(\widehat{Ta})/P_i(T)$ is the probability that T will have continuation a, in view of PEM, Q_i. This is the same as expression (12). Equation (14) is then a weighted sum of the probabilities for the continuation a, as given by all possible PEM's. The factor $f_i P_i(T)$ gives the weight of PEM Q_i, and $1/\sum_{j=1}^{\infty} f_j P_j(T)$ is the normalizing factor for all of the weights.

It would seem, then, that if T is a very long string, P'''' will make an evaluation based largely on the PEM of greatest weight. This is because while the f_i's are independent of T, $P_i(T)$ normally decreases exponentially as T increase in length. Also, if Q_i and Q_j are two different PEM's and Q_i is "better" than Q_j, then usually $P_i(T)/P_j(T)$ increases exponentially as T increases in length. Of greater import, however,

$f_i P_i(T)/f_j P_j(T)$, which is the relative weight of Q_i and Q_j, increases to arbitrarily large values for long enough T's. This suggests that for very long T, Eq. (14) gives almost all of the weight to the single "best" PEM.

Here we define "best" using one of the criteria defined by McCarthy (1956), i.e., PEM Q_i is "better" than PEM Q_j with respect to string T, if $P_i(T) > P_j(T)$.

This suggests that for very long T's, P'''' gives at least about as good predictions as any other PEM, and is much better than most of them.

There are some arguments that make it plausible that P'''' is a close approximation to P'''' of Eq. (11). If this is so, then it becomes likely that the PEM's of Sections 3.2 and 3.3 are also, for "sufficiently long T's," at least as good as any other PEM.

It should be noted that the arguments used to suggest the superiority of P'''' over other PEM's is similar to that used in Section 3.1.2.3 for the plausibility that P (of Eq. (1)) is largely machine independent for long enough T. Both arguments are, of course, extremely informal, and are meant only to suggest how a proof might possibly be found. ✒

Acknowledgments

Many of the basic ideas on induction that have been presented are the outgrowth of numerous discussions over many years with Marvin Minsky.

Discussions with Roland Silver and James Slagle have been particularly important in the analysis of the properties of Turing machines.

Criticism by Eugene Pendergraft has resulted in a much more readable paper, has done much to clarify the section on stochastic phrase structure grammars.

REFERENCES

Carnap, R. 1950. *Logical Foundations of Probability.* Chicago, IL: University of Chicago Press.

Chomsky, N. 1956. "Three Models for the Description of Language." *IRE Transactions on Electronic Computers* 2:113–124.

Green, Jr., B. F. 1961. "Computer Languages for Symbol Manipulation." *IRE Transactions on Electronic Computers* 10 (4): 729–735.

McCarthy, J. 1956. "Measures of the Value of Information." *Proceedings of the National Academy of Sciences of the United States of America* 42:654–655.

Solomonoff, R. J. 1959. "A Progress Report on Machines to Learn to Translate Languages and Retrieve Information." In *Advances in Documentation and Library Sciences, Part 2,* 3:941–953. New York, NY: Interscience.

———. 1960. "The Mechanization of Linguistic Learning." In *Proceedings of the Second International Congress of Cybernetics, September 1958,* 180–193. Namur, Belgium: Zator Company.

Turing, A. M. 1937. "On Computable Numbers, with an Application to the Entscheidungsproblem." *Proceedings of the London Mathematical Society* 42:230–265.

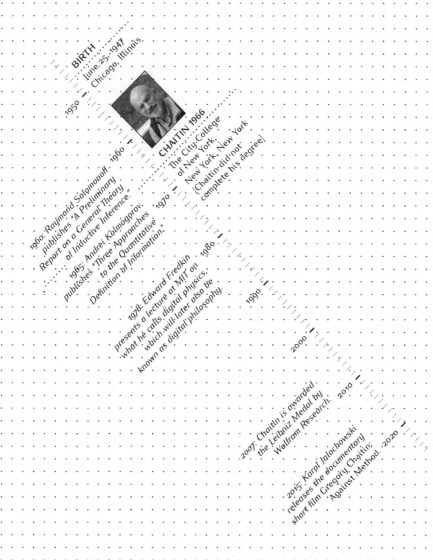

BIRTH
June 25, 1947
Chicago, Illinois,

1950

CHAITIN 1966
The City College
of New York,
New York, New York
[Chaitin did not
complete his degree]

1960: Raymond Solomonoff
publishes "A Preliminary
Report on a General Theory
of Inductive Inference."

1960

1965: Andrei Kolmogorov
publishes "Three Approaches
to the Quantitative
Definition of Information."

1970

1978, Edward Fredkin
presents a lecture at MIT on
what he calls digital physics,
which will later also be
known as digital philosophy.

1980

1990

2000

2007: Chaitin is awarded
the Leibniz Medal by
Wolfram Research.

2010

2015: Karol Jalochowski
releases the documentary
short film Gregory Chaitin;
Against Method. 2020

GREGORY JOHN CHAITIN

[26]

PORTRAIT OF THE ARTIST AS A YOUNG COMPLEXITY HACKER

Simon DeDeo, Carnegie Mellon University and Santa Fe Institute

G. J. Chaitin, "On the Length of Programs for Computing Finite Binary Sequences," in *Journal of the ACM* 13 (4): 547–569 (1966).

Used with permission of Journal of the Association for Computing Machinery; permission conveyed through Copyright Clearance Center, Inc.

Sometimes good things come from taking mathematics seriously. Artificial intelligence, for example, received a jump-start when Steve "Slug" Russell, a twenty-something hacker at MIT in the 1960s (Levy 1984), took a mathematical function seriously enough that he made it run on an IBM 704; it was the first interpreter for the computer language LISP (McCarthy 1981), and the ultimate ancestor to the Python code that runs our scientific and engineering projects today. Computer science often lives on this knife's-edge between mathematical order and fuse-blowing reality—the thrill of making mathematics run is part of the attraction of a discipline that picks up a virtual concept and asks "what would happen if this were a thing?" Antics like Russell's were one reason that nobody knew where to put computer science departments; some came out of electrical engineering, others applied mathematics, meeting in a no-man's land that even today makes the more disciplinarily inclined nervous.

Around the same time as Russell was putting one mathematical ghost into the machine, an even younger hacker, Gregory Chaitin, was working on something even stranger. The object Chaitin picked up was the ur-model of computation itself—the "Turing Machine," a philosophical thought experiment dreamed up by Alan Turing (1937) in Cambridge years earlier. In 1965, many would have said this was an unpromising beginning. We had proved, to our satisfaction, that Turing's model was "complete." Everything a computer could do, a Turing machine could do. We had gotten past these origins, and had far more appealing, if less philosophical, ways to talk about how to get computers to do what we wanted. These included John McCarthy's LISP, which Russell was, almost simultaneously, programming on the

IBM 704. We had real computers with real problems—ones that made Turing's mathematical model look positively irrelevant.

Perhaps it was the literalism of youth that led Chaitin to go back to Turing and to pretend, for a while, that his machine was real. Picking up a suggestion left by Claude Shannon a few years earlier, Chaitin asked: say you built it, how would it work? How would you make it more efficient? What are the limits to what we can squeeze out?

In asking this question, he foresaw, dimly, a grand edifice just coming into view, that of what came to be called "computational complexity," a place where mathematicians didn't just leave engineers to build systems, but took some of the engineer's mindset on board. Mathematicians are famously profligate; there is an infinity of prime numbers, for example, and they never wear out. If a mathematician uses prime numbers in a proof they rarely ask—except as a matter of aesthetics—whether they need to use so many. Engineers are the opposite: when people start using the things they make, those things wear out, and the more of them they use, the more upset the end-user gets.

In much of this paper, Chaitin asks questions like an engineer: Turing invented this thing, but what if the memory system was more expensive than the CPU? What if the CPU had constraints, like the ones on machines in the real world? What kind of trade-offs do we face, and can we make them—with a little clever design—less severe? The paper twists back and forth between the mind-numbingly tedious pretense that a Turing machine is something one might actually want to construct in a materially efficient fashion (e.g., the endless design specifications of section 1.3, and the excursion of section 2, which feel like a user manual for a science-fictional device), and the mathematically mysterious idea that some sequences of binary digits might be more difficult—as a matter of engineering—to calculate than others.

In doing so, the eighteen-year-old City College student stumbles upon something that the sixty-year-old Kolmogorov, a world away in Moscow, was also after, at quite literally the same moment in history:[1] an essential connection between that difficulty of calculation and its

---

[1] See chapter 31, this volume.

apparent mirror-world opposite: not how hard the sequence is to calculate, but how random it is. The two ideas seem a world apart. If I ask my dean at Carnegie Mellon to grant me full access to his computer infrastructure, he will be very displeased if, on inquiring about the result, I tell him that it was indistinguishable from a series of coin tosses. He will be even more irritated if I tell him that this was in fact *proof* that I had used his infrastructure to the utmost, with no repetition or redundancy.[2] Chaitin's paper, however, gives us good reason—indeed, as we now know, provably the best philosophical reason—to think that this is exactly correct (section 1.8).

These difficult sequences, as Chaitin points out, are not just random, they are also incomprehensible: we know they exist, but we cannot say what they are. The mystery hinges on a subtle distinction, that he points to at the end of section 2.4: if you give me a sequence, and it happens not to be difficult, I can eventually recognize it as such. But if you give me a difficult one, I can't; I will peer at it and peer at it, until you get bored and call a halt to things—like we sometimes do when command-escaping a program on a Mac—but your impatience tells me nothing about the answer.[3] Randomness exists, in other words, but as a negative theology: we can only point to what is not. The final part of section 2 dances right up to the edge of this distinction, asking questions about those easy sequences: how many there are, and how they are squeezed out by the vaster sea of the difficult. Chaitin swings between the philosopher, knowing these mysteries to be hidden, and the engineer, scheming, like Milton's Satan, to storm the heaven of the truly difficult with "hollow engines, long and round" (*Paradise Lost*, Book VI, 484); the battle ends, as he knows it will, in mathematical stalemate, but he comes as close as he logically can.

The final section, Part 3, serves as a coda to this drama. Having established the insurmountable challenge of describing the difficult, he turns to the meaning of recognizing the *easy*. Which, for fallen creatures like us, is still an achievement. Consider, he says, the sequences we

---

[2] My dean is also a professor of philosophy, so his amusement at the proof might be equal to his annoyance—but I don't fancy my chances.

[3] This is the distinction between what Chaitin describes as "recursive" and "recursively enumerable."

actually encounter in the real world, the ones that appear random, but that for some of us—the Einsteins, say—can suddenly be resolved. Some of that apparent randomness, Chaitin points out, may be *only* apparent; faced with a long, apparently random sequence of events, we may, in fact, be able to construct a machine (a *theory*) that reveals its unexpected simplicity: such a machine would compute the sequence needing just the littlest prompt. Chaitin's engineering metaphors give us a new way to talk about science: not as a matter of power over nature, but as an epistemic insight, a matter of explanation, and one that seems to match our psychological experience of the gap between pattern and randomness (Griffiths *et al.* 2018; Wojtowicz and DeDeo 2020).

The point is far from just a poetic one—it can, in fact, resolve the puzzle of the dean, raised earlier. Imagine that I did, indeed, burn up Carnegie Mellon's computer time to produce what looks like a random sequence. But now I return to my dean and say the following: do you remember that data we got, that everyone gave up on as truly random? That enormously long one? Well, look, here—I have a theory about what it really is, and wrote a computer program—quite a short one— and when I run the simulation, that's exactly what it makes. Depending on where that data came from, how much of it I could reproduce, and how short my program was, I may book a flight to Stockholm, or call the National Security Agency from a secure line.

In keeping with Chaitin's oscillation between machine engineer and mathematical savant, his understanding of the relationship between randomness and difficulty is not just of philosophical interest; it will return again and again with a decidedly practical bent. Cryptography, for example, depends upon the ability to take an ordinary message and turn it into an apparently random jumble—and questions about how Chaitin's quantities vary under different sorts of machine designs turn into claims about what ciphers can be broken, and by whom (Liu and Pass 2020).

There is a world hidden in the work that Chaitin began. His paper was funded in part by the precursor to the National Science Foundation's Research Experience for Undergraduates program, and it is fair to say that it might be—so far—the most successful REU in history. ❧

REFERENCES

Griffiths, T. L., D. Daniels, J. L. Austerweil, and J. B. Tenenbaum. 2018. "Subjective Randomness as Statistical Inference." *Cognitive Psychology* 103:85–109. https://doi.org/10.1016/j.cogpsych.2018.02.003.

Levy, S. 1984. *Hackers: Heroes of the Computer Revolution.* Garden City, NY: Doubleday.

Liu, Y., and R. Pass. 2020. "On One-way Functions and Kolmogorov Complexity." In *2020 IEEE 61st Annual Symposium on Foundations of Computer Science (FOCS),* 1243–1254. https://doi.org/10.1109/FOCS46700.2020.00118.

McCarthy, J. 1960. "Recursive Functions of Symbolic Expressions Their Computation by Machine, Part I." *Communications of the ACM* 3 (4): 184–195. https://doi.org/10.1145/367177.367199.

———. 1981. "History of LISP." In *History of Programming Languages,* edited by R. Wexelblat. New York, NY: Academic Press. http://jmc.stanford.edu/articles/lisp.html.

Turing, A. M. 1937. "On Computable Numbers, with an Application to the Entscheidungsproblem." *Proceedings of the London Mathematical Society* s2-42 (1): 230–265. https://doi.org/10.1112/plms/s2-42.1.230.

Wojtowicz, Z., and S. DeDeo. 2020. "From Probability to Consilience: How Explanatory Values Implement Bayesian Reasoning." *Trends in Cognitive Sciences* 24 (12): 981–993. https://doi.org/10.1016/j.tics.2020.09.013.

ON THE LENGTH OF PROGRAMS FOR COMPUTING FINITE BINARY SEQUENCES

Gregory J. Chaitin, City College of the City University of New York

Abstract

This paper was written in part with the help of NSF Undergraduate Research Participation Grant GY-161. The use of Turing machines for calculating finite binary sequences is studied from the point of view of information theory and the theory of recursive functions. Various results are obtained concerning the number of instructions in programs. A modified form of Turing machine is studied from the same point of view. An application to the problem of defining a patternless sequence is proposed in terms of the concepts here developed.

Introduction

In this paper the Turing machine is regarded as a general purpose computer and some practical questions are asked about programming it. Given an arbitrary finite binary sequence, what is the length of the shortest program for calculating it? What are the properties of those binary sequences of a given length which require the longest programs? Do most of the binary sequences of a given length require programs of about the same length?

The engineer meets the philosopher: Chaitin is tinkering, not with a machine, but an armchair thought experiment.

The questions posed above are answered in Part 1. In the course of answering them, the logical design of the Turing machine is examined as to redundancies, and it is found that it is possible to increase the efficiency of the Turing machine as a computing instrument without a major alteration in the philosophy of its logical design. Also, the following question raised by C. E. Shannon (1956) is partially answered: What effect does the number of different symbols that a Turing machine can write on its tape have on the length of the program required for a given calculation?

An early example of what would become the core of modern theoretical computer science: how does the ability of a machine to solve problems change with resource constraints?

In Part 2 a major alteration in the logical design of the Turing machine is introduced, and then all the questions about the lengths of programs which had previously been asked about the first computer are asked again. The change in the logical design may be described in the following terms: Programs for Turing machines may have transfers from any part of the program to any other part, but in the programs for the Turing machines which are considered in Part 2 there is a fixed upper bound on the length of transfers.

Part 3 deals with the somewhat philosophical problem of defining a random or patternless binary sequence. The following definition is proposed: Patternless finite binary sequences of a given length are sequences which in order to be computed require programs of approximately the same length as the longest programs required to compute any binary sequences of that given length. Previous work along these lines and its relationship to the present proposal are discussed briefly.

Part 1

1.1 We define an N-state M-tape-symbol Turing machine by an N-row by M-column table. Each of the NM places in this table must have an entry consisting of an ordered pair (i, j) of natural numbers, where i goes from 0 to N and j goes from 1 to $M + 2$. These entries constitute, when specified, the program of the N-state M-tape-symbol Turing machine. They are to be interpreted as follows: An entry (i, j) in the kth row and the pth column of the table means that when the machine is in its kth state and the square of its one-way infinite tape which is being scanned is marked with the pth symbol, then the machine is to go to its ith state if $i \neq 0$ (the machine is to halt if $i = 0$) after performing the operation of (1) moving the tape one square to the right if $j = M + 2$, (2) moving the tape one square to the left if $j = M + 1$, and (3) marking (overprinting) the square of the tape being scanned with the jth symbol if $1 \leq j \leq M$. Special names are given to the first, second and third symbols. They are, respectively, the blank (for unmarked square), 0 and 1.

A third example of how Chaitin brings the engineer's mindset to a philosophical problem: what if a Turing machine had the constraints common (in 1966, memory paging and restricted GOTOs) to the machines we have in the real world.

Chaitin's final flourish—a new definition of knowledge, pattern, and explanation.

A Turing machine may be represented schematically as follows:

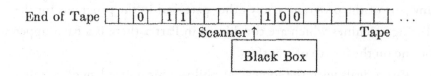

End of Tape | | 0 | 1 1 | | | | 1 0 0 | | | | | ...

Scanner ↑   Tape

Black Box

It is stipulated that

(1.1A) Initially the machine is in its first state and scanning the first square of the tape.

(1.1B) No Turing machine may in the course of a calculation scan the end square of the tape and then move the tape one square to the right.

(1.1C) Initially all squares of the tape are blank.

Since throughout this paper we shall be concerned with computing finite binary sequences, when we say that a Turing machine calculates a particular finite binary sequence (say, 01111000), we shall mean that the machine stops with the sequence written at the end of its tape, with all other squares of the tape blank and with its scanner on the first blank square of the tape. For example, the following Turing machine has just calculated the sequence mentioned:

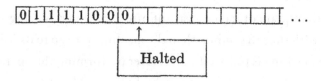

0 1 1 1 1 0 0 0 | | | | | | | | | | ...

↑

Halted

1.2 There are exactly $((N + 1)(M + 2))^{NM}$ possible programs for an N-state M-tape-symbol Turing machine. Thus to specify a single one of these programs requires $\log_2(((N + 1)(M + 2))^{NM})$ bits of information, which is asymptotic to $NM \log_2 N$ bits for M fixed and N large. Therefore a program for an N-state M-tape-symbol Turing machine (considering M to be fixed and N to be large) can be regarded as consisting of about $NM \log_2 N$ bits of information. It may be, however, that in view of the fact that different programs may cause the machine to behave in exactly the same way, a substantial portion of the information necessary to specify a program is redundant in its specification of the behavior of the machine. This in fact turns out to be the case. It will be shown in what follows that for M fixed and N large at least $1/M$ of the bits of information of a program are redundant. Later we shall be in a position to ask to what extent the remaining portion of $(1 - 1/M)$ of the bits is redundant.

The basic reason for this redundancy is that any renumbering of the rows of the table (this amounts to a renaming of the states of the machine) in no way changes the behavior that a given program will cause the machine to have. Thus the states can be named in a manner determined by the sequencing of the program, and this makes possible the omission of state numbers from the program. This idea is by no means new. It may be seen in most computers with random access memories. In these computers the address of the next instruction to be executed is usually 1 more than the address of the current instruction, and this makes it generally unnecessary to use memory space in order to give the address of the next instruction to be executed. Since we are not concerned with the practical engineering feasibility of a logical design, we can take this idea a step farther.

1.3 In the presentation of the redesigned Turing machine let us begin with an example of the manner in which one can take a program for a Turing machine and reorder its rows (rename its states) until it is in the format of the redesigned machine. In the process, several row numbers in the program are removed and replaced by $+$ or $++$ —this is how redundant information in the program is removed. The "operation codes" (which are 1 for "print blank," 2 for "print zero," 3 for "print one," 4 for "shift tape left" and 5 for "shift tape right") are omitted from the program; every time the rows are reordered, the op-codes are

Get out your pencils—or not. Much of this is essentially irrelevant to the core point, but it certainly reveals Chaitin's fertile literalism.

just carried along. The program used as an example is as follows:

row 1	1	9	7
row 2	8	8	8
row 3	9	6	1
row 4	3	2	0
row 5	7	7	8
row 6	6	5	4
row 7	8	6	9
row 8	9	8	1
row 9	9	1	8

To prevent confusion later, letters instead of numbers are used in the program:

row A	A	I	G
row B	H	H	H
row C	I	F	A
row D	C	B	J
row E	G	G	H
row F	F	E	D
row G	H	F	I
row H	I	H	A
row I	I	A	H

Row A is the first row of the table and shall remain so. Replace A by 1 throughout the table:

row 1	1	I	G
row B	H	H	H
row C	I	F	1
row D	C	B	J
row E	G	G	H
row F	F	E	D
row G	H	F	I
row H	I	H	1
row I	I	1	H

To find to which row of the table to assign the number 2, read across the first row of the table until a letter is reached. Having found an I,

1. replace it by a +,
2. move row I so that it becomes the second row of the table, and
3. replace I by 2 throughout the table:

row 1	1	+	G
row 2	2	1	H
row B	H	H	H
row C	2	F	1
row D	C	B	J
row E	G	G	H
row F	F	E	D
row G	H	F	2
row H	2	H	1

To find to which row of the table to assign the number 3, read across the second row of the table until a letter is found. Having found an H,

1. replace it by a +,
2. move row H so that it becomes the third row of the table, and
3. replace H by 3 throughout the table:

row 1	1	+	G
row 2	2	1	+
row 3	2	3	1
row B	3	3	3
row C	2	F	1
row D	C	B	J
row E	G	G	3
row F	F	E	D
row G	3	F	2

To find to which row of the table to assign the number 4, read across the third row of the table until a letter is found. Having failed to find one, read across rows 1, 2 and 3, respectively, until a letter is found. (A letter must be found, for otherwise rows 1, 2 and 3 are the whole program.) Having found a G in row 1,

1. replace it by a ++,
2. move row G so that it becomes the fourth row of the table, and
3. replace G by 4 throughout the table:

row 1	1	+	++
row 2	2	1	+
row 3	2	3	1
row 4	3	F	2
row B	3	3	3
row C	2	F	1
row D	C	B	J
row E	4	4	3
row F	F	E	D

The next two assignments proceed as in the cases of rows 2 and 3:

row 1	1	+	++
row 2	2	1	+
row 3	2	3	1
row 4	3	+	2
row 5	5	E	D
row B	3	3	3
row C	2	5	1
row D	C	B	J
row E	4	4	3

row 1	1	+	++
row 2	2	1	+
row 3	2	3	1
row 4	3	+	2
row 5	5	+	D
row 6	4	4	3
row B	3	3	3
row C	2	5	1
row D	C	B	J

To find to which row of the table to assign the number 7, read across the sixth row of the table until a letter is found. Having failed to find one, read across rows 1, 2, 3, 4, 5 and 6, respectively, until a letter is found. (A letter must be found, for otherwise rows 1, 2, 3, 4, 5 and 6 are the whole program.) Having found a D in row 5,

1. replace it by a ++,
2. move row D so that it becomes the seventh row of the table, and
3. replace D by 7 throughout the table:

row 1	1	+	++
row 2	2	1	+
row 3	2	3	1
row 4	3	+	2
row 5	5	+	++
row 6	4	4	3
row 7	C	B	J
row B	3	3	3
row C	2	5	1

After three more assignments the following is finally obtained:

row 1	1	+	++
row 2	2	1	+
row 3	2	3	1
row 4	3	+	2
row 5	5	+	++
row 6	4	4	3
row 7	+	++	++
row 8	2	5	1
row 9	3	3	3
row 10			

This example is atypical in several respects: The state order could have needed a more elaborate scrambling (instead of which the row of the table to which a number was assigned always happened to be the last row of the table at the moment), and the fictitious state used for the purposes of halting (state 0 in the formulation of Section 1.1) could have ended up as any one of the rows of the table except the first row (instead of which it ended up as the last row of the table).

The reader will note, however, that 9 row numbers have been eliminated (and replaced by $+$ or $++$) in a program of 9 (actual) rows, and that, in general, *this process will eliminate a row number from the program for each row of the program*. Note too that if a program is "linear" (i.e., the machine executes the instruction in storage address 1, then the instruction in storage address 2, then the instruction in storage address 3, etc.), only $+$ will be used; departures from linearity necessitate use of $++$.

There follows a description of the redesigned machine. In the formalism of that description the program given above is as follows:

10

(1, ,0)	(0, ,1)	(0, ,2)
(2, ,0)	(1, ,0)	(0, ,1)
(2, ,0)	(3, ,0)	(1, ,0)
(3, ,0)	(0, ,1)	(2, ,0)
(5, ,0)	(0, ,1)	(0, ,2)
(4, ,0)	(4, ,0)	(3, ,0)
(0, ,1)	(0, ,2)	(0, ,2)
(2, ,0)	(5, ,0)	(1, ,0)
(3, ,0)	(3, ,0)	(3, ,0)

Here the third member of a triple is the number of $+$'s, the second member is the op-code, and the first member is the number of the next state of the machine if there are no $+$'s (if there are $+$'s, the first member of the triple is 0). The number outside the table is the number of the fictitious row of the program used for the purposes of halting.

We define an N-state M-tape-symbol Turing machine by an $(N + 1) \times M$ table and a natural number $n(2 \leq n \leq N + 1)$. Each of the $(N + 1)M$ places in this table (with the exception of those in the nth row) must have an entry consisting of an ordered triple (i, j, k) of natural numbers, where k is 0, 1 or 2; j goes from 1 to $M + 2$; and

$$\begin{cases} i \text{ goes from 1 to } N + 1 & \text{if } k = 0, \\ i = 0 & \text{if } k \neq 0. \end{cases}$$

(Places in the nth row are left blank.) In addition:

(1.3.1) The entries in which $k = 1$ or $k = 2$ are N in number.

Entries are interpreted as follows:

(1.3.2) An entry $(i, j, 0)$ in the pth row and the mth column of the table means that when the machine is in the pth state and the square of its one-way infinite tape which is being scanned is marked with the mth symbol, then the machine is to go to its ith state if $i \neq n$ (if $i = n$, the machine is instead to halt) after performing the operation of (1) moving the tape one square to the right if $j = M + 2$, (2) moving the tape one square to the left if $j = M + 1$, and (3) marking (overprinting) the square of the tape being scanned with the jth symbol if $1 \leq j \leq M$.

(1.3.3) An entry $(0, j, 1)$ in the pth row and mth column of the table is to be interpreted in accordance with ($1.3.2$) as if it were the entry $(p + 1, j, 0)$.

(1.3.4) For an entry $(0, j, 2)$ in the pth row and mth column of the table the machine proceeds as follows:

(1.3.4a) It determines the number p' of entries of the form $(0, \ , 2)$ in rows of the table preceding the pth row or to the left of the mth column in the pth row.

(1.3.4b) It determines the first $p' + 1$ rows of the table which have no entries of the form $(0, \ , 1)$ or $(0, \ , 2)$. Suppose the last of these $p' + 1$ rows is the p''th row of the table.

(1.3.4c) It interprets the entry in accordance with ($1.3.2$) as if it were the entry $(p'' + 1, j, 0)$.

(1.4) In Section 1.2 it was stated that the programs of the N-state M-tape-symbol Turing machines of Section 1.3 require in order to be specified $(1 - 1/M)$ the number of bits of information required to specify the programs of the N-state M-tape-symbol Turing machines of Section 1.1. (As before, M is regarded to be fixed and N to be large.) This assertion is justified here. In view of ($1.3.1$), at most $N(3(M + 2))^{NM}(N + 1)^{N(M-1)}$ ways of making entries in the table of an N-state M-tape-symbol Turing machine of Section 1.3 count as programs. Thus only $\log_2$ of this number or asymptotically $N(M - 1) \log_2 N$ bits are required to specify the program of an N-state M-tape-symbol machine of Section 1.3.

Henceforth, in speaking of an N-state M-tape-symbol Turing machine, one of the machines of Section 1.3 will be meant.

(1.5) We now define two sets of functions which play a fundamental role in all that follows.

The members $L_M(\cdot)$ of the first set are defined for $M = 3, 4, 5, \cdots$ on the set of all finite binary sequences S as follows:

> An N-state M-tape-symbol Turing machine can be programmed to calculate S if and only if $N \geq L_M(S)$.

The second set $L_M(C_n)(M = 3, 4, 5, \cdots)$ is defined by
$$L_M(C_n) = \max_s L_M(S),$$
where S is any binary sequence of length n.

Finally, we denote by $_MC_n(M = 3, 4, 5, \cdots)$ the set of all binary sequences S of length n satisfying $L_M(S) = L_M(C_n)$.

(1.6) In this section it is shown that for $M = 3, 4, 5, \cdots$,

$$L_M(C_n) \sim (n/((M-1)\log_2 n)).$$

We first show that $L_M(C_n)$ is greater than a function of n which is asymptotically equal to $(n/((M-1)\log_2 n))$. From Section 1.4 it is clear that there are at most $2^{((1+\epsilon_N)N(M-1)\log_2 N)}$ different programs for an N-state M-tape-symbol Turing machine, where ϵ_x denotes a (not necessarily positive) function of x and possibly other variables which tends to zero as x goes to infinity with any other variables held fixed. Since a different program is required to calculate each of the 2^n different binary sequences of length n, we see that an N-state M-tape-symbol Turing machine can be programmed to calculate any binary sequence of length n only if

$$(1 + \epsilon_N)N(M-1)\log_2 N \geq n \text{ or } N \geq (1 + \epsilon_n)(n/((M-1)\log_2 n)).$$

It follows from the definition of $L_M(C_n)$ that

$$L_M(C_n) \geq (1 + \epsilon_n)(n/((M-1)\log_2 n)).$$

Next we show that $L_M(C_n)$ is less than a function of n which is asymptotically equal to $(n/((M-1)\log_2 n))$. This is done by showing

---

Margin notes:

"What machines can do what"—if your goal is to compute a sequence S (or, perhaps, simulate data that looks like S), how big (in tape and internal memory) does the machine need to be?

$L_M(C_n)$: the largest number of internal states you need, if you have M symbols, and you want to compute an arbitrary sequence of length n.

The longer the sequence, the more internal states you need; Chaitin now has the scaling formula. Double the length of the sequences, and you'll find you might need to (almost) double the number of distinct tape symbols.

how to construct for any binary sequence S of length not greater than $(1 + e_N)N(M - 1)\log_2 N$ a program which causes an N-state M-tape-symbol Turing machine to calculate S. The main idea is illustrated in the ease where $M = 3$ (see Figure 1).

This program is in the format of the machines of Section I.I. There are N rows in this table. The unspecified row numbers in Section I are all in the range from d to $f - 1$, inclusive. The manner in which they are specified determines the finite binary sequence S which the program computes.

Pencils out! (Again.)

The execution of this program is divided into phases. There are twice as many phases as there are rows in Section I. The current phase is determined by a binary sequence P which is written out starting on the second square of the tape. The nth phase starts in row 1 with the scanner on the first square of the tape and with

$$\begin{cases} P = 111 \cdots 1 & (i\ 1's) \text{ if } n = 2i + 1, \\ P = 111 \cdots 10 & (i\ 1's) \text{ if } n = 2i + 2. \end{cases}$$

Control then passes down column three through the $(i + 1)$-th row of the table, and then control passes to

$$\begin{cases} \text{row } i + 2, \text{ column 1 if } n = 2i + 1, \\ \text{row } i + 2, \text{ column 2 if } n = 2i + 2, \end{cases}$$

which (1) changes P to what it must be at the start of the $(n + 1)$-th phase, and (2) transfers control to a row in Section II. Suppose this row to be the mth row of Section II from the end of Section II.

Once control has passed to the row in Section II, control then passes down Section II until row f is reached. Each row in Section II causes the tape to be shifted one square to the left, so that when row f finally assumes control, the scanner will be on the mth blank square to the right of P. The following diagram shows the way things may look at this point if n is 7 and m happens to be 11:

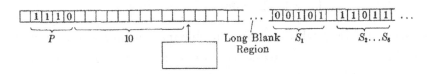

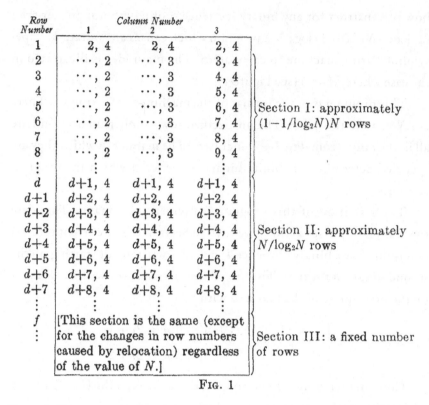

Fig. 1

Figure 1. This program is in the format of the machines of Section 1.1. There are N rows in this table. The unspecified row numbers in Section I are all in the range from d to $f - 1$, inclusive. The manner in which they are specified determines the finite binary sequence S which the program computes.

Now control has been passed to Section III. First of all, Section III accumulates in base-two on the tape a count of the number of blank squares between the scanner and P when f assumes control. (This number is $m - 1$.) This base-two count, which is written on the tape, is simply a binary sequence with a 1 at its left end. Section III then removes this 1 from the left end of the binary sequence. The resulting sequence is called S_n.

Note that if the row numbers entered in

$$\begin{cases} \text{row } i + 2, \text{ column 1 if } n = 2i + 1, \\ \text{row } i + 2, \text{ column 2 if } n = 2i + 2, \end{cases}$$

of Section I are suitably specified, this binary sequence S_n can be made any one of the 2^v binary sequences of length $v = $ (the greatest integer not greater than $\log_2(f - d) - 1$). Finally, Section III writes S_n in a region of the tape far to the right where all the previous $S_j(j = 1, 2, \cdots, n-1)$ have been written during previous phases, cleans up the tape so that only the sequences P and $S_j(j = 1, 2, \cdots, n)$ remain on it, positions the scanner back on the square at the end of the tape and, as the last act of phase n, passes control back to row 1 again.

The foregoing description of the workings of the program omits some important details for the sake of clarity. These follow.

It must be indicated how Section III knows when the last phase (phase $2(d-2)$) has occurred. During the nth phase, P is copied just to the right of $S_1, S_2, \cdots, S_n$ (of course a blank square is left between S_n and the copy of P). And during the $(n+1)$-th phase, Section III checks whether or not P is currently different from what it was during the nth phase when the copy of it was made. If it isn't different, then Section III knows that phasing has in fact stopped and that a termination routine must be executed.

The termination routine first forms the finite binary sequence S^* consisting of $S_1, S_2, \cdots, S_{2(d-2)}$, each immediately following the other. As each of the S_j can be any one of the 2^v binary sequences of length v if the row numbers in the entries in Section I are appropriately specified, it follows that S^* can be any one of the 2^w binary sequences of length $w = 2(d-2)v$. Note that

$$2(d-2)(\log_2(f-d) - 1) \geq w > 2(d-2)(\log_2(f-d) - 2),$$

so that

$$w \sim 2((1 - 1/\log_2 N)N)(\log_2(N/\log_2 N)) \sim 2N\log_2 N.$$

As we want the program to be able to compute any sequence S of length not greater than $(2 + \epsilon_N)N\log_2 N$, we have S^* consist of S followed to the right by a single 1 and then a string of 0's, and the termination routine removes the rightmost 0's and first 1 from S^*. Q.E.D.

The result just obtained shows that it is impossible to make further improvement in the logical design of the Turing machine of the kind described in Section 1.2 and actually effected in Section 1.3; if we let the number of tape symbols be fixed and speak asymptotically as the number of states goes to infinity, in our present Turing machines 100 percent of the bits required to specify a program also serve to specify the behavior of the machine.

Note too that the argument presented in the first paragraph of this section in fact establishes that, say, for any fixed s greater than zero, at most $n^{-s}2^n$ binary sequences S of length n satisfy

$$L_M(S) \leq (1 + \epsilon_n)(n/((M-1)\log_2 n)).$$

Thus we have:

For any fixed s greater than zero, at most $n^{-s}2^n$ binary sequences of length n fail to satisfy the double inequality:

$$(1 + \epsilon_n)(n/((M-1)\log_2 n)) \leq L_M(S)$$
$$\leq (1 + \epsilon_n')(n/((M-1)\log_2 n)).$$

1.7 It may be desirable to have some idea of the "local" as well as the "global" behavior of $L_M(C_n)$. The following program of 8 rows causes an 8-state 3-tape-symbol Turing machine to compute the binary sequence 01100101 of length 8 (this program is in the format of the machines of Section 1.1):

1,2	2,4	2,4
2,3	3,4	3,4
3,3	4,4	4,4
4,2	5,4	5,4
5,2	6,4	6,4
6,3	7,4	7,4
7,2	8,4	8,4
8,3	0,4	0,4.

And in general:

(1.7.1) $L_M(C_n) \leq n$.

From this it is easy to see that for m greater than n:

(1.7.2) $L_M(C_m) \leq L_M(C_n) + (m - n)$.

Also, for m greater than n:

(1.7.3) $L_M(C_m) + 1 \geq L_M(C_n)$.

For if one can calculate any binary sequence of length m greater than n with an M-tape-symbol Turing machine having $L_M(C_m)$ states, one can certainly program any M-tape-symbol Turing machine having $L_M(C_m) + 1$ states to calculate the binary sequence

$$\cdots\cdots\cdots\cdots\cdots\cdots\cdots10000000000\cdots\cdots\cdots\cdot0000000000$$

/ Any particular sequence of length n

/ This sequence of length $(m-n)$

and then—instead of immediately halting—to first erase all the 0's and the first 1 on the right end of the sequence. This last part of the program takes up only a single row of the table; in the format of the machines of Section 1.1 this row r is:

$$\text{row } r \quad r, 5 \quad r, 1 \quad 0, 1.$$

Together (1.7.2) and (1.7.3) yield:

(1.7.4) $|L_M(C_{n+1}) - L_M(C_n)| \leq 1$.

From (1.7.1) it is obvious that $L_M(C_1) = 1$, and with (1.7.4) and the fact that $L_M(C_n)$ goes to infinity with n it finally is concluded that:

(1.7.5) For any positive integer p there is at least one solution n of $L_M(C_n) = p$.

1.8 In this section a certain amount of insight is obtained into the properties of finite binary sequences S of length n for which $L_M(S)$ is close to $L_M(C_n)$. M is considered to be fixed throughout this section. There is some connection between the present subject and that of Shannon (1948, Pt. I, especially Th. 9).

The main result is as follows:

What are those "hard" sequences?

(1.8.1) For any $e > 0$ and $d > 1$ one has for all sufficiently large n: If S is any binary sequence of length n satisfying the statement that

(1.8.2) the ratio of the number of 0's in S to n differs from $\frac{1}{2}$ by more than e, then $L_M(S) < L_M(C_{[ndH(\frac{1}{2}+e, \frac{1}{2}-e)]})$.

Here $H(p,q)(p \geq 0, q \geq 0, p+q = 1)$ is a special case of the entropy function of Boltzmann statistical mechanics and information theory and equals

$$
\begin{cases}
0 & \text{if } p = 0 \text{ or } 1, \\
-p\log_2 p - q\log_2 q & \text{otherwise.}
\end{cases}
$$

Also, a real number enclosed in brackets denotes the least integer greater than the enclosed real. The H function comes up because the logarithm to the base-two of the $\displaystyle\sum_{|(k/n)-\frac{1}{2}|>e} \binom{n}{k}$ of binary sequences of length n satisfying (1.8.2) is asymptotic to $nH(\frac{1}{2}+e, \frac{1}{2}-e)$. This may be shown easily by considering the ratio of successive binomial coefficients and using the fact that $log(n!) \sim n\log n$.

To prove (1.8.1), first construct a class of effectively computable functions $M_n(\cdot)$ with the natural numbers from 1 to 2^n as range and all binary sequences of length n as domain. $M_n(S)$ is defined to be the ordinal number of the position of S in an ordering of the binary sequences of length n defined as follows:

1. If two binary sequences S and S' have, respectively, m and m' 0's, then S comes before (after) S' according as $|(m/n) - \frac{1}{2}|$ is greater (less) than $|(m'/n) - \frac{1}{2}|$.

2. If 1 does not settle which comes first, take S to come before (after) S' according as S represents (ignoring 0's to the left) a larger (smaller) number in base-two notation than S' represents.

The only essential feature of this ordering is that it gives small ordinal numbers to sequences for which $|(m/n) - \frac{1}{2}|$ has large values. In fact, as there are only $2^{(1+\epsilon_n)nH(\frac{1}{2}+e,\frac{1}{2}-e)}$ binary sequences S of length n satisfying (1.8.2), it follows that at worst $M_n(S)$ is a number which in base-two notation is represented by a binary sequence of length $\sim nH(\frac{1}{2}+e, \frac{1}{2}-e)$. Thus in order to obtain a short program for computing an S of length n satisfying (1.8.2), let us just give a program of fixed length r the values of n and $M_n(S)$ and have it compute $S(= M_n^{-1}(M_n(S)))$ from this data. The manner in which for n sufficiently large we give the values of n and $M_n(S)$ to the program is to pack them into a single binary sequence of length at most $[n(1 + (d-1)/2)H(\frac{1}{2} + e, \frac{1}{2} - e)] + 2(1 + [\log_2 n])$ as follows:

$$\cdots\cdots\cdots\cdots\cdots\cdots\cdots\cdots \cdot 01 \cdots\cdots\cdots\cdots\cdots\cdots\cdots\cdots$$

       /   /

The binary sequence representing $M_n(S)$ The binary sequence representing n
in base-two notation   with each of its bits doubled
(e.g., if $n = 43$, this is 110011001111)

Clearly both n and $M_n(S)$ can be recovered from this sequence. And this sequence can be computed by a program of $L_M(C_{[n(1+(d-1)/2)H(\frac{1}{2}+e,\frac{1}{2}-e))+} 2(1 + [\log_2 n]))$ rows.

Thus for n sufficiently large this many rows plus r is all that is needed to compute any binary sequence S of length n satisfying (1.8.2). And by the asymptotic formula for $L_M(C_n)$ of Section 1.6, it is seen that the total number of rows of program required is, for n sufficiently large, less than $L_M(C_{[ndH(\frac{1}{2}+e,\frac{1}{2}-e)]})$. Q.E.D.

From (1.8.1) and the fact that $H(p, q) \leq 1$ with equality if and only if $p = q = \frac{1}{2}$, it follows from $L_M(C_n) \sim (n/((M-1)\log_2 n))$ that, for example,

(1.8.3) For any $e > 0$, all binary sequences S in $_MC_n$, n sufficiently large, violate (1.8.2);

and more generally,

(1.8.4) Let $S_{n_1}, S_{n_2}, S_{n_3}, \cdots$ be any infinite sequence of distinct finite binary sequences of lengths, respectively, $n_1, n_2, n_3, \cdots$ which satisfies $L_M(S_{n_k}) \sim L_M(C_{n_k})$. Then as k goes to infinity, the ratio of the number of 0's in S_{n_k} to n_k tends to the limit $\frac{1}{2}$.

We now wish to apply (1.8.4) to programs for Turing machines. In order to do this we need to be able to represent the table of entries defining any program as a single binary sequence. A method is sketched here for coding any program $T_{N,M}$ occupying the table of an N-state M-tape-symbol Turing machine into a single binary sequence $C(T_{N,M})$ of length $(1 + \epsilon_N)N(M-1)\log_2 N$.

Pencils out! (Yet again.)

First, write all the members of the ordered triples entered in the table in base-two notation, adding a sufficient number of 0's to the left of the numerals for all numerals to be

(1) as long as the base-two numeral for $N + 1$ if they result from the first member of a triple,

(2) as long as the base-two numeral for $M + 2$ if they result from the second member, and

(3) as long as the base-two numeral for 2 if they result from the third member.

The only exception to this rule is that if the third member of a triple is 1 or 2, then the first member of the triple is not written in base-two notation; no binary sequences are generated from first members of such triples. Last, all the binary sequences that have just been obtained are joined together, starting with the binary sequence that was generated from the first member of the triple entered at the intersection of row 1 with column 1 of the table, then with the binary sequence generated from the second member of the triple $\cdots , \cdots$ from the third member $\cdots , \cdots$ from the first member of the triple entered at the intersection of row 1 with column 2, $\cdots$ from the second member $\cdots , \cdots$ from the third member $\cdots$, and so on across the first row of the table, then across the second row of the table, then the third, $\cdots$ and finally across the Nth row.

The result of all this is a single binary sequence of length $(1 + \epsilon_N)N(M-1)\log_2 N$ (in view of $(1.3.1)$) from which one can effectively determine the whole table of entries which was coded into it, if only one is given the values of N and M. But it is possible to code in these last pieces of information using only the rightmost $2(1 + [\log_2 N]) + 2(1 + [\log_2 M])$ bits of a binary sequence consequently of total length

$$(1 + \epsilon_N)N(M - 1)\log_2 N + 2(1 + [\log_2 N]) + 2(1 + [\log_2 M])$$
$$= (1 + \epsilon'_N)N(M - 1)\log_2 N,$$

by employing the same trick that was used to pack two separate pieces of information into a single binary sequence earlier in this section.

Thus we have a simple procedure for coding the whole table of entries $T_{N,M}$ defining a program of an N-state M-tape-symbol Turing machine and the parameters N and M of the machine into a binary sequence $C(T_{N,M})$ of $(1 + \epsilon_N)N(M - 1)\log_2 N$ bits.

We now obtain the result:

(1.8.5) Let $T_{L_M(S_1),M}, T_{L_M(S_2),M}, \cdots$ be an infinite sequence of tables of entries which define programs for computing, respectively, the distinct finite binary sequences $S_1, S_2, \cdots$. Then $L_M(C(T_{L_M(S_k),M})) \sim L_M(C_{n_k})$, where n_k is the length of $C(T_{L_M(S_k),M})$.

With (1.8.4) this gives the proposition:

(1.8.6) On the hypothesis of (1.8.5), as k goes to infinity, the ratio of the number of 0's in $C(T_{L_M(S_k),M})$ to its length tends to the limit $\frac{1}{2}$.

The proof of (1.8.5) depends on three facts:

(1.8.7a) There is an effective procedure for coding the table of entries $T_{N,M}$ defining the program of an N-state M-tape-symbol Turing machine together with the two parameters N and M into a single binary sequence $C(T_{N,M})$ of length $(1 + \epsilon_N)N(M - 1)\log_2 N$.

(1.8.7b) Any binary sequence of length not greater than $(1+\epsilon_N)N(M-1)\log_2 N$ can be calculated by a suitably programmed N-state M-tape-symbol Turing machine.

(1.8.7c) From a universal Turing machine program it is possible to construct a program for a Turing machine (with a fixed number r of rows) to take $C(T_{N,M})$ and decode it and to then imitate the calculations of the machine whose table of entries $T_{N,M}$ it then knows, until it finally calculates the finite binary sequence S which the program being imitated calculates, if S exists.

(1.8.7a) has just been demonstrated. (1.8.7b) was shown in Section 1.6. (The concept of a universal program is due to Turing 1937.)

The proof of (1.8.5) follows. From (1.8.7a) and (1.8.7b),

$$L_M(C(T_{L_M(S_k),M})) \leq (1 + \epsilon_k)L_M(S_k),$$

and from (1.8.7c) and the hypothesis of (1.8.5),

$$L_M(C(T_{L_M(S_k),M})) + r \geq L_M(S_k).$$

It follows that $L_M(C(T_{L_M(S_k),M})) = (1 + \epsilon_k)L_M(S_k)$, which is—since the length of $C(T_{L_M(S_k),M})$ is $(1+\epsilon_k)L_M(S_k)(M-1)\log_2 L_M(S_k)$ and

$$L_M(C_{(1+\epsilon_k)L_M(S_k)(M-1)\log_2 L_M(S_k)}) = (1 + \epsilon_k')L_M(S_k)$$

—simply the conclusion of $(1.8.5)$.

1.9 The topic of this section is an application of everything that precedes with the exception of Section 1.7 and the first half of Section 1.8. C. E. Shannon suggests [1, p. 165] that the state-symbol product NM is a good measure of the calculating abilities of an N-state M-tape-symbol Turing machine. If one is interested in *comparing* the calculating abilities of *large Turing machines whose M values vary over a finite range*, the results that follow suggest that $N(M - 1)$ is a good measure of calculating abilities. We have as an application of a slight generalization of the ideas used to prove $(1.8.5)$:

(1.9.1a) Any calculation which an N-state M-tape-symbol Turing machine can be programmed to perform can be imitated by any N'-state M'-tape-symbol Turing machine satisfying $(1+\epsilon_N)N(M-1)\log_2 N < (1 + \epsilon_{N'}')N'(M' - 1)\log_2 N'$ if it is suitably programmed.

And directly from the asymptotic formula for $L_M(C_n)$ we have:

(1.9.1b) If $(1 + \epsilon_N)N(M - 1)\log_2 N < (1 + \epsilon_{N'}')N'(M' - 1)\log_2 N'$, then there exist finite binary sequences which an N'-state M'-tape-symbol Turing machine can be programmed to calculate and which it is impossible to program an N-state M-tape-symbol Turing machine to calculate.

As $(1 + \epsilon_N)N(M - 1)\log_2 N = ((1 + \epsilon_{N'})N(M - 1))\log_2((1 + \epsilon_{N'})N(M - 1))$ and for x and x' greater than one, $x\log_2 x$ is greater (less) than $x'\log_2 x'$ according as x is greater (less) than x', it follows that the inequalities of $(1.9.1a)$ and $(1.9.1b)$ give the same *ordering* of calculating abilities as do inequalities involving functions of the form $(1 + \epsilon_N)N(M - 1)$.

Part 2

2.1 In this section we return to the Turing machines of Section 1.1 and add to the conventions $(1.1A)$, $(1.1B)$ and $(1.1C)$,

A new form of "universality"—you can trade internal memory and tape space against each other; a world where tape is expensive and a world where internal memory is expensive can still have equivalent capabilities.

(2.1D) An entry (i, j) in the pth row of the table of a Turing machine must satisfy $|i - p| \leq b$. In addition, while a fictitious state is used (as before) for the purpose of halting, the row of the table for this fictitious state is now considered to come directly after the actual last row of the program.

Here b is a constant whose value is to be regarded as fixed throughout Part 2. In Section 2.2 it will be shown that b can be chosen sufficiently large that the Turing machines thus defined (which we take the liberty of naming "bounded-transfer Turing machines") have all the calculating capabilities that are basically required of Turing machines for theoretical purposes (e.g., such purposes as defining what one means by "effective process for determining . . ."), and hence have calculating abilities sufficient for the proofs of Part 2 to be carried out.

(2.1D) may be regarded as a mere convention, but it is more properly considered as a change in the basic philosophy of the logical design of the Turing machine (i.e., the philosophy expressed by A. M. Turing 1937, Sec. 9).

Here in Part 2 there will be little point in considering the general M-tape-symbol machine. It will be understood that we are always speaking of 3-tape-symbol machines.

There is a simple and convenient notational change which can be made at this point; it makes all programs for bounded-transfer Turing machines instantly relocatable (which is convenient if one puts together a program from subroutines) and it saves a great deal of superfluous writing. Entries in the tables of machines will from now on consist of ordered pairs (i', j'), where i' goes from $-b$ to b and j' goes from 1 to 5. A "new" entry (i', j') is to be interpreted in terms of the functioning of the machine in a manner depending on the number p of the row of the table it is in; this entry has the same meaning that the "old" entry $(p + i', j')$ used to have.

Thus, halting is now accomplished by entries of the form (k, j) $(1 \leq k \leq b)$ in the kth row (from the end) of the table. Such an entry causes the machine to halt after performing the operation indicated by j.

2.2 In this section we attempt to give an idea of the versatility of the bounded-transfer Turing machine. It is here shown in two ways that b can

"Bounded Transfer"—what if the internal state space of the machine itself had constraints, not just on the number of states, but how they interlock? Unlike much of the rest of this paper, this section hasn't (yet) been associated with particularly fertile ideas.

The calculations above have shown that we can get by with a very small number of distinct tape symbols; from here on out, we can just use three (e.g., "0," "1," and "blank.")

Chaitin has shown that he can transfer some contemporary intuitions (e.g., that a computer program has libraries, subroutines, and so forth) to Turing's thought experiment.

be chosen sufficiently large so that any calculation which one of the Turing machines of Section 1.1 can be programmed to perform can be imitated by a suitably programmed bounded-transfer Turing machine.

As the first proof, b is taken to be the number of rows in a 3-tape-symbol universal Turing machine program for the machines of Section 1.1. This universal program (with its format changed to that of the bounded-transfer Turing machines) occupies the last rows of a program for a bounded-transfer Turing machine, a program which is mainly devoted to writing out on the tape the information which will enable the universal program to imitate any calculation which any one of the Turing machines of Section 1.1 can be programmed to perform. One row of the program is used to write out each symbol of this information (as in the program in Section 1.7), and control passes straight through the program row after row until it reaches the universal program.

Now for the second proof. To program a bounded-transfer Turing machine in such a manner that it imitates the calculations performed by a Turing machine of Section 1.1, consider alternate squares on the tape of the bounded-transfer Turing machine to be the squares of the tape of the machine being imitated. Thus

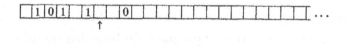

is imitated by

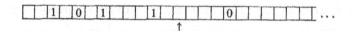

After the operation of a state (i.e., write 0, write 1, write blank, shift tape left, shift tape right) has been imitated, as many 1's as the number of the next state to be imitated are written on the squares of the tape of the bounded-transfer Turing machine which are not used to imitate the squares of the other machine's tape, starting on the square immediately to the right of the one on which is the scanner of the bounded-transfer Turing machine. Thus if in the foregoing situation the next state to be imitated is state number three, then the tape of the bounded-transfer Turing machine becomes

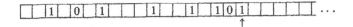

The rows of the table which cause the bounded-transfer Turing machine to do the foregoing (type I rows) are interwoven or braided with two other types of rows. The first of these (type II rows) is used for the sole purpose of putting the bounded-transfer Turing machine back in its initial state (row 1 of the table; this row is a type III row). They appear (as do the other two types of rows) periodically throughout the table, and each of them does nothing but transfer control to the preceding one. The second of these (type III rows) serve to pass control back in the other direction; each time control is about to pass a block of type I rows that imitate a particular state of the other machine while traveling through type III rows, the type III rows erase the rightmost of the 1's used to write out the number of the next state to be imitated. When finally none of these place-marking 1's is left, control is passed to the group of type I rows that was about to be passed, which then proceeds to imitate the appropriate state of the Turing machine of Section 1.1.

Thus the obstacle of the upper bound on the length of transfers in bounded-transfer Turing machines is overcome by passing up and down the table by small jumps, while keeping track of the progress to the desired destination is achieved by subtracting a unit from a count written on the tape just prior to departure.

Although bounded-transfer Turing machines have been shown to be versatile, it is not true that as the number of states goes to infinity, asymptotically 100 percent of the bits required to specify a program also serve to specify the behavior of the bounded-transfer Turing machine.

2.3 In this section the following fundamental result is proved.

(2.3.1) $L(C_n) \sim a^*n$, where a^* is, of course, a positive constant.

First it is shown that there exists an a greater than zero such that:

(2.3.2) $L(C_n) \geq an$.

It is clear that there are exactly $((5)(2b+1))^{3N}$ different ways of making entries in the table of an N-state bounded-transfer Turing machine; that

Back to the main question: what are those "hard" sequences, and how do their properties compose? For Kolmogorov (see elsewhere in this volume) these will be characteristics of the truly random.

is, there are $2^{((3\log_2(10b+5))N)}$ different programs for an N-state bounded-transfer Turing machine. Since a different program is required to have the machine calculate each of the 2^n different binary sequences of length n, it can be seen that an N-state bounded-transfer Turing machine can be programmed to calculate any binary sequence of length n only if

$$(3\log_2(10b+5))N \geq n \quad \text{or} \quad N \geq (1/(3\log_2(10b+5)))n.$$

Thus one can take $a = (1/(3\log_2(10b+5)))$.

Next it is shown that:

(2.3.3) $L(C_n) + L(C_m) \geq L(C_{n+m})$.

To do this we present a way of making entries in a table with at most $L(C_n) + L(C_m)$ rows which causes the bounded-transfer Turing machine thus programmed to calculate any particular binary sequence S of length $n + m$. S can be expressed as a binary sequence S' of length n followed by a binary sequence S'' of length m. The table is then formed from two sections which are numbered in the order in which they are encountered in reading from row 1 to the last row of the table. Section I consists of at most $L(C_n)$ rows. It is a program which calculates S'. Section II consists of at most $L(C_m)$ rows. It is a program which calculates S''. It follows from this construction and the definitions that (2.3.3) holds.

(2.3.2) and (2.3.3) together imply (2.3.1). This will be shown by a demonstration of the following general proposition:

(2.3.4) Let $A_1, A_2, A_3, \cdots$ be an infinite sequence of natural numbers satisfying

(2.3.5) $A_n + A_m \geq A_{n+m}$.

Then as n goes to infinity, (A_n/n) tends to a limit from above.

For all n, $A_n \geq 0$, so that $(A_n/n) \geq 0$; that is, $\{(A_n/n)\}$ is a set of reals bounded from below. It is concluded that this set has a greatest lower bound a^*. We now show that $\lim_{n\to\infty}(A_n/n) = a^*$. Since a^* is the greatest lower bound of the set $\{(A_n/n)\}$, for any e greater than zero there is a d for which

(2.3.6) $(A_d/d) < a^* + e$.

Every natural number n can be expressed in the form $n = qd+r$, where $0 \leq r < d$. From (2.3.5) it can be seen that for any $n_1, n_2, n_3, \cdots, n_{q+1}$,

$$\sum_{k=1}^{q+1} A_{n_k} \geq A_{\sum_{k=1}^{q+1} n_k}.$$

Taking $n_k = d\ (k = 1, 2, \cdots, q)$ and $n_{q+1} = r$ in this, we obtain

$$qA_d + A_r \geq A_{qd+r} = A_n,$$

which with (2.3.6) gives

$$qd(a^* + e) = (n - r)(a^* + e) \geq A_n - A_r$$

or

$$(1 - r/n)(a^* + e) \geq (A_n/n) - (A_r/n),$$

which implies

$$a^* + e \geq (A_n/n) + \epsilon_n$$

or

$$\varlimsup_{n \to \infty} (A_n/n) \leq a^* + e.$$

Since $e > 0$ is arbitrary, it can be concluded that

$$\varlimsup_{n \to \infty} (A_n/n) \leq a^*,$$

which with the fact that $(A_n/n) \geq a^*$ for all n gives

$$\lim_{n \to \infty} (A_n/n) = a^*.$$

2.4 In Section 2.3 an asymptotic formula analogous to a part of Section 1.6 was demonstrated; in this section a result is obtained which completes the analogy. This result is most conveniently stated with the aid of the notation $B(m)$ (where m is a natural number) for the binary sequence which is the numeral representing m in base-two notation (e.g., $B(6) = 110$).

(2.4.1) There exists a constant c such that those binary sequences S of length n satisfying

(2.4.2)

$$L(S) \leq L(C_n) - L(B(L(C_n))) - [\log_2 L(B(L(C_N)))]$$
$$-L(C_m) - [\log_2 L(C_m)] - c$$

are less than 2^{n-m} in number.

Say I have an n-term sequence. But I already have an algorithm to compute a (shorter) m-term sequence. Does that help?

For example: say I have a twenty-term sequence. In general, that can cost as much as $L(C_{20})$. But let's say I decide to compute some ten-term sequence, first, and then bootstrap off of that.

The cost of the ten-term sequence is (at worst) $L(C_{10})$. But I have an exponentially small number of sequences where I can shave $L(C_{10})$ bits off the maximal cost of $L(C_{20})$.

Put another way: it's hard to build a pseudo–random number generator. I can't "boost" randomness.

The proof of (2.4.1) is by contradiction. We suppose that those S of length n satisfying (2.4.2) are 2^{n-m} or more in number and we conclude that for any particular binary sequence $S^{\sim}$ of length n there is a program of at most $L(C_n) - 1$ rows that causes a bounded-transfer Turing machine to calculate $S^{\sim}$. This table consists of 11 sections which come one after the other. The first section consists of a single row which moves the tape one square to the left ($1, 4\ \ 1, 4\ \ 1, 4$ will certainly do this). The second section consists of exactly $L(B(L(C_n)))$ rows; it is a program for computing $B(L(C_n))$ consisting of the smallest possible number of rows. The third section is merely a repetition of the first section. The fourth section consists of exactly $[\log_2 L(B(L(C_n)))]$ rows. Its function is to write out on the tape the binary sequence which represents the number $L(B(L(C_n)))$ in base-two notation. Since this is a sequence of exactly $[\log_2 L(B(L(C_n)))]$ bits, a simple program exists for calculating it consisting of exactly $[\log_2 L(B(L(C_n)))]$ rows each of which causes the machine to write out a single bit of the sequence and then shift the tape a single square to the left (e.g., $0, 2\ \ 1, 4\ \ 1, 4$ will do for a 0 in the sequence). The fifth section is merely a repetition of the first section. The sixth section consists of at most $L(C_m)$ rows; it is a program consisting of the smallest possible number of rows for computing the sequence S^R of the m rightmost bits of $S^{\sim}$. The seventh section is merely a repetition of the first section. The eighth section consists of exactly $[\log_2 L(C_m)]$ rows. Its function is to write out on the tape the binary sequence which represents the number $L(C_m)$ in base-two notation. Since this is a sequence of exactly $[\log_2 L(C_m)]$ bits, a simple program exists for calculating it consisting of exactly $[\log_2 L(C_m)]$ rows each of which causes the machine to write out a single bit of the sequence and then shift the tape a single square to the left. The ninth section is merely a repetition of the first section. The tenth section consists of at most as many rows as the expression on the right-hand side of the inequality (2.4.2). It is a program for calculating one (out of not less than 2^{n-m}) of the sequences of length n satisfying (2.4.2) (which one it is depends on $S^{\sim}$ in a manner which will become clear from the discussion of the eleventh section; for now we merely denote it by S^L).

We now come to the last and crucial eleventh section, which consists *by definition* of $(c - 6)$ rows, and which therefore brings the total number of rows up to at most $1 + L(B(L(C_n))) + 1 + [\log_2 L(B(L(C_n)))] + 1 +$

$L(C_m) + 1 + [\log_2 L(C_m)] + 1 +$ (the expression on the right-hand side of the inequality (2.4.2)) $+ (c - 6) = L(C_n) - 1$.

When this section of the program takes over, the number and sequences $L(C_n)$, $L(B(L(C_n)))$, S^R, $L(C_m)$, S^L are written—in the above order—on the tape. Note, first of all, that section 11 can: (1) compute the value v of the right-hand expression of the inequality (2.4.2) from this data, (2) find the value of n from this data (simply by counting the number of bits in the sequence S^L), and (3) find the value of m from this data (simply by counting the number of bits in S^R). Using its knowledge of v, m and n, section 11 then computes from the sequence S^L a new sequence $S^{L'}$ which is of length $(n - m)$. The manner in which it does this is discussed in the next paragraph. Finally, section 11 adjoins the sequence S^R to the right of $S^{L'}$, positions this sequence which is in fact $S^{\sim}$ properly for it to be able to be regarded calculated, cleans up the rest of the tape, and halts scanning the square just to the right of $S^{\sim}$. $S^{\sim}$ has been calculated.

To finish the proof of (2.4.1) we must now only indicate how section 11 arrives at $S^{L'}$ (of length $(n - m)$) from v, m, n and S^L. (And it must be here that it is made clear how the choice of S^L depends on $S^{\sim}$.) By assumption, S^L satisfies

(2.4.3) $L(S^L) \le v$ and S^L is of length n.

Also by assumption there are at least 2^{n-m} sequences which satisfy (2.4.3). Now *section 11 contains a procedure which when given any one of some particular serially ordered set $_nQ_v$ of 2^{n-m} sequences satisfying (2.4.3), will find the ordinal number of its position in $_nQ_v$.* And the number of the position of S^L in $_nQ_v$ is the number of the position of $S^{L'}$ in the natural ordering of all binary sequences of length $(n - m)$ (i.e., $000 \cdots 00$, $000 \cdots 01$, $000 \cdots 10$, $000 \cdots 11$, $\cdots$, $111 \cdots 00$, $111 \cdots 01$, $111 \cdots 10$, $111 \cdots 11$). In the next and final paragraph of this proof, the foregoing italicized sentence is explained.

It is sufficient to give here a procedure for serially calculating the members of $_nQ_v$ in order. (That is, we define a serially ordered $_nQ_v$ for which there is a procedure.) By assumption we know that the predicate which is satisfied by all members of $_nQ_v$, namely,

$$(L(\cdots) \le v) \& (\cdots \text{ is of length } n),$$

is satisfied by at least 2^{n-m} sequences. It should also be clear to the reader on the basis of some background in Turing machine and recursive function theory (see especially Davis 1958, where recursive function theory is developed from the concept of the Turing machine) that the set Q of

all natural numbers of the form $2^n 3^v 5^e$, where e is the natural number represented in base-two notation by a binary sequence S satisfying

$$(L(S) \leq v) \ \& \ (S \text{ is of length } n)$$

is recursively enumerable. Let T denote some particular Turing machine which is programmed in such a manner that it recursively enumerates (or, to use E. Post's term, generates) Q. The definition of $_nQ_v$ can now be given:

$_nQ_v$ is the set of binary sequences of length n which represent in base-two notation the exponents of 5 in the prime factorization of the first 2^{n-m} members of Q generated by T whose prime factorizations have 2 with an exponent of n and 3 with an exponent of v, and their order in $_nQ_v$ is the order in which T generates them. Q.E.D.

It can be proved by contradiction that the set Q is not recursive. For were Q recursive, there would be a program which given any finite binary sequence S would calculate $L(S)$. Hence there would be a program which given any natural number n would calculate the members of C_n. Giving n to this program can be done by a program of length $[\log_2 n]$. Thus there would be a program of length $[\log_2 n] + c$ which would calculate an element of C_n. But we know that the shortest program for calculating an element of C_n is of length $\sim a^*n$, so that we would have for n sufficiently large an impossibility.

In a very twisty form, this is the Berry paradox (first described by Bertrand Russell.)

It should be emphasized that if $L(C_n)$ is an effectively computable function of n then the method of this section yields the following far stronger result:

There exists a constant c such that those binary sequences S of length n satisfying $L(S) \leq L(C_n) - L(C_m) - c$ are less than 2^{n-m} in number.

2.5 The purpose of this section is to investigate the behavior of the right-hand side of (2.4.2). We start by showing a result which is stronger for n sufficiently large than the inequality $L(C_n) \leq n$, namely, that the constant

a^* in the asymptotic evaluation $L(C_n) \sim a^* n$ of Section 2.3 is less than 1. This is done by deriving:

(2.5.1) For any s there exist n and m such that

$$
\begin{cases}
L(C_s) \leq L(C_n) + L(C_m) + c, \\
(n+m) \text{ is the smallest integral solution } x \text{ of the inequality,} \\
s \leq x + [\log_2 x] - 1.
\end{cases}
$$

From (2.5.1) it will follow immediately that if $e(n)$ denotes the function satisfying $L(C_n) = a^* n + e(n)$ (note that by Section 2.3 $(e(n)/n)$ tends to 0 *from above* as n goes to infinity), then for any s, $L(C_s) \leq L(C_n) + L(C_m) + c$ for some n and m satisfying $(n+m) = s - (1 + \epsilon_s) \log_2 s$, which implies

$$a^* s \leq a^*(s - (1 + \epsilon_s) \log_2 s) + e(n) + e(m) \quad \text{or}$$
$$(a^* + \epsilon_s) \log_2 s \leq e(n) + e(m).$$

Hence as n and m are both less than s and at least one of $e(n)$, $e(m)$ is greater than $(a^* + e_s) \log_2 s/2$, there are an infinity of n for which $e(n) \geq (a^* + \epsilon_n) \log_2 n/2$. That is,

(2.5.2)

$$\overline{\lim} \frac{L(C_n) - a^* n}{a^* \log_2 n} \geq \frac{1}{2}.$$

From (2.5.2) with $L(C_n) \leq n$ follows immediately

(2.5.3) $a^* < 1$.

The proof of (2.5.1) is presented by examples. The notation $T * U$ is used, where T and U are finite binary sequences for the sequence resulting from adjoining U to the right of T. Suppose it is desired to calculate some finite binary sequence S of length s, say $S = 010110010100110$ and $s = 15$. The smallest integral solution x of $s \leq x + [\log_2 x] - 1$ for this value of s is 12. Then S is expressed as $S' * S^T$ where S' is of length $x = 12$ and S^T is of length $s - x = 15 - 12 = 3$, so that $S' = 010110010100$ and $S^T = 110$. Next S' is expressed as $S^L * S^R$ where the length m of S^L satisfies $A * B(m) = S^T$ for some (possibly null) sequence A consisting entirely of 0's, and the length n of S^R is $x - m$. In this case $A * B(m) = 110$, so that $m = 6$, $S^L = 010110$ and $S^R = 010100$. The final result is that one has obtained the sequences S^L and S^R from the sequence S. And—this is the crucial point—if one is given the S^L and S^R resulting by the foregoing process from some unknown sequence S, one can reverse the procedure and determine S. Thus suppose $S^L = 1110110$ and $S^R = 01110110000$ are given. Then the length m of S^L is 7, the length n of S^R is 11, and the sum x of m and n is $7 + 11 = 18$. Therefore the length s of S must be $s = x + [\log_2 x] - 1 = 18 + 5 - 1 = 22$. Thus $S = S^L * S^R * S^T$, where S^T is of length $s - x = 22 - 18 = 4$, and so from $A * B(m) = S^T$ or $0 * B(7) = S^T$ one finds $S^T = 0111$. It is concluded that

$$S = S^L * S^R * S^T = 1110110011101100000111.$$

(For x of the form 2^h what precedes is not strictly correct. In such cases s may equal the foregoing indicated quantity or the foregoing indicated quantity minus one. It will be indicated later how such cases are to be dealt with.)

Let us now denote by F the function carrying (S^L, S^R) into S, and by F_R^{-1} the function carrying S into S^R, defining F_L^{-1} similarly. Then for any particular binary sequence S of length s the program of Figure 2 consists of at most

$$1 + L(F_L^{-1}(S)) + 1 + L(F_R^{-1}(S)) + 2 + (c - 4) \leq L(C_n) + L(C_m) + c$$

rows with $m + n = x$ being the smallest integral solution of $s \leq x + [\log_2 x] - 1$. As this program causes S to be calculated, the proof is easily seen to be complete.

The second result is:

(2.5.4) Let $f(n)$ be any effectively computable function that goes to infinity with n and satisfies $f(n + 1) - f(n) = 0$ or 1. Then there are an infinity of distinct n_k for which $L(B(L(C_{nk}))) < f(n_k)$.

This is proved from (2.5.5), the proof being identical with that of (1.7.5).

(2.5.5) For any positive integer p there is at least one solution n of $L(C_n) = p$. Let the n_k satisfy $L(C_{n_k}) = f^{-1}(k)$, where $f^{-1}(k)$ is defined to be the smallest value of j for which $f(j) = k$. Then since $L(C_n) \leq n$,

1,4	1,4	1,4
1,4	1,4	1,4

}Section I

\Section II:

}$L(F_L^{-1}(S))$ rows

}Section III

\Section IV:

}$L(F_R^{-1}(S))$ rows

$\overleftarrow{}^*$

\Section V:

}$c-4$ rows, by definition

FIG. 2

Figure 2. Section II is a program with the smallest possible number of rows for calculating $F_L^{-1}(S)$.

Section IV is a program with the smallest possible number of rows for calculating $F_R^{-1}(S)$.

Section V is a program that is able to compute F. It computes $F(F_L^{-1}(S), F_R^{-1}(S)) = S$, positions S properly on the tape, cleans up the rest of the tape, positions the scanner on the square just to the right of S and halts.

*Should x be of the form 2^h, another section is added at this point to tell Section V which of the two possible values s happens to have. This section consists of two rows; it is either

1,4	1,4	1,4	OR	1,4	1,4	1,4
1,2	1,2	1,2		1,3	1,3	1,3.

$f^{-1}(k) \leq n_k$. Noting that f^{-1} is an effectively computable function, it is easily seen that

$$L(B(L(C_{n_k}))) = L(B(f^{-1}(k))) \leq L(B(k)) + c \leq [\log_2 k] + c.$$

Hence, for all sufficiently large k,

$$L(B(L(C_{n_k}))) \leq [\log_2 k] + c < k = f(f^{-1}(k)) \leq f(n_k). \quad \text{Q.E.D.}$$

(2.5.4) and (2.4.1) yield:

(2.5.6) Let $f(n)$ be any effectively computable function that goes to infinity with n and satisfies $f(n+1) - f(n) = 0$ or 1. Then there are an infinity of distinct n_k for which less than $2^{n_k - f(n_k)}$ binary sequences S of length n_k satisfy $L(S) \leq L(Cn_k) - (a^* + \epsilon_k)f(n_k)$.

Part 3

3.1 Consider a scientist who has been observing a closed system that once every second either emits a ray of light or does not. He summarizes his observations in a sequence of 0's and 1's in which a zero represents "ray not emitted" and a one represents "ray emitted." The sequence may start

$$0110101110\cdots$$

and continue for a few thousand more bits. The scientist then examines the sequence in the hope of observing some kind of pattern or law. What

After the heavy lifting, this section might come as a relief—for early readers, it would serve as a way to connect these ideas to core concepts in logical positivism, as well as the theory of science itself.

does he mean by this? It seems plausible that a sequence of 0's and 1's is patternless if there is no better way to calculate it than just by writing it all out at once from a table giving the whole sequence:

My Scientific Theory

0

1

1

0

1

0

1

1

1

0

.

.

.

This would not be considered acceptable. On the other hand, if the scientist should hit upon a method by which the whole sequence could be calculated by a computer whose program is short compared with the sequence, he would certainly not consider the sequence to be entirely patternless or random. And the shorter the program, the greater the pattern he might ascribe to the sequence.

There are many genuine parallels between the foregoing and the way scientists actually think. For example, a simple theory that accounts for a set of facts is generally considered better or more likely to be true than one that needs a large number of assumptions. By "simplicity" is *not* meant "ease of use in making predictions." For although General or Extended Relativity is considered to be the simple theory par excellence, very extended calculations are necessary to make predictions from it. Instead, one refers to the number of arbitrary choices which have been made in specifying the theoretical structure. One naturally is suspicious of a theory the number of whose arbitrary elements is of an order of magnitude comparable to the amount of information about reality that it accounts for.

On the basis of these considerations it may perhaps not appear entirely arbitrary to define a patternless or random finite binary sequence as a sequence which in order to be calculated requires, roughly speaking, at least as long a program as any other binary sequence of the same length. A patternless or random infinite binary sequence is then defined to be one whose initial segments are all random. In making these definitions mathematically approachable it is necessary to specify the kind of computer referred to in them. This would seem to involve a rather arbitrary choice, and thus to make our definitions less plausible, but in fact both of the kinds of Turing machines which have been studied by such different methods in Parts I and 2 lead to precise mathematical definitions of patternless sequences (namely, the patternless or random finite binary sequences are those sequences S of length n for which $L(S)$ is approximately equal to $L(C_n)$, or, fixing M, those for which $L_M(S)$ is approximately equal to $L_M(C_n)$) whose provable statistical properties start with forms of the law of large numbers. Some of these properties will be established in a paper of the author to appear.[1]

A final word. In scientific research it is generally considered better for a proposed new theory to account for a phenomenon which had not previously been contained in a theoretical structure, before the discovery of that phenomenon rather than after. It may therefore be of some interest to mention that the intuitive considerations of this section antedated the investigations of Parts I and 2.

3.2 The definition which has just been proposed[2] is one of many attempts which have been made to define what one means by a patternless or random sequence of numbers. One of these was begun by R. von Mises (1939) with contributions by A. Wald (1937), and was brought to its culmination by A. Church (1940). K. R. Popper (1959) criticized this definition.

---

[1] The author has subsequently learned of work of P. Martin-Löf ("The Definition of Random Sequences," research report of the Institutionen för Försäkringsmatematik och Matematisk Statistik, Stockholm, Jan. 1966, 21 pp.) establishing statistical properties of sequences defined to be patternless on the basis of a type of machine suggested by A. N. Kolmogorov. Cf. footnote 2.

[2] The author has subsequently learned of the paper of A. N. Kolmogorov, Three approaches to the definition of the concept "amount of information," *Problemy Peredachi Informatsii* [Problems of Transmission of Information], *1*, 1 (1965), 3–11 [in Russian], in which essentially the definition offered here is put forth.

The definition given here deals with the concept of a patternless binary sequence, a concept which corresponds roughly in intuitive intent with the random sequences associated with probability $\frac{1}{2}$ of Church. However, the author does not follow the basic philosophy of the von Mises–Wald–Church definition; instead, the author is in accord with the opinion of Popper (1959, Sec. 57, footnote 1):

> I come here to the point where I failed to carry out fully my intuitive programme—that of analysing randomness as far as it is possible within the region of *finite* sequences, and of proceeding to *infinite* reference sequences (in which we need *limits* of relative frequencies) only afterwards, with the aim of obtaining a theory in which the existence of frequency limits follows from the random character of the sequence.

Nonetheless the methods given here are similar to those of Church; the concept of effective computability is here made the central one.

A discussion can be given of just how patternless or random the sequences given in this paper appear to be for practical purposes. How do they perform when subjected to statistical tests of randomness? Can they be used in the Monte Carlo method? Here the somewhat tantalizing remark of J. von Neumann (1963) should perhaps be mentioned:

> Any one who considers arithmetical methods of producing random digits is, of course, in a state of sin. For, as has been pointed out several times, there is no such thing as a random number—there are only methods to produce random numbers, and a strict arithmetical procedure of course is not such a method. (It is true that a problem that we suspect of being solvable by random methods may be solvable by some rigorously defined sequence, but this is a deeper mathematical question than we can now go into.) ʬ

Acknowledgment

The author is indebted to Professor Donald Loveland of New York University, whose constructive criticism enabled this paper to be much clearer than it would have been otherwise.

REFERENCES

Chaitin, G. J. 1966a. "On the Length of Programs for Computing Finite Binary Sequences by Bounded-Transfer Turing Machines." Abstract 66T-26, *Notices of The American Mathematical Society* 13.

———. 1966b. "On the Length of Programs for Computing Finite Binary Sequences by Bounded-Transfer Turing Machines II." Abstract 631-6. Erratum, p. 229, line 5: replace "*P*" by "*L*", *Notices of The American Mathematical Society* 13:228–229.

Church, A. 1940. "On the Concept of a Random Sequence." *Bulletin of American Mathematical Society* 46:130–135.

Davis, M. 1958. *Computability and Unsolvability.* New York, NY: McGraw–Hill.

Popper, K. R. 1959. *The Logic of Scientific Discovery.* Toronto, Canada: University of Toronto.

Shannon, C. E. 1948. "A Mathematical Theory of Communication." *The Bell System Technical Journal* 27 (3): 379–423.

———. 1956. "A Universal Turing Machine With Two Internal States." In *Automata Studies.* Princeton, NJ: Princeton University Press.

Turing, A. M. 1937. "On Computable Numbers, with an Application to the Entscheidungsproblem." In *Proceedings of the London Mathematical Society,* 42:230–265. 2. Also appears in Alan Turing Collection.

von Mises, R. 1939. *Probability, Statistics, and Truth.* New York, NY: MacMillan.

von Neumann, J. 1963. "Various Techniques Used in Connection with Random Digits." In *John von Neumann, Collected Works,* edited by A. H. Taub, vol. 5. New York, NY: MacMillan.

Wald, A. 1937. "Die Widerspruchsfreiheit des Kollektivbegriffes der Wahrscheinlichkeitsrechnung." *Ergebnisse eines mathematischen Kolloquiums* 8:38–72.

1930

BIRTH
April 24, 1933
Boston,
Massachusetts

1936: Thylacine
(Tasmanian tiger of wolf),
becomes extinct due to
hunting, habitat loss, and
competition with dogs;

1940

1944: George Gaylord
Simpson publishes Tempo
and Mode in Evolution,
bringing paleontology
into the orbit of the
modern synthesis.

1950

RAUP 1966
University of Rochester,
Rochester, New York

1960

1970

1977: Stephen J. Gould
publishes Ontogeny,
and Phylogeny.

1980

1980: Luis Alvarez, Walter
Alvarez, Frank Asaro, and
Helen Michel publish
their paper proposing
the Alvarez hypothesis.

1984: Raup and John
Sepkoski publish
"Periodicity of Extinctions
in the Geologic Past."

1990

2000: Sue, one of
the world's most
complete specimens
of Tyrannosaurus rex
ever discovered, is
unveiled at the Field
Museum of Chicago.

2000

DEATH
July 9, 2015
Sturgeon Bay,
Wisconsin
complications
after surgery
after a fall

2010

DAVID MALCOLM RAUP

[27]

MORPHOSPACES, THE POSSIBLE, AND THE ACTUAL

Ricard Solé, Universitat Pompeu Fabra and Santa Fe Institute

A recurrent topic in evolutionary biology is the problem of the role played by contingency versus the existence of convergence. In other words, we can ask if the repertoire of our biosphere's complex life forms is one in many or if there are instead strong constraints to the space of the possible. In the first scenario, the vagaries of fluctuating environments, along with the combinatorial possibilities of genomes and gene networks, would allow for an astronomic number of choices. In the latter, fundamental constraints affecting how morphologies can arise from developmental programs would lead to a different, but largely familiar, alternative biosphere. Both alternative paths can create complexity, and a legitimate question is: How can we define cartography of such complexity in terms of a space of the possible? If such a goal was reachable, what would such space look like? What evolutionary lessons could be learned from it? If evolution can freely explore the universe of possible forms over millions of years and under very different environmental conditions, we would expect that this space would have been more or less homogeneously visited (i.e., filled by different possible forms). Is that the case?

In 1966 paleontologist David Raup published a seminal paper that introduced the concept of a space of possible forms, using shell coiling as a case study. The choice made sense for two reasons. First, the shells of a large variety of invertebrates are coiled, and we have an accurate fossil record of them (shells are well preserved). Second, coiling allows us to exploit well-defined mathematical expressions that fully capture the main geometric features. Although a potentially large number of parameters could in principle be required to describe all possible shell morphologies, Raup was able to find three algebraically

D. M. Raup, "Geometric Analysis of Shell Coiling; General Problems," in *Journal of Paleontology* 40 (5): 1178–1190 (1966).

Used with permission of Cambridge University Press and the Society of Economic Paleontologists and Mineralogists; permission conveyed through Copyright Clearance Center, Inc.

independent main numbers that successfully allowed him to visualize all theoretical shells within a three-dimensional cube. This in itself was a considerable tour de force that previous studies had tried to address, with limited success. Four dimensions were the smallest number variables chosen by different authors, but the choices were plagued by the problem of lack of orthogonality: it was difficult to choose truly independent dimensions. Raup's clever solution involved the use of the so-called logarithmic model from which three parameters (W, D, T) could be numerically estimated from direct measurements. In a nutshell, these parameters capture the impact of three different geometric transformations (including translations and expansions) on the final geometry. In this way, Raup's work takes advantage of an earlier suggestion by D'Arcy Thompson (1942) that the many forms adopted by some structures in nature are in fact variations of a basic, simple model. Among these simple forms, the so-called logarithmic spiral was used as a minimal representation of coiled shells. This is a self-similar curve that several scholars used as a baseline to further mathematical extensions to account for the full three-dimensional problem.

One of these extensions was cleverly taken by Raup, who used a system of cylindrical coordinates to formally define a space of morphologies, or morphospace, which provided the first global picture of shell diversity as a single, static image. But the implications were far from static. Each species (fossil or extant) is assigned a specific point in the morphospace, and when many shells are located within this space, they appear clustered in highly nonrandom ways and large voids are observable. Empty, unoccupied spaces are actually a very common feature of most morphospaces, and as Raup argues, several explanations can be conjectured. Is this a consequence of anatomical or physiological constraints? Are these nonobserved but potential solutions hard to be reached by evolution? Do occupied domains correlate with particular adaptations to given life styles? To answer these questions, an evolutionary look to the underlying evolutionary biology is needed for each case study. But one fundamental message was clear from these early examples: the voids strongly point to evolutionary constraints. In other words, there are limits to evolutionary change due to the nature of the underlying generative mechanisms that produce organisms.

Morphospaces can be considered the other side of the coin of another crucial concept in evolutionary biology: the fitness (or adaptive) landscape. In abstract terms, the fitness landscape provides a high-dimensional picture of adaptation by mapping a set of traits (morphological or not) to a number that is intended to capture a fitness value. As George McGhee (2006) pointed out, adaptation does not enter into the construction of the original morphospaces, where the dimensions are geometric and the relevant measure is the frequency of occurrence of different observable shapes. By contrast, adaptation is a central feature of adaptive landscapes. However, both constructs share a common property: they allow us to identify nonexisting forms.

Raup's work triggered the creation of a new field that inspired scholars from very different areas. Although morphological features described as geometric shapes have been a common goal for many studies, it was soon realized that many abstractions could be introduced to exploit theoretical morphospaces moving beyond one-to-one parameterizations, where each point is defined by a well-defined vector. A very popular extension has been the use of principal component analysis, which allows us to use many different variables simultaneously. Here the set of data points associated to each item (a shell, an organism, or an artifact, each described by N different measures) are mapped onto a new, low-dimensional set of axes—the principal components—that are mutually orthogonal and separate noncorrelated variations. These statistical counterparts of the original proposal allowed the exploration of the time evolution of complex communities and their shape changes as mass extinctions introduced major disruptions on regional or even global scales. More importantly, Raup's work opened the door for a more general view, where each axis could include nongeometric features. This is the case, for example, of Niklas and Kerchner's (1984) 3D spaces of evolved plant morphogenesis, where one axis in their plan evolution space is the probability of branching, thus allowing the explicit introduction of modeling-related parameters and the observation of how the space is occupied through in silico evolution. In this context, qualitative spaces have also been defined in terms of the relative location between points, with no required quantification of their axes. By allowing actual rules of evolutionary change to become part of theoretical morphospaces, they become de facto evolutionary spaces and help us explore fundamental questions concerning convergence and innovation or the limits of bioengineering designs.

Since 2000, the conceptual framework of a space of the possible has been extended to topological measures: building them is not necessarily tied to a proper definition of distance. When applied to topological features of graphs, the use of this framework within network science has also revealed the importance of empty spaces as a hallmark of dynamic and structural constraints associated with network architecture. These studies show that while optimal solutions might explain the occupation of space in some cases, the densest parts of network morphospaces might also be the result of evolutionary tinkering, processes with little or no connection to adaptive traits. Finally, an important property of these spaces is that it is often possible to find sharp boundaries separating qualitatively different classes of structures. These boundaries define what is known as morphospace transitions, closely related to the well-known concept of phase transition, and have been found in very different context. Examples include the morphospaces of virus capsids, protocellular structures, and termite nests, to mention just a few examples. Such an equivalence is far from metaphorical and suggests new avenues for exploration that could uncover deep connections between evolution, development, and the class of universal laws found in the domain of statistical physics.

REFERENCES

Alberch, P. 1989. "The Logic of Monsters: Evidence for Internal Constraint in Development and Evolution." *Geobios* 22:21–57. https://doi.org/10.1016/S0016-6995(89)80006-3.

Avena-Koenigsberger, A., J. Goñi, R. Solé, and O. Sporns. 2015. "Network Morphospace." *Journal of the Royal Society Interface* 12 (103): 20140881. https://doi.org/10.1098/rsif.2014.0881.

Erwin, D. H. 2017. "The Topology of Evolutionary Novelty and Innovation in Macroevolution." *Philosophical Transactions of the Royal Society B: Biological Sciences* 372 (1735). https://doi.org/10.1098/rstb.2016.0422.

McGhee, G. R. 2006. *The Geometry of Evolution: Adaptive Landscapes and Theoretical Morphospaces.* Cambridge, UK: Cambridge University Press.

Niklas, K. J., and V. Kerchner. 1984. "Mechanical and Photosynthetic Constraints on the Evolution of Plant Shape." *Paleobiology* 10 (1): 79–101.

Ollé-Vila, A., S. Duran-Nebreda, N. Conde-Pueyo, R. Montañez, and R. Solé. 2016. "A Morphospace for Synthetic Organs and Organoids: The Possible and the Actual." *Integrative Biology* 8 (4): 485–503. https://doi.org/10.1039/C5IB00324E.

Thompson, D. W. 1942. *On Growth and Form.* Cambridge, UK: Cambridge University Press.

GEOMETRIC ANALYSIS OF SHELL COILING: GENERAL PROBLEMS

David M. Raup

Abstract

Among the shells of invertebrates that exhibit spiral growth, differences in form can be expressed by differences in geometric parameters. If three of these parameters are considered at a time, the spectrum of possible shell forms may be shown by a block diagram. Analog and digital computer constructions make it possible to visualize shell forms that are theoretically possible but do not occur in nature.

Actual species are not randomly distributed in the total spectrum of theoretically possible forms. Functional and evolutionary groups are confined to discrete regions of the spectrum. Rational explanations for several of the observed distributions are apparent and may be expressed in terms of shell function. For example, a bivalve must have non-overlapping whorls in order to have a functional hinge. This fact restricts the geometric range of both brachiopods and bivalved molluscs.

Ontogenetic change in coiling geometry may be interpreted as a compensation for the effects of increase in absolute size during growth.

Introduction

The shells of a wide variety of invertebrate animals have a coiled, or spiral, form. Examples may be found in many diverse groups: from the single-celled Foraminifera to highly complex groups such as the Mollusca and Brachiopoda. Coiling has developed independently in several quite distinct evolutionary lines. Its functional significance to the animal is not always the same, even within fairly homogeneous groups.

When one compares coiled shells from a variety of taxonomic groups, marked differences in form are evident. In spite of this variation, however, most types have important geometric characteristics in common which make rigorous comparison between them possible. The problem of defining parameters through which coiled forms can be analyzed has tempted many workers.

The literature of shell coining is long and varied. Perhaps the best known discussion is contained in D'Arcy Thompson's (1942) monumental volume "On Growth and Form." Thompson's treatment is essentially a review of earlier work published by others but it is valuable as a synthesis. More recently, work by Lison (1949), Owen (1953), Fukutomi (1953), Rudwick (1959), Stasek (1963), and others has added greatly to our knowledge of the coiling phenomenon.

As a result of these studies, there is general agreement that the bulk of the coiled forms observed in nature are but variations on one rather simple model. Several sets of parameters have been suggested to describe differences and similarities between coiled forms. But there have been few if any successful applications of this knowledge to the specific problems facing the zoologist or paleozoologist working with animals having a coiled shell. From the standpoint of application, the analysis of shell coiling has been little more than intellectual exercise. Its practical importance has never been established.

There are many reasons for this: I have discussed several of them in an earlier paper (Raup 1961), but the most important is that the basic relationships between shell geometry and shell function have not been clearly presented. The purpose of the present paper is to explore some of these basic relationships. The discussion will consider broad problems of the distribution of functional and taxonomic groups within the spectrum of geometrically possible forms. A subsequent paper (Raup 1967) will be a detailed analysis of coiling variation in the Ammonoidea.

Both papers are presented not only as an attempt to broaden the applicability of coiling analysis but also as an example of the methods of "theoretical morphology" (Raup and Michelson 1965). Using this approach, a conceptual or mathematical model is established for some aspect of morphology. The model in turn is used to formulate or describe the total spectrum of physically possible forms. This spectrum then serves as a framework through which actually occurring forms may be interpreted.

Acknowledgment is made to the donors of The Petroleum Research Fund, administered by the American Chemical Society, for support of this research. Also, the following persons contributed valuable help and advice at various stages of the study: H. H. Beaver, Z. P. Bowen, W.

Although not formulated in this way, D'Arcy Thompson's book provides a first glimpse into the concept of universal design rules that predate the conceptual development of the idea of morphospace.

H. Diment, Myra Keen, J. Kullmann, D. B. Macurda, Jr., A. Miller, O. Schindewolf, D. Schumann, A. Seilacher, J. Wendt, J. Wiedmann, and E. L. Yochelson. The illustrations were prepared by Robert M. Eaton, Richard W. Linfield, and Richard C. Pettis.

Geometric Models for Coiling

Moseley (1838) established a geometric model for shell coiling based on the logarithmic spiral. This model has been accepted by most zoologists and paleozoologists and is widely known through Thompson's review (1942). Moseley based his analysis primarily on gastropods but clearly intended that his model be applicable to essentially all coiled forms—both planispiral and helicoid.

Two years after Moseley's initial publication, Naumann (1840a) published a similar analysis but based his model on a more elaborate spiral. He argued that Moseley's logarithmic spiral did not provide a reasonable approximation of actual morphology. Considerable discussion in the literature followed (Moseley 1842; Naumann 1840b, 1845, 1848). Naumann's work was carried on and expanded by Müller (1850, 1853) and Grabau (1872). In the latter works, most of the species used were ammonoids and therein lies the reason for the differing interpretations of Naumann and Moseley. Ammonoids often show considerable ontogenetic change in geometry, particularly in whorl shape and degree of involution. Thus, it is commonly impossible to find a logarithmic spiral that fits the shell throughout ontogeny. Much of the work of Naumann and his students was an effort to produce an equation or set of equations that would satisfy the ammonoid shell throughout ontogeny. Moseley, on the other hand, considering a wider variety of shell form and emphasizing gastropods (where ontogenetic variation, though present, is minimal), found the logarithmic spiral to give the most consistent accuracy. Moseley's case was strengthened by the fact that he was able to present *a priori* justification for his model: that the logarithmic spiral provides for growth without change in shape. This constancy of shape is obviously of functional importance to the majority of coiled forms—where mode of life and shell functions do not change during post-metamorphic growth. Thompson (1942) provided

Moseley's work established the mathematical basis for the coordinate systems (he pioneered the use of polar coordinates) that allowed the definition of the geometry of shells. This work deeply influenced further developments and predates the mathematical tools applied to shape description in theoretical morphology (where cylindrical coordinates are used as a natural extension).

Ammonoids define a very diverse group of extinct marine molluscs with a typical spiral coiling usually confined to a single plane (they are *planispirals*) but also display more complex shapes that depart form this simple design.

many other examples of good conformity to the logarithmic model, drawn from a wide variety of taxonomic and functional types, and he thus further confirmed the general applicability of Moseley's model.

In view of the foregoing, the logarithmic spiral is used as a basis for the present analysis. This does not, however, relieve us of the problem of ontogenetic variation in ammonoids and other groups that display it. Rather, it puts this ontogenetic variation in another light. Change in geometry during growth may be looked upon as a genetically controlled departure from the norm, and as such must be interpreted in terms of the functional or adaptive advantage of the departure to the organism. This subject will be considered at length below and in another paper (Raup 1967).

The logarithmic model used here is that of Raup and Michelson (1965). Four basic parameters describe the general form of the coiled shell. They are: the shape of the generating curve (S), the whorl expansion rate (W), the position of the generating curve in relation to the axis (D), and the rate of whorl translation (T).

The generating curve is often equivalent to the outline of the growing edge of the shell. As such, its shape can only rarely be defined mathematically. An equation can be used when the generating curve approximates a simple geometric figure such as a circle or ellipse. More generally, however, a line drawing is used to describe the shape. The other three parameters can be defined numerically.

The coiled shell may be considered in a system of cylindrical coordinates (text-fig. 1). The y-axis coincides with the axis of coiling, θ expresses revolution of the generating curve about the axis, and r is the distance of any point from the axis. The *initial* generating curve may be defined conveniently by a set of arbitrary points (such as point A in text-fig. 1) and is so placed in the coordinate system that the geometric center (point B in text-fig. 1) has a y-value of zero.

If r_o is the initial distance of point A (or any other such point) from the axis then r_θ, the distance after θ revolutions, may be expressed as follows:

$$r_\theta = r_o W^{\theta/2\pi} \qquad (1)$$

where:

As defined, these are algebraically independent parameters. Lower-dimensional spaces are possible: the typical planispiral ammonoids studied by Raup in another paper, published a year later, required only two dimensions (D, W) and a simpler 2D morphospace.

W is the rate of whorl expansion.

In planispiral shells ($T = 0$) the y-value of the same point is expressed by:

$$y_\theta = y_o W^{\theta/2\pi} \tag{2}$$

where:

y_o is the initial y value of the point.

In planispiral forms, the geometric center of the generating curve has a constant y-value throughout growth ($y = 0$). In helicoid forms, on the other hand, the generating curve moves along the y-axis and equation (2) becomes:

$$y_\theta = y_o W^{\theta/2\pi} + r_c T \left(W^{\theta/2\pi} - 1 \right) \tag{3}$$

where:

T is the rate of translation defined as dy/dr, with respect to the center of the generating curve, and r_c is the r-value of the center of the initial generating curve.

Equations (1) and (3) can be used to locate any point on the generating curve where a known angular distance of growth separates it from the initial generating curve. These equations have been used extensively in programming digital computers for graphical construction of ideal shell forms (Raup 1962, 1963; Raup and Michelson 1965). In these programs, W and T are input constants for a given shell form. The shape of the generating curve (S) is defined by the coordinates of points on the initial generating curve. The coordinates of these points also fix the position (D) of the curve relative to the coiling axis. When dealing with simple, ideal generating curve shapes, as in text-fig. 1, a distance (D) is defined as the ratio between the r-value of the axial margin of the generating curve and that of the outer margin. D is thus zero when the generating curve is in contact with the coiling axis (as in many gastropods) and increases as the generating curve moves away from the axis (as in serpenticone ammonoids).

It should be emphasized that the four parameters (S, W, D, and T) do not completely describe the morphology of the coiled shell. The complete morphological picture would include the many features of surface ornamentation, growth rings, internal structure, shell thickness, and so on. The model is concerned *only* with general

Multiple extensions of the geometric approach were taken involving diverse geometric motifs, including fractal patterns of sutures that are common to many ammonoid groups as well as shell surface sculptures in bivalves, usually associated with regular color (Turing) patterns. In all these cases, a limited repertoire of design principles was also found.

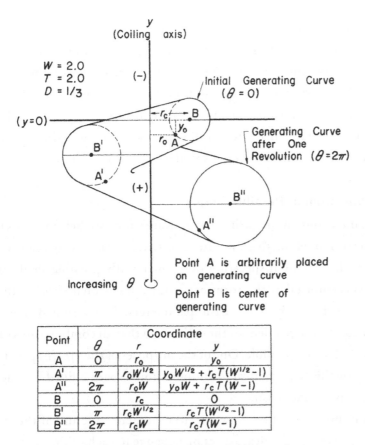

Text-fig. 1. One whorl of a hypothetical coiled shell in cylindrical coordinates.

Point	Coordinate		
	θ	r	y
A	0	r_0	y_0
A'	π	$r_0 W^{1/2}$	$y_0 W^{1/2} + r_c T(W^{1/2}-1)$
A''	2π	$r_0 W$	$y_0 W + r_c T(W-1)$
B	0	r_c	0
B'	π	$r_c W^{1/2}$	$r_c T(W^{1/2}-1)$
B''	2π	$r_c W$	$r_c T(W-1)$

form and includes only that ornamentation produced by the revolution of the generating curve about the axis. Furthermore, the model does not describe ontogenetic change in coiling, though this can sometimes be added as an elaboration of the basic equations. The model assumes dextral and orthostrophic coiling. Hyperstrophic coiling can be produced by assigning a negative sign to T.

All four parameters can be measured readily in nearly all specimen material, as long as the position of the coiling axis can be located. The shape of the generating curve is equivalent to the shape of the whorl cross-section. The position of the generating curve (including its distance from the axis) may be observed directly or from a suitably oriented photograph. Translation rate is equal to the calculated ratio of movement of the center of the generating curve along the coiling axis to movement away from the coiling axis. The expansion rate may be calculated from measurements of one linear dimension on any two replicas (growth stages) of the generating curve, as long as the angular distance between the two is known (the difference between the two θ's). An accurate estimate of expansion rate may be made even where less than a full whorl is observed (as in many bivalves). In the calculation of expansion rate, any external dimensions of the whorl or distances between prominent features of spiral ornamentation may be used.

The Spectrum of Possible Forms

As pointed out in an earlier paper Raup and Michelson (1965) the geometric model and the computer constructions based on it can be used to visualize the total spectrum of geometrically possible shell forms. This spectrum takes the form of a four-dimensional space with one dimension for each of the basic parameters. It is assumed that each parameter is independent of the others and that all combinations of the four variables are possible. One of the purposes of the present paper is to show how this hypothetical four-dimensional space is filled with actual species, living and fossil.

It is important, first, however, to have a clear picture of the effects on general morphological aspect of a change in each of the parameters. Text-figure 2 shows three series of hypothetical shell forms, each series starting from the same form. The initial form was chosen arbitrarily and is not intended to represent any particular taxonomic group. Nevertheless, it is a form commonly found in several groups.

In text-figure 2, increase in rate of translation (from $T = 0$ to $T = 3$) produces the relatively high-spired coiling types most common in gastropods and some heteromorph ammonoids. Note that accompanying this change is a decrease in the amount of overlap between successive whorls. In forms with a high degree of overlap, the organism does not deposit skeletal material over the entire generating curve, but rather uses the outer surface of the preceding whorl to enclose part of the new whorl. As overlap decreases, however (in this case through an increase in translation rate), that portion of the generating curve which is actually deposited by the organism becomes larger and larger. Only in cases where overlap of successive whorls is completely absent is the

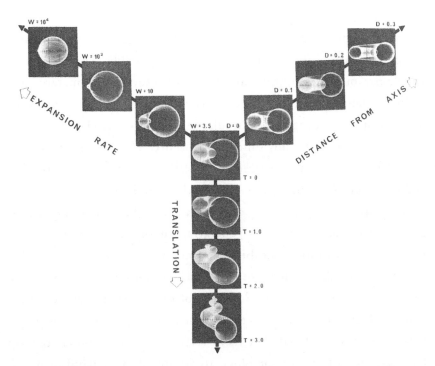

Text-fig. 2. Computer produced shell forms illustrating the morphological effects of change in whorl expansion rate (W), translation rate (T), and the distance from the generating curve to the axis (D).

total generating curve, as a closed figure, deposited by the organism. The effect of variable whorl overlap is an important factor in the functional analysis of coiled forms and will be considered in more detail below.

The increase in expansion rate shown in text-figure 2 (from $W = 3.5$ to $W = 10^4$) changes shell form from what may be called the "univalve region" of the four-dimensional space to the "bivalve region". As the bivalve region is approached, the opening of the shell (the trace of the last generating curve) becomes relatively larger and the umbo becomes relatively smaller.

Increase in the distance from the coiling axis to the generating curve (from $D = 0$ to $D = 0.3$) makes the shell more evolute and more umbilicate. In text-figure 2 this change is shown for a shell having a low value of W and zero translation. If the same change were to take place in a form having a high W the morphological effect would be to increase the relative length of the umbo.

Change in the shape of the generating curve is illustrated in text-figure 3. Depending on the means used to describe shape, almost any configuration of the generating curve is possible. The apparently simple parameter S could be subdivided into several parameters, each adding dimensions to the four-dimensional space. In text-figure 3, the illustration in the center has a circular generating curve. The upper and lower illustrations employ differently oriented ellipses. In this figure, S is defined as the ratio between axes of the generating curve parallel and normal to the coiling axis. Clearly this is only one kind of change in the shape of the generating curve which could be represented. This particular mode of change in generating curve shape is used in text-figure 3 because of its applicability to ammonoid geometry.

In text-figure 4 other possible combinations between the basic parameters are shown. Here the shape of the generating curve is held constant (a simple circle) and a *three*-dimensional space of geometrically possible forms is defined. The front vertical face of the block, the top face, and the interior of the block are occupied by helicoid forms (T greater than 0). The right hand vertical face contains planispiral forms ($T = 0$).

Comparable block diagrams could be constructed for other shapes of the generating curve. Changing generating curve shape would, of course, change the morphological aspect of the resulting shell forms but the general relations shown in text-figure 4 would not change appreciably. For example, the form shown in the upper left would remain gastropod in aspect regardless of the shape of the generating curve. We can, therefore, use text-figure 4 as a format for analysis of the distribution of real world geometric forms if it is kept in mind that elaboration of the generating curve would complicate the picture.

Problems of Terminology

For each of the taxonomic groups being considered here, a morphologic terminology has developed which serves the needs of that group. When the several groups are brought together under a single format as in text-figure 4, we find that the morphologic terminology often leads to confusion. In several instances one geometric element of the shell is

Several possible deviations from Raup's original choices can be considered, but all of them preserve the domains of definition of different, nonoverlapping classes of shells located on similar domains of the morphospace, thus indicating that the mathematical framework is robust.

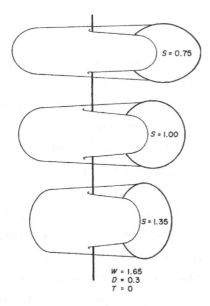

Text-fig. 3. Morphological effect of change in generating curve shape. The parameter S is defined here as the ratio between dimensions of the generating curve (parallel to and normal to the coiling axis).

given different names in different taxonomic or morphologic situations. For example, the opening of the shell (generally the outline of the last deposited generating curve) is termed *aperture* in coiled cephalopods and gastropods while in bivalves the term *commissure* is applied to the same feature.

Among bivalves, the term *interarea* in brachiopods and the term *ligament area* in pelecypods both refer to the same gemetric structure. In both cases the term applies to that portion of the shell deposited by the axial margin of the generating curve. Consider also the differing ways in which such simple dimensions as *length* are defined. In brachiopods the length dimension is generally defined as the maximum dimension through the beak and perpendicular to the coiling axis. In pelecypods, on the other hand, the length dimension runs approximately but not exactly parallel to the coiling axis. Length in gastropod shells also parallels the coiling axis whereas in coiled cephalopods we do not have a comparable dimension. Much of the variation in the definition of basic dimensions stems from the fact that shells are oriented differently with respect to geometry. The ventral surface of a brachiopod, for example, is totally different geometrically from the ventral surface of a pelecypod or coiled cephalopod.

The differences in terminology discussed above are, of course, completely legitimate in terms of the taxonomic groups to which they correspond. Most of the differences have their roots in fundamental anatomical differences or in differences in life position. It would, therefore, be unwise to attempt to make terminology uniform for the sake of geometric consistency. We can, however, superimpose on these terminologies a set of informal geometric terms which will have meaning in the context of the present analysis. For example, when referring to a portion of the last deposited generating curve (aperture or commissure) the term *axial margin* has been used. The axial margin of the last generating curve in brachiopod terminology would be the posterior margin of the commissure. In pelecypods it would be the dorsal margin of the commissure. In gastropods it would be the inner margin of the aperture and in cephalopods it would correspond to the dorsum.

Natural Occurrence of Coiling Types

The foregoing discussion has concentrated on defining the range of possible shell forms from a strictly geometric viewpoint. To reduce the scope to a manageable scale certain ideal conditions have been assumed, as follows: a simple and constant generating curve shape, perfect adherence to the model (that is, no ontogenetic variation), and orthostrophic, dextral coiling. There is probably no group of coiled organisms that fulfills all these conditions perfectly. However, the approximation in nature is generally close and we can proceed to estimate what parts of the total spectrum of forms is or has been used by actual organisms.

An attempt has been made in text-figure 4 to outline the regions in which representatives of four major taxonomic groups are concentrated: Brachiopoda, Pelecypoda, Gastropoda, and Ammonoidea. The regions are not intended to encompass all occurrences for a given group. As an example, the ammonoid region is shown as being confined to a small part of the planispiral face of the block (including values of W from approximately 1.25 to 3.0 and of D from 0 to 0.65). These limits include

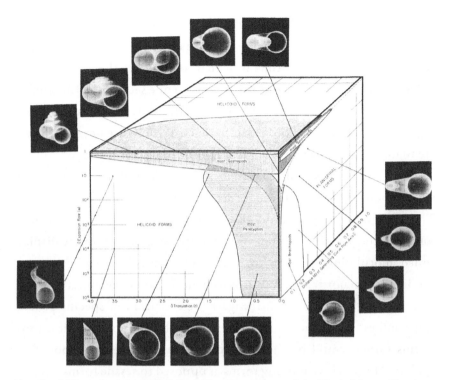

Text-fig. 4. Three dimensional block illustrating the spectrum of possible shell forms. The shape of the generating curve is assumed to be constant. The regions occupied by the majority of species in four taxonomic groups are outlined in the block. Species of these groups are not commonly found in the blank regions of the block.

perhaps 90% of all ammonoids: many of the remaining 10% fall in the interior of the block (turriculate forms).

Of the taxonomic regions shown in text-figure 4, only that of the ammonoids is actually based on measured data (Raup 1967). The regions for brachiopods, gastropods, and pelecypods are estimated from comparisons of computer-produced ideal forms and a representative array of species. In spite of the tentative nature of these regions, however, they are probably substantially correct. It cannot be questioned, for example, that brachiopods predominate in the high W, low D portion of the planispiral face. Similarly, the W values for pelecypods are on the average higher than for gastropods.

Inspection of text-figure 4 raises several questions. It should be noted, for example, that the bulk of the species in the four taxonomic groups are confined to *non-overlapping* regions which if taken together comprise a relatively small part of the block. Clearly, the distribution of actual species is not random. Do the relatively unused regions represent physiologically impossible shell forms or has the evolution of these taxa simply not had sufficient time in which to populate the entire block? Are some regions of the block suited only to one set of shell functions? Are swimming forms, for example, necessarily limited to certain discrete regions? The answers to these and similar questions are necessary if we are to understand fully the evolution of coiled organisms.

Text-figure 4 is representative of a wide variety of diagrams which could be drawn on the format of the three-dimensional block. The taxonomic range could be expanded, particularly to include foraminifera, nautiloids, and other groups of organisms that display coiled morphology. Going to lower taxonomic levels and thereby subdividing major taxonomic groups would also be meaningful. Such diagrams could be used to investigate the evolution of specific genera and families. From the point of view of shell function, distributions in this format could be shown of burrowing bivalves as opposed to epifaunal bivalves, swimming forms as opposed to sessile forms, etc.

Ontogenetic Change in Coiling Geometry

In the foregoing discussion the assumption has been made that the geometric characteristics of a shell are constant throughout ontogeny. It was pointed out earlier, however, that this is not always the case. In geometric terms, the effect of ontogenetic change is to shift the organism from one part of the geometric spectrum to another. Specific cases of ontogenetic variation in coiling fall principally into two categories: either the ontogenetic change is sudden (as in vermetid gastropods and in some heteromorph ammonoids) or the ontogenetic change is gradual, so gradual that some authors have argued that the logarithmic model does not apply.

In examples of the first kind of ontogenetic change it can often be shown that the change coincides with a major change in mode of life (such as from planktonic to benthonic). In view of the functional importance of shell form, it is not unreasonable that a change in mode of life during ontogeny should be coincident with a change in geometry.

These questions raise some of the most fundamental problems of evolutionary biology concerning the relative role played by form versus function. Forbidden solutions could be explained by developmental constraints, whereas occupied volumes could be connected to adaptation forces leading to optimal shapes.

An implicit assumption within the model is that there are no developmental processes (ontogeny) at play that can change qualitative shell properties. In this section, Raup raises a deep problem that became central in the development of evo-devo (and Thompson's ideas on the growth of forms): the importance of developmental paths as a key component of evolutionary change.

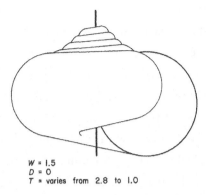

W = 1.5
D = 0
T = varies from 2.8 to 1.0

Text-fig. 5. Hypothetical shell form showing the morphological effect of ontogenetic change in translation rate.

Text-figure 5 shows an example of gradual ontogenetic change. The example is purely hypothetical (produced by computer) but it is of a type commonly found among gastropods. The ontogenetic change involves a gradual decrease in translation rate (T) from 2.8 to 1.0. All other parameters are held constant ($W = 1.5$, $D = 0.0$, and the generating curve is circular). The morphological result is an "extraconical" shell form: whorl overlap increases steadily and the spire of the shell is concave in lateral profile.

The amount of ontogenetic change shown by the example in text-figure 5 is considerable when compared with the total range in T exhibited by the gastropods (text-fig. 4). Cases such as this are uncommon but they do exist (and may even dominate certain genera and families). Quite a high degree of plasticity in geometry during growth is thus possible. It is important to note, however, that the plasticity is limited in kind. In text-figure 5, shell geometry has shifted from one part of the gastropod region (text-fig. 4) to another rather than across a boundary between major taxonomic regions.

In instances where ontogenetic change is gradual, many authors have suggested that the change is simply a relic of phylogeny. In certain cases, this may indeed be true. However, in the general case it seems more reasonable that the organism is adjusting during its growth to changes in the dynamics of shell function that are produced by growth itself. Such changes refer primarily to the effects of absolute size. Consider, for example, the problem of the pelecypod for which it is advantageous to maintain a constant relationship between the strength of its adductor musculature and the total mass of the shell. As the shell grows, following the ideal logarithmic model, the volume of the shell increases more rapidly than the area of the shell opening. (Volume increases as the cube of a linear dimension of the generating curve, whereas the area of the opening increases only as the square.) It would be entirely plausible, therefore, for the bivalve to alter its geometry during ontogeny in order to maintain a favorable ratio between area of the opening and volume of the shell.

Other effects of increase in absolute size include the strength of the shell wall in relation to shell size, and the amount of shell building material necessary to create a desired volume of shell interior. At this time, information is available only in a very few cases to interpret ontogenetic change rigorously in terms of compensation for increasing absolute size. Some of these will be considered later (Raup 1967). Other examples must wait for more detailed research.

The Problems of Bivalveness

In text-figure 4, the bivalve groups (pelecypods and brachiopods) have higher values of W than the univalves (gastropods and ammonoids). In fact the only region of overlap between these two major shell types is that small region in the neighborhood of $W = 10$, $T = 1$. This raises the question of what geometric characteristics a shell must have in order to operate as a bivalve.

It was noted earlier that change in one or more basic parameters may change the amount of overlap between successive whorls. If other factors are held constant, an increase in translation rate decreases the whorl overlap. Similarly, increases in expansion rate or in the distance between the generating curve and the axis both decrease whorl overlap. In a bivalve shell the hinge line is most important. In order for the two valves to articulate, the axial margin of the generating curve must be exposed. As was shown earlier, a form which has whorl overlap does not expose or even precipitate the axial margin of the generating curve.

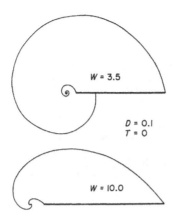

Text-fig. 6. Hypothetical shell forms illustrating the effect of whorl expansion rate on whorl overlap. The geometry of the upper form is typically univalve and that of the lower is typically bivalve.

Thus, we can postulate that *in order for a geometric form to operate as a equivalved bivalve, whorl overlap must be absent.*

Text-figure 6 shows two idealized shell forms. The upper one shows overlap of successive whorls whereas the lower has a geometry such that the whorls are completely separate. Were the former to function as a bivalve, the hinge and dentition structures would of necessity be deposited as a secondary secretion of the shell on the outside of the preceding whorl, and would have to shift position constantly during growth. There would be no space for the development of a ligament area or interarea. From this viewpoint, the lower illustration in text-figure 6 is readily adaptable to the bivalve form.

We can now return to the theoretical consideration of determining what part of the total spectrum of geometrically possible forms contains shells which lack whorl overlap and thus could be bivalves. If we assume a generating curve of constant shape, it is possible to calculate rigorously a surface in the three-dimensional block which will separate forms where whorls overlap from forms where there is no overlap. Along the surface itself, successive whorls are just in contact. This surface is sketched in text-figure 7. The upper form in text-figure 6 is derived from above this surface and the lower one from below the surface.

We can thus define the bivalve region as that region of the three-dimensional block lying below the surface just described. Note,

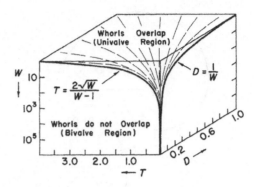

Whorls Overlap
(Univalve Region)

W 10

$T = \dfrac{2\sqrt{W}}{W-1}$

$D = \dfrac{1}{W}$

10^3

Whorls do not Overlap
(Bivalve Region)

10^5

1.0

0.6

0.2

D

3.0 2.0 1.0

$\longleftarrow T$

Text-fig. 7. Theoretical surface separating the univalve region from the bivalve region (format is that of text-fig. 4).

 The geometric model allows us to predict a bounded volume of the morphospace that could be occupied by bivalves, but it turns out that only a fraction of it is filled. Raup considers several constraints associated with geometrical requirements allowing wide valve opening, which require that the whorls of the two valves do not overlap.

however, that *bivalves do not occupy the entire region below the surface.* If the only requirements were those discussed above, the bivalves could occupy a larger part of the geometric range.

We may ask what is wrong from the viewpoint of the bivalve with the left side of the front helicoid face in text-figure 4. A geometric form in this region has a considerably higher internal volume than the typical bivalve. Compare, for example, the illustration in text-figure 4 on the front face at $T = 3.5$ and $W = 10$ with that at $T = .5$ and $W = 10^5$. The relative size of the opening in the latter case is much greater. One of the primary functions of the opening in the bivalve shell is to provide space for adductor muscles passing from one valve to the other. Furthermore, the required strength of the musculature must be proportional to the mass or volume of the whole shell. Strength of muscles is in turn proportional to their cross sectional areas. It is possible to imagine, therefore, a shell which would have too small an opening in relation to its total mass to accommodate the musculature necessary for valve opening and the same time provide space for other vital organs. As we move from left to right on the front helicoid face of the block we are moving geometrically from a region of high ratio between internal volume and the area of the opening, to a region having a more favorable ratio from the viewpoint of these relationships. It is probably for this reason that we find the pelecypods confined mostly to the region of relatively low translation. By a similar argument the brachiopods are plausibly confined to the left hand portion of the planispiral face of the block.

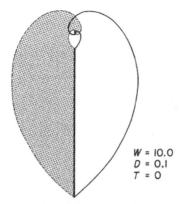

$W = 10.0$
$D = 0.1$
$T = 0$

Text-fig. 8. Hypothetical bivalve illustrating the necessity of interumbonal growth in equivalved bivalves.

Organisms using the bivalve shell form face other critical problems. Some of these have been discussed by Stasek (1963). Text-figure 8 shows a hypothetical shell identical to that in the lower of the two illustrations in text-figure 6. If we add to this shell its mirror image (dashed in text-figure 8), such that the two "shells" meet along the generating curve, we see that even though successive whorls do not overlap, this geometric form could not function as an *equivalved* bivalve because the two umbonal areas would conflict. Several taxonomic groups of bivalved organisms have developed means of avoiding this difficulty. One of these means is shown in text-figure 9. In this case, the axial margin of the whorl grows relatively more rapidly than the outer margin. Therefore, when two such valves are placed together along their growing edges the two umbos do not conflict and the space between them is sufficient for valve opening (see discussion of "interumbonal growth" by Stasek 1963).

In the discussion thus far, the term generating curve has been used for a geometric figure lying in a plane containing the coiling axis. If, as in text-figure 8, the trace of the generating curve is extended it will pass through the axis of the coiling. In the bivalve shown in text-figure 9 the generating curve does not coincide with the leading edge of the shell. Rather, we have what may be termed a *biological generating curve* which is at an angle to the *geometric generating curve*. The angle is large enough so that when two such shells are placed together the umbos do not interfere. It is evident, therefore, that equivalved bivalves are able to occupy the so-called bivalve

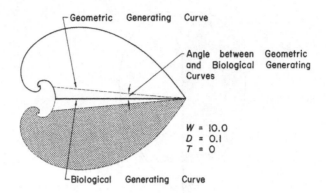

Text-fig. 9. Same shell form as in text-fig. 8 but with interumbonal growth (expressed by the angle between biological and geometric generating curves).

region in text-figure 7 only because of a secondary adaptation: that of depositing a biological generating curve which is not coincident with the geometric generating curve.

The angle between the biological and the geometric generating curves, in combination with other geometric parameters, will determine the degree to which a bivalve can open. Several species of the pelecypod genera *Arca* and *Cardium* have umbos that have been beveled as a result of wear. The wear is caused by the fact that the organism attempted to open farther than the geometry allowed. In working with coiling in pelecypods the angle between the biological and geometric generating curves should be used as an additional basic parameter. Text-figure 10 shows several possible morphologies resulting only from variations in this angle.

There are other geometric mechanisms used by bivalved organisms that serve to increase potential for wide valve opening. A very simple example is the use of an increase in W to decrease the relative size of the umbo, thus providing more space between the umbos (as in *Arca senilis* as described by Yonge 1955). Another mechanism involves pelecypods whose valves have different geometries. For example, the genera *Exogyra* and *Gryphaea* have one large valve and one small cap-like valve. Yet another class of solutions to the same problem is exemplified by the genus *Corculum*, as described by Bartsch (1947). Here, the two valves are approximately the same size but their geometries differ: the umbo of the left valve is displaced along the hinge line relative to the umbo of the right valve. When the shell opens, the two umbos move past each other.

The Problem of Univalveness

When considering the univalve shell we are relieved of the problem of requiring a functional hinge. Nevertheless, the univalve groups in text-figure 4 are confined to the upper part of the block and in general occupy a region not occupied by bivalves. At least one reason for this becomes apparent when we consider the primary functions of the shell in univalves.

The univalve shell serves in part for internal support of the soft part anatomy and in part for protection of the animal. The main function of the aperture is to provide access to the interior of the shell. The function of the shell is defeated if the size of the aperture becomes very large in relation to total shell volume. A large aperture inevitably reduces the *relative* amount of surface area insider the shell and detracts from the protective function of the shell. Returning to the basic relations shown in text-figures 2 and 4, we see that the ratio of apertural area to total shell volume varies systematically with changes in basic geometric parameters. It is thus reasonable that most univalve forms are confined to the upper regions of the three-dimensional block (i.e., relatively low expansion rate).

It should be noted further that the vast majority of univalve shells are above the surface which separates forms with overlapping whorls from those with separate whorls (text-fig. 7). In other words, univalves tend to have overlapping whorls. This is also reasonable geometrically. Where W is low (as in most univalves), the shell tends to be a tube which tapers rather gradually. If successive coils of this tube are not in contact, the strength of the coiled structure is lessened. Therefore, the presence of whorl overlap may be interpreted as serving to increase shell strength. This provides a second geometric reason for the concentration of univalves in the upper part of the block.

A few univalves depart radically from the foregoing generalizations. Limpets, for example, have large apertures. This is accomplished geometrically by a high expansion rate (W) and by a large angle between biological and geometric generating curves (see text-fig. 10). These facts do not nullify the reasoning applied above to typical univalves because the limpet shell type is used by organisms that live attached to a firm substratum and shell functions are not the same as for typical univalves. In a limpet, a large aperture serves to provide the necessary area for attachment of the foot to a

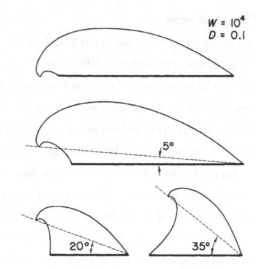

Text-fig. 10. Hypothetical shell forms illustrating the morphological effects of variation in the angle between biological and geometric generating curves. This angle is zero in the uppermost illustration.

substratum. As long as the animal remains attached, the protective function of aperture size is not a problem.

An additional problem posed by the geometric relations of univalves is the region in text-figure 4 where both univalves and bivalves are found (gastropods and pelecypods, respectively). In this region are found shells that are quite bulky in relation to aperture size. The region is thus typically univalve. Following the logic used earlier, a truly equivalved bivalve employing this geometry would have difficulty functioning as a normal bivalve. The musculature would be insufficiently strong to wield the massive valves. Also, the shell would be poorly adapted for burrowing and, if epifaunal, would be very sensitive to the attempts of predators to open the shell (because the predator would be offered a scissors-like mechanism for opening the shell).

The fact is that the majority of bivalves found in this overlap region are forms that are strongly *inequivalved* (such as *Exogyra*). The smaller of the two valves is simply a cap. By reducing the mass of one valve the problem of musculature and its strength is alleviated and the scissors mechanism is avoided. Furthermore, the geometry of the whole shell (articulated valves) provides an excellent functional unit for the sessile filter feeding organisms that generally occupy this region.

Conclusions

This analysis has been of a very general nature, being intended primarily as an introduction to a few general problems of interpreting coiling geometry and as an illustration of an approach to these problems. The basic model utilizes only four parameters and is obviously a simplification of the real situation. As soon as one attempts to consider some of the more subtle aspects of coiling variation, additional parameters are necessary (such as the angle between the biological and geometric generating curves). Regardless of the scale of the problem, however, the same type of logic may be applied.

Many questions remain to be answered. For example, why are brachiopods confined to the planispiral face of the three-dimensional block in text-figure 4 and why are pelecypods not found on this face? It is tempting to answer this question simply in terms of phylogeny: that is, to conclude that pelecypods have by chance never evolved the capability of truly planispiral coiling. To draw this conclusion is to discard the question and thereby to ignore the possibility of a rigorous functional explanation (perhaps in terms of musculature and hingement) for the coiling difference between the two phylogenetic groups.

Finally, it should be emphasized that the present study has not treated several important groups of coiled shells, particularly the nautiloids and foraminifera. The addition of these groups will be necessary for a complete understanding of the coiling phenomenon.

Further research found, for example, that the constrained range of forms might be the result of optimal use of shell materials. In this case, adding an extra parameter e that introduces thickness as a scaling law W^e. Here isometric growth (the one considered in Raup's paper) would be obtained for $e = 1$.

Although extra dimensions might prove useful to improve the description of forms, additional parameters might not necessarily provide great insight. Instead, different dimensions, even low-dimensional spaces (such as size versus shape or information theory-based quantities) can efficiently capture relevant complexity.

REFERENCES

Bartsch, P. 1947. "The Little Hearts (Corculum) of the Pacific and Indian Oceans." *Pacific Science* 1:221–226.

Fukutomi, T. 1953. "A General Equation Indicating the Regular Forms of Mollusca Shells, and Its Application to Geology, Especially in Paleontology (I)." *Geophysics Bulletin* (Hokkaido University) 3:63–82.

Grabau, A. H. 1872. "Über due Naumann'sche Conchospirale und ihre Bedeutung für die Conchyliometrie." University Leipzig, Inaugural dissert. (Leipzig), 1–77.

Lison, L. 1949. *Recherches sur la Forme et la Mécanique de Développement des Coquilles des Lamellibranches.* Brussels, Belgium: Memoirs of the Royal Institute of Natural Sciences of Belgium.

Moseley, H. 1838. "On the Geometrical Forms of Turbinated and Discoid Shells." *Philosophical Transactions of the Royal Society of London,* 351–370.

———. 1842. "On Conchyliometry." *The Philosophical Magazine: A Journal of Theoretical Experimental and Applied Physics* 21:300–305.

Müller, J. H. T. 1850. "Beiträge zur Conchyliometrie." *Ännalen der Physik,* 533–544.

———. 1853. "Zweiter Beitrag zur Conchyliometrie." *Ännalen der Physik,* 323–327.

Naumann, C. F. 1840a. "Beitrag zur Conchyliometrie." *Ännalen der Physik* 126:223–236.

———. 1840b. "Über die Spiralen der Ammoniten." *Ännalen der Physik,* 245–259.

———. 1845. "Über die wahre Spirale der Ammoniten." *Ännalen der Physik,* 538–543.

———. 1848. "Über die logarithmische Spiral von Nautilus pompilius und Ammonites galeatus." *Ber. Verh. k. sächs. Gesell. Wissen.* 2:26–34.

Owen, G. 1953. "The shell in the Lamellibranchia." *Quarterly Journal Microscopical Science* 94:57–70.

Raup, D. M. 1961. "The Geometry of Coiling in Gastropods." *Proceedings Of The National Academy of Sciences* 47:602–609.

———. 1962. "Computer as Aid in Describing Form in Gastropod Shells." *Science* 138:150–152.

———. 1963. "Analysis of Shell Form in Gastropods." In *GSA Special Papers,* 73:222. Boulder, CO: Geological Society of America.

———. 1967. "Geometric Analysis of Shell Coiling: Coiling in Ammonoids." *Journal of Paleontology* 41 (1): 43–65.

Raup, D. M., and A. Michelson. 1965. "Theoretical Morphology of the Coiled Shell." *Science* 147:1294–1295.

Rudwick, M. J. S. 1959. "The Growth and Form of Brachiopod Shells." *Geological Magazine* 96:1–24.

Stasek, C. R. 1963. "Geometrical Form and Gnomonic Growth in Bivalved Mollusca." *Journal of Morphology* 112:213–231.

Thompson, D. W. 1942. *On Growth and Form.* 1116. Cambridge, UK: Cambridge University Press.

Yonge, C. M. 1955. "A Note on Arca Senilia Senilis Lamarck." In *Proceedings of the Malacological Society of London,* edited by H. E. Quick, 31:202–208.

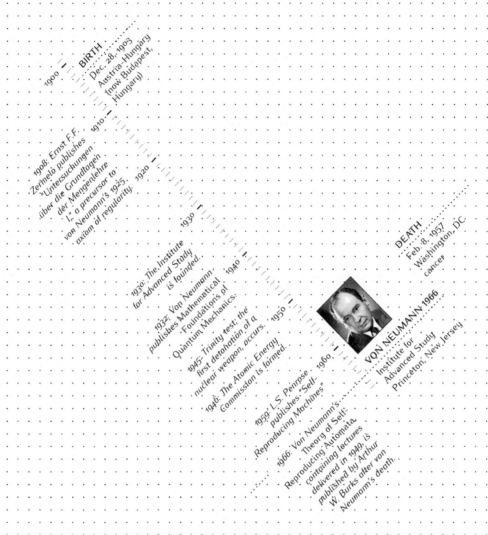

BIRTH
Dec. 28, 1903
Austria–Hungary
(now Budapest,
Hungary)

1900

1908: Ernst F.F.
Zermelo publishes
"Untersuchungen
über die Grundlagen
der Mengenlehre
I," a precursor to
von Neumann's 1925
axiom of regularity.

1910

1920

1930: The Institute
for Advanced Study
is founded.

1930

1932: Von Neumann
publishes Mathematical
Foundations of
Quantum Mechanics.

1940

1945: Trinity test; the
first detonation of a
nuclear weapon, occurs.

1946: The Atomic Energy
Commission is formed.

1950

1959: L.S. Penrose
publishes "Self-
Reproducing Machines"

1960

1966: Von Neumann's
Theory of Self-
Reproducing Automata,
containing lectures
delivered in 1949, is
published by Arthur
W. Burks after von
Neumann's death.

DEATH
Feb. 8, 1957
Washington, DC
cancer

VON NEUMANN 1966
Institute for
Advanced Study
Princeton, New Jersey

JOHN VON NEUMANN

[28]

SELF-REPRODUCING IDEAS

Neil Gershenfeld, Massachusetts Institute of Technology

John(ny) von Neumann is most widely known for what's called the von Neumann computing architecture. He never called it that, and in fact wrote about it only in an influential but fairly dreadful document (von Neumann 1945). That this was not a document for the ages is apparent in its title: "First Draft of a Report on the EDVAC." It never got beyond a first draft, and it filters his thoughts on how to program a computer through the severe limitations of the system he was programming (1k memory, 1k operations per second).

This report enshrined a technological limitation that we've spent decades recovering from. The division of labor between expensive vacuum tubes and slow serial memories is mirrored in what can be thought of as a physics mistake in the Turing machine that influenced him (Turing 1937). This was a theoretical construct that introduced computational universality and undecidability, but in it the tape storing data is distinct from the head processing it. That's unphysical: memory transistors are as universal as the transistors used in a processor, but data must be shuttled from the former to the latter to be operated in. Only recently have computer architectures overcome that bottleneck by mixing processing with memory.

Even though the canon of computer science credits von Neumann's architecture and Turing's machine to them as foundational contributions, both recognized the limitations of disembodied computing. Turing's final work was on the morphogenesis problem of how genes give rise to form (Turing 1952), and von Neumann studied the related problem of self-reproduction. The latter was published posthumously following his untimely death in 1957, based on lectures he gave at the University of Illinois in 1949 (von Neumann 1966). In these notes his experimental projections are almost entirely wrong, but only now are the profound

J. von Neumann, "Theory of Self-Reproducing Automata," in *Theory of Self-Reproducing Automata*, ed. A. W. Burks, University of Illinois Press (1966).

Reprinted with permission of Marina von Neumann Whitman.

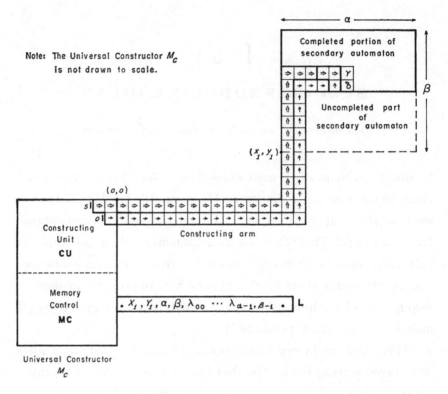

Figure 50. Operation of the constructing arm. *Reproduced from von Neumann (1966).*

ideas he introduced being realized. At its heart is figure 50 (my favorite figure in any paper), showing how a computation can communicate its own construction.

To study this problem von Neumann invented cellular automata (CA) with Stan Ulam (Shannon 1958; Ulam *et al.* 1969), and provided a constructive proof of a self-reproducing system. This launched a small industry seeking the simplest description of a system that can reproduce itself (Langton 1984, 1995), and led to the recognition of the computational universality of CA models of physics (Margolus 1984), and to computational models based on reconfiguration (Gershenfeld *et al.* 2010) and construction (Deutsch and Marletto 2015). This problem in turn inspired early attempts at mechanical self-reproduction (Penrose 1959), which was followed by doing this in electromechanical systems (Griffith, Goldwater, and Jacobson 2005; Zykov *et al.* 2005), and with robots making robots (Abdel-Rahman *et al.* 2022).

Unusually, given von Neumann's mathematical rigor, he introduced a key concept of "complication" without defining it beyond an ability "to do things." He doesn't quite mean complexity; he's getting at the minimum requirements for a system to reproduce and adapt. His description of complexity anticipates important results to come, including the work he presented in lectures at Caltech in 1952 on computing reliably with unreliable devices (von Neumann 1956), and the recognition of the physical limits of computing (Landauer 1961; Bennett 1982).

To see why the study of self-reproducing automata is so timely over fifty years later, consider an updated version of von Neumann's numbers (Gershenfeld 2020). A brain has about 10^{15} synapses, which fire around 100 Hz, and so can do approximately 10^{17} ops per second. A 100 petaflop computer can do 10^{17} ops per second, and has 10^7 processor cores with 10^8 transistors per core, and 10^{15} memory bits with 1 transistor per bit, for about 10^{15} transistors. And so they've reached parity in size and speed; it shouldn't be surprising that they can now do similar things. But the chip fab making the supercomputer can process 10^4 wafers per month, with 10^5 mm^2 per wafer, and 10^8 transistors per mm^2, for a total of 10^{10} transistors per second. You, on the other hand, have 10^{13} cells, each with about 10^5 ribosomes per cell, running at about 1 Hz, and so you're placing 10^{18} amino acids per second. That's an eight order of magnitude difference in fabricational rather than computational capacity!

That gap is what von Neumann identified in these notes, anticipating that closing it lies at the convergence of digital communication and computation with fabrication. His computing architecture had a good fifty-year run with Moore's Law; we're just at the beginning of the same kind of scaling for turning bits into atoms (and *vice versa*), with even greater implications (Gershenfeld, Gershenfeld, and Cutcher-Gershenfeld 2017). ❧

REFERENCES

Abdel-Rahman, A., C. Cameron, B. Jenett, M. Smith, and N. Gershenfeld. 2022. "Self-Replicating Hierarchical Modular Robotic Swarms." *Communications Engineering* 1 (1): 35. https://doi.org/10.1038/s44172-022-00034-3.

Bennett, C. H. 1982. "The Thermodynamics of Computation—A Review." *International Journal of Theoretical Physics* 21 (12): 905–940. https://doi.org/10.1007/BF02084158.

Deutsch, D., and C. Marletto. 2015. "Constructor Theory of Information." *Proceedings of the Royal Society A: Mathematical, Physical, and Engineering Sciences* 471 (2174): 20140540. https://doi.org/10.1098/rspa.2014.0540.

Gershenfeld, N. 2020. "Scaling." In *Possible Minds: Twenty-Five Ways of Looking at AI*, edited by J. Brockman. New York, NY: Penguin.

Gershenfeld, N., D. Dalrymple, K. Chen, A. Knaian, F. Green, E. D. Demaine, S. Greenwald, and P. Schmidt-Nielsen. 2010. "Reconfigurable Asynchronous Logic Automata: (RALA)." *ACM Sigplan Notices* 45 (1): 1–6. https://doi.org/10.1145/1707801.1706301.

Gershenfeld, N., A. Gershenfeld, and J. Cutcher-Gershenfeld. 2017. *Designing Reality: How to Survive and Thrive in the Third Digital Revolution*. London, UK: Hachette UK.

Griffith, S., D. Goldwater, and J. M. Jacobson. 2005. "Self-Replication from Random Parts." *Nature* 437 (7059): 636. https://doi.org/10.1038/437636a.

Landauer, R. 1961. "Irreversibility and Heat Generation in the Computing Process." *IBM Journal of Research and Development* 5 (3): 183–191. https://doi.org/10.1147/rd.53.0183.

Langton, C. G. 1984. "Self-Reproduction in Cellular Automata." *Physica D: Nonlinear Phenomena* 10 (1–2): 135–144. https://doi.org/10.1016/0167-2789(84)90256-2.

———. 1995. *Artificial Life: An Overview*. Cambridge, MA: MIT Press.

Margolus, N. 1984. "Physics-Like Models of Computation." *Physica D: Nonlinear Phenomena* 10 (1–2): 81–95. https://doi.org/10.1016/0167-2789(84)90252-5.

Penrose, L. S. 1959. "Self-Reproducing Machines." *Scientific American* 200 (6): 105–117. https://doi.org/10.1038/scientificamerican0659-105.

Shannon, C. E. 1958. "Von Neumann's Contributions to Automata Theory." *Bulletin of the American Mathematical Society* 64 (3): 123–129. https://doi.org/10.1090/S0002-9904-1958-10214-1.

Turing, A. M. 1937. "On Computable Numbers, with an Application to the Entscheidungsproblem." *Proceedings of the London Mathematical Society* s2-42:230–265. https://doi.org/10.1112/plms/s2-42.1.230.

———. 1952. "The Chemical Basis of Morphogenesis." *Philosophical Transactions of the Royal Society of London* 237 (641): 37–72. https://doi.org/10.1098/rstb.1952.0012.

Ulam, S., H. W. Kuhn, A. W. Tucker, and C. E. Shannon. 1969. "John von Neumann, 1903–1957." In *The Intellectual Migration: Europe and America, 1930–1960*, edited by D. Fleming and B. Bailyn, 235–269. Cambridge, MA: Harvard University Press.

von Neumann, J. 1945. *First Draft of a Report on the EDVAC*. Contract No. W-670-ORD-4926, June 30, 1945.

———. 1956. "Probabilistic Logics and the Synthesis of Reliable Organisms from Unreliable Components." In *Automata Studies*, edited by C. E. Shannon and J. McCarthy, 34:43–98. Princeton, NJ: Princeton University Press. https://doi.org/10.1515/9781400882618-003.

———. 1966. *Theory of Self-Reproducing Automata*. Edited by A. W. Burks. Urbana-Champaign, IL: University of Illinois Press.

Zykov, V., E. Mytilinaios, B. Adams, and H. Lipson. 2005. "Self-Reproducing Machines." *Nature* 435 (7039): 163–164. https://doi.org/10.1038/435163a.

THEORY OF SELF-REPRODUCING AUTOMATA

John von Neumann

FOURTH LECTURE

The Role of High and Extremely High Complication

Comparisons between computing machines and the nervous systems. Estimates of size for computing machines, present and near future.

Estimates for size for the human central nervous system. Excursus about the "mixed" character of living organisms. Analog and digital elements. Observations about the "mixed" character of all componentry, artificial as well as natural. Interpretation of the position to be taken with respect to these.

Evaluation of the discrepancy in size between artificial and natural automata. Interpretation of this discrepancy in terms of physical factors. Nature of the materials used.

The probability of the presence of other intellectual factors. The role of complication and the theoretical penetration that it requires.

Questions of reliability and errors reconsidered. Probability of individual errors and length of procedure. Typical lengths of procedure for computing machines and for living organisms—that is, for artificial and for natural automata. Upper limits on acceptable probability of error in individual operations. Compensation by checking and self-correcting features.

Differences of principle in the way in which errors are dealt with in artificial and in natural automata. The "single error" principle in artificial automata. Crudeness of our approach in this case, due to the lack of adequate theory. More sophisticated treatment of this problem in natural automata: The role of the autonomy of parts. Connections between this autonomy and evolution.

After the broad general discussions of the last two lectures I would like to return to the subject of the specific automata which we know. I would like to compare artificial automata, specifically computing machines, with natural automata, particularly the human nervous system. In order to do this, I must say a few things in both cases about components and I must make certain comparisons of sizes.

As I mentioned before, in estimating the size of the human nervous system one is limited to a figure which is not very well established, but which is probably right in its order of magnitude. This is the statement that there are 10^{10} neurons in the human brain. The number of nerves present elsewhere in the human organism is probably much smaller than this. Also, a large number of these other nerves originate in the brain anyway. The largest aggregation of nerves of the periphery is on the retina, and the optic nerve going from the retina to the brain is part of the brain.

A current estimate is 10^{15} synapses.

Compared to this, the number of vacuum tubes involved in the computing machines we know of is very small, a million times smaller. The largest existing computing machine, the ENIAC, has 2×10^4 vacuum tubes. Another large computing machine, the SSEC, which belongs to the IBM Company, contains a mixture of vacuum tubes and relays, about 10 thousand of each. The fastest computing machines now under construction are designed to have several thousand vacuum tubes, perhaps 3 thousand. The reason for this difference in size between the ENIAC and the fast machines now under construction is a difference in the treatment of memory, which I will discuss later.

A large computer now has 10^{15} transistors.

So the human nervous system is roughly a million times more complicated than these large computing machines. The increase in complexity from these computing machines to the central nervous system is more than the increase in complexity from a single vacuum tube to these computing machines. Even measuring complexity on a logarithmic scale, which is highly generous, we have not yet come half the way. I think that in any sensible definition of complexity, it would be much less than half way.

There is, however, a factor in favor of these machines: they're faster than the human brain. The time in which a human nerve can respond is about $\frac{1}{2}$ millisecond. However, that time is not a fair measure of the speed of the neuron, because what matters is not the time in which the neuron responds, but the time in which it recovers, the time from one response to the next potential response. That time is, at best, 5 milliseconds. In the case of a vacuum tube it's difficult to estimate the speed, but present designs call for repetition rates which are not much in excess of a million per second.

Thus, the nervous system has a million times as many components as these machines have, but each component of the machine is about 5 thousand times faster than a neuron. Counting what can be done, hour by hour, the nervous system outperforms the machine by a factor of roughly 200. This estimate, however, favors the automaton, because an *n*-fold increase in size brings much more than an *n*-fold increase in what can be done. What can be done is a matter of the interrelationships between the components, and the number of interrelationships increases with the square of the number of components. And apart from this, what can be done depends on certain minima. Below a certain minimum level of complexity you cannot do a certain thing, but above this minimum level of complexity you can do it.

[Von Neumann next compared the human nervous system and computers with respect to volume. The decisive factor is the space in which the control and amplifying functions are performed. In the case of the vacuum tube this is essentially the space between the cathode and the control grid, which is of the order of magnitude of a millimeter. In the case of the nerve cell it is the thickness of the nerve membrane, which is of the order of 1 micron. The ratio in size is about 1000 to 1, and this is also the ratio in voltage, so that the intensity of the field which is used for control and amplification is about the same in the vacuum tube and the nerve cell. This means that differences in total energy dissipation are mainly due to differences in size. "A discrepancy of 10^3 in linear size means a discrepancy of 10^9 in volume, and probably a not very different discrepancy in energy." See also *Collected Works* 5.299-302 and *The Computer and the Brain* 44-52.

He then calculated the energy which is dissipated "per elementary act of information, that is, per elementary decision of a two-way alternative and per elementary transmittal of 1 unit of information." He did this for three cases: the thermodynamical minimum, the vacuum tube, and the neuron.

In the third lecture he said that thermodynamical information is measured by the logarithm, to the base two, of the number of alternatives involved. The thermodynamical information in the case of two alternatives

Clocks are now measured in gigahertz.

This ratio is now approximately 1:1.

This is both trivially wrong, and profoundly right. It's wrong because the challenge in high-performance computing is to maintain linear scaling with system size. And it's right because there are important problems (like AI) which appear to have a scale threshold beyond which performance significantly improves.

is thus one, "except that this is not the unit in which you measure energy. Entropy is energy only if you specify the temperature. So, running at low temperature you can say what energy should be dissipated." He then computed the thermodynamical minimum of energy per elementary act of information from the formula $kT \log_e N$ ergs, where k is Boltzmann's constant (1.4×10^{-16} ergs per degree), T is the temperature in absolute units, and N is the number of alternatives. For a binary act $N = 2$, and taking the temperature to be about 300 degrees absolute, he obtained 3×10^{-14} ergs for the thermodynamical minimum.

Von Neumann then estimated that the brain dissipates 25 watts, has 10^{10} neurons, and that on the average a neuron is activated about 10 times per second. Hence the energy dissipation per binary act in a nerve cell is roughly 3×10^{-3} ergs. He estimated that a vacuum tube dissipates 6 watts, is activated about $100,000$ times per second, and thus dissipates 6×10^2 ergs per binary act.]

Superconducting logic can now switch with zeptojoule energies.

So our present machinery is about 200 thousand times less efficient than the nervous system is. Computing machines will be improved in the next few years, perhaps by replacing vacuum tubes with amplifying crystals, but even then they will be of the order of 10 thousand times less efficient than the nervous system. The remarkable thing, however, is the enormous gap between the thermodynamical minimum (3×10^{-14} ergs) and the energy dissipation per binary act in the neuron (3×10^{-3} ergs). The factor here is 10^{11}. This shows that the thermodynamical analysis is missing a large part of the story. Measured on a logarithmic scale, the gap between our instrumentation, which is obviously amateurish, and the procedures of nature, which show a professional touch, is about half the gap between the best devices we know about and the thermodynamical minimum. What this gap is due to I don't know. I suspect that it's due to something like a desire for reliability of operation.

Thus, for an elementary act of information, nature does not use what, from the point of view of physics, is an elementary system with two stable states, such as a hydrogen atom. All the switching organs used are much larger. If nature really operated with these elementary systems, switching organs would have dimensions of the order of a few angstroms, while the smallest switching organs we know have dimensions of the order of thousands or tens of thousands of angstroms. There is obviously something which forces one to use organs several orders of magnitude larger than is required by the strict thermodynamical argument. Thus, though the observation that information is entropy tells an important part of the story, it by no means tells the whole story. There is a factor of 10^{11} still to be accounted for.

[Von Neumann then discussed memory components. Vacuum tubes, which are switching organs, may be used for memory. But since the standard circuit for storing a binary digit has two tubes, and additional tubes are needed for transmitting the information in and out, it is not feasible to build a large memory out of vacuum tubes. "The actual devices which are used are of such a nature that the store is effected, not in a macroscopic object like a vacuum tube, but in something which is microscopic and has only a virtual existence." Von Neumann describes two devices of this sort: acoustic delay line storage and cathode ray tube storage.

Solid-state memories have now displaced most other kinds of storage.

An acoustic delay line is a tube which is filled with a medium such as mercury and which has a piezo-electric crystal at each end. When the transmitting crystal is stimulated electrically, it produces an acoustic wave that travels through the mercury and causes the receiving crystal to produce an electrical signal. This signal is amplified, reshaped, and retimed and sent to the transmitting crystal again. This acoustic–electrical cycle can be repeated indefinitely, thereby providing storage. A binary digit is represented by the presence or absence of a pulse at a given position at a given time, and since the pulses circulate around the system, the digit is not stored in any fixed position. "The thing which remembers is nowhere in particular."

Information may be stored in a cathode ray tube in the form of electric charges on the inside surface of the tube. A binary digit is represented by the charge stored in a small area. These charges are deposited and sensed by means of the electron beam of the cathode ray tube. Since the area associated with a given binary digit must be recharged frequently, and since this area may be moved by changing the position of the electron beam, this memory is also virtual. "The site of the memory is really nowhere organically, and the mode of control produces the memory organ in a virtual sense, because no permanent physical changes ever occur."]

There's therefore no reason to believe that the memory of the central nervous system is in the switching organs (the neurons). The size of the human memory must be very great, much greater than 10^{10} binary units. If you count the impressions which a human gets in his life or other things which appear to be critical, you obtain numbers like 10^{15}. One cannot place much faith in these estimates, but I think it likely that the memory capacity of the human nervous system is greater than 10^{10}. I don't know how legitimate it is to transfer our experience with computing machines to natural systems, but if our experience is worth anything it is highly unlikely that the natural memory should be in switching organs or should consist of anything as unsophisticated and crude as the modification of a switching organ. It has been suggested that memory consists in a change of threshold at a synapse. I don't know if this is true, but the memory of computing machines does not consist of bending a grid. A comparison between artificial automata and the central nervous system makes it probable that the memory of the latter is more sophisticated and more virtual than this. Therefore, I think that all guesses about what the memory of the human organism is, and where it sits, are premature.

This is now understood in great detail; while important changes happen around the synapse, it is the locus of memory.

Another thing of which I would like to talk is this. I have been talking as if a nerve cell were really a pure switching organ. It has been pointed out by many experts in neurology and adjacent fields that the nerve cell is not a pure switching organ but a very delicate continuous organ. In the lingo of computing machinery one would say it is an analog device that can do vastly more than transmit or not transmit a pulse. There is a possible answer to this, namely, that vacuum tubes, electromechanical relays, etc. are not switching devices either, since they have continuous properties. They are all characterized by this, however, that there is at least one way to run them where they have essentially an all-or-none response. What matters is how the component runs when the organism is functioning normally. Now nerve cells do not usually run as all-or-none organs. For instance, the method of translating a stimulus intensity into a frequency of response depends on fatigue and the time of recovery, which is a continuous or analog response. However, it is quite clear that the all-or-none character of a neuron is a very important part of the story.

The human organism is not a digital organ either, though one part of it, the nervous system, is essentially digital. Almost all the nervous stimuli end in organs which are not digital, such as a contracting muscle or an organ which causes secretions to produce a chemical. To control the production of a chemical and rely on the diffusion rate of a chemical is to employ a much more sophisticated analog procedure than we ever use in analog computing machines. The most important loops in the human system are of this nature. A system of nervous stimuli goes through a complicated network of nerves and then controls the operation of what is essentially a chemical factory. The chemicals are distributed by a very complicated hydrodynamical system, which is completely analog. These chemicals produce nervous stimuli which travel in a digital manner through the nervous system. There are loops where this change from digital into analog occurs several times. So the human organism is essentially a mixed system. But this does not decrease the necessity for understanding the digital part of it.

Computing machines aren't purely digital either. The way we run them now, their inputs and outputs are digital. But it's quite clear that we need certain non-digital inputs and outputs. It's frequently desirable to display the result, not in digits, but, say, as a curve on an oscilloscope screen. This is an analog output. Moreover, I think that the important applications of these devices will come when you can use them to control complicated machinery, for example, the flight of a missile or of a plane. In this case the inputs will come from an analog source and the outputs will control an analog process. This whole trans-continuous alternation between digital and analog mechanisms is probably characteristic of every field.

The digital aspect of automata should be emphasized at the present time, for we now have some logical tools to deal with digital mechanisms, and our understanding of digital mechanisms is behind our understanding of analog mechanisms. Also, it appears that digital mechanisms are necessary for complicated functions. Pure analog mechanisms are usually not suited for very complicated situations. The only way to handle a complicated situation with analog mechanisms is to break it up into parts and deal with the parts separately and alternately, and this is a digital trick.

Let me now come to the following question. Our artificial automata are much smaller than natural automata in what they do and in the number of components they have, and they're phenomenally more expensive in terms of space and energy. Why is this so? It's manifestly hopeless to produce a true answer at the present time: We can hardly explain why two objects are different if we understand one a little and the other not at all. However, there are some obvious discrepancies in the tools with which we operate, which make it clear that we would have difficulty in going much further with these tools.

The materials which we are using are by their very nature not well suited for the small dimensions nature uses. Our combinations of metals, insulators, and vacuums are much more unstable than the materials used by nature; that they have higher tensile strengths is completely incidental. If a membrane is damaged it will reconstruct itself, but if a vacuum tube develops a short between its grid and cathode it will not reconstruct itself. Thus the natural materials have some sort of mechanical stability and are well balanced with respect to mechanical properties, electrical properties, and reliability requirements. Our artificial systems are patchworks in which we achieve desirable electrical traits at the price of mechanically unsound things. We use techniques which are excellent for fitting metal to metal but are not very good for fitting metal to vacuum. To obtain millimeter spacings in an inaccessible vacuum space is a great mechanical achievement, and we will not be able to decrease the size by large factors here. And so the differences in size between artificial and natural automata are probably connected essentially with quite radical differences in materials.

Transistor features are now on atomic scales.

[Von Neumann proceeded to discuss what he thought was a deeper cause of the discrepancy in size between natural and artificial automata. This is that many of the components of the natural system serve to make the system reliable. As he noted in the third lecture, actual computing elements function correctly with a certain probability only, not with certainty. In small systems the probability that the whole system will behave incorrectly is relatively small and may often be neglected, but this is not the case with large systems. Thus error considerations become more important as the system becomes more complex.

Von Neumann made some very rough calculations to justify this conclusion. Assuming that the system is designed in such a way that the failure of a single element would result in failure of the whole system, he calculated the error probability required for a given mean free path between system errors. For the human nervous system he used the following figures: 10^{10} neurons; each neuron activated 10 times per second on the average; a mean free path between fatal errors of 60 years (the average life span). Since 60 years is about 2×10^9 seconds, the product of these numbers is 2×10^{20}.

Hence an error probability of 0.5×10^{-20} for each activation of an element is required under these assumptions. For a digital computer he used the figures: 5×10^3 vacuum tubes, 10^5 activations per tube per second, and a desired mean free path between system errors of 7 hours (about 2×10^4 seconds). An error probability of 10^{-13} per tube activation is required for this degree of reliability. Compare the calculations at *Collected Works* 5.366—367.

He pointed out that vacuum tubes, and artificial components generally, do not have an error probability as low as 10^{-13}, and that neurons probably do not either. We try to design computing machines so that they will stop when they make an error and the operator can then locate it and correct it. For example, a computer may perform a certain operation twice, compare the results, and stop if the results differ.]

It's very likely that on the basis of the philosophy that every error has to be caught, explained, and corrected, a system of the complexity of the living organism would not run for a millisecond. Such a system is so well integrated that it can operate across errors. An error in it does not in general indicate a degenerative tendency. The system is sufficiently flexible and well organized that as soon as an error shows up in any part of it, the system automatically senses whether this error matters or not. If it doesn't matter, the system continues to operate without paying any attention to it. If the error seems to the system to be important, the system blocks that region out, by-passes it, and proceeds along other channels. The system then analyzes the region separately at leisure and corrects what goes on there, and if correction is impossible the system just blocks the region off and bypasses it forever. The duration of operability of the automaton is determined by the time it takes until so many incurable errors have occurred, so many alterations and permanent by-passes have been made, that finally the operability is really impaired. This is a completely different philosophy from the philosophy which proclaims that the end of the world is at hand as soon as the first error has occurred.

To apply the philosophy underlying natural automata to artificial automata we must understand complicated mechanisms better than we do, we must have more elaborate statistics about what goes wrong, and we must have much more perfect statistical information about the milieu in which a mechanism lives than we now have. An automaton can not be

Until recently computers did restore the state of every bit after every operation; thermodynamic limits are now leading to a return to computing reliably with unreliable parts.

separated from the milieu to which it responds. By that I mean that it's meaningless to say that an automaton is good or bad, fast or slow, reliable or unreliable, without telling in what milieu it operates. The characteristics of a human for survival are well defined on the surface of the earth in its present state, though for most types of humans you must actually specialize the situation a little further than this. But it is meaningless to argue how the human would survive on the bottom of the ocean or in a temperature of 1000 degrees centigrade. Similarly, in discussing a computing machine it is meaningless to ask how fast or how slow it is, unless you specify what type of problems will be given to it.

It makes an enormous difference whether a computing machine is designed, say, for more or less typical problems of mathematical analysis, or for number theory, or combinatorics, or for translating a text. We have an approximate idea of how to design a machine to handle the typical general problems of mathematical analysis. I doubt that we will produce a machine which is very good for number theory except on the basis of our present knowledge of the statistical properties of number theory. I think we have very little idea as to how to design good machines for combinatorics and translation.

What matters is that the statistical properties of problems of mathematical analysis are reasonably well known, and as far as we know, reasonably homogeneous. Consider some problems in mathematical analysis which look fairly different from each other and which by mathematical standards are very different: finding the roots of an equation of the tenth order, inverting a matrix of the twentieth order, solving a proper value problem, solving an integral equation, or solving an integral differential equation. These problems are surprisingly homogeneous with respect to the statistical properties which matter for a computing machine: the fraction of multiplications to other operations, the number of memory references per multiplication, and the optimal hierarchic structure of the memory with respect to access time. There's vastly less homogeneity in number theory. There are viewpoints under which number theory is homogeneous, but we don't know them.

So, it is true for all these automata that you can only assign them a value in combination with the milieu which they have to face. Natural automata are much better suited to their milieu than any artifacts we know.

It is therefore quite possible that we are not too far from the limits of complication which can be achieved in artificial automata without really fundamental insights into a theory of information, although one should be very careful with such statements because they can sound awfully ridiculous 5 years later.

[Von Neumann then explained why computing machines are designed to stop when a single error occurs. The fault must be located and corrected by the engineer, and it is very difficult for him to localize a fault if there are several of them. If there is only one fault he can often divide the machine into two parts and determine which part made the error. This process can be repeated until he isolates the fault. This general method becomes much more complicated if there are two or three faults, and breaks down when there are many faults.]

The fact that natural organisms have such a radically different attitude about errors and behave so differently when an error occurs is probably connected with some other traits of natural organisms, which are entirely absent from our automata. The ability of a natural organism to survive in spite of a high incidence of error (which our artificial automata are incapable of) probably requires a very high flexibility and ability of the automaton to watch itself and reorganize itself. And this probably requires a very considerable autonomy of parts. There is a high autonomy of parts in the human nervous system. This autonomy of parts of a system has an effect which is observable in the human nervous system but not in artificial automata. When parts are autonomous and able to reorganize themselves, when there are several organs each capable of taking control in an emergency, an antagonistic relation can develop between the parts so that they are no longer friendly and cooperative. It is quite likely that all these phenomena are connected.

FIFTH LECTURE

Re-Evaluation of the Problems of Complicated Automata—Problems of Hierarchy and Evolution

Analysis of componentry and analysis of integration. Although these parts have to appear together in a complete theory, the present state of our information does not justify this yet.

The first problem: Reasons for not going into it in detail here. Questions of principle regarding the nature of relay organs.

The second problem: Coincides with a theory of information and of automata. Reconsideration of the broader program regarding a theoretical discussion of automata as indicated at the end of the second lecture.

Synthesis of automata. Automata which can effect such syntheses.

The intuitive concept of "complication." Surmise of its degenerative character: In connection with descriptions of processes by automata and in connection with syntheses of automata by automata.

Qualifications and difficulties regarding this concept of degeneracy.

Rigorous discussion: Automata and their "elementary" parts. Definition and listing of elementary parts. Synthesis of automata by automata. The problem of self-reproduction.

Main types of constructive automata which are relevant in this connection: The concept of a general instruction. The general constructive automaton which can follow an instruction. The general copying automaton. The self-reproducing combination.

Self-reproduction combined with synthesis of other automata: The enzymatic function. Comparison with the known major traits of genetic and mutation mechanisms.

The questions on which I've talked so far all bear on automata whose operations are not directed at themselves, so that they produce results which are of a completely different character than themselves. This is obvious in each of the three cases I have referred to.

It is evident in the case of a Turing automaton, which is a box with a finite number of states. Its outputs are modifications of another entity, which, for the sake of convenience, I call a punched tape. This tape is not itself an object which has states between which it can move of its own accord. Furthermore, it is not finite, but is assumed to be infinite in both directions. Thus this tape is qualitatively completely different from the automaton which does the punching, and so the automaton is working into a qualitatively different medium.

This distinction between the head and the tape is the architectural mistake which it's taken decades to recover from.

This is equally true for the automata discussed by McCulloch and Pitts, which are made of units, called neurons, that produce pulses. The inputs and outputs of these automata are not the neurons but the pulses. It is true that these pulses may go to peripheral organs, thereby producing entirely different reactions. But even there one primarily thinks, say, of feeding the pulses into motor or secretory organs, so it is still true that the inputs and outputs are completely different from the automaton itself.

Finally, it is entirely true for computing machines, which can be thought of as machines which are fed, and emit, some medium like punched tape. Of course, I do not consider it essentially different whether the medium is a punched card, a magnetic wire, a magnetized metal tape with many channels on it, or a piece of film with points photographed on it. In all these cases the medium which is fed to the automaton and which is produced by the automaton is completely different from the automaton. In fact, the automaton doesn't produce any medium at all; it merely modifies a medium which is completely different from it. One can also imagine a computing machine with an output of pulses which are fed to control completely different entities. But again, the automaton is completely different from the electrical pulses it emits. So there's this qualitative difference.

A complete discussion of automata can be obtained only by taking a broader view of these things and considering automata which can have outputs something like themselves. Now, one has to be careful what one means by this. There is no question of producing matter out of nothing. Rather, one imagines automata which can modify objects similar to themselves, or effect syntheses by picking up parts and putting them together, or take synthesized entities apart. In order to discuss these things, one has to imagine a formal set-up like this. Draw up a list of unambiguously defined elementary parts. Imagine that there is a practically unlimited supply of these parts floating around in a large container. One can then imagine an automaton functioning in the following manner: It also is floating around in this medium; its essential activity is to pick up parts and put them together, or, if aggregates of parts are found, to take them apart.

This is an axiomatically shortened and simplified description of what an organism does. It's true that this view has certain limitations, but they are not fundamentally different from the inherent limitations of the axiomatic method. Any result one might reach in this manner will depend quite essentially on how one has chosen to define the elementary parts. It is a commonplace of all axiomatic methods that it is very difficult to give rigorous rules as to how one should choose the elementary parts, so that whether the choice of the elements was reasonable is a matter of common sense judgment. There is no rigorous description of what choice is reasonable and what choice is not.

First of all, one may define parts in such numbers, and each of them so large and involved, that one has defined the whole problem away. If you chose to define as elementary objects things which are analogous to whole living organisms, then you obviously have killed the problem, because you would have to attribute to these parts just those functions of the living organism which you would like to describe or to understand. So, by choosing the parts too large, by attributing too many and too complex functions to them, you lose the problem at the moment of defining it.

One also loses the problem by defining the parts too small, for instance, by insisting that nothing larger than a single molecule, single atom, or single elementary particle will rate as a part. In this case one would probably get completely bogged down in questions which, while very important and interesting, are entirely anterior to our problem. We are interested here in organizational questions about complicated organisms, and not in questions about the structure of matter or the quantum mechanical background of valency chemistry. So, it is clear that one has to use some common sense criteria about choosing the parts neither too large nor too small.

Even if one chooses the parts in the right order of magnitude, there are many ways of choosing them, none of which is intrinsically much better than any other. There is in formal logics a very similar difficulty, that the whole system requires an agreement on axioms, and that there are no rigorous rules on how axioms should be chosen, just the common sense rules that one would like to get the system one is interested in and would not like to state in his axioms either things which are really terminal theorems of his theory or things which belong to vastly anterior fields. For example, in axiomatizing geometry one should assume theorems from set theory, because one is not interested in how to get from sets to numbers, or from numbers to geometry. Again, one does not choose the more sophisticated theorems of analytic number theory as axioms of geometry, because one wants to cut in at an earlier point.

Even if the axioms are chosen within the common sense area, it is usually very difficult to achieve an agreement between two people who have done this independently. For instance, in the literature of formal logics there are about as many notations as there are authors, and anybody who has used a notation for a few weeks feels that it's more or less superior to any other. So, while the choice of notations, of the elements, is enormously important and absolutely basic for an application of the axiomatic method, this choice is neither rigorously justifiable nor humanly unambiguously justifiable. All one can do is to try to submit a system which will stand up under common sense criteria. I will give an indication of how one system can be constructed, but I want to emphasize very strongly how relatively I state this system.

I will introduce as elementary units neurons, a "muscle," entities which make and cut fixed contacts, and entities which supply energy, all defined with about that degree of superficiality with which the formal theory of McCulloch and Pitts describes an actual neuron. If you describe muscles, connective tissues, "disconnecting tissues," and means of providing metabolic energy, all with this degree of schematization, you wind up with a system of elements with which you can work in a reasonably uncomplicated manner. You probably wind up with something like 10 or 12 or 15 elementary parts.

By axiomatizing automata in this manner, one has thrown half of the problem out the window, and it may be the more important half. One has resigned oneself not to explain how these parts are made up of real things, specifically, how these parts are made up of actual elementary particles, or even of higher chemical molecules. One does not ask the most intriguing, exciting, and important question of why the molecules or aggregates which in nature really occur in these parts are the sort of things they are, why they are essentially very large molecules in some cases but large aggregations in other cases, why they always lie in a range beginning at a few microns and ending at a few decimeters. This is a very peculiar range for an elementary object, since it is, even on a linear scale, at least five powers of ten away from the sizes of really elementary entities.

These things will not be explained; we will simply assume that elementary parts with certain properties exist. The question that one can then hope to answer, or at least investigate, is: What principles are involved in organizing these elementary parts into functioning organisms, what are the traits of such organisms, and what are the essential quantitative characteristics of such organisms? I will discuss the matter entirely from this limited point of view.

[At this point von Neumann made the remarks on information, logic, thermodynamics, and balance which now appear at the end of the Third Lecture. They are placed there because that is where von Neumann's detailed outline located them. Those remarks are relevant to the present discussion because the concept of complication which von Neumann introduced next belongs to information theory.]

There is a concept which will be quite useful here, of which we have a certain intuitive idea, but which is vague, unscientific, and imperfect. This concept clearly belongs to the subject of information, and quasi-thermodynamical considerations are relevant to it. I know no adequate name for it, but it is best described by calling it "complication." It is effectivity in complication, or the potentiality to do things. I am not thinking about how involved the object is, but how involved its purposive operations are. In this sense, an object is of the highest degree of complexity if it can do very difficult and involved things.

This is the key (lack of a) definition.

I mention this because when you consider automata whose normal function is to synthesize other automata from elementary parts (living organisms and such familiar artificial automata as machine tools), you find the following remarkable thing. There are two states of mind, in each of which one can put himself in a minute, and in each of which we feel that a certain statement is obvious. But each of these two statements is the opposite or negation of the other!

And herself, and themself . . .

Anybody who looks at living organisms knows perfectly well that they can produce other organisms like themselves. This is their normal function, they wouldn't exist if they didn't do this, and it's plausible that this is the reason why they abound in the world. In other words, living organisms are very complicated aggregations of elementary parts, and by any reasonable theory of probability or thermodynamics highly improbable. That they should occur in the world at all is a miracle of the first magnitude; the only thing which removes, or mitigates, this miracle is that they reproduce themselves. Therefore, if by any peculiar accident there should ever be one of them, from there on the rules of probability do not apply, and there will be many of them, at least if the milieu is reasonable. But a reasonable milieu is already a thermodynamically much less improbable thing. So, the operations of probability somehow leave a loophole at this point, and it is by the process of self-reproduction that they are pierced.

Furthermore, it's equally evident that what goes on is actually one degree better than self-reproduction, for organisms appear to have gotten more elaborate in the course of time. Today's organisms are phylogenetically descended from others which were vastly simpler than they are, so much simpler, in fact, that it's inconceivable how any kind of description of the later, complex organism could have existed in the earlier one. It's not easy to imagine in what sense a gene, which is probably a low order affair, can contain a description of the human being which will come from it. But in this case you can say that since the gene has its effect only within another human organism, it probably need not contain a complete description of what is to happen, but only a few cues for a few alternatives. However, this is not so in phylogenetic evolution. That starts from simple entities, surrounded by an unliving amorphous milieu, and produces something more complicated. Evidently, these organisms have the ability to produce something more complicated than themselves.

The other line of argument, which leads to the opposite conclusion, arises from looking at artificial automata. Everyone knows that a machine tool is more complicated than the elements which can be made with it, and that, generally speaking, an automaton A, which can make an automaton B, must contain a complete description of B and also rules on how to behave while effecting the synthesis. So, one gets a very strong impression that complication, or productive potentiality in an organization, is degenerative, that an organization which synthesizes something is necessarily more complicated, of a higher order, than the organization it synthesizes. This conclusion, arrived at by considering artificial automata, is clearly opposite to our early conclusion, arrived at by considering living organisms.

I think that some relatively simple combinatorial discussions of artificial automata can contribute to mitigating this dilemma.

There are many important counter-examples to this, such as starting with a foundry and ending up with a machine shop (Gingery 2014).

Appealing to the organic, living world does not help us greatly, because we do not understand enough about how natural organisms function. We will stick to automata which we know completely because we made them, either actual artificial automata or paper automata described completely by some finite set of logical axioms. It is possible in this domain to describe automata which can reproduce themselves. So at least one can show that on the site where one would expect complication to be degenerative it is not necessarily degenerative at all, and, in fact, the production of a more complicated object from a less complicated object is possible.

He almost reaches threshold theorems here.

The conclusion one should draw from this is that complication is degenerative below a certain minimum level. This conclusion is quite in harmony with other results in formal logics, to which I have referred a few times earlier during these lectures.[1] We do not now know what complication is, or how to measure it, but I think that something like this conclusion is true even if one measures complication by the crudest possible standard, the number of elementary parts. There is a minimum number of parts below which complication is degenerative, in the sense that if one automaton makes another the second is less complex than the first, but above which it is possible for an automaton to construct other automata of equal or higher complexity. Where this number lies depends upon how you define the parts. I think that with reasonable definitions of parts, like those I will partially indicate later, which give one or two dozen parts with simple properties, this minimum number is large, in the millions. I don't have a good estimate of it, although I think that one will be produced before terribly long, but to do so will be laborious.

There is thus this completely decisive property of complexity, that there exists a critical size below which the process of synthesis is degenerative, but above which the phenomenon of synthesis, if properly arranged, can become explosive, in other words, where syntheses of automata can proceed in such a manner that each automaton will produce other automata which are more complex and of higher potentialities than itself.

----

[1] [See the end of the Second Lecture.]

Now, none of this can get out of the realm of vague statement until one has defined the concept of complication correctly. And one cannot define the concept of complication correctly until one has seen in greater detail some critical examples, that is, some of the constructs which exhibit the critical and paradoxical properties of complication. There is nothing new about this. It was exactly the same with conservation and non-conservation properties in physics, with the concepts of energy and entropy, and with other critical concepts. The simplest mechanical and thermodynamic systems had to be discussed for a long time before the correct concepts of energy and entropy could be abstracted from them.

[Von Neumann only briefly described the kinds of elements or parts he planned to use. There are neurons like those of McCulloch and Pitts. There are elements "that have absolutely no function except that they are rigid and produce a geometrical tie between their ends." Another kind of element is called a "motor organ" and a "muscle-like affair"; it contracts to zero length when stimulated. There is an organ which, when pulsed, "can either make or break a connection." He said that less than a dozen kinds of elements are needed. An automaton composed of these parts can catch other parts which accidentally come in contact with it; "it is possible to invent a system by which it can sense" what part it has caught.

In June of 1948 von Neumann gave three lectures on automata at the Institute for Advanced Study to a small group of friends. He probably did this in preparation for the Hixon Symposium which took place in September of that year.[2] These lectures contained the most detailed description of the parts of his self-reproducing automaton that I know of. For this reason, I have attempted to reconstruct, from the notes and memories of the audience, what he said about these parts and how they would function.

A detailed design is shown in figure 50 in the introduction.

Von Neumann described eight kinds of parts. All seem to have been symbolized with straight lines; inputs and outputs were indicated at the ends and/or the middle. The temporal reference frame was discrete,

---

[2]["The General and Logical Theory of Automata." *Collected Works* 5.288-328. It will be recalled that the Illinois lectures were delivered in December of 1949.]

each element taking a unit of time to respond. It is not clear whether he intended this list to be complete; I suspect that he had not yet made up his mind on this point.

Four of the parts perform logical and information processing operations. A *stimulus organ* receives and transmits stimuli; it receives them disjunctively, that is, it realizes the truth-function "*p* or *q*." A *coincidence organ* realizes the truth-function "*p* and *q*." An *inhibitory organ* realizes the truth-function "*p* and not-*q*." A *stimuli producer* serves as a source of stimuli.

The fifth part is a *rigid member*, from which a rigid frame for an automaton can be constructed. A rigid member does not carry any stimuli; that is, it is an insulated girder. A rigid member may be connected to other rigid members as well as to parts which are not rigid members. These connections are made by a *fusing organ* which, when stimulated, welds or solders two parts together. Presumably the fusing organ is used in the following way. Suppose point *a* of one girder is to be joined to point *b* of another girder. The active or output end of the fusing organ is placed in contact with points *a* and *b*. A stimulus into the input end of the fusing organ at time *t* causes points *a* and *b* to be welded together at time $t+1$. The fusing organ can be withdrawn later. Connections may be broken by a *cutting organ* which, when stimulated, unsolders a connection.

The eighth part is a *muscle*, used to produce motion. A muscle is normally rigid. It may be connected to other parts. If stimulated at time *t* it will contract to length zero by time $t+1$, keeping all its connections. It will remain contracted as long as it is stimulated. Presumably muscles can be used to move parts and make connections in the following way. Suppose that muscle 1 lies between point *a* of one girder and point *b* of another girder, and muscle 2 lies between point *a* and the active end *c* of a fusing organ. When both muscles are stimulated, they will contract, thereby bringing points *a*, *b*, and *c* together. When the fusing organ is stimulated, it will weld points *a* and *b* together. Finally, when the stimuli to the muscles are stopped, the muscles will return to their original length, at least one end of muscle 1 separating from the point *ab*. Von Neumann does not seem to have discussed the question of how the connections between muscles and other parts are made and broken.

Von Neumann conceived of an automaton constructing other automata in the following manner. The constructing automaton floats on a surface, surrounded by an unlimited supply of parts. The constructing automaton contains in its memory a description of the automaton to be constructed. Operating under the direction of this description, it picks up the parts it needs and assembles them into the desired automaton. To do this, it must contain a device which catches and identifies the parts that come in contact with it. The June, 1948 lectures contain only a few remarks on how this device might operate. Two stimulus units protrude from the constructing automaton. When a part touches them tests can be made to see what kind of part it is. For example, a stimulus organ will transmit a signal; a girder will not. A muscle might be identified by determining that it contracts when stimulated.

Von Neumann intended to disregard the fuel and energy problem in his first design attempt. He planned to consider it later, perhaps by introducing a battery as an additional elementary part. Except for this addition, von Neumann's early model of self-reproduction deals with the geometrical-kinematic problems of movement, contact, positioning, fusing, and cutting, and ignores the truly mechanical and chemical questions of force and energy. Hence I call it his *kinematic model* of self-reproduction. This early model is to be contrasted with his later *cellular model* of self-reproduction, which is presented in Part II of the present work.

In his June, 1948 lectures von Neumann raised the question of whether kinematic self-reproduction requires three dimensions. He suspected that either three dimensions or a Riemann surface (multiply-connected plane) would be needed. We will see in Part II that only two dimensions are required for self-reproduction in von Neumann's cellular model. This is a strong indication that two dimensions are sufficient for kinematic self-reproduction.

We return now to the Illinois lectures. Von Neumann discussed the general design of a self-reproducing automaton. He said that it is in principle possible to set up a machine shop which can make a copy of any machine, given enough time and raw materials. This shop would contain a machine tool B with the following powers. Given a pattern or object X, it would search over X and list its parts and their connections, thereby obtaining a description of X. Using this description, the tool B would then make a copy of X. "This is quite close to self-reproduction, because you can furnish B with itself."]

But it is easier, and for the ultimate purpose just as effective, not to construct an automaton which can copy any pattern or specimen given to it, but to construct an automaton which can produce an object starting from a logical description. In any conceivable method ever invented by man, an automaton which produces an object by copying a pattern will go first from the pattern to a description and then from the description to the object. It first abstracts what the thing is like, and then carries it out. It's therefore simpler not to extract from a real object its definition, but to start from the definition.

To proceed in this manner one must have axiomatic descriptions of automata. You see, I'm coming quite close to Turing's trick with universal automata, which also started with a general formal description of automata. If you take those dozen elements I referred to in a rather vague and general way and give exact descriptions of them (which could be done on two printed pages or less), you will have a formal language for describing automata unambiguously. Now any notation can be expressed as a binary notation, which can be recorded on a punched tape with a single channel. Hence any automaton description could be punched on a piece of tape. At first, it is better not to use a description of the pieces and how they fit together, but rather a description of the consecutive steps to be used in building the automaton.

[Von Neumann then showed how to construct a binary tape out of rigid elements. See Figure 2. A binary character is represented at each intersection of the basic chain; "one" is represented by an attached rigid element, "zero" by the absence of a side element. Writing and erasing are accomplished by adding and removing side elements.]

I have simplified unnecessarily, just because of a purely mathematical habit of trying to do things with a minimum of notation. Since I'm using a binary notation, all I'm attaching here is no side chain, or a one-step side chain. Existing languages and practical notations use more symbols than the binary system. There is no difficulty in using more symbols here;

you simply attach more complex side chains. In fact, the very linearity of our logical notation is completely unnecessary here. You could use more complicated looped chains, which would be perfectly good carriers for a code, but it would not be a linear code. There is reason to suspect that our predilection for linear codes, which have a simple, almost temporal sequence, is chiefly a literary habit, corresponding to our not particularly high level of combinatorial cleverness, and that a very efficient language would probably depart from linearity.[3]

There is no great difficulty in giving a complete axiomatic account of how to describe any conceivable automaton in a binary code. Any such description can then be represented by a chain of rigid elements like that of Figure 2. Given any automaton X, let $\phi(X)$ designate the chain which represents X. Once you have done this, you can design a universal machine tool A which, when furnished with such a chain $\phi(X)$, will take it and gradually consume it, at the same time building up the automaton X from the parts floating around freely in the surrounding milieu. All this design is laborious, but it is not difficult in principle, for it's a succession of steps in formal logics. It is not qualitatively different from the type of argumentation with which Turing constructed his universal automaton.

Another thing which one needs is this. I stated earlier that it might be quite complicated to construct a machine which will copy an automaton that is given it, and that it is preferable to proceed, not from original to copy, but from verbal description to copy. I would like to make one exception; I would like to be able to copy linear chains of rigid elements. Now this is very easy. For the real reason it is harder to copy an existing automaton than its description is that the existing automaton does not conform with our habit of linearity, its parts being connected with each other in all possible directions, and it's quite difficult just to check off the pieces that have already been described.[4] But it's not difficult to copy a linear chain of rigid elements. So I will assume that

---

[3] [The programming language of flow diagrams, invented by von Neumann, is a possible example. See p. 13 of the Introduction to the present volume.]

[4] [Compare Sec. 1.6.3 of Part II, written about 3 years later. Here von Neumann gives a more fundamental reason for having the constructing automaton work from a description of an automaton rather than from the automaton itself.]

there exists an automaton B which has this property: If you provide B with a description of anything, it consumes it and produces two copies of this description.

Please consider that after I have described these two elementary steps, one may still hold the illusion that I have not broken the principle of the degeneracy of complication. It is still not true that, starting from something, I have made something more subtle and more involved. The general constructive automaton A produces only X when a complete description of X is furnished it, and on any reasonable view of what constitutes complexity, this description of X is as complex as X itself. The general copying automaton B produces two copies of $\phi(X)$, but the juxtaposition of two copies of the same thing is in no sense of higher order than the thing itself. Furthermore, the extra unit B is required for this copying.

Now we can do the following thing. We can add a certain amount of control equipment C to the automaton $A + B$. The automaton C dominates both A and B, actuating them alternately according to the following pattern. The control C will first cause B to make two copies of $\phi(X)$. The control C will next cause A to construct X at the price of destroying one copy of $\phi(X)$. Finally, the control C will tie X and the remaining copy of $\phi(X)$ together and cut them loose from the complex $(A + B + C)$. At the end the entity $X + \phi(X)$ has been produced.

Now choose the aggregate $(A + B + C)$ for X. The automaton $(A+B+C)+\phi(A+B+C)$ will produce $(A+B+C)+\phi(A+B+C)$. Hence auto-reproduction has taken place.

[The details are as follows. We are given the universal constructor $(A+B+C)$, to which is attached a description of itself, $\phi(A+B+C)$. Thus the process of self-reproduction starts with $(A+B+C)+\phi(A+B+C)$. Control C directs B to copy the description twice; the result is $(A+B+C)+\phi(A+B+C)+\phi(A+B+C)$. Then C directs A to produce the automaton $A + B + C$ from one copy of the description; the result is $(A+B+C)+(A+B+C)+\phi(A+B+C)$. Finally, C ties the new automaton and its description together and cuts them loose. The final result consists of the two automata $(A+B+C)$ and $(A+B+C)+\phi(A+B+C)$. If B were to copy the description thrice, the process would start with one copy of $(A+B+C)+\phi(A+B+C)$ and terminate with two copies of this automaton. In this way, the universal constructor reproduces itself.]

This is not a vicious circle. It is quite true that I argued with a variable X first, describing what C is supposed to do, and then put something which involved C for X. But I defined A and B exactly, before I ever mentioned this particular X, and I defined C in terms which apply to any X. Therefore, in defining A, B, and C, I did not make use of what X is to be, and I am entitled later on to use an X which refers explicitly to A, B, and C. The process is not circular.

The general constructive automaton A has a certain creative ability, the ability to go from a description of an object to the object. Likewise, the general copying automaton B has the creative ability to go from an object to two copies of it. Neither of these automata, however, is self-reproductive. Moreover, the control automaton C is far from having any kind of creative or reproductive ability. All it can do is to stimulate two other organs so that they act in certain ways, tie certain things together, and cut these things loose from the original system. Yet the combination of the three automata A, B, and C is auto-reproductive. Thus you may break a self-reproductive system into parts whose functioning is necessary for the whole system to be self-reproductive, but which are not themselves self-reproductive.

You can do one more thing. Let X be $A + B + C + D$, where D is any automaton. Then $(A + B + C) + \phi(A + B + C + D)$ produces $(A+B+C+D)+\phi(A+B+C+D)$. In other words, our constructing automaton is now of such a nature that in its normal operation it produces another object D as well as making a copy of itself. This is the normal function of an auto-reproductive organism: it creates byproducts in addition to reproducing itself.

The system $(A + B + C + D)$ can undergo processes similar to the process of mutation. One of the difficulties in defining what one means by self-reproduction is that certain organizations, such as growing crystals, are self-reproductive by any naive definition of self-reproduction, yet nobody is willing to award them the distinction of being self-reproductive. A way around this difficulty is to say that self-reproduction includes the ability to undergo inheritable mutations as well as the ability to make another organism like the original.

Consider the situation with respect to the automaton $(A+B+C+D) + \phi(A + B + C + D)$. By a mutation I will simply mean a random change of one element anywhere. If an element is changed at random in one of the automata A, B, or C, the system will usually not completely reproduce itself. For example, if an element is changed in C, C may fail to stimulate A and B at the proper time, or it may fail to make the connections and disconnections which are required. Such a mutation is lethal.

If there is a change in the description $\phi(A+B+C+D)$, the system will produce, not itself, but a modification of itself. Whether the next generation can produce anything or not depends on where the change is. If the change is in A, B, or C, the next generation will be sterile. If the change occurs in D, the system with the mutation is exactly like the original system, except that D has been replaced by D'. This system can reproduce itself, but its by-product will be D' rather than D. This is the normal pattern of an inheritable mutation.

So, while this system is exceedingly primitive, it has the trait of an inheritable mutation, even to the point that a mutation made at random is most probably lethal, but may be non-lethal and inheritable. ✤

REFERENCES

Von Neumann, J. 1966a. In *Theory of Self-Reproducing Automata*, edited by A. W. Burks, 13. Urbana, IL: University of Illinois Press.

———. 1966b. "Copying: Use of Descriptions vs. Originals." In *Theory of Self-Reproducing Automata*, edited by A. W. Burks, 122–123. Urbana, IL: University of Illinois Press.

———. n.d. "The General and Logical Theory of Automata." In *John Von Neumann Collected Works*, 5:288–328.

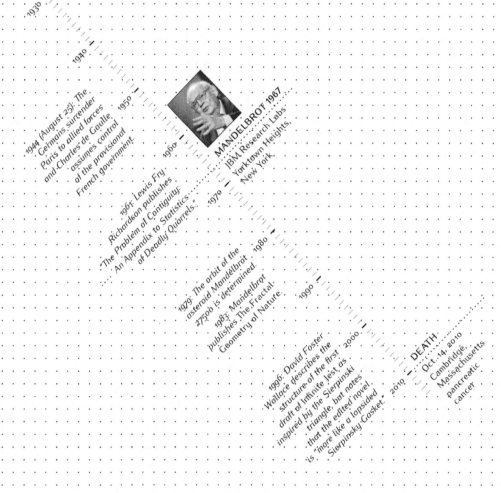

1918: Gaston Julia publishes "Memoir on the Iteration of Rational Functions."

1920

BIRTH
Nov. 20, 1924
Warsaw, Poland

1930

1940

1944 (August 25): The Germans surrender Paris to allied forces and Charles de Gaulle assumes control of the provisional French government.

1950

MANDELBROT 1967
IBM Research Labs
Yorktown Heights,
New York.

1960

1961: Lewis Fry Richardson publishes "The Problem of Contiguity; An Appendix to Statistics of Deadly Quarrels."

1970

1979: The orbit of the asteroid Mandelbrot 27500 is determined.

1980

1983: Mandelbrot publishes The Fractal Geometry of Nature.

1990

1996: David Foster Wallace describes the structure of the first draft of Infinite Jest as inspired by the Sierpinski triangle, but notes that the edited novel is "more like a lopsided Sierpinsky Gasket."

2000

DEATH
Oct. 14, 2010
Cambridge,
Massachusetts
pancreatic
cancer

2010

BENOIT B. MANDELBROT

[29]

FRACTALS, SELF-SIMILARITY, AND POWER LAWS

Geoffrey B. West, Santa Fe Institute

Few foundational concepts underlying complexity science have sparked the imagination and been embraced by both the academic and nonacademic community more than that of fractals. Most people are familiar with the idea. Simply put, fractals are objects that look approximately the same at all scales or at any level of magnification. Each subunit looks like a scaled-down version of the original whole with the same geometrical pattern repeating itself over and over as the resolution changes. For example, any branch of a tree when isolated looks like a scaled-down version of the original tree. This *self-similar property* embodied in fractals is ubiquitous throughout nature, ranging, to varying degrees, from circulatory and neural systems to transport systems, clouds, financial markets, and river and social networks. Indeed, the fascination with fractals largely derives from the remarkable observation that underlying the crinkliness, roughness, discontinuity, messiness, and apparent arbitrariness of the continuously evolving and adapting complex world around us lies a hidden regularity encapsulated in fractal-like structures.

This insight was pioneered by the mathematician Benoit Mandelbrot, who introduced the term *fractal* in 1975 when elaborating on ideas he had developed in his seminal 1967 paper "How Long Is the Coast of Britain? Statistical Self-Similarity and Fractional Dimension." This work and its rhetorical title were inspired by an equally seminal paper published in 1961 with the marvelously obscure title "The Problem of Contiguity: An Appendix to Statistics of Deadly Quarrels," written by the little-known polymath Lewis Fry Richardson. A passionate pacifist, Richardson had attempted to develop a quantitative theory for the origins of war and conflict and made the dubious hypothesis that the probability of

B. B. Mandelbrot, "How Long is the Coast of Britain? Statistical Self-Similarity and Fractional Dimension," in *Science* 156 (3775): 636–638 (1967).

Reprinted with permission from AAAS.

war between neighboring states was proportional to the length of their common border, so he turned his attention to measuring their lengths . . . and thereby discovered fractals, self-similarity, and power laws.

Implicit in the measurement process is the assumption that as the resolution of the measuring instrument increases, the result converges to an increasingly accurate fixed number, which is an objective property of the system (e.g., the length of this room is 9.73 meters or the height of the Empire State Building is 443.2 meters). However, when Richardson carried out this standard iterative procedure using calipers on detailed maps, he discovered that the finer the scale—and therefore the greater the accuracy—the longer the border got rather than converging to some specific value. Unlike lengths of rooms, shoes, or molecules, the lengths of borders and coastlines continually increased with increasing resolution, apparently violating the basic laws of measurement. Equally surprising, Richardson discovered that these lengths (L) increased systematically with resolution (G). When he plotted L versus G on a logarithmic scale, it revealed a simple straight line (fig. 1); in Mandelbrot's notation, $\log L = \log M + (1-D) \log G$, where M and D are constants with $(1-D)$ being the slope of the line. Mathematically, this is equivalent to the simple *power law*, $L = MG^{1-D}$, whose *exponent* is $(1-D)$.

This discovery was extremely strange since it indicated that, contrary to the belief going back several thousand years, some lengths are *not* an objective fixed property of the system but seem to depend on the resolution used to make the measurement.

So, what's going on here? Unlike living rooms, borders and coastlines are not straight lines; rather, they are squiggly and meandering. If a straight ruler or yardstick of length 200 km is laid between two points on a coastline or border, as is effectively done when surveying, then all of the many meanderings and wiggles in between are obviously missed (see fig. 1). However, with a 100-km-long ruler, the measuring process becomes sensitive to all the meanderings and wiggles previously missed whose scale is bigger than 100 km. This finer resolution follows these wiggles, thereby leading to an estimate necessarily larger than the coarser 200-km scale. Likewise, the 100-km scale is blind to similar meanderings and wiggles whose scale is smaller than 100 km, but which would be included if the resolution is increased to 50 km, leading to a further increase in the length.

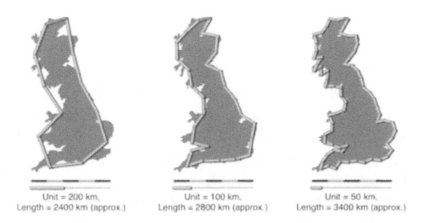

Figure 1. Measuring the lengths of a coastline using different resolutions (Britain in the example).

Thus, we can readily understand how such measured lengths continuously increase with increasing resolution. More challenging is to explain the origin of *self-similarity*, namely, that the wiggles and squiggles at one scale are, on average, nonlinearly scaled versions of the wiggles and squiggles at another, as expressed mathematically by the power law.

The lengths increase systematically with resolution following a power law as indicated by the examples in the graph. The slope gives the fractal dimension for the coastline: the more squiggly it is, the steeper the slope.

Crinkliness, or fractality, is quantified by the slopes of the straight lines on Richardson's logarithmic plots: the steeper the slope, the more crinkly or fractal the curve. For smooth curves, like circles, the slope is zero ($D = 1$), since its length does not change with resolution but converges to a definite value, as in the living room example. However, for rugged coastlines like the west coast of Britain, the slope is non-zero (0.25). For more crinkly coastlines like Norway with its fjords and multiple bays and inlets successively branching into increasingly smaller bays and inlets, the slope is 0.52. On the other hand, the South African coast has a slope of only 0.02, closely approximating a smooth curve. To appreciate what these numbers mean, imagine increasing the resolution by a factor of two, then the measured length of the west coast of Britain increases by about 25 percent and of Norway by over 50 percent. These are enormous effects, which had been completely overlooked until Richardson stumbled across them just eighty years ago. The take-home message is clear: *In general, it is meaningless to quote the value of a measured length without stating the resolution used to make it.* It is as meaningless as quoting a length as $1,543$, 27, or 1.289176 without giving the units; just as we need to know if it's miles, centimeters, or angstroms, we need to know the resolution.

To formalize these surprising observations, Mandelbrot introduced the concept of a *fractional* (later called fractal) *dimension*, D, defined by adding 1 to the exponents of the power law (the value of the slopes). Thus, for the South African coast $D = 1.02$, for Norway 1.52, and so on. The point of adding the 1 was to connect the idea of fractals to the conventional concept of ordinary dimensions. The meaning of a fractional dimension is through the scaling properties expressed by the power law.

Recall that a smooth line is one-dimensional, a smooth surface two-dimensional, and a volume three-dimensional. Thus, the South African coast is very close to being a smooth line because its fractal dimension is 1.02, very close to 1, whereas Norway is far from it because its fractal dimension of 1.52 is so much greater than 1. You could imagine an extreme case in which the line is so crinkly and convoluted that it effectively fills an entire area. Consequently, even though it's still a line with "ordinary" dimensions 1, it *scales as if* it were an *area* having fractal dimension 2. This curious gain of an effective additional dimension is a general feature of space-filling and plays an important role, for example, in organisms where networks need to penetrate "everywhere" and fill all of the space to service all cells.

Mathematicians had recognized for a long time that there were geometries outside of the classical Euclidean geometry that has formed the basis for mathematics and physics since ancient times. The traditional framework assumes that lines and surfaces are smooth and continuous. Novel concepts of multiple discontinuities and crinkliness were viewed as fascinating formal extensions of mathematics but not generally perceived as playing any significant role in the real world. It was Benoit Mandelbrot who made the crucial insight that, quite to the contrary, crinkliness, discontinuity, roughness, and self-similarity—in a word, fractality—are, in fact, ubiquitous features of the complex world we live in.

It is astonishing that this insight had alluded the greatest mathematicians, physicists, and natural philosophers for over 2,000 years. Like many great leaps, Mandelbrot's insight now seems almost obvious; after all, everyone is familiar with cauliflowers, vascular networks, streams, rivers, and mountain ranges, all of which are now perceived as fractals. Perhaps, like the erroneous Aristotelian assumption that heavier things "obviously" fall faster, the Platonic ideal of smoothness embodied in Euclidean geometry was so firmly engrained that it had to wait a very long time for someone to actually check it in the real world. That great discovery fell to Lewis Fry Richardson, though, as remarked by Mandelbrot, "unfortunately it attracted no attention." Equally ironic, Richardson's original motivation led him to another surprising discovery, namely, that the frequency distribution of different size wars also follows power law scaling, indicating that conflicts are approximately self-similar: a large war is just a scaled-up version of a small conflict governed by its fractal dimension. Among his many other accomplishments, Richardson pioneered the modern strategy for weather forecasting, conceived well before the development of modern computers, by augmenting the fundamental equations of hydrodynamics with continuously updated real-time weather data.

Mandelbrot put the concept of fractals on a sound mathematical footing, but equally importantly he realized that they are generalizable far beyond considerations of borders and coastlines to almost anything that can be measured. Examples include brains, crumpled paper, lightning, music, art, and time series like electrocardiograms and the stock market. Thus, the pattern of fluctuations in financial markets during an hour of trading is, on average, the same as that for a day, a month, a year, or a decade; the stock market is a self-similar fractal repeating itself across all time scales following a power law quantified by its fractal dimension.

Having revealed to the world the extraordinary universality of fractals, Mandelbrot's passion remained more impassioned with their mathematics than with understanding their physical mechanistic origins. Consequently, his great insight did not receive quite the appreciation in the physics community and scientific establishment that it deserved, despite broad recognition in many quarters, and especially with those developing the science of complexity. ✦

HOW LONG IS THE COAST OF BRITAIN? STATISTICAL SELF-SIMILARITY AND FRACTIONAL DIMENSION

Benoit Mandelbrot, Thomas J. Watson Research Center

Abstract

Geographical curves are so involved in their detail that their lengths are often infinite or, rather, undefinable. However, many are statistically "self-similar," meaning that each portion can be considered a reduced-scale image of the whole. In that case, the degree of complication can be described by a quantity D that has many properties of a "dimension," though it is fractional; that is, it exceeds the value unity associated with the ordinary, rectifiable, curves.

Seacoast shapes are examples of highly involved curves such that each of their portion can—in a statistical sense—be considered a reduced-scale image of the whole. This property will be referred to as "statistical self-similarity." To speak of a length for such figures is usually meaningless. Similarly, "the left bank of the Vistula, when measured with increased precision, would furnish lengths ten, hundred or even thousand times as great as the length read off the school map" (Steinhaus 1954, where earlier references are listed). More generally, geographical curves can be considered as superpositions of features of widely scattered characteristic size; as ever finer features are taken account of, the measured total length increases, and there is usually no clearcut gap between the realm of geography and details with which geography need not be concerned.

Quantities other than length are thus needed to discriminate between various degrees of complication for a geographical curve. When a curve is self-similar, it is characterized by an exponent of similarity, D, which possesses many properties of a dimension, though it is usually a fraction greater than the dimension 1 commonly attributed to curves. We shall reexamine in this light some empirical observations by Richardson (1961). I propose to interpret them as implying, for

At the outset Mandelbrot immediately introduces the concept of "self-similarity" that he had pioneered in his papers of just a few years earlier on time series in financial markets and noise more generally. It wasn't until 1975 that he coined the term "fractal" to generalize the concept beyond geometric curves (such as borders and coastlines) or time series in order to put the concept on a formal mathematical basis. For most practical purposes, the terms fractal and self-similar are synonymous and expressible as simple power laws, as explained in the ensuing pages.

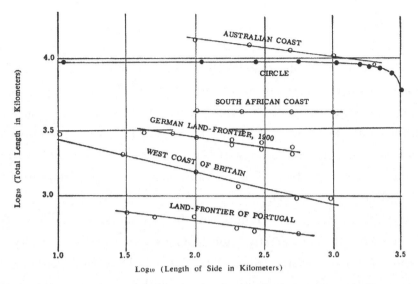

Figure 1. Richardson's data concerning measurements of geographical curves by way of polygons which have equal sides and have their corners on the curve. For the circle, the total length tends to a limit as the side goes to zero. In all other cases, it increases as the side becomes shorter, the slope of the doubly logarithmic graph being in absolute value equal to $D - 1$. (Reproduced from Richardson 1961, Fig. 17, by permission.)

example, that the dimension of the west coast of Great Britain is $D = 1.25$. Thus, the so far esoteric concept of "random figure of fractional dimension" is shown to have simple and concrete applications and great usefulness.

Self-similarity methods are a potent tool in the study of chance phenomena, including geostatistics, as well as economics (Mandelbrot 1964) and physics (Mandelbrot 1965, 1967).[1] In fact, many noises have dimensions D contained between 0 and 1, so that the scientist ought to consider dimension as a continuous quantity ranging from 0 to infinity.

Returning to the claim made in the first paragraph, let us review the methods used when attempting to measure the length of a seacoast. Since a geographer is unconcerned with minute details, he may choose a positive scale G as a lower limit to the length of geographically meaningful features. Then, to evaluate the length of a coast between two of its points A and B, he may draw the shortest inland curve joining

To his credit, Mandelbrot gives due recognition to Steinhaus and Richardson, both of whom had earlier realized the inherent problem of measuring the lengths of meandering or crinkly geographical features. Although Steinhaus focused more on the conceptual mathematics of the paradox, it was the more practically minded Richardson who saw that the dependence on scale can be well approximated by a power law. As Mandelbrot ruefully remarks, Richardson got little recognition for his remarkable insight and seminal observations; Steinhaus got even less!

---

[1] Very similar considerations apply in turbulence, where the characteristic sizes of the "features" (that is, the eddies) are also very widely scattered, as was first pointed out by Richardson himself in the 1920s.

A and B while staying within a distance G of the sea. Alternatively, he may draw the shortest line made of straight segments of length at most G, whose vertices are points of the coast which include A and B. There are many other possible definitions. In practice, of course, one must be content with approximations to shortest paths. We shall suppose that measurements are made by walking a pair of dividers along a map so as to count the number of equal sides of length G of an open polygon whose corners lie on the curve. If G is small enough, it does not matter whether one starts from A or B. Thus, one obtains an estimate of the length to be called $L(G)$.

Unfortunately, geographers will disagree about the value of G, while $L(G)$ depends greatly upon G. Consequently, it is necessary to know $L(G)$ for several values of G. Better still, it would be nice to have an analytic formula linking $L(G)$ with G. Such a formula, of an entirely empirical character, was proposed by Lewis F. Richardson but unfortunately it attracted no attention. The formula is $L(G) = MG^{1-D}$, where M is a positive constant and D is a constant at least equal to unity. This D, a "characteristic of a frontier, may be expected to have some positive correlation with one's immediate visual perception of the irregularity of the frontier. At one extreme, $D = 1.00$ for a frontier that looks straight on the map. For the other extreme, the west coast of Britain was selected because it looks like one of the most irregular in the world; it was found to give $D = 1.25$. Three other frontiers which, judging by their appearance on the map were more like the average of the world in irregularity, gave $D = 1.15$ for the land frontier of Germany in about A.D. 1899; $D = 1.14$ for the land frontier between Spain and Portugal and $D = 1.13$ for the Australian coast. A coast selected as looking one of the smoothest in the atlas, was that of South Africa and for it, $D = 1.02$."

Richardson's empirical finding is in marked contrast with the ordinary behavior of smooth curves, which are endowed with a well-defined length and are said to be "rectifiable." Thus, to quote Steinhaus again, "a statement nearly adequate to reality would be to call most arcs encountered in nature not rectifiable. This statement is contrary to the belief that not rectifiable arcs are an invention of mathematicians and that natural arcs are rectifiable: it is the opposite that is true."

Ironically, the crux of the paper is in its first three pages where Mandelbrot succinctly reviews the pioneering work of Steinhaus and Richardson, thereby bringing their revolutionary observations to the attention of the broader scientific community. He then made the leap, which is somewhat tentative here, that this phenomenon (namely, the dependence of measured quantities on scale) is, in fact, a very general, deep, and ubiquitous characteristic of nature. This had to wait till the publication of his classic book *The Fractal Geometry of Nature* in 1983.

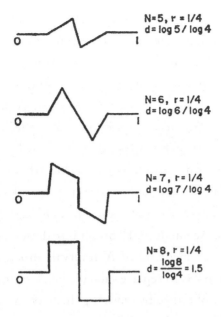

Figure 2. Nonrectifiable self-similar curves can be obtained as follows. Step 1: Choose any of the above drawings. Step 2: Replace each of its N legs by a curve deduced from the whole drawing through similarity of ratio $(1/4)$. One is left with a curve made of N^2 legs of length $(1/4)^2$. Step 3: Replace each leg by a curve obtained from the whole drawing through similarity of ratio $(1/4)^2$. The desired self-similar curve is approached by an infinite sequence of these steps.

I interpret Richardson's relation as contrary to the belief that curves of dimension greater than one are an invention of mathematicians. For that, it is necessary to review an elementary feature of the concept of dimension and to show how it naturally leads to the consideration of fractional dimensions.

To begin, a straight line has dimension one. Hence, for every positive integer N, the segment $(0 \leqslant x < X)$ can be exactly decomposed into N nonoverlapping segments of the form $[(n-1)X/N \leqslant x < nX/N]$, where n runs from 1 to N. Each of these parts is deducible from the whole by a similarity of ratio $r(N) = 1/N$. Similarly, a plane has dimension two. Hence, for every perfect square N, the rectangle $(0 \leqslant x < X; 0 \leqslant y < Y)$ can be decomposed exactly into N nonoverlapping rectangles of the form $[(k-1)X/\sqrt{N} \leqslant x < kX/\sqrt{N}; (h-1)Y/\sqrt{N} \leqslant y < hY/\sqrt{N}]$, where k and h run from 1 to $\sqrt{N}$. Each of these parts is deducible from the whole by a similarity of ratio $r(N) = 1/\sqrt{N}$. More generally, whenever $N^{1/D}$ is a positive integer, a D-dimensional rectangular parallelepiped can be decomposed into N parallelepipeds

The idea that certain geometries could be described as having non-integer dimensions had already been considered by mathematicians, the best known of whom was Felix Hausdorff; however, they were regarded as bizarre curiosities that had little, if anything, to do with the "real world." Hence this slightly defensive remark that they are "an invention of mathematicians" (a similar remark had already been made by Steinhaus).

As an example, Mandelbrot gives here a calculation of the Haussdorff dimension (which he later called the fractal dimension) for a "non-rectifiable self-similar curve"—one introduced by Koch. Such curves have increasing discontinuity in their derivative as their length increases, simulating increasing, self-similar roughness. Though relatively simple, the calculation is not very elegant; much better to look at later papers, or better still, books on fractals. Curiously, Mandelbrot fails to reference or even mention Hausdorff, perhaps assuming that we all know what he's referring to!

Given that Mandelbrot spent much of his life vehemently arguing that nature is dominated by fractals (or, rather, fractal-like geometry) and that Euclidean straight lines and smooth surfaces are the rare exception, it is amusing that in this seminal paper he makes the remark that "self-similar figures are seldom encountered in nature." As a mathematician, he of course meant *exact* self-similar figures. Hence the qualifier of a "statistical form of self-similarity."

deducible from the whole by a similarity of ratio $r(N) = 1/N^{1/D}$. Thus, the dimension D is characterized by the relation $D = -\log N / \log r(N)$.

This last property of the quantity D means that it can also be evaluated for more general figures that can be exactly decomposed into N parts such that each of the parts is deducible from the whole by a similarity of ratio $r(N)$, or perhaps by a similarity followed by rotation and even symmetry. If such figures exist, they may be said to have $D = -\log N / \log r(N)$ for dimension (5).[2] To show that such figures exist, it suffices to exhibit a few obvious variants of von Koch's continuous nondifferentiable curve. Each of these curves is constructed as a limit. Step 0 is to draw the segment $(0, 1)$. Step 1 is to draw either of the kinked curves of Fig. 2, each made up of N intervals superposable upon the segment $(0, \frac{1}{4})$. Step 2 is to replace each of the N segments used in step 1 by a kinked curve obtained by reducing the curve of step 1 in the ratio $r(N) = \frac{1}{4}$. One obtains altogether N^2 segments of length $1/16$. Each repetition of the same process adds further detail; as the number of steps grows to infinity, our kinky curves tend toward continuous limits and it is obvious by inspection that these limits are self-similar, since they are exactly decomposable into N parts deducible from the whole by a similarity of ratio $r(N) = \frac{1}{4}$ followed by translation. Thus, given N, the limit curve can be said to have dimension $D = -\log N / \log r(N) = \log N / \log 4$. Since N is greater than 4 in our examples, the corresponding dimensions all exceed unity. Let us now consider length: at step number s, our approximation is made of N^8 segments of length $G = (\frac{1}{4})^8$, so that $L = (N/4)^8 = G^{1-D}$. Thus, the length of the limit curve is infinite, even though it is a "line." (Note that it is not excluded for a plane curve to have a dimension equal to 2. An example is Peano's curve, which fills up a square.)

Practical application of this notion of dimension requires further consideration, because self-similar figures are seldom encountered in nature (crystals are one exception). However, a statistical form of self-

---

[2] The concept of "dimension" is elusive and very complex, and is far from exhausted by the simple considerations of the kind used in this paper. Different definitions frequently yield different results, and the field abounds in paradoxes. However, the Hausdorff–Besicovitch dimension and the capacitary dimension, when computed for random self-similar figures, have so far yielded the same value as the similarity dimension.

similarity is often encountered, and the concept of dimension may be further generalized. To say that a (closed) plane figure is chosen at random implies several definitions. First, one must select a family of possible figures, usually designated by Ω. When this family contains a finite number of members, the rule of random choice is specified by attributing to each possible figure a well-defined probability of being chosen. However, Ω is in general infinite and each figure has a zero probability of being chosen. But positive probabilities can be attached to appropriately defined "events" (such as the event that the chosen figure differs little—in some specified sense—from some specified figure).

For the family Ω, together with the definition of events and their probabilities, to be self-similar, two conditions are needed. First, each of the possible figures must be constructible by somehow stringing together N figures, each of which is deduced from a possible figure by a similarity of ratio r; second, the probabilities must be so specified that the same value is obtained whether one selects the overall figure at one swoop or as a string. (The value of N may either be arbitrary, or chosen from some specific sequence, such as the perfect squares relative to nonrandom rectangles, or the integral powers of $4, 5, 6,$ or 7 encountered in the curves built as in Fig. 2.) In case that the value of r is specified by choosing N, one can consider $-\log N / \log r$ a similarity dimension. More usually, however, given r, N will take different values for different figures of Ω. As one considers points "sufficiently far" from each other, the details on a "sufficiently fine" scale may become asymptotically independent, in such a way that $-\log N / \log r$ almost surely tends to some limit as r tends to zero. In that case, this limit may be considered a similarity dimension. Under wide conditions, the length of approximating polygons will asymptotically behave like $L(G) \sim G^{1-D}$.

To specify the mathematical conditions for the existence of a similarity dimension is not a fully solved problem. In fact, even the idea that a geographical curve is random raises a number of conceptual problems familiar in other applications of randomness. Therefore, to return to Richardson's empirical law, the most that can be said with perfect safety is that it is compatible with the idea that geographical curves are random self-similar figures of fractional

From the perspective of a "science of complexity," and especially that of a physicist, it's surprising that nowhere in the paper is there any consideration or curiosity about the mechanistic or dynamic origins of fractality or self-similarity. Indeed, at best, this was of secondary interest to Mandelbrot; his interest was to reveal their underlying formal mathematical structure, which ultimately led to the concept of the "Mandelbrot set" for the space such idealized geometric objects occupy.

Surprisingly for a renowned mathematician, Mandelbrot did not occupy a regular tenured position in a university till very late in life (in his mid-70s) when he was appointed the Sterling Professor of Mathematical Sciences at Yale. In addition to being the "father of fractals," his other great claim to fame is that he was the oldest professor in Yale's history to receive tenure!

dimension D. Empirical scientists having to be content with less than perfect inductions, I favor the more positive interpretation stated at the beginning of this report. ☙

REFERENCES

Mandelbrot, B. 1964. "The Variation of Certain Speculative Prices." In *The Random Character of Stock Market Prices,* edited by P. H. Cootner, 297. Also in *The Random Character of Stock Market Prices,* P. H. Cootner, ed. (MIT Press, Cambridge, Mass., 1964), p. 297.

———. 1965. "Self-Similar Error Clusters in Communication Systems and Concept of Conditional Stationarity." *IEEE Transactions on Communication Technology* 13:71.

———. 1967. "Some Noises WithI/fspectrum, a Bridge Between Direct Current and White Noise." *IEEE Transactions on Communication Technology* 13:289.

Richardson, L. F. 1961. "The Problem of Contiguity: An Appendix to Statistics of Deadly Quarrels." *General Systems Yearbook* 6:139.

Steinhaus, H. 1954. "Length, Shape, and Area." *Colloquium Mathmaticum* 3:1–13.

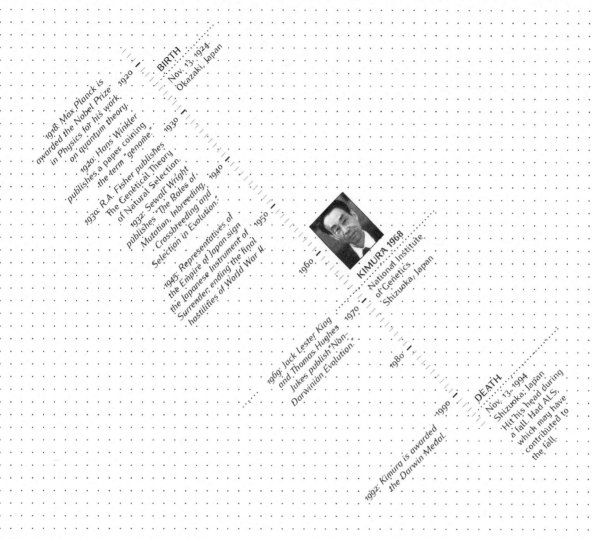

1918: Max Planck is
awarded the Nobel Prize
in Physics for his work
on quantum theory.

1920

BIRTH
Nov. 13, 1924.
Okazaki, Japan

1920: Hans Winkler
publishes a paper coining
the term "genome."

1930

1930: R.A. Fisher publishes
The Genetical Theory
of Natural Selection.

1932: Sewall Wright
publishes "The Roles of
Mutation, Inbreeding,
Crossbreeding and
Selection in Evolution."

1940

1945: Representatives of
the Empire of Japan sign
the Japanese Instrument of
Surrender, ending the final
hostilities of World War II.

1950

KIMURA 1968
National Institute
of Genetics.
Shizuoka, Japan

1960

1969: Jack Lester King
and Thomas Hughes
Jukes publish "Non-
Darwinian Evolution."

1970

1980

DEATH
Nov. 13, 1994.
Shizuoka, Japan
Hit his head during
a fall. Had ALS,
which may have
contributed to
the fall.

1990

1992: Kimura is awarded
the Darwin Medal.

MOTOO KIMURA

[30]

ORIGINS OF THE NEUTRAL THEORY

Carl T. Bergstrom, University of Washington, and
Michael Lachmann, Santa Fe Institute

By establishing a compelling case for neutral evolution at the molecular level, Motoo Kimura's 1968 *Nature* paper laid an important cornerstone for our modern understanding of biology. While Kimura's short report has become the canonical citation that biologists use when referencing the neutral theory of evolution, many biologists are unaware of the beautiful way in which it drives to this conclusion by bringing deep theoretical insights to bear on newly-obtained empirical evidence.

M. Kimura, "Evolutionary Rate at the Molecular Level," *Nature* 217: 624–626 (1968).

Reprinted with permission of Springer Nature.

Let's begin with some context. In the 1930s and 1940s, biologists unified a Darwinian view of evolution with the emerging field of transmission genetics through intensive theoretical and empirical work across the span of biology. The vision of evolution that emerged from this "modern evolutionary synthesis" was—despite support for the notion of neutral characters in the writings of Charles Darwin, Julian Huxley, Ernst Mayr, and others—predominantly panselectionist. Evolutionary change was taken to be almost exclusively the consequence of natural selection. Where variation was observed, it demanded a selective explanation: either a selective change was underway, or polymorphism was maintained by balancing selection in favor of heterozygous individuals (Gould 1983; Dietrich 1994; Provine 1990).

This so-called modern synthesis was crafted before its architects knew the underlying molecular basis of inheritance. DNA was not decisively shown to be the hereditary material until the 1940s and 1950s (Avery, MacLeod, and McCarty 1944; Hershey and Chase 1952). Its structure was only revealed in 1953 (Watson and Crick 1953). And most importantly, the genetic code by which nucleotide triplets specify amino acids was not worked out until 1961–1966 (Nirenberg 1968).

As a result, it was unclear what room there might be for neutral characters in a mathematical theory of biological evolution. Kimura had long been intrigued by the idea of neutral evolution, but his intuitions obtained traction neither with the selectionist Fisherian school, nor with Sewall Wright and his followers, who felt that gene interactions were ubiquitous and sufficiently complex to ensure that nearly all allelic differences had selective effects. Still, in 1964 Kimura and geneticist James Crow went through the exercise of working out the population genetics of neutral loci, should such exist (Kimura and Crow 1964). The rationale that they provided should inspire theoreticians everywhere.

> It is not the purpose of this article to discuss the plausibility of such a system of isoalleles, or the evidence for or against. Instead, we propose to examine some of the population genetic consequences of such a system if it does exist. The probability seems great enough to warrant such an inquiry.

Working out the dynamics of a plausible imagined world is a fruitful exercise no matter what the true state of affairs turns out to be. If the imagined world turns out to be accurate, one has gotten a head start on understanding it. If it turns out to be inaccurate, the exercise may nonetheless lead to unexpected insights about reality.

Before an understanding of the genetic code, notions of neutral evolution had focused on neutral phenotypes. The discovery of how DNA codes for amino acid sequences opened the door to thinking about neutrality at the molecular level. Kimura took every advantage of this in his 1968 paper included here.

When Kimura wrote this paper, there was no way to directly assess the fitness effects of molecular variation in populations. The genius of the paper was to recognize that one didn't need to measure fitness consequences directly. If one can estimate the rate at which new variants are fixed in a population, this has strong implications about the intensity of selection that could have been involved.

Thus the 1968 paper begins with what is essentially an exercise in Fermi estimation. In the absence of data on molecular variation within populations, Kimura had to rely on estimates of variation between populations—in this case, divergence in protein sequence across vertebrate species. He estimates that we should see roughly one nucleotide substitution in a population every two years.

That figure, Kimura observes, is far higher than can be supported by panselectionist explanations. Here Kimura needed some basic theory about the cost of natural selection, and turned to work that J. B. S. Haldane had published several years earlier (Haldane 1957). In that paper, Haldane estimated that a population could reasonably sustain itself while undergoing one substitution every 300 generations. Kimura himself had derived an alternative—and in our view more elegant— formulation in papers published shortly thereafter (Kimura 1960, 1961). That result is worth describing in detail.

In these papers, Kimura explored a concept he called *substitutional load*. For a favored allele to replace a disfavored one by natural selection, individuals carrying the disfavored allele must reproduce less rapidly than those carrying the favored variant. This takes a toll on the Malthusian (geometric-mean) growth rate of the population. Kimura developed a simple mathematical model suggesting that this cost, integrated over the entire period during which a substitution occurs, is independent of the strength of selection against the disfavored allele. Whether the disfavored allele suffers a huge fitness cost for a few generations or a tiny fitness cost for eons, the ultimate effect on the growth rate of the population is the same.

It is worth mentioning that in addition to deriving an estimate of the cost of a gene substitution, Kimura's 1961 paper establishes a fundamental link between the *cost of natural selection* and the *amount of information* that natural selection encodes into the genome. A substitutional load that reduces the growth rate of the population by a factor L can encode at most $\mathrm{Log}_2 L$ bits in the genome. Researchers have been slow to develop an information-theoretic view of natural selection, but we believe that such a theory will be a critical component of a mature theory of biological evolution.

Based on this theory, Kimura concludes that natural selection could not be the primary driver of molecular evolution. Given the rate of amino acid substitution, the cost of this on populations would be far too high to be sustainable. This inference thus provided a grounding for the neutral theory. It is important to be clear about what the neutral theory says. It does not suggest that most amino acid changes will have no phenotypic effects, nor does it mean that most changes will have no fitness consequences. The core claim of the neutral theory is that most of the variation observed in populations and that most substitutions observed over time are neutral, or nearly so (Ohta 1992).

Over the past half-century, Kimura's argument that many amino acid substitutions are driven by mechanisms other than selection has become generally accepted, though attention has shifted somewhat. For decades after Kimura's paper was published, genetic drift—random fluctuation of allele frequencies due to finite population sizes (Wright 1931)—was seen as the primary driver of neutral substitution. Population geneticists today put more emphasis on genetic draft, the happenstance of where a neutral variant arises on a selectively favored or disfavored genetic background (Gillespie 2000). The neutral theory has also been expanded well beyond amino acid sequence. In animals and plants, only a small fraction of the genome codes for amino acid sequences to be transcribed to mRNA—the rest of the genome either codes for other types of RNA molecules, or is composed of introns, retroviruses, repetitive elements, and so forth. Most of these regions are under weaker selection than protein coding regions, and their function is less well understood. An ongoing debate rages around whether these domains are entirely non-functional, but whatever the resolution, these arguments do not contradict Kimura's model (Pennisi 2012; Doolittle 2013).

We conclude by noting that, while Kimura's empirical inferences about the importance of non-selective processes in evolution are broadly (if not universally) accepted, the adequacy of the theoretical argument that he used to reach this conclusion remains unresolved. The problem is essentially that Haldane–Kimura arguments about substitution load rely on very simple models of reproduction and gene interactions. In a sexually reproducing population with gene interactions, the substitution load may be substantially lower than Kimura's estimates. Arguments to this effect appeared the same year that Kimura's paper was published (Maynard Smith 1968; Sved 1968) and the issue remains unresolved today.

In some sense that resolution is irrelevant to the importance of Kimura's 1968 paper as a foundational contribution to the science of complex systems. Regardless of how things play out, the paper stands as a remarkable illustration of how theory in one domain can be combined with empirical evidence in another to make powerful and testable predictions about a complex system—predictions that have largely been confirmed in the decades since the publication of this work. ❧

REFERENCES

Avery, O. T., C. M. MacLeod, and M. McCarty. 1944. "Studies on the Chemical Nature of the Substance Inducing Transformation of Pneumococcal Types: Induction of Transformation by a Desoxyribonucleic Acid Fraction Isolated from Pneumococcus Type III." *Journal of Experimental Medicine* 79 (2): 137–158. https://doi.org/10.1084/jem.79.2.137.

Dietrich, M. R. 1994. "The Origins of the Neutral Theory of Molecular Evolution." *Journal of the History of Biology* 27:21–59. https://doi.org/10.1007/BF01058626.

Doolittle, W. F. 2013. "Is Junk DNA Bunk? A Critique of ENCODE." *Proceedings of the National Academy of Sciences* 110 (14): 5294–5300. https://doi.org/10.1073/pnas.1221376110.

Gillespie, J. H. 2000. "Genetic Drift in an Infinite Population: The Pseudohitchhiking Model." *Genetics* 155 (2): 909–919. https://doi.org/10.1093/genetics/155.2.909.

Gould, S. J. 1983. "The Hardening of the Modern Synthesis." In *Dimensions of Darwinism,* edited by M. Grene. Cambridge, UK: Cambridge University Press.

Haldane, J. B. S. 1957. "The Cost of Natural Selection." *Journal of Genetics* 55:511–524. https://doi.org/10.1007/BF02984069.

Hershey, A. D., and M. Chase. 1952. "Independent Functions of Viral Protein and Nucleic Acid in Growth of Bacteriophage." *Journal of General Physiology* 36 (1): 39–56. https://doi.org/10.1085/jgp.36.1.39.

Kimura, M. 1960. "Optimum Mutation Rate and Degree of Dominance as Determined by the Principle of Minimum Genetic Load." *Journal of Genetics* 57:21–34. https://doi.org/10.1007/BF02985336.

———. 1961. "Natural Selection as the Process of Accumulating Genetic Information in Adaptive Evolution." *Genetical Research* 2 (1): 127–140. https://doi.org/10.1017/S0016672300000616..

Kimura, M., and J. F. Crow. 1964. "The Number of Alleles That Can Be Maintained in a Finite Population." *Genetics* 49 (4): 725–738. https://doi.org/10.1093/genetics/49.4.725.

Maynard Smith, J. 1968. "'Haldane's Dilemma' and the Rate of Evolution." *Nature* 219:1114–1116. https://doi.org/10.1073/pnas.1221376110.

Nirenberg, M. 1968. "Genetic Memory." *JAMA* 206 (9): 1973–1977. https://doi.org/10.1001/jama.1968.03150090049012.

Ohta, T. 1992. "The Nearly Neutral Theory of Molecular Evolution." *Annual Review of Ecology and Systematics* 23:263–286. https://doi.org/10.1146/annurev.es.23.110192.001403.

Pennisi, E. 2012. "ENCODE Project Writes Eulogy for Junk DNA." *Science* 337 (6099): 1159–1161. https://doi.org/10.1126/science.337.6099.1159.

Provine, W. B. 1990. "The Neutral Theory of Molecular Evolution in Historical Perspective." In *Population Biology of Genes and Molecules,* edited by N. Takahata and J. F. Crow, 17–31. Tokyo, Japan: Baifukan.

Sved, J. A. 1968. "Possible Rates of Gene Substitution in Evolution." *The American Naturalist* 102 (925): 283–293. https://doi.org/10.1086/282542.

Watson, J. D., and F. H. C. Crick. 1953. "Molecular Structure of Nucleic Acids: A Structure for Deoxyribose Nucleic Acid." *Nature* 171:737–738. https://doi.org/10.1038/171737a0.

Wright, S. 1931. "Evolution in Mendelian Populations." *Genetics* 16 (2): 97–159. https://doi.org/10.1093/genetics/16.2.97.

EVOLUTIONARY RATE AT THE MOLECULAR LEVEL

Motoo Kimura, National Institute of Genetics

Abstract

Calculating the rate of evolution in terms of nucleotide substitutions seems to give a value so high that many of the mutations involved must be neutral ones.

Comparative studies of haemoglobin molecules among different groups of animals suggest that, during the evolutionary history of mammals, amino-acid substitution has taken place roughly at the rate of one amino-acid change in 10^7 yr for a chain consisting of some 140 amino-acids. For example, by comparing the α and β chains of man with those of horse, pig, cattle and rabbit, the figure of one amino-acid change in 7×10^6 yr was obtained (Zuckerkandl and Pauling 1965). This is roughly equivalent to the rate of one amino-acid substitution in 10^7 yr for a chain consisting of 100 amino-acids.

A comparable value has been derived from the study of the haemoglobin of primates (Buettner-Janusch and Hill 1965). The rate of amino-acid substitution calculated by comparing mammalian and avian cytochrome c (consisting of about 100 amino-acids) turned out to be one replacement in 45×10^6 yr (Margoliash and Smith 1965). Also by comparing the amino-acid composition of human triosephosphate dehydrogenase with that of rabbit and cattle (Kaplan 1965), a figure of at least one amino-acid substitution for every 2.7×10^6 yr can be obtained for the chain consisting of about 1,110 amino-acids. This figure is roughly equivalent to the rate of one amino-acid substitution in 30×10^6 yr for a chain consisting of 100 amino-acids. Averaging those figures for haemoglobin, cytochrome c and triosephosphate dehydrogenase gives an evolutionary rate of approximately one substitution in 28×10^6 yr for a polypeptide chain consisting of 100 amino-acids.

I intend to show that this evolutionary rate, although appearing to be very low for each polypeptide chain of a size of cytochrome c, actually amounts to a very high rate for the entire genome.

First, the DNA content in each nucleus is roughly the same among different species of mammals such as man, cattle and rat (see, for example, Sager and Ryan 1961). Furthermore, we note that the G–C content of DNA is fairly uniform among mammals, lying roughly within the range of 40–44 per cent (Sueoka 1961). These two facts suggest that nucleotide substitution played a principal part in mammalian evolution.

Current estimates are slightly lower, around 3.2×10^9 bases in the haploid human genome.

In the following calculation, I shall assume that the haploid chromosome complement comprises about 4×10^9 nucleotide pairs, which is the number estimated by Muller (1958) from the DNA content of human sperm. Each amino-acid is coded by a nucleotide triplet (codon), and so a polypeptide chain of 100 amino-acids corresponds to 300 nucleotide pairs in a genome. Also, amino-acid replacement is the result of nucleotide replacement within a codon. Because roughly 20 per cent of nucleotide replacement caused by mutation is estimated to be synonymous (Kimura 1968), that is, it codes for the same amino-acid, one amino-acid replacement may correspond to about 1.2 base pair replacements in the genome. The average time taken for one base pair replacement within a genome is therefore

$$28 \times 10^6 \text{yr} \div \left(\frac{4 \times 10^9}{300} \right) \div 1.2 \doteqdot 1.8 \text{yr}$$

Kimura's estimate of annual substitution rate is just a bit lower than the current estimate.

This means that in the evolutionary history of mammals, nucleotide substitution has been so fast that, on average, one nucleotide pair has been substituted in the population roughly every 2 yr.

This figure is in sharp contrast to Haldane's well known estimate (Haldane 1957) that, in horotelic evolution (standard rate evolution), a new allele may be substituted in a population roughly every 300 generations. He arrived at this figure by assuming that the cost of natural selection per generation (the substitutional load in my terminology, Kimura 1960) is roughly 0.1, while the total cost for one allelic substitution is about 30. Actually, the calculation of the cost based on Haldane's formula shows that if new alleles produced by nucleotide replacement are substituted in a population at the rate of one substitution every 2 yr, then the substitutional load becomes so large that no mammalian species could tolerate it.

Thus the very high rate of nucleotide substitution which I have calculated can only be reconciled with the limit set by the substitutional load by assuming that most mutations produced by nucleotide replacement are almost neutral in natural selection. It can be shown that in a population of effective size N_e, if the selective advantage of the new allele over the pre-existing alleles is s, then, assuming no dominance, the total load for one gene substitution is

$$L(p) = 2\left\{\frac{1}{u(p)} - 1\right\}$$
$$\int_0^{4Sp} \frac{e^y - 1}{y}dy - 2e^{-4S}\int_{4Sp}^{4S} \frac{e^y}{y}dy + 2\log_e\left(\frac{1}{p}\right) \qquad (1)$$

where $S = N_e s$ and p is the frequency of the new allele at the start. The derivation of the foregoing formula will be published elsewhere. In the expression given here $u(p)$ is the probability of fixation given by (Kimura 1957)

$$u(p) = \left(1 - e^{-4Sp}\right) / \left(1 - e^{-4S}\right) \qquad (2)$$

Now, in the special case of $|2N_e s| \leqslant 1$, formulae 1 and 2 reduce to

$$L(p) = 4N_e s \log_e(1/p) \qquad (1')$$

$$u(p) = p + 2N_e sp(1 - p) \qquad (2')$$

Formula ($1'$) shows that for a nearly neutral mutation the substitutional load can be very low and there will be no limit to the rate of gene substitution in evolution. Furthermore, for such a mutant gene, the probability of fixation (that is, the probability by which it will be established in the population) is roughly equal to its initial frequency as shown by equation ($2'$). This means that new alleles may be produced at the same rate per individual as they are substituted in the population in evolution.

This brings the rather surprising conclusion that in mammals neutral (or nearly neutral) mutations are occurring at the rate of roughly 0.5 per yr per gamete. Thus, if we take the average length of one generation in the history of mammalian evolution as 4 yr, the mutation rate per generation

By "no dominance," Kimura means that the heterozygote has a fitness halfway between the fitnesses of the homozygotes.

Note that Kimura's model also assumes that the fitness effect of each locus is independent of every other locus, i.e., that there is no epistasis. John Maynard Smith (1968) relaxed this assumption and found that in the presence of the right kinds of epistasis— namely threshold selection— substitution load can be lower.

This is one of our favorite results on mathematical population genetics because it is both counterintuitive and simple. Why should neutral substitutions occur in the population at the same rate that neutral mutations arise in individuals? Imagine the line of individuals stretching over time from some distant ancestor of yours to you. If we assume that mutations in your lineage don't affect anything (i.e., are neutral), then the rate at which your genome differs from your ancestor is simply the rate at which mutations accumulate along your lineage.

In the limit as time gets large, most of the differences between you and your ancestor will be substitutions that are fixed in the population.

for neutral mutations amounts to roughly two per gamete and four per zygote (5×10^{-10} per nucleotide site per generation).

Such a high rate of neutral mutations is perhaps not surprising, for Mukai (1964) has demonstrated that in *Drosophila* the total mutation rate for "viability polygenes" which on the average depress the fitness by about 2 per cent reaches at least some 35 per cent per gamete. This is a much higher rate than previously considered. The fact that neutral or nearly neutral mutations are occurring at a rather high rate is compatible with the high frequency of heterozygous loci that has been observed recently by studying protein polymorphism in human and *Drosophila* populations (Harris 1966; Hubby and Lewontin 1966; Lewontin and Hubby 1966).

Lewontin and Hubby (1966) estimated that in natural populations of *Drosophila pseudoobscura* an average of about 12 per cent of loci in each individual is heterozygous. The corresponding heterozygosity with respect to nucleotide sequence should be much higher. The chemical structure of enzymes used in this study does not seem to be known at present, but in the typical case of esterase-5 the molecular weight was estimated to be about 10^5 by Narise and Hubby (1966). In higher organisms, enzymes with molecular weight of this magnitude seem to be common and usually they are "multimers" (Fincham 1966). So, if we assume that each of those enzymes comprises on the average some 1,000 amino-acids (corresponding to molecular weight of some 120,000), the mutation rate for the corresponding genetic site (consisting of about 3,000 nucleotide pairs) is

$$u = 3 \times 10^3 \times 5 \times 10^{-10} = 1.5 \times 10^{-6}$$

per generation. The entire genome could produce more than a million of such enzymes.

In applying this value of u to *Drosophila* it must be noted that the mutation rate per nucleotide pair per generation can differ in man and *Drosophila*. There is some evidence that with respect to the definitely deleterious effects of gene mutation, the rate of mutation per nucleotide pair per generation is roughly ten times as high in *Drosophila* as in man (Muller 1967; Kimura 1967). This means that the corresponding mutation rate for *Drosophila* should be $u = 1.5 \times 10^{-5}$ rather than $u = 1.5 \times 10^{-6}$. Another consideration allows us to suppose that $u =$

Recent experimental work shows that, in microbes from viruses to *E. coli*, a large fraction of mutations are neutral or nearly so. These include but are not limited to synonymous mutations.

With the term "multimer," Kimura is referring to several identical or different proteins linked together to form a protein complex.

This sentence assumes that the entire genome constitutes protein coding sequence. We now know this is far from the case. The human genome codes for about 20,000 proteins and a number of functional RNA products. The remainder is made of non-coding DNA with varying degrees of functionality.

1.5×10^{-5} is probably appropriate for the neutral mutation rate of a cistron in *Drosophila*. If we assume that the frequency of occurrence of neutral mutations is about one per genome per generation (that is, they are roughly two to three times more frequent than the mutation of the viability polygenes), the mutation rate per nucleotide pair per generation is $1/\left(2 \times 10^{8}\right)$, because the DNA content per genome in *Drosophila* is about one-twentieth of that of man (Nations 1958). For a cistron consisting of 3, 000 nucleotide pairs, this amounts to $u = 1.5 \times 10^{-5}$.

Kimura and Crow (1964) have shown that for neutral mutations the probability that an individual is homozygous is $1/\left(4N_{e}u + 1\right)$, where N_{e} is the effective population number, so that the probability that an individual is heterozygous is $H_{e} = 4N_{e}u/\left(4N_{e}u + 1\right)$. In order to attain at least $H_{e} = 0.12$, it is necessary that at least $N_{e} = 2,300$. For a higher heterozygosity such as $H = 0.35$, N_{e} has to be about 9,000. This might be a little too large for the effective number in *Drosophila*, but with migration between subgroups, heterozygosity of 35 per cent may be attained even if N_{e} is much smaller for each subgroup.

We return to the problem of total mutation rate. From a consideration of the average energy of hydrogen bonds and also from the information on mutation of rIIA gene in phage T_{4}, Watson (1965) obtained $10^{-8} \sim 10^{-9}$ as the average probability of error in the insertion of a new nucleotide during DNA replication. Because in man the number of cell divisions along the germ line from the fertilized egg to a gamete is roughly 50, the rate of mutation resulting from base replacement according to these figures may be $50 \times 10^{-8} \sim 50 \times 10^{-9}$ per nucleotide pair per generation. Thus, with 4×10^{9} nucleotide pairs, the total number of mutations resulting from base replacement may amount to $200 \sim 2,000$. This is 100–1,000 times larger than the estimate of 2 per generation and suggests that the mutation rate per nucleotide pair is reduced during evolution by natural selection (Muller 1967; Kimura 1967).

Finally, if my chief conclusion is correct, and if the neutral or nearly neutral mutation is being produced in each generation at a much higher rate than has been considered before, then we must recognize the great importance of random genetic drift due to finite population number (Wright 1931) in forming the genetic structure of biological populations. The significance of random genetic drift has been deprecated during the

This is the key point to which Kimura's entire paper is driving. Having provided evidence that many substitutions must be neutral or nearly so, Kimura concludes that genetic drift has to play an important role in evolutionary change.

past decade. This attitude has been influenced by the opinion that almost no mutations are neutral, and also that the number of individuals forming a species is usually so large that random sampling of gametes should be negligible in determining the course of evolution, except possibly through the "founder principle" (Mayr 1965). To emphasize the founder principle but deny the importance of random genetic drift due to finite population number is, in my opinion, rather similar to assuming a great flood to explain the formation of deep valleys but rejecting a gradual but long lasting process of erosion by water as insufficient to produce such a result. ❧

REFERENCES

Buettner-Janusch, J., and R. L. Hill. 1965. "Evolution of Hemoglobin in Primates." In *Evolving Genes and Proteins: A Symposium Held at the Institute of Microbiology of Rutgers, the State University, with Support from the National Science Foundation,* edited by V. Bryson and H. J. Vogel, 167–181. New York, NY: Academic Press.

Fincham, J. R. S. 1966. *Genetic Complementation.* New York, NY: W. A. Benjamin.

Haldane, J. B. S. 1957. "The Cost of Natural Selection." *Journal of Genetics* 55:511–524.

Harris, H. 1966. "Enzyme Polymorphisms in Man." *Proceedings of the Royal Society B* 164 (995): 298–310.

Hubby, J. L., and R. C. Lewontin. 1966. "A Molecular Approach to the Study of Genic Heterozygosity in Natural Populations. I. The Number of Alleles at Different Loci in *Drosophila Pseudoobscura.*" *Genetics* 54 (2): 577–594.

Kaplan, N. O. 1965. "Evolution of Dehydrogenases." In *Evolving Genes and Proteins: A Symposium Held at the Institute of Microbiology of Rutgers, the State University, with Support from the National Science Foundation,* edited by V. Bryson and H. J. Vogel, 243–277. New York, NY: Academic Press.

Kimura, M. 1957. "Some Problems of Stochastic Processes in Genetics." *The Annals of Mathematical Statistics* 28:882–901.

———. 1960. "Optimum Mutation Rate and Degree of Dominance as Determined by the Principle of Minimum Genetic Load." *Journal of Genetics* 57:21–34.

———. 1967. "On the Evolutionary Adjustment of Spontaneous Mutation Rates." *Genetics Research* 9:23–34.

———. 1968. "Genetic Variability Maintained in a Finite Population Due to Mutational Production of Neutral and Nearly Neutral Isoalleles." *Genetical Research* 11:247–269.

Kimura, M., and J. F. Crow. 1964. "The Number of Alleles that Can Be Maintained in a Finite Population." *Genetics* 49:725–738.

Lewontin, R. C., and J. L. Hubby. 1966. "A Molecular Approach to the Study of Genic Heterozygosity in Natural Populations. II. Amount of Variation and Degree of Heterozygosity in Natural Populations of *Drosophila Pseudoobscura*." *Genetics* 54 (2): 595–609.

Margoliash, E., and E. L. Smith. 1965. "Structural and Functional Aspects of Cytochrome *c* in Relation to Evolution." In *Evolving Genes and Proteins: A Symposium Held at the Institute of Microbiology of Rutgers, the State University, with Support from the National Science Foundation,* edited by V. Bryson and H. J. Vogel, 221–242. New York, NY: Academic Press.

Mayr, E. 1965. *Animal Species and Evolution.* Cambridge, MA: Harvard University Press.

Mukai, T. 1964. "The Genetic Structure of Natural Populations of Drosphilia Melanogaster. I. Spontaneous Mutation Rate of Polygenes Controlling Viability." *Genetics* 50 (1): 1–19.

Muller, H. J. 1958. "Evolution by Mutation." *Bulletin of the American Mathematical Society* 64:137–160.

———. 1967. "The Gene Material as the Initiator and the Organizing Basis of Life." In *Heritage from Mendel,* edited by R. A. Brink, 419–448. Madison, WI: Wisconsin Press.

Narise, S., and J. L. Hubby. 1966. "Purification of Esterase-5 from *Drosophila Pseudoobscura*." *Biochimica et Biophysica Acta (BBA) - Enzymology* 122:281–288.

Nations, United. 1958. *Report of the United Nations Scientific Committee on the Effects of Atomic Radiation.* Technical report 17 (A/3838). New York, NY: United Nations.

Sager, R., and F. J. Ryan. 1961. *Cell Heredity.* New York, NY: John Wiley and Sons.

Sueoka, N. 1961. "Variation and Heterogeneity of Base Composition of Deoxyribonucleic Acids: A Compilation of Old and New Data." *Journal of Molecular Biology* 3:31–40.

Watson, J. D. 1965. *Molecular Biology of the Gene.* New York, NY: W. A. Benjamin.

Wright, S. 1931. "Evolution in Mendelian Populations." *Genetics* 16 (2): 97–159.

Zuckerkandl, E., and L. Pauling. 1965. "Evolutionary Divergence and Convergence in Proteins." In *Evolving Genes and Proteins: A Symposium Held at the Institute of Microbiology of Rutgers, the State University, with Support from the National Science Foundation,* edited by V. Bryson and H. J. Vogel, 97–166. New York, NY: Academic Press.

BIRTH
April 25, 1903,
Tambov, Russia
(then the
Russian Empire)

1900

1906: Andrey Markov
publishes "Extension of
the Law of Large Numbers,
to Dependent Quantities"
in its original Russian. 1910

1918: The Romanov
family is executed in
Yekaterinburg, Russia.

1920

1936: Mathematician
Nikolai Luzin is convicted
in Russia of anti-Soviet
behavior as a part of
Stalin's Great Purge. 1940

1930

1950

KOLMOGOROV 1968
Moscow State
University
Moscow, Russia

1960: Raymond
Solomonoff publishes "A
Preliminary Report on
a General Theory of
Inductive Inference." 1960

1966: Gregory Chaitin 1970
publishes "On the Length
of Programs for Computing
Finite Binary Sequences."

DEATH
October 20, 1987
Moscow, Russia
(SFSR)
cause of death
unknown

1980

ANDREI NIKOLAEVICH KOLMOGOROV

[31]

INSPIRING, ENIGMATIC, INCOMPLETE

Simon DeDeo, Carnegie Mellon University and Santa Fe Institute

Written near the end of the productive stage of his career, Kolmogorov's "Three Approaches" is a work of maddening genius. Alternately inspiring, enigmatic, and incomplete, the text spawned entire subfields in computer science, mathematics, and philosophy—and, at the same time, a thousand misconceptions. Though it is unquestionably part of the complexity-science canon, few papers are as misread and misunderstood by outsiders. Perhaps one should expect nothing less from a paper that proposes a quantitative measure of information, structure, complexity, and order that can never, in the end, be calculated. To read "Three Approaches" is to see a mind at the height of its powers, straining for a new ontology of form beyond anything previously conceived.

To understand Kolmogorov's ambition—to do justice to it—one must first understand that he is writing in the shadow of a paper written seventeen years prior: Claude Shannon's "Mathematical Theory of Communication" (1948). Shannon's paper was the origin point of modern information theory, and the heart of the probabilistic approach that Kolmogorov intends to transcend.

Shannon focused on the transmission of information in a statistical sense—a matter of repeated, independent, communicative acts that Kolmogorov rather dismissively likens to a flow of congratulatory telegrams. For Shannon, the establishment of a codebook, or look-up table, enables one to communicate, to a receiver, one of a number of different possible messages. One codebook, call it A, is more efficient than another codebook, B, insofar as the average number of symbols one transmits, over the course of multiple engagements, using codebook A, is shorter than what one would have transmitted using codebook B.[1]

A. N. Kolmogorov, "Three Approaches to the Quantitative Definition of Information," in *International Journal of Computer Mathematics* 2 (1–4): 157–168 (1968).

Reprinted by permission of Taylor & Francis Ltd.

---

[1] For a gentle introduction, see https://sites.santafe.edu/~simon/it.pdf.

Among other things, Shannon's work formalized the intuition that one should use short sequences to transmit common letters, and long sequences to transmit rare ones—something that Samuel Morse, the inventor of Morse code, clearly understood when he assigned "dot" to symbolize the letter E, and the far longer "dash dash dot dot" to symbolize the letter Z.

The properties of the most efficient codebook characterize the information content, or "entropy," of a process; calculate the property of the codebook, and you quantify the information. Once you know the probabilities, this quantity is ridiculously easy to compute, and Shannon gives us the formula. Kolmogorov does so too, as equation 8, using Shannon's own notation, including the use of H for entropy although—presumably for political reasons, since he is required to write for a patriotic Soviet audience at the height of the Cold War—he can neither cite nor name the American originator.

For nearly all intents and purposes—and, as Kolmogorov admits, for all practical engineering work—Shannon's answer settled the matter. But the matter was settled at significant cost. Information now attached to channels and streams, to a predetermined *set* of things one might say. We could no longer talk about the "information" contained in a object or an event, because a message only has information relative to what it might have said instead. If there are only three types of congratulatory telegrams—one complimenting your looks, one your brains, and one both—the "information" contained in "well done beautiful stop" depends upon how often other messages chose to refer to brains as well. The role of the ensemble is pervasive: in Shannon's theory, for example, we cannot say that this particular room is "messy" or "disordered," only that "it looks like this room is drawn from a large number of rooms that we would describe equivalently." My students struggle with this necessary mental reorientation from object to set. Kolmogorov refused it.

War and Peace, he points out, clearly contains information. But, if we are to make sense of it under the Shannon scheme, what are the range of alternatives against which it ought to be compared? If we take Tolstoy to be communicating a vision of human life, what are the alternative views he might have communicated, and by writing *War and*

Peace, ruled out? Kolmogorov first considers the standard answer that Shannon arrived at: that we should see Tolstoy's novel as unfolding, sentence by sentence, with the information contained in his choices between synonyms, say, or among grammatically correct alternatives.

In this picture, if there are three ways to complete the sentence "Natasha fell in love from the moment she entered the ___," then (in the Shannon formula), Tolstoy added $\log_2(3)$, or around 1.5, bits of information by the stroke of a pen. Indeed, Kolmogorov, in his playful way, considers this possibility in a discussion of the statistics of Russian poetry and prose. He discards it, however, pointing out that it quickly leads to counterintuitive conclusions. Whatever it looks like moment-to-moment, *War and Peace* as a whole is not a sequence of disconnected selections made in sequence but, rather, the unfolding of a vision according to a plan. In a similar fashion, Kolmogorov points to the "information" contained in an organism like a cockroach: we might understand it as a sequence of switch-flips engineered by the molecular biology of the genetic code, and thus against the background of all the mutant cockroaches that might arise through microevolution, but that seems to neglect the fact that the organism's form—the true structure we care about—was guided by an entirely separate process, of macro-scale natural selection.

To talk about the information in an object, in other words, requires that one go from Shannon's "option" view to a deeper notion of "plan" or (in Kolmogorov's terminology) "algorithm." Kolmogorov must exchange the Shannon codebook for something far stranger: the computer program. He first considers the relative notion: imagine writing a computer program that takes as input one object (say, the text of Tolstoy's diaries, or a description of the Carboniferous's chemical environment), and outputs another (say, *War and Peace*, or the shape and form of the cockroach). Regardless of what such programs look like in their details, for Kolmogorov, the critical question is how short they can be after all the necessary accompanying data is included. The shorter the program, the more information the first object contains about the second.

Given this, he then can define the information contained in an object *simpliciter*: the length of the shortest program that generates it *ab initio*, from the empty string. "Simple" objects, ones with little algorithmic information, have succinct programs that generate them; the Mandelbrot set may look complicated, but only a short program is needed to cover a wall with its patterns. "Complex," "information-bearing" objects, meanwhile, have only long programs, full of exception cases and details. To get this story going, Kolmogorov has to invoke a set of ideas from theoretical computer science, including the idea of a "universal partially recursive function": what we would refer to today as a sufficiently expressive computer language, like LISP or Python.

The mathematical proofs in Kolmogorov's paper are so simple as to be essentially implicit, and it is mostly a matter of notation for him to define what today we call Kolmogorov complexity, the formalization of the account above. Given a set of objects, and a way of referring to them (their "names"—e.g., the text in an encoding like ASCII, or the coordinates of all their pixels), the Kolmogorov Complexity of object x, written $K_A(x)$, is "the shortest program, written in sufficiently general computer language A, that reproduces the name of object y." Some somersaults are required to show that, if you have two different languages, A and B, then $K_A(x)$ and $K_B(x)$ will differ by, at most, a constant that sometimes favors A, and sometimes favors B, but whose bound does not depend on the particular choice of x. Pick a language, and (as long as the objects you're looking at are complicated enough, or seen with sufficient context) the details won't matter.

There's only one problem, as Kolmogorov somewhat grudgingly acknowledges: $K_A(x)$ might be well-defined, but it is not, in general, computable. Every object x has a shortest program that generates its name (in the worst case, the program is just the name itself). But finding the shortest program requires cycling through all possible programs of different lengths, running them, and seeing which eventually terminate by printing the required name. When you start to do this, you discover that when you run some programs, they never complete. You might think to yourself that you could spot the programs that enter infinite loops ahead of time, but a crucial result at the heart of computer science, due to Alan Turing (1936), says that solving this so-called "halting problem" is impossible.

$K_A(x)$, in other words, turns out to be one of those strange objects whose existence is not in question—it is a well-defined object, not a "square circle"—but whose knowability would imply a logical contradiction. That does not, unfortunately, prevent people from referring to it *en passant*: the possibility of knowing it is so tantalizing that I've been to plenty of talks where the speakers have referred to, for example, the idea of "approximating" $K_A(x)$ as a solution to the problem of statistical induction. But what's uncomputable is uncomputable and, as Frank Ramsey once said, you can't "whistle it, either."[2]

If $K_A(x)$ is a purely notional object, it might seem that Kolmogorov's work is a bust. In fact, of course, it's not—for two reasons. First, $K_A(x)$ might be unknowable for any particular x, but there's an enormous amount one can say about it anyway. What Kolmogorov himself is really after—although it's only gestured at in the final paragraphs—is a foundation for the theory of probability itself.

This requires a little exposition, because what Shannon took for granted—that probability is a relatively simple matter to define—is false. Even today, as David Wallace (2012, chapter 4) points out in his account of the interpretation of quantum mechanics, the circularity at the heart of defining probability in terms of frequencies is hard to escape. We might say, for example, that if a coin has "probability 0.5" of turning up heads, it means that, when you toss it hundreds of times, the frequency of heads is very close to 50%. It turns out, however, that mostly what you're saying when you do that is something like "the probability that the frequency of heads is within two percentage points of 50% is close to 99%"—i.e., you've defined probability in a circular fashion.

Kolmogorov wanted a definition of randomness that didn't include probability, and $K_A(x)$ provides one: an object x in a set of size N is random if $K_A(x)$ is close to $\log(N)$, or, informally, if the best computer program for producing it is simply one that saves the name in memory and prints it right back out. It turns out that nearly all

---

[2] For extensive discussion of the temptations and frustrations of $K_A(x)$'s uncomputability, see DeDeo (2020).

sequences are like this: random in this philosophically novel sense, with no clever, succinct summary. Even though you can't compute $K_A(x)$ for any particular x, its existence thus provides a way to define probabilitistic notions in a well-founded sense—the theory today known as algorithmic randomness.

There's another use for $K_A(x)$, however, since $K_A(x)$ is knowable if you are willing, as Kolmogorov suggests, to consider "reasonable" restrictions on the nature of the program: restrictions, for example, on the kinds of "programs" (really, patterns of reasoning) one usually "runs", and how those patterns actually play out in a particular life-world and context. Succinctness in general may be unknowable, but succinctness relative to a culture or a psychology is clearly a compelling phenomenon that we can grasp and respond to in daily life (Chater and Loewenstein 2016). Computer scientists, meanwhile, took Kolmorogov's notion of reasonable in a very different direction; considering different constraints on the resources a program might use led to our modern theory of *computational complexity*. Despite its uncomputability, Kolmogorov's measure appears as a limit point in proofs surrounding the most important conjectures in theoretical computer science today—including the security of cryptographic systems (Hirahara *et al.* 2023).

Kolmogorov was alert to both the cognitive and the mathematical, and his article, full of technical fireworks, has an unexpected conclusion:: a report on a series of experiments that attempt to measure the "reasonable" Kolmogorov complexity of literary texts. This is the conditional complexity—in this case, the "minimal length of a program that can complete a passage of text, given the text so far." Kolmogorov reports two estimates, that involved the participation of his collaborator, Natasha G. Rychkova.

Thirty years later, in a tribute to Kolmorogov that she edited, Rychkova talked in passing about these unusual experiments:

> *[Kolmogorov] came up with experiments on guessing contin-*
> *uations in the early sixties, building on the experiments of*
> *Claude Shannon. He was then extremely passionate about it,*
> *he was burning, he was rushed. He developed the methodol-*
> *ogy, explained to me how to carry out experiments, and found*

many interested people (mathematicians who he considered not devoid of literary talent, and non-mathematicians from literary circles). We conducted several dozen experiments, I calculated estimates using the formula that was proposed, of course, also by Kolmogorov. He himself participated in guessing twice... And, of course, I didn't feel any telepathic connection with the authors (mind you, deceased ones) nor do I feel it now, it's just that after conducting many experiments with others, I had already gotten used to the methodology. (Shiryaev 2006, 410)

Some accounts of Kolmogorov's life (e.g., Gessen 2009, chapter 3) suggest he ran a rather "boy's club" inner circle; Rychkova's fond memoir of Kolmorogov as a mentor, which include joining in the hijinks of his research group, suggests she, at least, found a home among friends.

Even with this information, however, it's hard to know exactly what the two were after, and there are gaps in this passage—notably, in the connection of their Shannon-style estimates to the algorithmic notion—although one can, with a little charity, fill them in. One possibility is that she presented subjects with a fragment of a text—a sentence, or a paragraph, say—and asked the person to guess the next word, or even, perhaps, to provide some more coarse-grained continuation of the plot. The number of guesses required for the person to get close enough then provides an estimate (really, in the Shannon sense, an upper bound) of the residual uncertainty. If, half the time, it takes two guesses to get a correct answer, and the other half the time it takes one guess, then the residual uncertainty is around one bit. For Kolmogorov to report an error range of "0.9 to 1.1"—i.e., an error of around 10%—she must have conducted hundreds, if not thousands, of trials.

Such a setup, however, fails to explain the humorous remark that Rychkova's less successful guessers accused her of telepathic communication with the authors of the text. Her set-up, then, must have at least suggested to the subjects that she herself was engaged in guessing, more successfully, along with them—or at least scolding them for poor intuition. In the midst of such a technical tour de force—and with the context of Kolmogorov's grand ambition in view—this brief flash of human complexity is nothing short of a delight.

There is an extraordinary vision in Kolmogorov's work. In the past, we might have pointed to its position in this history of the theory of computer science and statistical inference; today, by contrast, what draws our attention is perhaps more the thoughtful attention to the limitations of Shannon's compelling—but, in the final analysis, too-simple—answer for how to understand the complexity of human culture and biological evolution. Its unexpected resonances well-deserve it the status of a perennial classic, and a permanent place in the complexity canon. ⸎

Acknowledgments

I thank Roman Tikhonov, Gülce Kardeş, and Artemy Kolchinsky for helpful comments.

REFERENCES

Chater, N., and G. Loewenstein. 2016. "The Under-Appreciated Drive for Sense-Making." *Journal of Economic Behavior & Organization* 126:137–154. https://doi.org/10.1016/j.jebo.2015.10.016.

DeDeo, S. 2020. *Mutual Explainability, or, A Comedy in Computerland.* Fqxi Prize Essay. https://s3.amazonaws.com/fqxi.data/data/essay-contest-files/DeDeo_Comedy_in_Computerlan.pdf.

Gessen, M. 2009. *Perfect Rigor: A Genius and the Mathematical Breakthrough of the Century.* Boston, MA: Houghton Mifflin Harcourt.

Hirahara, S., R. Ilango, Z. Lu, M. Nanashima, and I. C. Oliveira. 2023. *A Duality between One-Way Functions and Average-Case Symmetry of Information.* Cryptology ePrint Archive, Paper 2023/424. https://eprint.iacr.org/2023/424.

Kolmogorov, A. N., and N. G. Rychkova. 2000. "Russian Poetry Rhythm Analysis and Probability Theory." *Theory of Probability & Its Applications* 44 (2): 375–385. https://doi.org/10.1137/S0040585X97977616.

Shannon, C. E. 1948. "A Mathematical Theory of Communication." *Bell System Technical Journal* 27 (4): 623–656. https://doi.org/10.1002/j.1538-7305.1948.tb00917.x.

Shiryaev, A. N., ed. 2006. *Kolmogorov: In the Memories of Students.* Machine translated by Google and corrected by Artemy Kolchinsky. Moscow, Russia: MTsNMO Publishing House.

Turing, A. M. 1936. "On Computable Numbers, with an Application to the *Entscheidungsproblem.*" *Proceedings of the London Mathematical Society* 42 (1): 230–265. https://doi.org/10.1112/plms/s2-42.1.230.

Wallace, D. 2012. *The Emergent Multiverse: Quantum Theory according to the Everett Interpretation.* Oxford, UK: Oxford University Press. https://doi.org/10.1093/acprof:oso/9780199546961.001.0001.

THREE APPROACHES TO THE QUANTITATIVE DEFINITION OF INFORMATION

A. N. Kolmogorov, Moscow State University

There are two common approaches to the quantitative definition of "information": combinatorial and probabilistic. The author briefly describes the major features of these approaches and introduces a new algorithmic approach that uses the theory of recursive functions.

1. The Combinatorial Approach

Assume that a variable x is capable of taking values in a finite set X containing N elements. We say that the "entropy" of the variable x is

$$H(x) = \log_2 N.$$

By giving x a definite value

$$x = a$$

we "remove" this entropy and communicate "information"

$$I = \log_2 N.$$

If the variables $x_1, x_2, ..., x_k$ are capable of independently taking values in sets respectively containing $N_1, N_2, ..., N_k$ members, then

$$H(x_1, x_2, ..., x_k) = H(x_1) + H(x_2) + \cdots + H(x_k). \tag{1}$$

Transmission of a quantity of information I requires

$$I' = \begin{cases} I & \text{for integral } I \\ [I] + 1 & \text{for fractional } I \end{cases}$$

binary digits. For example, the number of different "words" consisting of k zeros and ones and one 2 is

$$2^k(k+1).$$

In both the English translation and the original Russian, Kolmogorov uses "H" as the symbol for entropy, following Shannon's choice, which, in turn, goes back to the notation used in statistical physics by Ludwig Boltzmann.

To do this calculation, first consider the number of different symbols, of length k, composed of zeros and ones—at each point, there are two choices, so there are 2^k possibilities. Now you just have to figure out where to insert the number "two"; for each of those 2^k strings there are $(k+1)$ possibilities.

Hence, the information content of such a message is

$$I = k + \log_2(k+1),$$

i.e., the "coding" of such words in a purely binary system requires *

$$I' \approx k + \log_2 k$$

zeros and ones.

Discussions of information theory do not usually go into this combinatorial approach at any length, but I consider it important to emphasize its logical independence of probabilistic assumptions. Suppose, for example, that we are faced with the problem of coding a message written in an alphabet consisting of s letters, it being known that the frequencies

$$p_r = \frac{s_r}{s} \tag{2}$$

of occurrence of individual letters in a message of length n satisfy the inequality

$$X = -\sum_{r=1}^{s} p_r \log_2 p_r \leqq h. \tag{3}$$

It is easy to see that for large n, the binary logarithm of the number of messages satisfying requirement (2) has the asymptotic estimate

$$H = \log_2 N \sim nh.$$

In transmitting such messages, therefore, it is sufficient to use approximately nh binary digits.

A universal coding method that permits the transmission of any sufficiently long message in an alphabet of s letters with no more than nh binary digits is not necessarily excessively complex; in particular, it is not essential to begin by determining the frequencies p_r for the entire message. In order to make this clear, it is sufficient to note that by splitting the message S into m segments $S_1, S_2, ..., S_m$, we obtain the inequality.

$$X \geq \frac{1}{n}[n_1 x_1 + n_2 x_2 + \cdots + n_m x_m]. \tag{4}$$

However, I will not go into the details of this special problem here. It is only important for me to show that the mathematical problems

---

*Here and in what follows $f \approx g$ indicates that the difference $f - g$ is bounded, while $f \sim g$ indicates that the ratio $f : g$ approaches one.

associated with a purely combinatorial approach to the measure of information are not limited to trivialities.

It is perfectly natural to take a purely combinatorial approach to the notion of the "entropy of language" if we have in mind an estimate of its "flexibility," an index of the diversity of the possibilities for developing a language with a given dictionary and given rules for the construction of sentences. M. Ratner and N. Svetlova obtained the following estimate for the binary logarithm of the number N of Russian texts of length n, expressed as the "number of symbols including spaces," composed of words in S. I. Ozhegov's Russian dictionary and subject only to the requirements of "grammatical correctness"

$$h = \frac{\log_2 N}{n} = 1.9 \pm 0.1.$$

This is considerably larger than the upper estimate for the "entropy of literary texts" that can be obtained by various methods of "guessing continuations." This discrepancy is quite natural, since literary texts must meet many requirements beyond simple "grammatical correctness."

It is more difficult to estimate the combinatorial entropy of texts subject to definite, more elaborate constraints. It would, for example, be of interest to estimate the entropy of Russian texts that could be regarded as sufficiently accurate (in terms of content) translations of a given foreign-language text. It is only "residual entropy" that makes it possible to translate poetry, where the "entropy cost" of adhering to a given meter and rhyme scheme can be calculated rather accurately. It can be shown that the classical rhyming iambic tetrameter, with certain natural restraints on the frequency of syllables, etc., requires a freedom in handling verbal material characterized by a "residual entropy" of the order of 0.4 (this estimate is based on the above method of measuring the length of a text in terms of the "number of symbols, including spaces"). On the other hand, if we take into account the fact that the stylistic limitations of a particular genre probably reduce the above estimate of the "total" entropy from 1.9 to no more than 1.1–1.2, the situation becomes remarkable both in the case of translation and in the case of original poetry.

Close to Shannon's value for English, which was approximately 2.4. Ozhegov's additional constraint of "grammatical correctness" might explain why his answer is 0.5 bits lower. Both Kolmogorov and Shannon are excessively vague about the methods behind these results, in part because of their connection to military cryptography.

Kolmogorov's first signal that something is wrong with Shannon. Ozhegov's Shannon-like analysis of Russian says that each new letter has 1.9 bits of entropy; equivalently, the number of possible sentences nearly quadruples with each letter. Kolmogorov points out that that's far too high. If a word is (say) five letters long, then there should be 1.9^5, or around 25 possibilities, but in practice, you (or Google autocomplete) can very often guess correctly on the first or second try. That's because sentences have to make sense (and humans are profoundly uncreative).

"As constraints of sound and sense pile up, poets run out of possibilities."

We're not just constrained by sense (see note above); we might also be constrained by sound, which further cuts down on allowable combinations. For his 0.4 estimate, Kolmogorov is referencing work he's done with Rychkova, finally published as Kolmogorov and Rychkova (2000).

Kolmogorov cares a lot about binary classifications of "possible/not-possible," in contrast to Shannon's concern for "probable/improbable." This is in part because Kolmogorov has great reservations about the mathematical foundations of probability theory.

I trust the reader of a utilitarian bent will forgive me this example, but it should be noted that the broader problem of measuring the information connected with creative human endeavor is of the utmost significance.

At this point, let us turn to a discussion of the extent to which a purely combinatorial approach permits one to estimate the information conveyed by a variable x with respect to a related variable y. The relation between the variables x and y, which respectively take values in the sets X and Y, consists in that not all pairs (x, y) belonging to the Cartesian product $X \times Y$ are "possible." The set U of possible pairs determines the set Y_a of y such that for a given $a \, \epsilon \, X$

$$(a, y) \, \epsilon \, U.$$

It is natural to define the conditional entropy by the equation

$$H(y/a) = \log_2 N(Y_a) \qquad (5)$$

(where $N(Y_x)$ is the number of members of Y_x) and the information conveyed by x with respect to y by the formula

$$I(x : y) = H(y) - H(y/x). \qquad (6)$$

For the case shown in the table, for example, we have

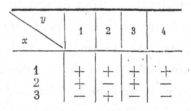

"+" here refers to allowable combinations; for example, if $x = 1$, all values of y are permitted; if $x = 2$, only two of them are. Tables like these, with yes/no constraints, are reminiscent of Noam Chomsky's strict delineation of sentences into grammatical and ungrammatical; Kolmogorov's "-" is the linguist's "starred" sentence.

Clearly, $H(y/x)$ and $I(x : y)$ are functions of x (whereas y takes the form of a "bound variable").

It is not difficult to introduce in a purely combinatorial conception the notion of the "quantity of information necessary to designate an object x with given requirements imposed on the accuracy of the designation." (Apropos of this see the extensive literature on the "ϵ-entropy" of sets in metric spaces.)

It is obvious that

$$H(x/x) = 0, \quad I(x : x) = H(x). \qquad (7)$$

The Probabilistic Approach

The possible advantages of further developing information theory on the basis of definitions (5) and (6) have been overshadowed by the fact that if we make the variables x and y "random variables" with given joint probability distributions, we can obtain a considerably richer system of concepts and relationships. Paralleling the quantities introduced in §1, here we have

$$H_W(x) = -\sum_x p(x) \log_2 p(x), \qquad (8)$$

$$H_W(y/x) = -\sum_y p(y/x) \log_2 p(y/x), \qquad (9)$$

$$I_W(x:y) = H_W(y) - H_W(y/x). \qquad (10)$$

As before, $H_W(y/x)$ and $I_W(x:y)$ are functions of x, and we have the inequalities

$$H_W(x) \lesseqgtr H(x), \quad H_W(y/x) \lesseqgtr H(y/x), \qquad (11)$$

where the equality holds when the corresponding distributions (on both X and Y_x) are uniform. The quantities $I_W(x:y)$ and $I(x:y)$ are not related by an inequality of a particular direction. As in §1,

$$H_W(x/x) = 0, \quad I_W(x:x) = H_W(x). \qquad (12)$$

The difference lies in the fact that we can form the mathematical expectations

$$MH_W(y/x), \quad MI_W(x:y),$$

while the quantity

$$I_W(x,y) = MI_W(x:y) = MI_W(y:x) \qquad (13)$$

symmetrically characterizes the "closeness of the relation" between x and y.

However, it should be noted that the probabilistic approach gives rise to a paradox: In the combinatorial approach, $I(x:y)$ is always non-negative, which is natural in a naive conception of information content, but $I_W(x:y)$ may be negative. Now only the averaged quantity $I_W(x,y)$ is a true measure of the information content.

These equations are a *long time coming*; all of the previous results can be derived from them by setting probabilities to zero for the "forbidden" combinations, and $1/N$ for the remaining N allowed ones.

For Shannon, there are things you might see that *increase* your uncertainty: I might learn that my friend is drunk, and thus become more uncertain about what he'll do next. Kolmogorov thinks that "negative" information like this is a paradox.

The probabilistic approach is natural in the theory of information transmission over communications channels carrying "bulk" information consisting of a large number of unrelated or weakly related messages obeying definite probabilistic laws. In this type of problem there is a harmless and (in applied work) deep-rooted tendency to mix up probabilities and frequencies within a sufficiently long time sequence (which is rigorously justified if it is assumed that "mixing" is sufficiently rapid). In practice, for example, it can be assumed that the problem of finding the "entropy" of a flow of congratulatory telegrams and the channel "capacity" required for timely and undistorted transmission is validly represented by a probabilistic treatment even with the usual substitution of empirical frequencies for probabilities. If something goes wrong here, the problem lies in the vagueness of our ideas of the relationship between mathematical probability theory and real random events in general.

But what real meaning is there, for example, in asking how much information is contained in "War and Peace"? Is it reasonable to include this novel in the set of "possible novels," or even to postulate some probability distribution for this set? Or, on the other hand, must we assume that the individual scenes in this book form a random sequence with "stochastic relations" that damp out quite rapidly over a distance of several pages?

Actually, we are just as much in the dark over the fashionable question of the "quantity of hereditary information" necessary, say, for the reproduction of particular form of *roach*. Still, within the limits of the probabilistic approach, two variants are possible. In the first variant, we must consider the set of "possible forms" with a probability distribution of uncertain origin in this set. In the second variant, the characteristics of the form are assumed to be a set of weakly dependent random variables. The real nature of the mechanism of mutation provides arguments favoring the second variant, but these arguments are undermined if we assume that natural selection causes a system of consistent characteristics to appear.

An Algorithmic Approach

Actually, it is most fruitful to discuss the quantity of information "conveyed by an object" (x) "about an object" (y). It is not an accident,

---

The crux: Shannon's notion of information relies upon thinking in terms of an ensemble of possible messages. But this makes it impossible to talk about "unrepeatable" events like the creation of *War and Peace* or (as he'll suggest later) the development of an embryo. If Tolstoy is sending us a message, it's not on analogy with picking from one of a well-defined range of "celebratory telegrams." So what's the alternative?

Quarrels with the probabilistic model. The natural way to apply Shannon information theory to biology is to say the structure of an organism is encoded in a series of "switch flips" during development: the DNA "transmits" information in the code. But that seems incompatible with the fact that it's the environment (natural selection), not the DNA, that's ultimately responsible for picking out this range of "roach forms" over all the other possibilities.

that in the probabilistic approach this has led to a generalization to the case of continuous variables, for which the entropy is infinite but, in a large number of cases,

$$I_W(x, y) = \iint P_{xy}(dxdy) \log_2 \frac{P_{xy}(dxdy)}{P_x(dx)P_y(dy)}$$

is finite. The real objects that we study are very (infinitely) complex, but the relationships between two separate objects diminish as the schemes used to describe them become simpler. While a map yields a considerable amount of information about a region of the earth's surface, the microstructure of the paper and the ink of the paper have no relation to the microstructure of the area shown on the map.

In practice, we are most frequently interested in the quantity of information "*conveyed by an individual object x about an individual object y.*" It is true, as we have already noted, that such an individual quantitative estimate of information is meaningful only when the quantity of information is sufficiently large. It is, for example, meaningless to ask about the quantity of information conveyed by the sequence

0 1 1 0

about the sequence

1 1 0 0.

But if we take a perfectly specific table of random numbers of the sort commonly used in statistical practice, and for each of its digits we write the unit's digit of the units of its square according to the scheme

0 1 2 3 4 5 6 7 8 9
0 1 4 9 6 5 6 9 4 1,

the new table will contain approximately

$$(\log_2 10 - \frac{8}{10})n$$

bits of information about the initial sequence (where n is the number of digits in the tables).

Kolmogorov is going to provide a definition of information that's fundamentally relative. While the final analysis is extremely complicated in its ultimate details, what we usually want to know is "what's relevant about one thing for understanding another."

This "square" sequence is the first example of Kolmogorov's conception of aboutness: two processes related to each other not as a matter of statistical regularity, but as a matter of *computation*. To get the lower sequence from the upper, run a computer program.

Accordingly, below we propose to define

$$I_A(x : y)$$

so that some indeterminacy remains. Different equivalent variants of this definition will lead to values equivalent only in the sense that $I_{A_1} \approx I_{A_2}$, i.e.,

$$|I_{A_1} - I_{A_2}| \leqq C_{A_1 A_2},$$

where the constant $C_{A_1 A_2}$ depends on the two basic ways of defining the universal methods of programming A_1 and A_2.

Consider an "indexed domain of objects," i.e., a countable set

$$X = \{x\},$$

with a finite sequence $n(x)$ of zeros and ones, beginning with a one, associated with each element as its index. Denote the length of the sequence $n(x)$ by $l(x)$, and assume that:

1) the correspondence between X and the set D of binary sequences of the form described above is one-to-one;

2) $D \subset X$, the function $n(x)$ on D is generally recursive (Uspenskii 1960), and for $x \in D$

$$l(n(x)) \leqq l(x) + C,$$

where C is a constant;

3) together with x and y, the set X contains the ordered pair (x, y), whose index is a generally recursive function of the indices of x and y and

$$l(x, y) \leqq C_x + l(y),$$

where C_x depends only on x.

Not all of these requirements are essential, but they do simplify the discussion. The end result of the construction is invariant under transition to a new indexing $n'(x)$ that has the same properties as the old system, and can be generally recursively expressed in terms of it; moreover, X retains its properties when embedded in a larger system X' (provided that, for the members of the initial system, the index n' in the expanded system

When sequences are short enough, there might be a number of different ways to relate them. The different ways to relate them may produce different estimates of the final complexity—but we want to make sure that this difference doesn't depend on the sequences themselves.

Here we go! Every possible object (binary sequence) x is going to get a "name," $n(x)$, which is also a binary sequence. In the traditional twisty way of computer science, because the names are also sequences, we can talk not only about the length of a name, $l(x)$, but also the length of the name of the name, $l(n(x))$. Constraint (2) says the naming system is "efficient"—at worst, the length of the name of the name is just the length of the name.

What if we want to name a pair of sequences, x and y, together? Kolmogorov says that we can assume the name of this "correspondence" has a key property: it's less than the length of y plus some constant, C_x, that depends only on x. This is easy to satisfy: if we name x and y separately, C_x is just $l(x)$, with maybe a little overhead, of length $\log(l(x))$, to specify the breakpoint.

can be generally recursively expressed in terms of the initial index n). The new "complexity" K and quantity of information remain equivalent under these transformations in the sense of $\approx$.

As the "relative complexity" of an object y with a given x, we will take the minimal length $l(p)$ of the "program" p for obtaining y from x. The definition thus formulated depends on the "programming method," which is nothing other than the function

$$\varphi(p, x) = y,$$

that associates on object y with a program p and an object x.

In accordance with the views now universally accepted in modern mathematical logic, we must assume that the function φ is partially recursive. For any such function we have

$$K_\varphi(y/x) = \begin{cases} \min\limits_{\varphi(p,x)=y} l(p) \\ \infty \text{ if there is no } p \text{ such that } \varphi(p, x) = y, \end{cases}$$

In this case a function

$$v = \varphi(u)$$

of $u \in X$ with range $v \in X$ is said to be partially recursive if it generates a partially recursive function of the index transformation

$$n(v) = \Psi[n(u)].$$

In order to understand the definition, it is important to note that, in general, partially recursive functions are not defined everywhere, and there is no fixed method for determining whether application of the program p to an object k will lead to a result or not. As a result, the function $K_\varphi(y/x)$ cannot be effectively calculated (generally recursive) even if it is known to be finite for all x and y.

Fundamental theorem. There exists a partially recursive function $A(p, x)$ such that for any other partially recursive function $\varphi(p, x)$ we have the inequality

$$K_A(y/x) \leqq K_\varphi(y/x) + C_\varphi,$$

where the constant C_φ does not depend on x or y.

Consider the "square" sequence at the beginning of this section; here x is the original sequence, and p might be the program "square each number and take the units digit."

The essence of Kolmogorov's definition: the "complexity," K, of y given x is the shortest program p that, given x as an input, produces y. K is relative to a "programming method" φ, however.

"A function that translates between objects implies a function that translates between names."

$K_\varphi(y|x)$ is well defined, but (crazily enough!) we can not, in general, calculate it for all values. When we cycle through all programs looking for a good translation, we may hit one that goes into an infinite loop. Thanks to Alan Turing ("views now universally accepted"), we know that we can't spot these ahead of time!

The proof is based on the existence of a *universal* partially recursive function

$$\Phi(n, u),$$

which has the property that by fixing an appropriate index n, we can use the formula

$$\varphi(u) = \Phi(n, u)$$

to obtain any other partially recursive function. The function $A(p, x)$ we require is given by the formula[*]

$$A((n, q), x) = \Phi(n, (q, x)).$$

Indeed, if

$$y = \varphi(p, x) = \Phi(n, (p, x)),$$

then

$$A((n, p), x) = y,$$
$$l(n, p) \leqq l(p) + C_n.$$

We will call functions $A(p, x)$ that satisfy the requirements of the fundamental theorem (and the programming methods defined by them) *asymptotically optimal*. It is clear that the corresponding "complexity" $K_A(y/x)$ is finite for all x and y. For two such functions A_1 and A_2

$$|K_{A_1}(y/x) - K_{A_2}(y/x)| \leqq C_{A_1 A_2},$$

where $C_{A_1 A_2}$ does not depend on x and y, i.e., $K_{A_1}(y/x) - K_{A_2}(y/x)$.

Finally,

$$K_A(y) = K_A(y/1)$$

can be taken for the "complexity of y" and we can define the "quantity of information conveyed by x about y" by the formula

$$I_A(x : y) = K_A(y) - K_{A_1}(y/x).$$

It is easy to show[†] that this quantity is always essentially positive,

$$I_A(x : y) \geqq 0,$$

---

[*]$\Phi(n, u)$ is defined only when $n \in D$, and $A(p, x)$ is defined only when p is of the form (n, q) $n \in D$.

[†]By choosing a "comparison function" of the form $\varphi(p, x) = A(p, 1)$, we obtain $K_A(y/x) \leqq K_\varphi(y/x) + C_\varphi = K_A(y) + C_\varphi$.

What about that weird "φ"? It turns out we'll be able to find a "universal" Φ, called A, that we can then keep constant and use for all sequence pairs.

To modern eyes, this is a very complicated way of saying "don't worry about whether your program p is written in language A_1 or A_2. When both are sufficiently general, you can include a bit of code that translates any program written in A_1 into A_2, or vice versa—code whose length, $C_{A_1 A_2}$, doesn't depend on the program you're translating."

Victory!—in contrast to Shannon, the information that x gives about y is always positive (or bounded from below). Both x and y are definite objects: e.g., "Tolstoy's diaries" and *War and Peace*.

which means that $I_A(x\colon y)$ is no less than some negative constant C that depends only on the characteristics of the selected programming method. As we have already noted, the theorem was designed for application to a quantity of information so large that, in comparison, $|C|$ is negligibly small.

Note, finally, that $K_A(x/x) \approx 0$, $I_A(x\colon x) \approx K_A(x)$.

Of course, one can avoid the indeterminacies associated with the constant C_φ, etc., by considering particular domains of the objects X, indexing, and the function A, but it is doubtful that this can be done without explicit arbitrariness. One must, however, suppose that the different "reasonable" variants presented here will lead to "complexity estimates" that will converge on hundreds of bits instead of tens of thousands. Hence, such quantities as the "complexity" of the text of "War and Peace" can be assumed to be defined with what amounts to uniqueness. Experiments on guessing continuations of literary texts make it possible to obtain an upper estimate for the conditional complexity in the presence of a given consumption of "a priori information" (about language, style, textual content) available to the guesser. In tests conducted at the Moscow State University Department of Probability Theory, such upper estimates fluctuated between 0.9 and 1.4. The estimates of the order of 0.9–1.1 obtained by N. G. Rychkova have led less successful guessers to suggest that she telepathically communicated with the authors of the texts.

I believe that the approach proposed here yields, in principle, a correct definition of the "quantity of hereditary information," although it would be difficult to obtain a reliable estimate of this quantity.

Conclusion

The concepts discussed in §3 have one important disadvantage: They do not allow for the "difficulty" of preparing a program p for passing from an object x to an object y. By introducing appropriate definitions, it is possible to prove rigorously formulated mathematical propositions that can be legitimately interpreted as an indication of the existence of cases in which an object permitting a very simple program, i.e., with a very small complexity $K(x)$, can be restored by short programs only as the result of computations of a thoroughly unreal duration. Sometime in the future,

I intend to study the relationship between the necessary complexity of a program

$$K^t(x)$$

and its permissible difficulty t. The complexity $K(x)$ that was obtained in §3, is, in this case, the minimum of $K^t(x)$ on the removal of constraints on t.

It is beyond the scope of this article to consider the use of the constructions of §3 in providing a new basis for probability theory. Roughly speaking, the situation is as follows: If a finite set M, containing a very large number of members N, admits determination by means of a program of length negligibly small in comparison with $\log_2 N$, then almost all members of M have complexity $K(x)$ close to $\log_2 N$. The elements $x \in M$ of this complexity are also treated as "random" members of the set M. An incomplete discussion of this idea may be found in Kolmogorov (1963). ❧

REFERENCES

Kolmogorov, A. N. 1963. "On Tables of Random Numbers." *Sankhyā: The Indian Journal of Statistics* 25 (4): 369–376.

Kolmogorov, A. N., and N. G. Rychkova. 2000. "Russian Poetry Rhythm Analysis and Probability Theory." *Theory of Probability & Its Applications* 44 (2): 375–385. https : / / doi . org / 10 . 1137 / S0040585X97977616.

Uspenskii, V. A. 1960. *Lectures on Computable Functions [in Russian]*. Matematičeskaya Logika i Osnovaniya Matematiki Gosudarstv. Izdat. Fiz.-Mat. Lit. Moscow, Russia.

BIRTH
1920 — January 20, 1920
Gomel,
Byelorussian SSR
(now Belarus)

1922: the Byelorussian
SSR becomes a founding
constituent republic
of the Soviet Union.

1930

June 1940: the USSR 1940
annexes Lithuania,
Latvia, and Estonia.

1950

1956: The groundbreaking
Heat Balance of 1960
the Earth's Surface
is published.

BUDYKO 1969
Leningrad Polytechnic
Institute (now Peter the
Great St. Petersburg
Polytechnic University).
St. Petersburg, Russia

1972: Budyko begins work 1970
at the Main Physical
Observatory, established
a century earlier with
support from Alexander
von Humboldt.

1975: Wallace S. Broecker 1980
publishes "Climatic
Change: Are We on the
Brink of a Pronounced
Global Warming?"—the
first use of the term
"global warming." 1990

1991: Belarus officially
gains independence
from Russia as the
Soviet Union dissolves. 2000

DEATH
December 10, 2001
St. Petersburg,
Russia
cause of death
unknown

MIKHAIL·IVANOVICH·BUDYKO

[32]

A FAULTY FOUNDATION SUPPORTS A POWERFUL IDEA: MIKHAIL BUDYKO AND HIS WORK ON THE ICE–ALBEDO FEEDBACK

Daniel P. Schrag, Harvard University
and Santa Fe Institute

Introduction

In 1969, the Soviet geophysicist Mikhail Budyko published this short article in the journal *Tellus*. It contained a discussion of how changes in both solar radiation and volcanic activity on Earth may have created the changes in climate observed in the geologic past, in particular trying to explain the Pleistocene ice ages. This was a slightly obscure topic for Budyko, who had already published many seminal works on climate physics and the heat budget of the Earth; his 1956 book *Heat Balance of the Earth's Surface* is widely credited as offering a more quantitative approach to climatology relative to much preceding work. Moreover, the central argument in the 1969 *Tellus* article—the idea that changes in volcanic activity were primarily responsible for past variations in Earth's climate—is false. Given his extraordinary contributions to physical climatology, one might think that this paper could easily be forgiven and overlooked. And yet it remains Budyko's most-cited work published in English, a profound influence on multiple areas within climatology, including the history of Earth's glaciations, the sensitivity of Earth's climate in the future to changes in glaciation, and the risks that nuclear war could lead to a global climate catastrophe called "nuclear winter." The story of how such a paper could offer a foundation to multiple ideas in climate science yields insight into how science advances, one (erroneous) idea at a time.

M. I. Budyko, "The Effect of Solar Radiation Variations on the Climate of the Earth," in *Tellus* 21 (5): 611–619 (1969).

The Footing

Before summarizing the core ideas in Budyko's famous paper, it is worth describing the scientific footing on which his argument stands. When this paper was published, 110 years had passed since John Tyndall (1863) described the ability of carbon dioxide to absorb radiant heat, giving him the claim to the discovery of the "greenhouse effect." It had been seventy-three years since Svante Arrhenius (1896) had published his seminal work, "On the Influence of Carbonic Acid in the Air upon the Temperature of the Ground," in which he described how carbon dioxide accumulation in the atmosphere from burning coal would warm the Earth's climate. In a popular 1903 book, Arrhenius calculated that a doubling of carbon dioxide in the atmosphere would lead to an increase in Earth's temperature by 4 degrees Celsius—within the range of modern estimates for Earth's climate sensitivity. In 1957, Roger Revelle is credited with first using the term "global warming." He had written many papers echoing the concerns expressed decades earlier by Arrhenius. And in 1958, Charles David Keeling, whom Revelle had brought to the new Scripps Institute of Oceanography, started measuring atmospheric carbon dioxide at the top of Mauna Loa, Hawaii. By 1969, Keeling had already demonstrated the increasing trend in atmospheric carbon dioxide concentration that continues to this day. In addition, Syukuro Manabe, at the Geophysical Fluid Dynamics Laboratory in Princeton, New Jersey, had published in the 1960s on early general circulation models of Earth's atmosphere—far more sophisticated than the simple energy-balance models that Budyko was using (Manabe, Smagorinsky, and Strickler 1965); and in the same year that Budyko wrote his paper, Manabe had published with Kirk Bryan the first general circulation model that coupled the atmosphere and the ocean (Manabe and Bryan 1969). Despite the Cold War, all of this work outlining the basic physics and chemistry of the importance of greenhouse gases on Earth's temperature was familiar to Budyko, although he took a simpler, more analytical approach to understanding the fundamental driving forces that controlled Earth's climate through energy-balance models, usually in just two dimensions.

The Faulty Foundation

Budyko's paper in *Tellus* starts with a brief discussion of the Quaternary (Pleistocene) glaciations, seeking to explain what causes these large climate fluctuations. To explore this, he extrapolates from modern observations to calculate how the driving forces compare with the observed climate response. Thus, he compares Earth's temperature from 1880 through 1960 with measurements of direct solar radiation measured at various stations in Europe and America on days without clouds. The graph of solar radiation shows two peaks: a sharper peak around 1895, and a longer, broader peak that reaches a maximum between 1930 and 1940. Budyko concludes that the two curves (solar radiation and temperature) look "more or less similar," and then works out a scaling relationship, assuming that changes in solar radiation must be the primary cause of the temperature changes. He employs this relationship along with a basic expression of energy balance (i.e., that incoming solar radiation minus what is reflected by Earth's albedo must equal the outgoing radiation of heat at steady state). He then takes a leap:

> *Thus, it seems probable that present changes of the Earth's temperature are determined mainly by the atmosphere transparency variations that depend on the level of volcanic activity. If the present changes in volcanic activity cause radiation variations by several tenths of per cent and the planetary temperature variations by several tenths of a degree, one can believe that in the past respective variations of radiation and temperature reached appreciably larger values.*

Budyko is essentially saying that modern changes in Earth's temperature are dominated by volcanoes; in particular, how volcanic dust affects the transparency of Earth's atmosphere to sunlight. And because he presumes that volcanic activity was greater in the past (without a clear justification), such volcanic activity must have driven even larger swings in climate, such as the Pleistocene ice ages, in the geologic past.

What is fascinating in this analysis is that Budyko ignored the role of greenhouse gases—from Tyndall to Arrhenius to Keeling. By presuming that the intensity of solar radiation, moderated by volcanic emissions and the transparency of the atmosphere, was the primary cause of climate fluctuations, rather than changes in greenhouse gas concentrations, Budyko jumped down a rabbit hole that would inevitably lead to a series of faulty conclusions. It is remarkable that anyone would push past this basic misstep—and yet the key insights in this paper follow from these erroneous assumptions.

The Bedrock of Budyko's Energy Balance

From his faulty conclusions about the role of volcanic activity in relationship to twentieth-century global temperature variability, Budyko then turns to the question of glacial cycles and immediately focuses on the effect of ice albedo on the climate. Using a very simple, two-dimensional energy balance model for the Earth, Budyko derives a set of expressions that allows him to calculate the surface temperature and the ice cover at any latitude. He explores how the temperature distribution is affected by small changes in solar radiation, concluding, "Comparatively small changes of radiation—only by 1.0–1.5%—are sufficient for the development of ice cover on the land and oceans that reaches temperate latitudes." This is the core result that he was looking for, as he is trying to explain how ice sheets during the glaciations expanded down to temperate latitudes, such as the Laurentide ice sheet over North America that extended to New York City along its eastern margin. Based on his previous discussion of the role of volcanic activity in changing the transparency of the Earth's atmosphere, he concludes,

> *Taking into consideration that according to the data of geological investigations the level of volcanic activity for long periods of time in the past changed by a factor of several times, one can believe that the influence of long-period variations of volcanic activity is a probable factor of glaciation development.*

What is novel about Budyko's simple approach is his treatment of the effect of albedo on the Earth's energy balance and surface temperature. For over a century, scientists had explored the effect of changes in the Earth's orbit around the sun to explain cycles of glaciation (Croll 1864), hypothesizing that the changes in various aspects of the Earth's orbit around the sun led to changes in whether glaciers could grow or shrink. In the 1930s, Mutin Milankovitch introduced the important idea that it was cold summers and not cold winters that were critical for the growth of ice sheets; Milankovitch reasoned that it was always cold enough for snow to fall in the winter in high latitudes, but it was essential for that snow to survive the warmer summers in order for ice sheets to grow. Milankovitch focused on the obliquity or tilt of the Earth's axis, which varies with a 41,000-year period, as a major factor controlling the strength of the seasonal cycle, and hence the growth or demise of glaciation. But, for Milankovitch, the ice sheets were responding to seasonal changes in solar radiation due to the tilt of the Earth's axis of rotation.

It was Budyko who focused on the ways that glaciation affects the radiation budget by reflecting more or less incoming solar radiation back to space. With these simple equations of energy balance, Budyko recognized that the growth of ice sheets from the poles towards lower latitudes has a profound effect on temperature, identifying one of the critical feedbacks that we accept now as a core explanation for the ice-age cycles. Indeed, Budyko discusses the Milankovitch hypothesis in the *Tellus* paper, concluding that the radiation changes driven by orbital cycles are likely too small to change the latitude of glaciation by a large amount.

> *Emphasizing the necessity of further study of the problem on the effect of annual radiation variation on the glaciation, it should be noted that the above-obtained result casts some doubt on the hypothesis that the effect of the Earth's orbit changes is sufficient for the explanation of the quaternary glaciations.*

Thus, despite his faulty conclusions about the role of volcanic activity, his model of how the albedo of ice sheets is coupled to surface temperature was a major contribution towards understanding the ice-age cycles. His criticism of Milankovitch and other authors who invoked astronomical explanations for the ice-age cycles was correct but misleading. The orbital changes by themselves are not sufficient to explain the glaciations. But with amplifiers (i.e., positive feedbacks) such as the effect of ice on the planetary albedo, the orbital variations are sufficient to explain the waxing and waning of ice sheets. Of course, aside from ice albedo, the other major feedback that we believe controls the ice age cycles is the carbon dioxide levels in the atmosphere. We can excuse Budyko's omission of any discussion of greenhouse forcing as it was not until 1982 that ice core scientists first reconstructed carbon dioxide levels in the ancient atmosphere through the air trapped in bubbles in ice (Neftel *et al.* 1982). And it was over a decade later that long ice cores from the interior of Antarctica were able to provide reconstructions of carbon dioxide over the past 400,000 years (Petit *et al.* 1999).

Legacy of the Budyko's Exploration of Ice and Planetary Albedo

What may be most interesting about the legacy of Budyko's *Tellus* paper is that it has impacted communities with little interest in Quaternary glaciations. Much of the impact came from a short section of Budyko's paper where he discusses what we now call a "runaway ice albedo feedback." Budyko describes how different changes in solar radiation would affect the latitude of ice sheets and the surface temperature.

> *When radiation decreases by 1.6% the ice cover reaches the mean latitude of about 50°, after that it starts shifting towards lower latitudes up to the equator as a result of self-development. At the same time the planetary temperature drops sharply and reaches the value of several tens of degrees below zero.*

This simple analysis provided the insight that an expansion of glaciation to lower and lower latitudes could cross a threshold that would become unstable; the surface temperature would plummet, encasing the entire planet in ice.

One application of this idea was the concept of nuclear winter—the idea that nuclear weapons could inject enough soot into the stratosphere to block sunlight and freeze the whole planet. In the West, discussion of the effect of nuclear weapons on weather began in the 1950s, and most scientific treatments focused on the soot and aerosol release that would cool the planet by reducing incoming solar radiation. Soot and aerosols in the stratosphere would last a few years to perhaps a decade at most, depending on how high they were injected. On the other hand, if aerosol-driven cooling were to cause a dramatic expansion of glaciation towards the equator, locking the Earth in a frozen state as Budyko describes in the *Tellus* paper, then the catastrophe would last for millions of years. In detail, the relationship between nuclear explosions, soot in the stratosphere, and an expansion of glaciation is complicated, as the soot would eventually fall out, darkening the ice surface and lowering the albedo. Regardless of whether the effect was realistic, the concept that perturbations to the incoming solar radiation could have large and long-lasting impacts on surface temperatures grew out of Budyko's simple calculations. And Budyko himself certainly played a role in the discussion of nuclear winter inside the Soviet Union.

A final influence is less societally relevant but perhaps even more important to history of life on Earth (at least thus far . . .). From the 1940s through the '60s, Brian Harland at Cambridge University studied glaciations recorded in pre-Cambrian rocks around the world, but particularly in Svalbard, Norway. Harland argued that there had been a "great infra-Cambrian Ice Age," even writing a *Scientific American* article about it in 1964 (Harland and Rudwick 1964). Harland had no awareness of climate physics, so could not explain why it had happened. In his *Tellus* paper, Budyko shows no awareness that the runaway ice–albedo feedback that he theorizes could actually have happened in Earth history. In the 1990s, geologists began to put these two ideas together. Joe Kirschvink first coined the term "Snowball Earth" to describe the aftermath of a runaway glacial catastrophe (Kirschvink 1992). More detailed work by Hoffman and colleagues in 1998 brought much of the geologic and geochemical evidence together with Budyko's physical insights (Hoffman *et al.* 1998), eventually convincing the geologic community that Snowball Earth glaciations had happened, and had played a major role in the evolution of atmospheric oxygen and the evolution of life (Laakso and Schrag 2017).

Summary

In a short paper in 1969, Mikhail Budyko laid out his thinking about the causes of the Quaternary ice ages, attributing them to fluctuations in volcanic activity that changed the transparency of the Earth's atmosphere to solar radiation, amplified by changes in the Earth's surface albedo due to glaciation. The core idea in the paper was incorrect, and Budyko completely ignored the role of greenhouse gases, including carbon dioxide. But his simple model of the Earth's energy balance offered a powerful insight into the interaction between solar radiation, ice sheets, and surface temperature. The paper offered the foundation for the important idea of an ice–albedo feedback that is central to the discovery that global glaciations (Snowball Earths) occurred at multiple times in Earth history. The threat of an ice–albedo catastrophe may also have influenced thinking about the potential for nuclear winter. ❧

REFERENCES

Arrhenius, S. 1896. "On the Influence of Carbonic Acid in the Air upon the Temperature of the Ground." *Philosophical Magazine and Journal of Science,* 5th ser., 41:237–276.

Croll, J. 1864. "On the Physical Cause of the Change of Climate during Geological Epochs." *The London, Edinburgh, and Dublin Philosophical Magazine and Journal of Science* 28 (187): 121–137. https://doi.org/10.1080/14786446408643733.

Harland, W. B., and J. S. Rudwick. 1964. "The Great Infra-Cambrian Ice Age." *Scientific American* 211 (2): 28–36. https://doi.org/10.1038/scientificamerican0864-28.

Hoffman, P. F., A. J. Kaufman, G. P. Galverson, and D. P. Schrag. 1998. "A Neoproterozoic Snowball Earth." *Science* 281 (5381): 1342–1346. https://doi.org/10.1126/science.281.5381.134.

Keeling, C. D. 1960. "The Concentration and Isotopic Abundances of Carbon Dioxide in the Atmosphere." *Tellus* 12 (2): 200–203. https://doi.org/10.1111/j.2153-3490.1960.tb01300.x.

Kirschvink, J. L. 1992. "Late Proterozoic Low-Latitude Global Glaciation: The Snowball Earth." In *In the Proterozoic Biosphere: A Multidisciplinary Study,* edited by J. Schopf and C. Klein, 51–52. Cambridge, UK: Cambridge University Press.

Laakso, T. A., and D. P. Schrag. 2017. "A Theory of Atmospheric Oxygen." *Geobiology* 15 (3): 366–384. https://doi.org/10.1111/gbi.12230.

Manabe, S., and K. Bryan. 1969. "Climate Calculations with a Combined Ocean-Atmosphere Model." *Journal of the Atmospheric Sciences* 26 (4): 786–789. https://doi.org/10.1175/1520-0469(1969)026<0786:CCWACO>2.0.CO;2.

Manabe, S., J. Smagorinsky, and R. F. Strickler. 1965. "Simulated Climatology of a General Circulation Model with a Hydrologic Cycle." *Monthly Weather Review* 93 (12): 769–798. https://doi.org/10.1175/1520-0493(1965)093<0769:SCOAGC>2.3.CO;2.

Neftel, A., H. Oeschger, J. Schwander, B. Stauffer, and R. Zumbrunn. 1982. "Ice Core Sample Measurements Give Atmospheric CO_2 Content during the Past 40,000 Yr." *Nature* 295:220–223. https://doi.org/10.1038/295220a0.

Petit, J., J. Jouzel, D. Raynaud, N. I. Barkov, J.-M. Barnola, and I. Basile. 1999. "Climate and Atmospheric History of the Past 420,000 Years from the Vostok Ice Core, Antarctica." *Nature* 399:429–436. https://doi.org/10.1038/20859.

Tyndall, J. 1863. *Heat Considered as a Mode of Motion: Being a Course of Twelve Lectures Delivered at The Royal Institution of Great Britain in the Season of 1862.* London, UK: Longman, Green, Longman, Roberts & Green.

THE EFFECT OF SOLAR RADIATION VARIATIONS ON THE CLIMATE OF THE EARTH

M. I. Budyko

Abstract

It follows from the analysis of observation data that the secular variation of the mean temperature of the Earth can be explained by the variation of short-wave radiation, arriving at the surface of the Earth. In connection with this, the influence of long-term changes of radiation, caused by variations of atmospheric transparency on the thermal regime is being studied. Taking into account the influence of changes of planetary albedo of the Earth under the development of glaciations on the thermal regime, it is found that comparatively small variations of atmospheric transparency could be sufficient for the development of quaternary glaciations.

As paleogeographical research including materials on paleotemperature analyses has shown (Bowen 1966, *et al.*), the Earth's climate has long differed from the present one. During the last two hundred million years the temperature difference between the poles and equator has been comparatively small and there were no zones of cold climate on the Earth. By the end of the Tertiary period the temperature at temperate and high latitudes had decreased appreciably, and in the Quaternary time subsequent increase in the thermal contrast between the poles and equator took place, that was followed by the development of ice cover on the land and oceans at temperate and high latitudes.

The size of Quaternary glaciations changed several times, the present epoch corresponding to the moment of a decrease in the area of glaciations that still occupy a considerable part of the Earth's surface.

To answer the question of in what way the climate will change in future, it is necessary to establish the causes of Quaternary glaciations initiation and to determine the direction of their development. Numerous studies on this problem contain various and often contradictory hypotheses on the causes of glaciations. The absence of the generally accepted viewpoint as regards this seems to be explained by the fact that the existing hypotheses were based mainly on qualitative considerations allowing different interpretation.

Taking into account this consideration, we shall examine in the present paper the possibility of using quantitative methods of physical climatology to study the problem in question.

Firstly we shall dwell upon the problem of climate change regularities during the last century. Fig. 1 represents the secular variation of annual temperature in the northern hemisphere that was calculated from the maps of temperature anomalies for each month for the period of 1881 to 1960 which were compiled at the Main Geophysical Observatory. Line 1 in this figure characterizes the values of anomalies that are not smoothed, line 2 the anomalies averaged by ten-year periods.

As is seen from this figure, a rise in temperature that began at the end of last century stopped in about 1940, and a fall in temperature started. The temperature in the northern hemisphere that increased in the warming period by 0.6°C then decreased by the middle of the fifties by 0.2°C. A comparatively short-period rise in temperature with smaller amplitude was also observed in the last years of the XIXth century.

The curve of secular temperature variation can be compared with the curve of secular variation of direct solar radiation with cloudless sky that was drawn by the data from a group of stations in Europe and America with the longest-period series of observations. This curve presenting the values of solar radiation smoothed for ten-year periods corresponds to line 3 in Fig. 1. As is seen from the above figure, the direct radiation had two maxima—a short-period one at the end of the XIXth century and a longer-period one with the maximum values of radiation in the thirties.

The problem of the causes of secular variation of direct radiation was already discussed by Humphreys (1929, and others) who considered that it was determined by the change in the atmospheric transparency due to the propagation of volcanic eruption dust in it. Having agreed to this point of view that is confirmed by many new data, it should be suggested that a decrease in radiation after 1940 could also depend on the increase of dust in the atmosphere due to man's activity.

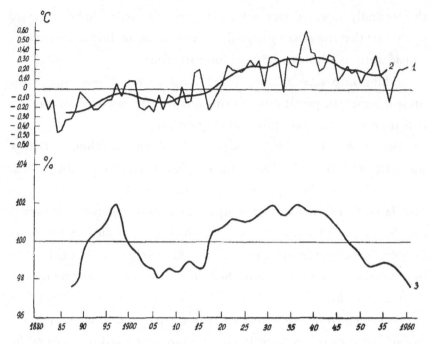

Figure 1. Secular variation of temperature and direet radiation.

As can be seen from Fig. 1, the curves of secular variations of temperature and radiation are more or less similar.

To find out the dependence between the radiation change and that of temperature, let us compare the radiation and thermal regimes of the northern hemisphere for two thirty-year periods: 1888-1917 and 1918-1947. It follows from the data given in Fig. 1 that the temperature in the latter of these periods was by 0.33°C higher than that in the former, and the direct radiation by 2.0% higher.

To estimate the corresponding change in total radiation, it should be taken into account that the atmospheric transparency changes after volcanic eruptions as a result of propagation of dust with particles of the order of 1μ in the lower stratosphere. This dust considerably increases the short-wave radiation diffusion, as a result of which the planetary albedo of the Earth becomes higher. Because of the radiation diffusion by dust mainly in the direction of an incident ray (Mie effect) the direct radiation decreases with diffusion to a greater extent than the total radiation does. Using the calculation method developed by K. S. Shifrin and his collaborators (Shifrin and Minin 1957; Shifrin and Pyatovskaya

1959), one can estimate the ratio of decrease in total radiation to that in direct radiation.

Such a calculation shows that this ratio computed for the average annual conditions changes slightly with the change of latitude, and on an average for the Earth equals 0.15.

Thus, the difference in total radiation for the periods under consideration amounts to 0.30%. In this case the ratio of temperature change to the change of radiation turns out to be equal to 1.1°C per 1% of radiation change.

This value should be compared with the values of similar ratio obtained as a result of calculating the radiation influence on the thermal regime of the Earth.

To determine the dependence of temperature on solar radiation with the average relationship between temperature, air humidity and other factors influencing the long-wave radiation, we used the results of calculations of monthly mean values of radiation at the outer boundary of the atmosphere that were made when preparing *Atlas of the Heat Balance of the Earth* (1963).

On the basis of these data relating to each month for 260 stations an empirical formula was derived

$$I = a + BT - (a_1 + B_1T)\, n \qquad (1)$$

where I = outgoing radiation in kcal/cm^2 month,

T = temperature at the level of Earth's surface in°C,

n = cloudiness in fractions of unit,

the values of dimensional coefficients of which equal: $a = 14.0$; $B = 0.14$; $a_1 = 3.0$; $B_1 = 0.10$.

The root-mean-square deviation of the results of calculation by this formula from the initial data accounts for less than 5% of the radiation values.

Comparing formula (1) with similar dependence that can be obtained from the work by Manabe and Wetherald (1967) Manabe and Wetherald (1967), it is possible to conclude that they practically coincide for the conditions of cloudless sky and differ in considering the cloudiness effect on radiation.

For mean annual conditions, the equation of the heat balance of the Earth-atmosphere system has the following form:

$$Q(1 - \alpha) - I = A \qquad (2)$$

where Q = solar radiation coming to the outer boundary of the atmosphere;

α = albedo;

A = gain or loss of heat as a result of the atmosphere and hydrosphere circulation, including heat redistribution of phase

water transformations.

Taking into account that for the Earth as a whole $A = 0$, we shall find from formulae (1) and (2) the dependence of the Earth's mean temperature on the value of solar radiation. In this case it turns out that the change of solar radiation by 1%, with the average for the Earth value of cloudiness equal to 0.50 and constant albedo equal to 0.33, causes the temperature change by $1.5°$.

This result can be compared with similar estimate obtained from the work by Manabe and Wetherald from which it follows that with constant relative air humidity the mean temperature at the Earth's surface changes by $1.2°$ solar radiation changes by 1%.

It is clear that both of these values agree satisfactorily with the relation between changes in temperature and radiation that was obtained from observational data. One can believe that some excess of the computed temperature changes as compared to observational data reflects the thermal inertia effect of oceans the heating or cooling of which smooths the Earth's temperature variations in comparison with the computed values for stationary conditions.

Thus, it seems probable that present changes of the Earth's temperature are determined mainly by the atmosphere transparency variations that depend on the level of volcanic activity.

If the present changes in volcanic activity cause radiation variations by several tenths of per cent and the planetary temperature variations by several tenths of a degree, one can believe that in the past respective variations of radiation and temperature reached appreciably larger values.

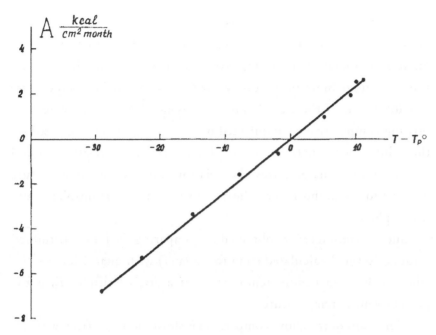

Figure 2. The dependence of horizontal heat transfer upon temperature difference.

It is evident that the number of volcanic eruptions for the given interval of time is different with constant mean level of volcanic activity for statistic reasons, these differences being the greater, the longer general period of time being considered. The standard of volcanic activity in different geological epochs is also known to change noticeably in connection with the change of tectonic processes intensity.

Since the volcanic activity variations caused by tectonic factors are characterized by long periods of time to calculate the influence of radiation variations associated with them on the thermal regime, changes in the Earth's albedo should be taken into account that are due to expansion or reduction of the area covered with ice on the land and oceans.

As observations from meteorological satellites have shown (see Raschke, Möller, and Bandeen 1968), the albedo of the Earth-atmosphere system over areas with ice cover is greater than that over ice-free areas, due to which fact the change in area covered with ice increases the radiation variation effect on thermal regime.

To estimate the radiation variation influence on the temperature of latitudinal zones, taking into account the indicated effect, one of numerical models of the average latitudinal temperature distribution should be used. Since in this case we are only interested in temperature distribution near the Earth's surface it is possible to use, instead of existing comparatively complicated models, a simple scheme based on the solution of equations (1) and (2) to which the relation should be added that characterizes the relationship between temperature distribution and horizontal heat transfer in the atmosphere and hydrosphere.

Such a relation can be obtained by comparing the mean latitudinal values of term A calculated from formula (1) with quantities $T - T_p$, where T is annual mean temperature at a given latitude, T_p is the planetary mean temperature.

The result of the above comparison is shown in Fig. 2 from which it follows that the corresponding dependence can be expressed in the form of equation

$$A = \beta \left(T - T_p \right) \tag{3}$$

where $\beta = 0.235 \, \text{kcal} / \text{cm}^2$ month degree

From formulae (1), (2) and (3), taking into consideration that for the Earth as a whole $A = 0$, we obtain equations

$$T = \frac{Q(1 - \alpha) - a + a_1 n + \beta T_p}{\beta + B - B_1 n} \tag{4}$$

$$T_p = \frac{Q_p \left(1 - \alpha_p \right) - a + a_1 n}{B - B_1 n} \tag{5}$$

(where Q_p and α_p are planetary values of radiation and albedo) by which the average latitudinal annual mean temperatures were computed for present climatic conditions of the northern hemisphere. The values of Q, Q_p accepted in this calculation correspond to the value of solar constant $1.92 \, \text{cal} / \text{cm}^2$ min, the albedo, according to observational data available, at the latitudes of $0°$ to $60°$ is considered to be equal to 0.32, at the latitude of $70°$ to 0.50, at the latitude of $80°$ to 0.62. In the calculation, the influence of deviations of cloudiness values from its mean planetary value equal to 0.50 on temperature is neglected.

The possibility of such an assumption results from the conclusion established in the calculations made using the above formulae concerning a comparatively weak effect of cloudiness on the mean indices of thermal regime within a rather wide range of conditions. Such a conclusion drawn, taking into account the dependence of albedo on cloudiness, implies that the effect of cloudiness on the change in absorbed radiation in a number of cases is compensated for by its influence on the outgoing long-wave radiation. The results of calculating the contemporary average latitudinal distribution of temperature are presented in Fig. 3 where they correspond to line T_0. As is seen, these results are in good agreement with the observed temperature at different latitudes that is represented in Fig. 3 by line T. Such an agreement allows us to use the scheme described for evaluation of the radiation variation effect on the Earth's thermal regime and glaciations.

The southern boundary of the existing ice cover on the seas and land in the Arctic corresponds to the mean latitude of 72°N. Let us consider that with a decrease in solar radiation the surface of ice cover expands in accordance with the extension of the surface area with temperature equal to or lower than the temperature observed now at 72°N. In this case let us assume that albedo on the ice-covered area is equal to 0.62 and at the southern boundary of this ice cover to 0.50.

It follows from the above values of albedo that with the change of ice cover area the mean albedo of the Earth changes by value $0.30\,S$ where coefficient 0.30 corresponds to the difference of albedo values with the presence and absence of ice cover, and quantity $S = lq$, ($l =$ the ratio of ice area change to the whole area of the Earth, $q =$ the ratio of mean radiation in the same zone of ice area change to the mean value of radiation for the Earth as a whole).

To take into account the influence of the glaciation area change on the annual mean temperature of the Earth, we shall use formula

$$\Delta T_p = \frac{Q_p}{B - B_1 n} \left[\frac{\Delta Q_p}{Q_p} (1 - \alpha_p - 0.30\,S) - 0.30\,S \right] \qquad (6)$$

which is obtained from formulae (1) and (2), where ΔT_p is the Earth's temperature change with the change of mean radiation Q_p by value ΔQ_p.

From (1), (2), (3), (6) we shall deduce a formula for temperature at some latitude where T_p' is the existing mean temperature of the Earth.

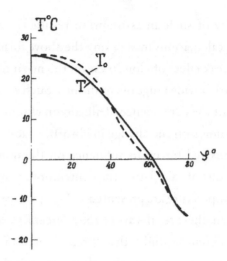

Figure 3. The average latitudinal temperature distribution.

Using this formula and considering the dependence of values Q and S on latitude, one can compute the position of glaciation boundary for different values of $\Delta Q_p / Q_p$. By this formula it is also possible to calculate the distributions of temperature at different latitudes that correspond to these values. The results of such a calculation are shown in Fig. 4, where lines $T_{1.0}$ and $T_{1.5}$ correspond to temperature distributions with the decrease in radiation income by 1.0% and 1.5% respectively. In the above-mentioned calculation the interrelationship between the thermal regimes of the northern and southern hemispheres is neglected (which assumption is reasonable with the similar change of thermal regime in both hemispheres). It is assumed in calculation that the relative decrease in radiation at different latitudes is the same.

Fig. 5 represents the values obtained from this calculation for the mean planetary temperature T_p and mean latitude to which glaciation extends φ_0 depending on relative radiation changes. As is seen from this figure, the radiation variation effect on thermal regime considerably increases as a result of glaciation development, the corresponding dependence becoming nonlinear.

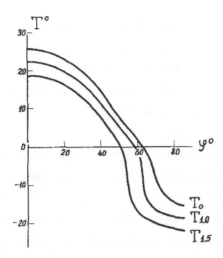

Figure 4. The dependence of temperature distribution on radiation amount.

$$T = \frac{Q(1-\alpha)\left(1 + \frac{\Delta Q_p}{Q_p}\right) - a + a_1 n + \beta T_p' + \frac{\beta Q_p}{B - B_1 n}\left[\frac{\Delta Q_p}{Q_p}\left(1 - \alpha_p - 0.30S\right) - 0.30S\right]}{\beta + B - B_1 n}$$

(7)

If with the decrease in radiation by 1% the mean temperature of the Earth drops by 5°, then with the decrease in radiation by 1.5% such a drop reaches 9°. Simultaneously with the above temperature drop the glaciation displacement $10 - 18°$ to the south takes place, i.e. the distances approximately corresponding to the expansion of quaternary glaciations. When radiation decreases by 1.6% the ice cover reaches the mean latitude of about 50°, after that it starts shifting towards lower latitudes up to the equator as a result of self-development. At the same time the planetary temperature drops sharply and reaches the value of several tens of degrees below zero.

A conclusion on the possibility of complete glaciation of the Earth after ice cover reaches some critical latitude follows from the calculation, using the above formulae, of the values of decrease in radiation necessary for further movement of ice to the equator. Such a calculation shows that to the south of critical latitude ice will move to the equator with the decrease in radiation by less than 1.6%, and at lower latitudes ice will move in the indicated direction with the existing values of radiation and even with its values exceeding those in the present epoch.

It should be noted that similar conclusion from other considerations was drawn previously by Öpik (1953, *et al.*) who considered, however, that for glaciating the Earth a considerable decrease in solar constant is necessary. The possibility of existence of complete glaciation of the Earth with the present value of solar constant was mentioned in the author's works (Budyko 1961, 1966).

Thus, the present thermal regime and glaciations of the Earth prove to be characterized by high instability. Comparatively small changes of radiation—only by 1.0-1.5%—are sufficient for the development of ice cover on the land and oceans that reaches temperate latitudes.

It should be noted that such changes in radiation are only several times as great as its variations observed due to the changeability of volcanic activity in the last century.

Taking into consideration that according to the data of geological investigations the level of volcanic activity for long periods of time in the past changed by a factor of several times (see Ronov 1959), one can believe that the influence of long-period variations of volcanic activity is a probable factor of glaciation development.

This conclusion is confirmed by the fact, established by Fuchs and Patterson, of correspondence between the main epochs of quaternary glaciations and the periods of considerable increase in volcanic activity in a number of regions of low latitudes (1947).

Though in this paper the author has no possibility to discuss numerous other hypotheses as to be causes of quaternary glaciations, nevertheless it is necessary to dwell upon popular idea concerning the influence of changes of the Earth's orbit elements on glaciations.

Such a conception substantiated by Milankovich (1930, and others) and other authors is shared by many specialists studying quaternary glaciations.

As is known, the effect of changes in the Earth's orbit elements leads to appreciable redistribution of radiation amount coming to different latitudes. Considering these changes and using the model of latitudinal temperature distribution suggested by him, Milankovich concluded that with the changes of orbit elements at temperate and high latitudes considerable changes in temperature occur that can result in glaciation.

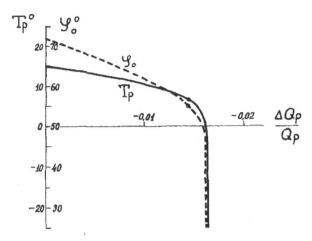

Figure 5. The dependence of the Earth's temperature and ice cover boundary on radiation variations.

It should be mentioned that the model of temperature distribution suggested by Milankovich did not take into account horizontal heat transfer in the atmosphere and hydrosphere due to which it had to overestimate considerably the influence of changes in radiation in a given latitudinal zone on the thermal regime of the same zone.

To verify the hypothesis of Milankovich, there were calculated, using the above-mentioned scheme, changes in thermal regime and glaciations for the case of considerable change of the Earth's orbit elements 22 thousand years ago which is usually associated with the last glaciation. The calculations made have shown that though the variations of orbit elements influence in a definite way the thermal regime and glaciation, this influence is comparatively small and corresponds to possible displacement of the glaciation boundary by a little less than 1° of latitude. It should be borne in mind that such a calculation allows for the change in annual radiation totals. According to Milankovich, the main influence on the glaciation is exerted by the variations of the summer radiation values that at latitudes 65 − 75° are 2 to 3 times as large as the variations of annual values. Emphasizing the necessity of further study of the problem on the effect of annual radiation variation on the glaciation, it should be noted that the above-obtained result casts some doubt on the hypothesis that the effect of the Earth's orbit changes is sufficient for the explanation of the quaternary glaciations.

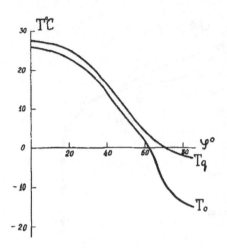

Figure 6. Ice cover effect on temperature distribution.

Now we shall proceed to the question of why the volcanic activity variations, that occurred during the whole history of the Earth, did not result in the development of glaciations during hundreds of millions of years previous to the quaternary period.

It has been established in geological investigations that in the pre-quaternary time the gradual rise of continents level took place. This caused weakening of water circulation in the oceans between low and high latitudes.

It was ascertained long ago (Budyko 1948, *et al.*) that the heat transfer between the equator and the poles in the hydrosphere is a considerable portion of the corresponding transfer in the atmosphere, in connection with which the changes in water circulation in the oceans should influence essentially the thermal regime at high and temperature latitudes.

To clear up this question, temperature distribution was calculated using the above-mentioned scheme for the case of absence of ice at high latitudes.

The results of such calculations are shown in Fig. 6 where line T_0 represents the present-day temperature distribution, and line T_q temperature distribution with the absence of polar glaciations. In these calculations the albedo at high latitudes is accepted to be equal to the albedo of ice-free areas and the coefficient β is considered to be equal to its value accepted above.

As is seen from Fig. 6, the polar ice changing little the temperature at low latitudes considerably decreases the temperature at high latitudes. As a result, the mean difference in temperature between the pole and the equator decreases and the annual mean temperature in polar zone turns out to be equal to several degrees below zero.

One can believe that with ice-free regime the meridional heat transfer in the polar ocean will increase as compared to present conditions since this ocean, that is now isolated from the atmosphere by ice, will give off a considerable amount of heat to the atmosphere through turbulent heat exchange.

If to consider that with the absence of ice the Arctic Ocean receives additionally an amount of heat equal to the mean value coming now to the ice-free areas of the oceans at high latitudes, the mean air temperature in the Arctic must be somewhat higher than the above value, i.e. close to zero.

This result is in agreement with the conclusions drawn using other methods in previous works by the author Budyko (1961, 1962a, 1966), L. R. Rakipova (1962, 1966), Donn and Shaw (1966), and others. It confirms once more the possibility of existence of ice-free regime in the polar basin in the present epoch and at the same time indicates high instability of such a regime.

It is evident that with the annual mean temperature in the Central Arctic close to water freezing point comparatively small anomalies of radiation income may lead to ice restoration.

Thus, with the present distribution of continents and oceans the existence of two climatic regimes is possible one of which is characterized by the presence of polar ice and large thermal contrast between the pole and the equator, and the other by the absence of glaciation and small meridional mean gradient of temperature.

Both of these regimes are unstable since even small variations of solar radiation income could be sufficient either for freezing of the ice-free polar ocean or melting of the existing ice. Such a peculiarity of climatic regime seems to determine the main features of climate variations in the Quaternary period.

In the periods of decreased volcanic activity the temperature distribution corresponded to ice-free regime which characterizes the climate of comparatively warm inter-ice epochs. When volcanic activity increased, ice formed firstly in the arctic seas, and then greater or smaller glaciations were developed on the land.

As it was mentioned in the author's work (Budyko 1968), in the mesozoic era and in the paleogene the northern polar basin was connected with the oceans of low latitudes with much wider straits as compared to the Quaternary period. In this case the heat income to the polar basin as a result of activity of sea currents seemed to exceed those values that are observed at high latitudes under present conditions. If this income was 1.5 to 2 times as great as its present mean value for the ice-free areas, then according to the calculations by the above formulae, the annual mean temperature in the Arctic reached $10°$, which fact excluded the possibility of glaciation even with appreciable anomalies of radiation.

During the Tertiary period the isolation of polar basin from the tropic regions of ocean gradually developed, which caused the temperature decrease near the pole and approaching of temperature distribution to the values characteristic of inter-ice epochs.

It follows from the above considerations that the present epoch is a part of glacial period since any noticeable increase in volcanic activity should lead to new glaciation development.

Moreover, it seems probable that one of the following glaciers expansion could reach the critical latitude after which the complete glaciation of the Earth would set in. Such a possibility was on the point of being realized in the period of maximum quaternary glaciation when the temperature of the Earth and the position of ice cover corresponded to dots plotted on lines T_p and φ_0 in Fig. 5.

As is seen from this figure, the ice cover under these conditions has moved about 0.8 of the way from the present ice boundary to the critical latitude.

From such a viewpoint the Quaternary History of the Earth seems to be the period of coming climatic catastrophe due to which the existence of higher forms of organic life on our planet may be exterminated.

When estimating the probability of such a catastrophe being realized in future, the character of man's activity should be taken into account which influences to some extent the climate at present. Without touching upon the possibility of implementing in future some projects of active influence on the climate which could affect the glaciation development, ever increasing influence of man's activity on the energy budget of the Earth should be mentioned.

All the energy used by man is transformed into heat, the main portion of this energy being an additional source of heat as compared to the present radiation gain. Simple calculations show (Budyko 1961) that with the present rate of growth of using energy the heat produced by man in less than two hundred years will be comparable with the energy coming from the sun. Since glaciations are greatly influenced by the changes in energy budget which are a small part of solar radiation income then it is probable that in the comparatively near future the possibility of glaciation expansion will be excluded and there will appear the reverse one of polar ice melting on the land and oceans with all the changes in the Earth's climate that are associated with it.

It should be mentioned that the conclusions stated in this paper on the effect of changes in solar radiation on climate have been drawn as a result of using a strongly schematized model of the Earth's thermal regime. It is considered desirable to make similar calculations with the use of more general models. ✍

REFERENCES

Bowen, R. 1966. *Paleotemperature Analysis.* Amsterdam: Elsevier Publishing Company.

Budyko, M. I. 1948. "The Heat Balance of the Northern Hemisphere. (In Russian)." *Proceedings of the Main Geophysical Observatory* 18.

———. 1961. "On the Thermal Zones of the Earth. (In Russian)." *Meteorology and Hydrology,* no. 11.

———. 1962a. "Polar Ice and Climate. (In Russian)." *Proceedings Ac. Sci. USSR ser. geograph.,* no. 6.

———. 1962b. "Some Ways of Climate Modification. (In Russian)." *Meteorology and Hydrology,* no. 2.

———. 1963. "Atlas of the Heat Balance of the Earth. (In Russian)." *Idrometcorozdat, Moscoue* (Moscow), 69.

———. 1966. "Polar Ice and Climate." In *Proceedings of the Symposium on the Arctic Heat Budget and Atmospheric Circulation.*

———. 1968. "On the Causes of Climate Variations." *Sveriges Meteorologiska och Hydrologiska Institut Meddelanden,* B, no. 28.

Donn, W. L., and M. Shaw. 1966. "The Heat Budgets of Ice-Free and Ice-Covered Arctic Ocean." *Journal of Geophysical Research* 71 (4): 1087–1093.

Fuchs, V. S., and T. T. Patterson. 1947. "The Relation of Volcanicity and Orogeny to Climate Change." *Geological Magazine* 84 (6): 321–333.

Humphreys, N. J. 1929. *Physics of the Air.* 2nd ed. New York.

Manabe, S., and R. Wetherald. 1967. "Thermal Equilibrium of the Atmosphere with a Given Distribution of Relative Humidity." *Journ. of Atmosph. Sciences* 24 (3).

Milankovich, M. 1930. *Matematische Klimalehre und Astronomische Theorie der Klimaschwanungen.*

Öpik, E. J. 1953. "On the Causes of Palaeoclimatic Variations and of the Ice Ages in Particular." *Journal of Glaciology* 2 (13).

Rakipova, L. R. 1962. "Climate Change When Influencing the Arctic Basin Ice. (In Russian)." *Meteorology and Hydrology,* no. 9.

———. 1966. "The Influence of the Arctic Ice Cover on the Zonal Distribution of Atmospheric Temperature." In *Proceedings of the Symposium on the Arctic heat budget and atmospheric circulation.*

Raschke, E., F. Möller, and W. R. Bandeen. 1968. "The Radiation Balance of Earth-atmosphere System." *Sveriges Meteorologiska och Hydrologiska Institut Meddelanden,* B, no. 28.

Ronov, A. B. 1959. "To the Post-Cambrian Geochemical History of the Atmosphere and Hydrosphere. (In Russian)." *Geochemistry,* no. 5.

Shifrin, K. S., and I. N. Minin. 1957. "To the Theory of Non-Horizontal Visibility. (In Russian)." *Proceedings of the Main Geophysical Observatory* 68.

Shifrin, K. S., and N. V. Pyatovskaya. 1959. *Tables of Slant Visibility Range and Day Sky Brightness. (In Russion).* Leningrad.

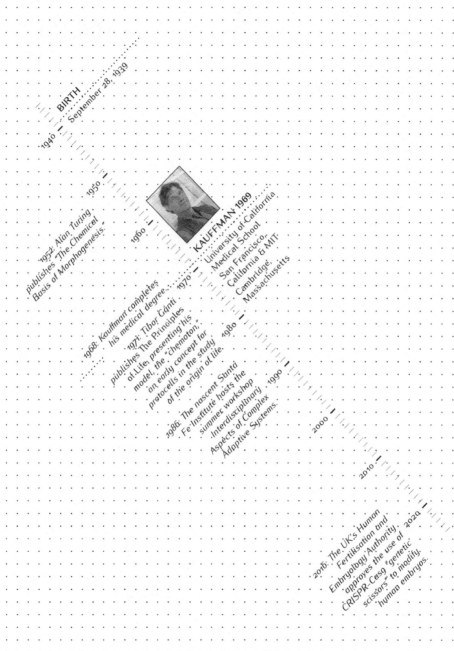

BIRTH — September 28, 1939

1940

1950

1952: Alan Turing
publishes "The Chemical
Basis of Morphogenesis."

1960

KAUFFMAN 1969
University of California,
Medical School
San Francisco,
California & MIT,
Cambridge,
Massachusetts

1968: Kauffman completes
his medical degree.

1970

1971: Tibor Gánti
publishes The Principles
of Life, presenting his
model, the "chemoton,"
an early concept for
protocells in the study
of the origin of life.

1980

1986: The nascent Santa
Fe Institute hosts the
summer workshop
Interdisciplinary
Aspects of Complex
Adaptive Systems.

1990

2000

2010

2016: The UK's Human
Fertilisation and
Embryology Authority
approves the use of
CRISPR-Cas9 "genetic
scissors" to modify
human embryos.

2020

STUART ALAN KAUFFMAN

[33]

ATTRACTORS OF A RANDOM NETWORKED DYNAMICAL SYSTEM HAVE SOMETHING TO SAY ABOUT LIFE

Sanjay Jain, University of Delhi
and Santa Fe Institute

Ignorance as Virtue

Stuart Kauffman's work extends a hallowed tradition in statistical physics to a new domain: the system that governs the switching on and off of an organism's genes. The fundamental postulate of statistical mechanics, originating in the work of Ludwig Boltzmann and Josiah Willard Gibbs, is an acknowledgement and celebration of ignorance. It asserts that for an isolated thermodynamic system at equilibrium all microstates of the system that are compatible with the macroscopic constraints of isolation (e.g., having the same fixed total energy E, volume V, and number of particles N) are equally probable. The statement of "equal probability" is an acknowledgment of complete ignorance or the maximization of entropy. However, this assertion of ignorance, circumscribed by what we do know about the system, is a source of great power. It defines a statistical ensemble, or a probability distribution over microstates, parameterized by E, V, and N, from which one can compute the average of any desired function of the microstates. Amazingly, averages computed from the theory agree with observations.

In the 1950s, Eugene Wigner introduced a statistical ensemble of matrices of a high-dimension N to describe the spacing of energy levels observed in individual atomic nuclei. Wigner's hypothesis was tantamount to saying that certain properties of a complex-enough quantum mechanical system (like an atomic nucleus) are identical to the averages of a suitably chosen random ensemble of systems. These properties, too difficult to derive theoretically for any particular

S. A. Kauffman, "Metabolic Stability and Epigenesis in Randomly Constructed Genetic Nets," in *Journal of Theoretical Biology* 22 (3): 437–467 (1969).

Reprinted with permission from Elsevier.

system, could be easily calculated from the ensemble and agreed with experiments. Random matrices have since been applied as a powerful tool in many different areas, including condensed matter physics, biology, and finance.

Kauffman's paper extends the tradition of making a virtue of ignorance and extracting insight from randomness to a most unlikely domain of systems: the cells of a developing embryo. These cells, sculpted by four billion years of evolution and displaying clockwork regularity and cooperativity in time and space—witness the complex yet repeatable appearance of form and different cell types as an embryo develops from a single cell to an adult—are hardly systems one expects to be described by a random construction. However, Kauffman constructs a class of randomly structured dynamical systems and suggests that their behavior is, in certain respects, similar to that of cells of a multicellular organism.

Genetic Interactions

In an organism, the time-dependent activity pattern of a gene depends upon other genes. As an approximation a gene may be thought to have only two states of activity: on or off. In the on state the gene is transcribed or read by the cellular machinery and its product, a protein, is produced. On a certain characteristic timescale, the concentration of the protein rises to a level that has significant downstream effects. A protein (called a transcription factor) can bind to the promoter region of other specific genes and switch them on (if it is an activator for the genes in question) or off (if it is an inhibitor). Whether a gene is on or off depends upon the collective effect of the various transcription factors binding to its promoter region. The binding of transcription factors is dependent on their concentration level, which in turn depends on the on–off state of the genes encoding them at an earlier time. In this way the on–off state of a gene at one instant can influence the state of other genes at later times. Feedback in this network make the dynamics complicated.

Random Boolean Networks

In the late 1960s the network of regulatory connections between genes was unknown for all organisms—only the connections between a few pairs of genes were known. Further, the logical rule governing a gene's regulation—specifying which configurations of its set of input genes turned this gene on and which configurations turned it off—was also known only for a few genes. Kauffman constructed the network of N genes randomly, each gene being influenced by K other randomly chosen genes in the network (or each node receiving inputs from K randomly chosen other nodes in the network). Further, the logical rule for each gene was also generated randomly from the set of all Boolean functions with K Boolean inputs (there being $2^{(2^K)}$ such functions). This defined an ensemble of dynamical systems characterized by N and K and generalized the model of Walker and Ashby (1966), which also employed a random network but with the same function at every node.

Attractors and Cell Types

Kauffman simulated these dynamical systems on the computer for values of N up to a few thousand (with most results for $N = 400$), $K = 1, 2, 3$, and studied their attractors. An *attractor* is the set of states in which the system eventually settles down after a transient, starting from some initial condition. A system can have multiple attractors. The set of initial conditions that all lead the system into a particular attractor is called the *basin of attraction* of the attractor.

Earlier work by Waddington (1940, 1957), Delbruck (1949), and Thom (1968) had recognized that various cell types ought to be considered attractors of an underlying biochemical dynamical system. Monod and Jacob (1961) had given examples of simple genetic circuits with more than one attractor. Kauffman's paper was the first to provide a concrete and simple dynamical model of an entire system of genes, which therefore allowed the hypothesis that cell types are attractors of a complex genetic regulatory system to be framed and tested.

Identifying cell types as attractors of a dynamical system immediately explains, conceptually,

1. The discreteness, or distinctiveness from each other, of the various cell types.

2. How the number of cell types present in an embryo can grow with time during ontogeny; a subset of cells in one attractor can be pushed into another attractor's basin of attraction by a perturbation or a systematic transformation of their local environment that takes them across the basin boundary, thereby bringing into existence a hitherto-absent cell type.

Furthermore, Kauffman found that random Boolean networks with $K = 2$ also shared with organisms the following properties:

3. There are rather few cell types in any organism. While the number of possible configurations of the system, 2^N, grows exponentially with N, Kauffman claimed that the number A of attractors for $K = 2$ systems is small and grows only as a power, $A \sim N^\alpha$, with the exponent $\alpha = 0.5$. A more recent estimate is even smaller, suggesting that α is close to 0.1 in these models with asynchronous update (Rozum *et al.* 2021).

4. In any given cell type a large fraction of genes does not change their state over time.

5. A constrained sequence of cell types arises as an embryo develops. Kauffman found that each attractor upon perturbation could transition into only a few other attractors with any significant probability.

The genetic regulatory network in any organism is, of course, far from random (as are the energy levels of any particular atomic nucleus). Nevertheless, the fact that *certain* features of organisms are reproduced by a random ensemble (and that *certain* features of the energy levels of atomic nuclei are reproduced by random matrices) means that we have a plausible and simple explanation of at least those features. In fact, it is an argument for why those features should generically arise. Of course, the random model is not appropriate for asking more specific questions about any particular organism—just as one does not expect Wigner's random matrix model, which explains level statistics of nuclei, to tell us the half-life of U-235.

Kauffman's model in this sense provides insight into certain qualitative features of organisms. This holds despite the fact that several of the quantitative predictions and provocative claims made by Kauffman in the paper have not proven correct. The latter is in part a consequence of new biological discoveries. For example, the number of genes in multicellular organisms has turned out to be much smaller than estimated by Kauffman. Further, phenomena such as alternate splicing, post translational modifications, and intrinsically disordered protein domains make the context of an individual gene's expression much more complicated than the relatively simple transcriptional regulation known when Kauffman's paper was written.

Connection with Other Areas

It is worth mentioning that attractors of randomly constructed systems have been employed for several different kinds of complex adaptive systems, for example in neuroscience for conceptualizing associative memory (Hopfield 1982); in ecology to illuminate the tension between complexity and stability (May 1972), and in the origin of life field to model self-organization of pre-biotic autocatalytic sets (Farmer, Kauffman, and Packard 1986; Jain and Krishna 1998).

Kauffman's paper has motivated the construction of non-random Boolean models for a wide range of biological phenomena including bacterial metabolism, eukaryotic cell cycle, cancers, and ecosystem dynamics (many compiled under the Cell Collective, Helikar *et al.* 2012). The reason for the popularity of these models is their simplicity: One does not need detailed biological information such as rate constants to construct them—only Boolean or "logical" causal relationships between nodes is needed—and yet one can often draw important qualitative conclusions at the system level or test certain hypotheses about its architecture. Boolean models have also cross-fertilized the disciplines of biology and engineering in elucidating the control properties of complex systems (Sugita 1963, Thomas 1973; for a review see Abou-Jaoudé *et al.* 2016).

The Edge of Chaos

Kauffman observed in this paper that for large N, networks with the smallest possible value of K ($K = 1$) and those with the largest possible value ($K = N$) showed qualitatively different behavior—and neither resembled that of biological systems. The behavior of $K = 2$ systems, also qualitatively different from both of the above, was, however, similar to biological systems. Subsequent work (Derrida and Pomeau 1986) showed that $K = 2$ was indeed special in the space of these systems, marking a transition between an "ordered phase" ($K < 2$) and a "disordered or chaotic phase" ($K > 2$). This, together with work on cellular automata (Langton 1986; Packard 1988) prompted the question: Are biological systems in some sense poised near the edge of order and chaos?

From the work of several people on Boolean models, reviewed in Kauffman (1993), the following broad conclusions seem to follow: A system belonging to the ordered phase typically spends most of its time in a small set of states (in one of the attractors) and any small perturbation of the state of the system quickly dies off, returning the system to the attractor. In other words, the system exhibits "homeostasis." In the chaotic phase, the system wanders over a large set of states, and small perturbations, instead of dying down, grow. Further, small structural perturbations to the system (in which an input connection to a node or the Boolean function at a node is altered) do not change the attractors significantly if the system is in the ordered phase but do in the disordered phase. In other words, the system is more robust to structural perturbations in the ordered phase. A system that is in the ordered phase but *close to the boundary* of the disordered phase is robust to most perturbations; however, the occasional structural perturbation can cause a significant change in attractors leading to new stable patterns of on–off nodes.

Living systems are typically robust to both state perturbations (e.g., transient environmental changes, within bounds) as well as structural perturbations (e.g., most mutations). Therefore, the ordered phase of Boolean network models describes them better than the disordered phase. Being in the ordered phase and also close to the boundary of the disordered phase could further endow living systems with a flexibility that enables them to occasionally take advantage of novel genetic perturbations to modify their phenotype. In other words, sitting in the ordered phase at the edge between order and chaos could confer greater evolvability to living systems (Kauffman 1993).

Are living systems sitting thus? The matter is not settled. One approach has been to analyze the existing Boolean models of biological systems. A Boolean dynamical system being at the phase boundary between order and disorder, or at "criticality," depends not only on the local connectivity K, but also on the global topology of the network and the choice of the Boolean rules at the nodes. Many studies have argued that existing Boolean models of living systems are close to criticality (see, e.g., Daniels *et al.* 2018), but recent work challenges this conclusion (Park *et al.* 2023). Also, there are suggestions that organisms could achieve both the flexibility and homeostasis they display by other architectural means than being close to the edge of chaos (Samal and Jain 2008). Existing evidence for criticality in living systems as well as open questions are reviewed in Roli *et al.* (2018) and Mora and Bialek (2011).

Irrespective of the outcome of this debate for living systems, the above development has contributed an important perspective on the origins of evolvability in complex adaptive systems.

Summary

Kauffman's 1969 article:

1. introduced a class of mathematical models of dynamics that have become paradigmatic in the field of complex systems. These are perhaps the simplest imaginable models that capture several aspects of real complex systems: a large number of nonidentical components, their nontrivial underlying network topology, and their nonlinear dynamics with complex feedback and control.

FOUNDATIONAL PAPERS IN COMPLEXITY SCIENCE

2. In applying this class of models to genetic regulatory networks the paper established that the mathematical notions of an "attractor" and its "basin of attraction" in dynamical systems theory are central to biology, thereby concretizing a powerful theoretical conceptualization of several biological phenomena including cell differentiation and embryogenesis in multicellular organisms.

3. It brought from statistical mechanics the idea that randomness at the level of components can translate to regularities at the systemic level, in effect boldly postulating a new source of order in living systems (that Kauffman has later referred to as "order for free").

4. It was the starting point of the hypothesis, still under debate, that real complex adaptive systems, including living systems, are situated near the edge between order and chaos.

More generally, Kauffman's work has brought a conjunction of dynamical systems theory and statistical physics into the mainstream of thinking about complex adaptive systems, sensitizing us to the sometimes unexpected and simple relationship between architecture and outcome. ☙

Acknowledgments

I would like to thank Parth Pratim Pandey, Areejit Samal, Priyotosh Sil, Jasbir Singh, Ajay Subbaroyan, and Atiyab Zafar for discussion and pointing out relevant references, and Sienna Latham for valuable editorial advice.

REFERENCES

Abou-Jaoudé, W., P. Traynard, P. T. Monteiro, J. Saez-Rodriguez, T. Helikar, D. Thieffry, and C. Chaouiya. 2016. "Logical Modeling and Dynamical Analysis of Cellular Networks." *Frontiers in Genetics* 7. https://doi.org/10.3389/fgene.2016.00094.

Bornholdt, S., and S. Kauffman. 2019. "Ensembles, Dynamics, and Cell Types: Revisiting the Statistical Mechanics Perspective on Cellular Regulation." *Journal of Theoretical Biology* 467:15–22. https://doi.org/10.1016/j.jtbi.2019.01.036.

Daniels, B. C., H. Kim, D. Moore, S. Zhou, H. B. Smith, B. Karas, S. A. Kauffman, and S. I. Walker. 2018. "Criticality Distinguishes the Ensemble of Biological Regulatory Networks." *Physical Review Letters* 121 (13): 138102. https://doi.org/10.1103/PhysRevLett.121.138102.

Delbruck, M. 1949. *Unités Biologiques Douées de Continuité Génétique.* Paris, France: Publications du Centre National de la Recherche Scientifique.

Derrida, B., and Y. Pomeau. 1986. "Random Networks of Automata: A Simple Annealed Approximation." *Europhysics Letters* 1 (2): 45. https://doi.org/10.1209/0295-5075/1/2/001.

Farmer, J. D., S. A. Kauffman, and N. H. Packard. 1986. "Autocatalytic Replication of Polymers." *Physica D: Nonlinear Phenomena* 22 (1): 50–67. https://doi.org/10.1016/0167-2789(86)90233-2.

Greil, F., and B. Drossel. 2005. "Dynamics of Critical Kauffman Networks under Asynchronous Stochastic Update." *Physical Review Letters* 95 (4): 048701. https://doi.org/10.1103/PhysRevLett.95.048701.

Helikar, T., B. Kowal, S. McClenathan, M. Bruckner, T. Rowley, A. Madrahimov, B. Wicks, M. Shrestha, K. Limbu, and J. A. Rogers. 2012. "The Cell Collective: Toward an Open and Collaborative Approach to Systems Biology." See also https://cellcollective.org. *BMC Systems Biology* 6:96. https://doi.org/10.1186/1752-0509-6-96.

Hopfield, J. J. 1982. "Neural Networks and Physical Systems with Emergent Collective Computational Abilities." *Proceedings of the National Academy of Sciences* 79 (8): 2554–2558. https://doi.org/10.1073/pnas.79.8.2554.

Jain, S., and S. Krishna. 1998. "Autocatalytic Sets and the Growth of Complexity in an Evolutionary Model." *Physical Review Letters* 81 (25): 5684–5687. https://doi.org/10.1103/PhysRevLett.81.5684.

Kauffman, S. A. 1993. *The Origins of Order: Self-Organization and Selection in Evolution.* New York, NY: Oxford University Press.

Klemm, K., and S. Bornholdt. 2005. "Stable and Unstable Attractors in Boolean Networks." *Physical Review E* 72 (5): 055101(R). https://doi.org/10.1103/PhysRevE.72.055101.

Langton, C. G. 1986. "Studying Artificial Life with Cellular Automata." *Physica D: Nonlinear Phenomena* 22 (1–3): 120–149. https://doi.org/10.1016/0167-2789(86)90237-X.

May, R. 1972. "Will a Large Complex System be Stable?" *Nature* 238:413–414. https://doi.org/10.1038/238413a0.

Mihaljev, T., and B. Drossel. 2006. "Scaling in a General Class of Critical Random Boolean Networks." *Physical Review E* 74 (4): 046101. https://doi.org/10.1103/PhysRevE.74.046101.

Monod, J., and F. Jacob. 1961. "General Conclusions: Teleonomic Mechanisms in Cellular Metabolism, Growth, and Differentiation." *Cold Spring Harbor Symposia Quantitative Biology* 26:389–401. https://doi.org/10.1101/SQB.1961.026.01.048.

Mora, T., and W. Bialek. 2011. "Are Biological Systems Poised at Criticality?" *Journal of Statistical Physics* 144:268–302. https://doi.org/10.1007/s10955-011-0229-4.

Packard, N. H. 1988. "Adaptation toward the Edge of Chaos." In *Dynamic Patterns in Complex Systems: Proceedings of a Conference, Sponsored by Florida Atlantic University, Held in Honor of Hermann Haken on the Occasion of his 60th Birthday,* edited by J. A. S. Kelso, A. J. Mandell, and M. F. Shlesinger, 293–301. Singapore: World Scientific.

Park, H. K., F. X. Costa, L. M. Rocha, R. Albert, and J. C. Rozum. 2023. "Models of Cell Processes are Far from the Edge of Chaos." *PRX Life* 1 (023009). https://doi.org/10.1103/PRXLife.1.023009.

Roli, A., M. Villani, A. Filisetti, and R. Serra. 2018. "Dynamical Criticality: Overview and Open Questions." *Journal of Systems Science and Complexity* 31:647–663. https://doi.org/10.1007/s11424-017-6117-5.

Rozum, J. C., J. G. T. Zañudo, X. Gan, D. Deritei, and R. Albert. 2021. "Parity and Time Reversal Elucidate Both Decision-Making in Empirical Models and Attractor Scaling in Critical Boolean Networks." 7 (29). https://doi.org/10.1126/sciadv.abf8124.

Samal, A., and S. Jain. 2008. "The Regulatory Network of *E. Coli* Metabolism as a Boolean Dynamical System Exhibits both Homeostasis and Flexibility of Response." *BMC Systems Biology* 2 (21). https://doi.org/10.1186/1752-0509-2-21.

Samuelsson, B., and C. Troein. 2003. "Superpolynomial Growth in the Number of Attractors in Kauffman Networks." *Physical Review Letters* 90 (9): 098701. https://doi.org/10.1103/PhysRevLett.90.098701.

Sugita, M. 1963. "Functional Analysis of Chemical Systems *in Vivo* Using a Logical Circuit Equivalent. II. The Idea of a Molecular Automaton." *Journal of Theoretical Biology* 4 (2): 179–192. https://doi.org/10.1016/0022-5193(63)90027-4.

Thom, R. 1968. "Une Théorie Dynamique de la Morphogenèse." In *Towards a Theoretical Biology I,* edited by C. H. Waddington. Reprinted in English translation in Thom (1983): *Mathematical Models of Morphogenesis.*

Thomas, R. 1973. "Boolean Formalization of Genetic Control Circuits." *Journal of Theoretical Biology* 42 (3): 563–585. https://doi.org/10.1016/0022-5193(73)90247-6.

Waddington, C. H. 1940. *Introduction to Modern Genetics.* London, UK: (George Allen and Unwin, Ltd.

———. 1957. *Strategy of the Genes.* London, UK: Routledge. https://doi.org/10.4324/9781315765471.

Walker, C. C., and W. R. Ashby. 1966. "On Temporal Characteristics of Behavior in Certain Complex Systems." *Kybernetik* 3:100–108. https://doi.org/10.1007/BF00299903.

Wigner, E. 1955. "Characteristic Vectors of Bordered Matrices with Infinite Dimensions." *Annals of Mathematics* 62 (3): 548–564. https://doi.org/10.2307/1970079.

METABOLIC STABILITY AND EPIGENESIS IN RANDOMLY CONSTRUCTED GENETIC NETS

S. A. Kauffman

"The world is either the effect of cause or chance. If the latter, it is a world for all that, that is to say, it is a regular and beautiful structure." —Marcus Aurelius

Abstract

Proto-organisms probably were randomly aggregated nets of chemical reactions. The hypothesis that contemporary organisms are also randomly constructed molecular automata is examined by modeling the gene as a binary (on-off) device and studying the behavior of large, randomly constructed nets of these binary "genes". The results suggest that, if each "gene" is directly affected by two or three other "genes", then such random nets: behave with great order and stability; undergo behavior cycles whose length predicts cell replication time as a function of the number of genes per cell; possess different modes of behavior whose number per net predicts roughly the number of cell types in an organism as a function of its number of genes; and under the stimulus of noise are capable of differentiating directly from any mode of behavior to at most a few other modes of behavior. Cellular differentiation is modeled as a Markov chain among the modes of behavior of a genetic net. The possibility of a general theory of metabolic behavior is suggested.

1. Introduction

A living thing is a complex net of interactions between thousands or millions of chemical species. A fundamental task of biology is to account for the origin and nature of metabolic stability in such systems in terms of the mechanisms which control biosynthesis. In the thermodynamics of gases, the mathematical laws of statistics bridge the gap between a chaos of colliding molecules and the simple order of the gas laws. In biology, a gene specifies a protein, and the output of one gene can control the rate of output of a second. The mathematical laws which engage large nets of interacting genes into biosynthetic coherence remain to be elucidated.

In this article I report the behavior of large nets of randomly interconnected binary (on-off) "genes". The motives for this choice of model are many.

The analogy of genetic repression and derepression with digital computers has suggested to several authors (Jacob and Monod 1963; Apter 1966; Bonner 1965; Sugita 1963; Kauffman 1967) that the genome embodies complex switching circuits which constitute a program for metabolic stability and cell differentiation, rather than providing a coded description of these phenomena.

It is a fundamental question whether metabolic stability and epigenesis require the genetic regulatory circuits to be precisely constructed. Has a fortunate evolutionary history selected only nets of highly ordered circuits which alone insure metabolic stability; or are stability and epigenesis, even in nets of randomly interconnected regulatory circuits, to be expected as the probable consequence of as yet unknown mathematical laws? Are living things more akin to precisely programmed automata selected by evolution, or to randomly assembled automata whose characteristic behavior reflects their unorderly construction, no matter how evolution selected the surviving forms?

In this article I present evidence that large, randomly connected feedback nets of binary "genes" behave with stability comparable to that in living things; that these systems undergo short stable cycles in the states of their constituents; that the time course of these behavior cycles parallels and predicts the time required for cell replication in many phyla; that the number of distinguishable modes of behavior of one randomly constructed net predicts with considerable accuracy the number of cell types in an organism which embodies a genetic net of the same size; that, like cells, a randomly connected genetic net is capable of differentiating directly from any one mode of behavior to at most a few of its other modes; and that these restricted transition possibilities between modes of behavior allow us to state a theory of differentiation which deduces the origin, sequence, branching, and cessation of differentiation as the expected behavior of randomly assembled genetic nets.

Mathematical insight into the behavior of randomly connected feedback systems is slight. Goodwin (1963) has treated the gene as a continuously oscillating biochemical element whose output of mRNA is repressed by the protein specified. To study coupled systems of such biochemical oscillators, Goodwin was constrained by the conditions of integrability to restrict cross-coupling between genes to be symmetrically repressive and form a linear sequence in which no gene represses more than its two neighbors. There is no reason, however, to suppose that the crossreactions between real genes are similarly constrained. To study the behavior of nets with arbitrarily complex couplings requires us to abandon the effort to obtain an integral of motion for the system (Goodwin 1963).

Several considerations suggest the advantage of modeling the gene as a binary device, able only to be on or off. The most fundamental of measures is the binary category scale. Use of these simplest devices facilitates study of the behavior of truly complex nets; the behavior of randomly connected, but then fixed, nets of binary components should provide a reliable guide to the behavior of similar systems whose components' behavior are described by continuous or probabilistic functions; synthesis of mRNA is, in fact, probably an all or none binary process; the number of repressor molecules per gene is thought to be less than about 12 (Bretscher 1968), therefore it seems preferable to treat the activity of a gene as a discrete, not continuous, function of its input.

To study the behavior of randomly interconnected nets requires a definition of the population from which equiprobable sampling is to be done. A distinct advantage in the choice of a binary model for gene activity is that the number of different possible rules by which a finite number (K) of inputs may affect the output behavior of a binary element is finite -2^{2K} (see Fig. 1). This allows construction of switching nets which are random in two different, but well defined, senses: the K inputs to each binary "gene" may be chosen at random; the effect of those inputs on the recipient element's output behavior may be randomly decided by assigning at random to each element one of the possible 2^{2K} Boolean functions of its inputs. Once built, the nets I have studied remained fixed in the choice of inputs to each gene, and their effect on its output.

In the original published version of the paper the typo 2^{2K} appears in a number of places. It should be read as $2^{(2^K)}$.

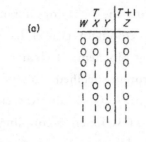

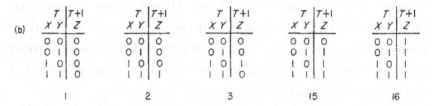

Figure 1. (a) W, X, and Y are each binary devices which act as inputs to Z, another binary device. The 3×8 matrix of 1 and 0 below W, X, Y list the eight possible configurations of input values to element Z. The column under Z assigns to it the value it will assume one moment after each input configuration. (a) is one of the $2^{2^3} = 256$ Boolean functions of three variables. (b) The $2^{2^2} = 16$ Boolean functions of two input variables are derived by filling the column under Z with 1 and 0 in all possible (16) ways. Function 1 is *contradiction*, 2 is *and*, 16 is *tautology*.

The number of genes whose products directly affect the output of any gene is not known. Therefore, I have studied nets in which each gene has direct inputs from all genes, nets with one input per gene, nets with two inputs per gene, and nets with three inputs per gene.

Since the autonomous, undriven behavior of a system must be elucidated before the effect of exogeneous inputs can be understood, I have studied the behavior of switching nets free of external inputs. A bacterium in a constant environment undergoes autonomous changes in the concentrations of molecular species, and the sea urchin, in a similarly homogeneous surrounding, develops in an orderly sequence of states from its zygote. Since constant external input to a net is equivalent to a similar net held free of external input, stable oscillations of chemical species and cell differentiation seem to be largely autonomous behaviors of metabolic nets.

The study of randomly constructed but deterministic switching nets forms a poorly developed area of automata theory. Walker and Ashby (1966) have examined the effect of the choice of Boolean function on the behavior of randomly interconnected nets of binary elements.

They simulated nets in which each of the 100 elements received a feedback input from itself, and randomly assigned inputs from two other elements. For each experiment, all elements of the net were assigned the same Boolean function.

These nets embody behavior cycles (described in detail below). They found that the choice of the Boolean function assigned to all the elements markedly affected the length of these behavior cycles. Some functions (e.g. "and") yield very short cycles, others (e.g. "exclusive or") yield cycles of immense length.

Since there is no reason to suppose that, in living genetic reaction nets, all elements are assigned the same Boolean function, I have studied nets in which all the 2^{2K} possible Boolean functions are assigned randomly, one to each element.

2. Genetic Model

On these considerations, the gene is modeled as a binary device able to realize any one, but only one, of the possible Boolean functions of its K inputs. If the activity of a formal gene, for brevity, gene, at any time is 1, then the value of all its output lines at time $T+1$ is simultaneously 1. Thus, the state of the outputs of a gene at $T+1$ depends on its activity at time T alone. For our logical analysis, it is sufficient to allow time to occur in discrete, clocked moments: $T = 1, 2, 3 \ldots$.

A *formal genetic net* is constructed by choosing a value of N, the number of elements comprising the net, and of K, the number of input lines to any gene. Each gene in the net receives exactly K inputs, one from each of K formal genes in N. Inputs arise only from members of N. On the average, each element has K output lines. Nets are randomly constructed in two distinct senses. The K inputs to each gene are chosen randomly; to each gene one of the 2^{2K} Boolean functions of its K inputs is assigned randomly. After being assembled, these nets are deterministic. We assume that all genes compute one step in one clocked time unit.

Such a genetic net is a finite sequential automation, a machine with a finite number of states and a function mapping each state into a subsequent state (see Fig. 2). A state of the net is described by a row

The model described in the next four paragraphs introduced a new framework of extreme simplicity for modeling complex networked systems of non-identical components. Versions of this model where the input connections and the Boolean function at each node are chosen with an eye on empirical facts have found many practical applications.

which lists the present value, 1 or 0, of each of the N elements of the net. Each gene can be independently on or off, thus there are just 2^N distinct states of a net of N binary elements.

If the system is placed in some state at time T, then at $T + 1$ each gene scans the present value of each of its K inputs, consults its Boolean function, and assumes the value specified by the function for that input configuration. The net passes from a state to only one subsequent state; therefore, although two states may converge on to a single subsequent state, no state may diverge on to two subsequent states. (The system is state determined.)

There are a finite number of states. As the system passes along a sequence of states from any arbitrarily chosen initial state, it must eventually re-enter a state previously passed. Thereafter, the system cycles continuously through the re-entered set of states, called a *cycle*. The *cycle length* is defined as the number of states on a re-enterant cycle of behavior. A state which re-enters itself, a cycle of length one, is called an equilibrial state. Since more than one state may converge on a single state, the state re-entered need not be the arbitrarily chosen initial state. The *transient (or run-in) length* is the number of states between the arbitrarily chosen initial state and the first state encountered on a cycle. A *confluent* is the set of states leading into, or on, a cycle; the *size* of a *confluent* is the number of states comprising it. Each state lies on a single confluent [(see Fig. 2c)].

A formal genetic net must contain at least one behavior cycle; it may contain more. By releasing the net from many different states, each of which runs to only one cycle, the total number of different cycles reached may be counted. The *number of cycles* embodied in a net is the number of different behavior cycles of which the net is capable. Since no state can diverge on to two subsequent states, no state on one cycle can simultaneously be on a second cycle. Different cycles in one net are behaviorally isolated from one another.

A *distance measure* comparing two states of the net may be defined as the number of genes with different values in the two states. (For example, the state (00000) of a 5 gene net, and the state (00111) differ in the value of three elements.) This distance is used as a measure of dissimilarity

This rule is referred to as the "synchronous" update rule; all nodes are updated together.

What Kauffman calls "cycle" is now usually referred to as "attractor."

"Confluent" of a cycle is the same as "basin of attraction" of the attractor.

Kauffman notes that different attractors are almost by definition behaviorally distinct, a satisfying feature in identifying them with distinct cell types.

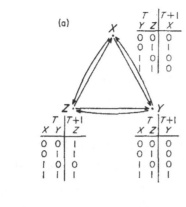

(a)

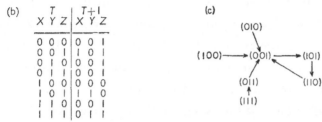

(b)

T			T+1		
X	Y	Z	X	Y	Z
0	0	0	0	0	1
0	0	1	1	0	1
0	1	0	0	0	1
0	1	1	0	0	1
1	0	0	0	0	0
1	0	1	1	1	0
1	1	0	0	0	1
1	1	1	0	1	1

(c)

Figure 2. (a) A net of three binary elements, each of which receives inputs from the other two. The Boolean function assigned to each element is shown beside the element. (b) All possible states of the 3-element net are shown in the left 3×8 matrix below T. The subsequent state of the net at time $T + 1$, shown in the matrix on the right, is derived from the inputs and functions shown in (a). (c) A kimatograph showing the sequence of state transitions leading into a state cycle of length 3. All states lie on one confluent. There are three run-ins to the single state cycle.

between subsequent states on a transient as the system approaches a cycle, between subsequent states along cycles, and between cycles.

As the net passes along a sequence of states on a cycle, one unit of noise may be introduced by arbitrarily changing the value of a single gene for one time moment. After perturbation, the system may return to the cycle perturbed, or run into a different cycle. In a net of size N there are just N states which differ from any state in the value of just one gene. By perturbing all states on each cycle to all states a distance of one, a matrix may be obtained listing the total number of times the system returned to the cycle perturbed, or ran into any of the other possible cycles. Dividing the value in each cell of this matrix by its row total yields the corresponding matrix of transition probabilities between cycles, under the drive of random, one unit, noise. Such a matrix is a Markov chain. The probability of transition from one cycle to a second need not be identical with the probability of transition from the second

Here is a quantitative measure of the accessibility of one attractor from another.

to the first. Thus, state noise may induce asymmetric probabilities of transition between the independent behavior cycles of the net.

3. Totally Connected Nets, $K = N$

In random nets in which each element receives an input from all elements, the state subsequent to each state is chosen by sampling at random from an infinite supply of the 2^N distinct states of the net. The characteristics of such a random mapping of a finite set (2^N) of numbers into itself has been solved (Rubin and Sitgreave 1954). The expected length of the behavior cycle is the square root of the number (2^N) in the set. Therefore, in totally connected nets with 200 elements and 2^{200} states, the expected cycle length is $2^{100} \sim 10^{30}$ states. If the transition from one state to the next required one microsecond, then the time required for a net of 200 elements to traverse its cycle is about $10,000,000$ times Hubble's age of the universe. Totally connected, random nets are biologically impossible.

4. One Connected Net, $K = 1$

Random nets in which each element receives just one input are no more biologically reasonable than totally connected nets. The structure of a one connected net breaks into separate loops of elements (as in Fig. 2c with the direction of all arrows reversed). State cycles arise whose lengths are a maximum of two times the lowest common multiple of the set of structural loop lengths. For random nets as small as 200, the state cycles generally exceed several millions of states in length (Slone 1967). One connected random nets possess behavior cycles capable of realization by no earthly organism.

Kauffman's conclusion that $K = 2$ random Boolean networks are qualitatively different from $K = 1$ and $K = N$, and share some properties with living systems, still stands. It is also the first hint for the (later) idea that living systems might be located near the boundary between order and chaos.

5. Two Connected Nets, $K = 2$

The behavior of randomly interconnected, deterministic nets in which each element received just two inputs from other elements is biologically reasonable. I have studied nets of 15, 50, 64, 100, 191, 400, 1024, 4096 and 8191 elements both by simulation on digital computers and analytically. Nets of 1000 elements possess $2^{1000} \sim 10^{300}$ possible states. The typical net is restricted to cycle among 12 of these states.

The program used constructs a net of size N by random assignment of the two inputs and one of the $2^{2^2} = 16$ Boolean functions to each binary gene. The net is placed in an arbitrary initial state (for example, with each gene switched off) and, at successive time moments, computes its next state. Each of the sequence of states along a run-in is compared with all previous states, and when the present state is identical to a state of the system x moments previously, a cycle whose length is x states has been identified. If undisturbed, the system would cycle through these x states repeatedly.

5.1. CYCLES

Cycle lengths in such nets are exceptionally short. Data was obtained for at least 100 nets at each of several different sizes, and a histogram of the cycle lengths found in each size net was compiled. Figure 3(a) presents a histogram of cycle lengths found in nets of 400 elements which used all 16 Boolean functions of two inputs equiprobably. The distribution of cycle lengths is markedly skewed toward short cycle lengths. Generally, the modal cycle length is less than the median length, which, in turn, is less than the mean cycle length. Here the modal length is 2, the median is 8, and the mean is 98. Equilibrial states (those which successively become themselves) are common.

Among the 16 Boolean functions of two inputs [see Fig. 1(b)], two are tautology and contradiction. An element assigned tautology is switched on regardless of the previous input values. An element assigned contradiction is constantly off. Thus, $2/16 = 1/8$ of the elements in a $K = 2$ random net are foci of constancy. These foci might be thought necessary to produce short behavior cycles. This is untrue. Nets were also studied in which these two functions were disallowed and the remaining 14 Boolean functions assigned equiprobably. The effect is to increase slightly the expected cycle length in nets of any given size and to shift the distribution of cycle lengths in nets of a given size from that found with all 16 Boolean functions. In Fig. 3(b) is the histogram of cycles from nets of 400 elements which used neither tautology nor contradiction. The distribution is still strongly skewed toward short cycle lengths, but the number of cycles of length one (equilibrial states) has decreased. The mode here is 12, the median is 32, and the mean is 209.

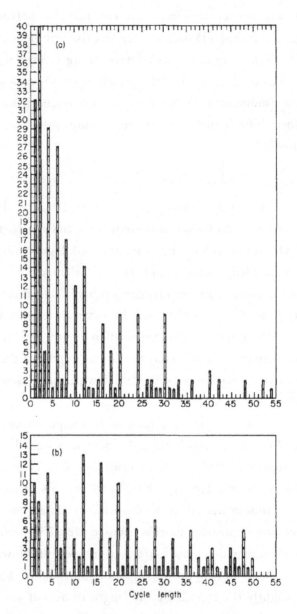

Figure 3. (a) A histogram of the lengths of state cycles in nets of 400 binary elements which used all 16 Boolean functions of two variables equiprobably. The distribution is skewed toward short cycles. (b) A histogram of the lengths of state cycles in nets of 400 binary elements which used neither tautology nor contradiction, but used the remaining 14 Boolean functions of 2 variables equiprobably. The distribution is skewed toward short cycles.

Deletion of tautology and contradiction has increased the median cycle length in nets of 400 elements from 8 to 32 states. The distribution of cycle lengths is remarkable also in the preponderance of even numbered cycle lengths.

Because the distribution of cycle lengths is highly skewed, the median cycle length seems the most representational length for nets of any size. In Fig. 4, the log of the median cycle length is plotted against the log of the size net, for nets with all 16 functions, and separately for nets without tautology and contradiction. The values in each condition appear non-linear in the log / log plot. The curves are initially steep, and flatten at larger values of N. In nets with tautology and contradiction allowed, the asymptotic log cycle length against $\log N$ is ~ 0.3. In nets with tautology and contradiction disallowed, the asymptotic log cycle length $\sim 0.6 \log N$. Disallowing tautologies and contradictions appears to double the asymptotic slope in the log/log plot. In this condition, the expected cycle length is just slightly greater than the square root $N(0.5$ in the log/log plot). As N increases, the median cycle length initially increases rapidly, then progressively slowly. By projection, nets of $1,000,000$ elements, with tautology and contradiction disallowed, possess behavior cycles of about 1000 states in length—an extreme localization of behavior among $2^{1,000,000}$ possible states.

5.2. TRANSIENTS

For nets of a given size, the lengths of run-ins to cycles appears uncorrelated with the length of the cycle to which the transient ran (Fig. 5). The longest transients found were about the same length as the longest cycles found. Like cycle length, the distribution of transient lengths is highly skewed toward short lengths.

5.3. ACTIVITY

When the system is released from an arbitrary initial state, the number of elements which change value (the activity) per state transition decreases rapidly. In nets of 100 elements, using all 16 Boolean functions, the number of elements which change value at the first state transition is about $0.4N$. This decreases, along a curve nearly fitted by a negative exponential with a half decay of $3 - 4$ state transitions, to a minimum

This figure and the accompanying text suggest that the typical number of states in an attractor for $K = 2$ networks grows asymptotically as a power of N (or slower). This quantitative claim in the paper, arrived at by the limited computational resources available at that time, was unchallenged for three decades, but was later proved incorrect. It was finally shown analytically that mean cycle lengths grow with N faster than any power (Mihaljev and Drossel 2006).

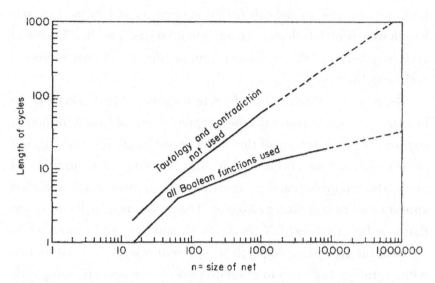

Figure 4. Log median cycle length as a function of $\log N$, in nets using all 16 Boolean functions of two inputs (all Boolean functions used), and in nets disallowing these two functions (tautology and contradiction not used). The asymptotic slopes are about 0.3 and 0.6.

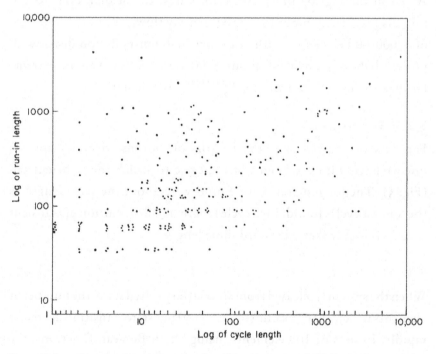

Figure 5. A scattergram of run-in length and cycle length in nets of 400 binary elements using neither tautology nor contradiction. Run-in length appears uncorelated with cycle length. A log / log plot was used merely to accommodate the data.

activity of 0 to $0.25N$ per state transition along the cycle. For larger nets, the half decay should require more transitions. Thus, as the system approaches a cycle, states become progressively more similar. One would expect that all states which differ from cycle states in the value of only one element would themselves be located a very few state transitions from that cycle.

The number of genes which change value during a cycle varies between 0 and 35 in nets of 100 elements using all 16 Boolean functions. The consequence is that most genes are constant throughout the cycle, and the cycle states are highly similar.

5.4. NUMBER OF CYCLES

The number of different state cycles—that is, the number of independent and different modes of behavior in these nets—are as surprisingly small as cycles are short.

By computer simulation, nets of 15, 50, 64, 100, 191 and 400 elements were studied. For each net, the system was placed successively in 50 arbitrarily chosen initial states, and the cycle discovered from each initial state was compared with previously discovered state cycles of that net. The median number of cycles per net is low; the distribution of the number of cycles per net around the median is skewed toward few cycles. In Fig. 6 is a histogram of the number of cycles per net, where $N = 400$, and neither tautology nor contradiction was allowed. The median number of cycles per net was 10. Presence or absence of tautology and contradiction does not seem to affect the number of cycles per net.

The log of the median number of cycles per net is plotted against $\log N$ in Fig. 7. The data appears to fall on a straight line with a slope of 0.5. Log number of cycles $\sim 0.5 \log N$. The expected number of modes of behavior is about $\sqrt{N}/2$. The number of cycles initially rises rapidly, then progressively slowly. By projection, nets of 1000 elements will have about 16 cycles, and nets of $1,000,000$ about 500 modes of behavior.

Since only 50 run-ins to each net were made, the data probably underestimates the number of cycles per net. However, 200 run-ins per

This feature of the model is reminiscent of mammalian cell types, in which the majority of genes are either maximally on or off, with a smaller fraction having intermediate levels of expression.

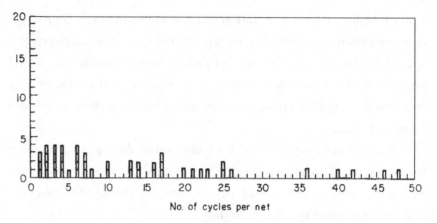

Figure 6. A histogram of the number of cycles per net in nets of 400 elements using neither tautology nor contradiction, but the remaining Boolean functions of two inputs equiprobably. The median is 10 cycles per net. The distribution is skewed toward few cycles.

The claim in figure 7 and the text above, about the N dependence of the number, A, of attractors in $K = 2$ networks, has taken many twists and turns. Interestingly, it is still not completely settled after more than five decades. For the synchronous update considered by Kauffman, A was shown analytically to grow faster than any power of N (Samuelsson and Troein 2003). However, a more realistic asynchronous update scheme, in which nodes are not updated together, but one by one in random order or with fluctuating delays, was found to destabilize most of those attractors and restore an approximate power law, $A \sim N^\alpha$. The exponent α was given an analytical upper bound $\alpha < \ln 4$ (Greil and Drossel 2005) and a numerical estimate $\alpha \cong 0.5$ (Klemm and Bornholdt 2005). A smaller value of $\alpha = 0.12 \pm 0.05$ has been claimed recently (numerical estimate by Rozum et al. 2021).

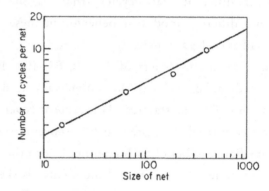

Figure 7. The median number of cycles per net as N increases appears linear in a log / log plot. The slope is about 0.5. The expected number of cycles is slightly less than square root N.

net rarely revealed more than 10% more cycles than had the first 50 run-ins of the 200; the data in Fig. 7, therefore, seems a good guide for the comparison of the number of cycles per net among nets of different sizes.

5.5. DISTANCE BETWEEN CYCLES

The minimum possible difference between states on two distinct cycles is 1—a difference in the value of a single element. This distance occurs frequently but the minimum distance may be as large as $0.3N$. Figure 8 is a scattergram of minimum distances between cycles correlated with the length of the cycles in many nets of 100 elements using all 16 Boolean functions. The median minimum distance between cycles is 5. The average distance between cycles is about 10. When a net embodies many cycles, these frequently form sets within which each cycle is a minimum distance of one from one or two members of the set. Between sets, the distance is larger and may be as great as $0.3N$.

5.6. NOISE PERTURBATIONS

The effect of state noise on the behavior of $K = 2$ random nets has been studied by perturbing the system as it traverses a cycle by arbitrarily reversing the value of a single gene for a single time moment. The perturbed net may either return to the behavior cycle from which it was dislodged, or run in to a different cycle. The program first built a net, then explored it from 50 randomly chosen initial states, and stored the different state cycles discovered. Then all states which differed by the value of one gene from each state of the first cycle discovered were tried, and the cycle to which each of these states ran was stored. From this, a row listing the number of times perturbation by one unit of noise shifted the system from the first behavior cycle to each of the cycles was compiled. The procedure was repeated for all remaining cycles, generating a square matrix listing of the transitions between cycles induced by all possible single units of noise. Division of the number in each cell of the matrix by the row total results in a matrix of transition probabilities under the drive of random (1 unit) noise, which is a Markov chain (see Fig. 10). Such chains are characterized by ergodic sets of states, transient states and absorbing states. If each behavior cycle in a binary net is considered a state of a Markov chain, then an ergodic set of cycles is defined to be a set in which each cycle can reach all members of the set by some path through them, but cannot reach a cycle outside the set. A transient cycle lies outside any ergodic set. Once the system reaches an ergodic region, it cannot return to the transient cycle. An absorbing cycle is an ergodic set consisting of a single cycle which always returns to itself after perturbation. Markov chains may, of course, have more than one ergodic region; each or all may be accessible from a single or several transient cycles.

Perturbation has been studied in nets ranging from 15 to 2000 elements. Nets larger than 400 elements used all 16 Boolean functions. In those of less than 400, both conditions—with and without tautology and contradiction—were simulated. In general, the net returns to the

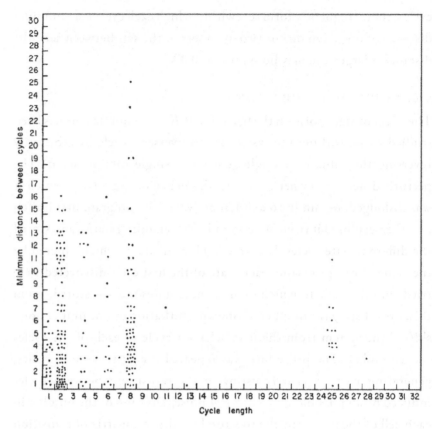

Figure 8. A scattergram of the minimum distance between cycles and cycle length in nets of 100 elements using all 16 Boolean functions of two variables. Minimum distance between cycles appears uncorrelated with cycle length. The median minimum distance is $0.05N$.

cycle perturbed with probabilities between 0.85 and 0.95. Behavior in randomly connected binary nets is highly stable to infrequent noise.

One might have supposed that infrequent noise could induce a shift from each cycle to all others. This proves untrue. Transitions from a cycle are highly restricted; each cycle generally can shift to only one to six other cycles with probabilities of 0.01 to 0.05, and to a few others with probabilities between 0.01 to 0.0001. Most cycles cannot be directly reached from any single cycle [see Figs 9(a) and 9(b)].

Despite the restricted transition possibilities from each cycle in many instances, the entire cycle set forms one ergodic region. Equally frequently, a subset of the cycles forms one ergodic region, and the remaining cycles are transient cycles leading into the ergodic region, but not reachable from it. In the latter case, under infrequent noise, the

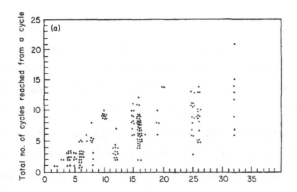

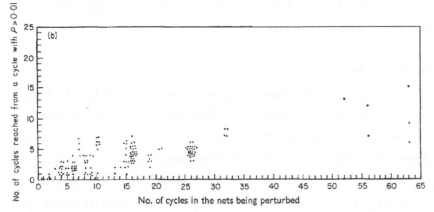

Figure 9. (a) The *total* number of cycles reached from each cycle after it was perturbed in all possible ways by one unit of noise correlated with the number of cycles in the net being perturbed. The data is from nets using neither tautology nor contradiction, with $N = 191$, and 400. (b) The number of cycles reached from each cycle with a probability greater than 0.01 in the same nets as those of (a). In nets using all 16 Boolean functions, the total number of cycles reached from each cycle is about the same as the data in (b).

system may progressively restrict the locale of its activity to the ergodic subset of cycles.

In no case when all possible single units of state noise were explored has more than one ergodic region been found. Restriction of perturbation to the first $0.6N$ of the N genes, however, has on one occasion yielded two ergodic regions. Further restriction of perturbation to $0.05N$ renders multiple ergodic sets probable.

One of the nets studied is presented in Fig. 10. The set of cycles form a single ergodic region, with transients leading into it. One would expect that in systems with several hundred cycles, more than a single ergodic region would be found.

5.7. $K = 3$ NETS

The occurrence of short cycle lengths and few cycles in random nets seems not to depend narrowly on an interconnection of two inputs per gene. I have simulated nets of 15, 20, 25 and 50 elements, each receiving three inputs from other elements, and allowed use of all $2^{2^3} = 256$ Boolean functions of three variables. Cycles were slightly longer, the number of cycles about the same as comparable nets of connectivity two. These characteristic behaviors of random nets seem to require only low connectivity to occur. The rate of their failure as K approaches N will require careful delineation.

6. Discussion

It is surprising that randomly constructed nets, in which each element is directly affected by two others, embody short, stable behavior cycles. The immense restriction of behavior in a $K = 2$ net of 1000 elements, limited to cycles a few hundred states in length, can only be appreciated in contrast to an expected state cycle length of 10^{150} in a totally connected $(K = N)$ net of the same size. 10^{150} assumes its appropriate proportion when one remembers that 10^{23} estimates the age of the universe in microseconds.

Schrödinger (1944) noted that high molecular specificity, guaranteed by quantum stabilization, is required for the precision of biosynthesis in living things. The behavior of these randomly connected nets discloses an unsuspected, and, I believe, fundamental corollary to that precision. A molecular reaction net of high specificity *is* a net of low connectivity. High specificity appears necessary both for precision of product formation, and to yield a system whose global chemical oscillatory behavior is brief and stable.

The hypothesis that living genetic nets are randomly assembled does not imply that one gene of these nets lacks a specific effect on a second. It asserts that if the "wiring diagram" of the specific repression and derepression connections between genes were known, it would be topologically indistinguishable from a "wiring diagram" generated by random assignment of specific interactions between genes. The hypothesis is consistent with both the random modifications of protein

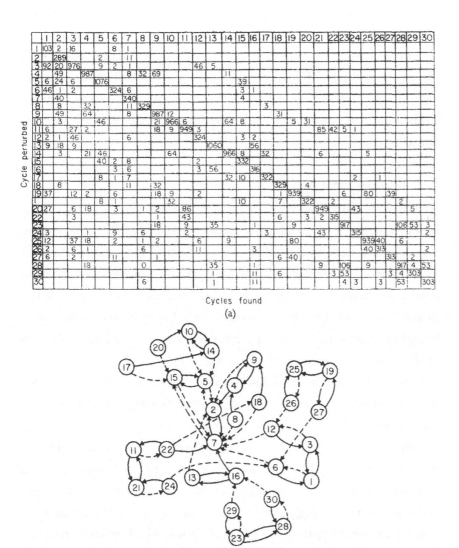

Cycles found

(a)

(b)

This figure shows a network of attractors—indicating how accessible attractors are from each other via perturbations. The paths from one attractor to another are constrained and a hierarchical structure of transitions emerges spontaneously from the model. This picture provides the first concrete way of imagining how Waddington's epigenetic landscape can arise from genetic interactions, and constitutes one of the significant insights from the model. A single attractor encapsulates the configurations of all the genes, and this network of attractors is an example of how higher-level structures and processes spontaneously emerge in complex systems from interactions among the components, even when those interactions are random.

Figure 10. (a) A matrix listing the 30 cycles of one net and the total number of times one unit of perturbation shifted the net from each cycle to each cycle. The system generally returns to the cycle perturbed. Division of the value in each cell of the matrix by the total of its row yields the matrix of transition probabilities between modes of behavior which constitute a Markov chain. The transition probabilities between cycles may be asymmetric. (b) Transitions between cycles in the net shown in (a). The solid arrows are the most probable transition to a cycle other than the cycle perturbed, the dotted arrows are the second most probable. The remaining transitions are not shown. Cycles 2, 7, 5 and 15 form an ergodic set into which the remaining cycles flow. If *all* the transitions between cycles are included, the ergodic set of cycles becomes: 1, 2, 3, 5, 6, 12, 13, 15, 16. The remainder are transient cycles leading into this single ergodic set.

structure induced by mutation, and the lack of steric similarity between the molecule mediating end-product inhibition of an enzyme, and the substrate of that enzyme.

Biologically reasonable behavior in random nets occurs only if each element is directly affected by about the same low number of other elements as are macromolecules in living things. This correspondence lends support to the hypothesis that living metabolic nets are randomly constructed.

7. Cell Cycle Time

Among the most characteristic cyclic phenomena in cells is their replication. Van't Hof and Sparrow (1963) have studied the minimum division cycle time in cells of several species of higher plants. In their Fig. 3 [reproduced as Fig. 11(a)] they show the minimum cell replication time as a function of the DNA content per cell nucleus in six species of plants. The data fall nearly on a straight line. The authors conclude that, in higher organisms, minimum cell replication time is a linear function of the DNA content per nucleus [see Fig. 11(a)].

Projection of this linear function predicts that cells without DNA will require several hours to replicate; bacteria with little DNA per cell require about 30 min to replicate. A curve of replication time from organisms with little DNA per cell to higher organisms must start near the origin, rise rapidly as the amount of DNA per cell increases, then rise more slowly as the DNA per cell continues to increase. Van't Hof and Sparrow (1963) suggest the assumption of a second mechanism to control the time required for cell replication which would provide a steep linear slope from the origin, and intersect their observed linear function among higher plants. Choice of control mechanism would depend upon the nuclear content of DNA.

I wish to show that a single principle, the hypothesis that living things are typical randomly interconnected reaction nets, is able to predict cell replication time as a function of the number of genes per cell throughout a wide range of phyla.

Estimates of the time required to switch a gene on or off lie between 5 and 90 seconds (Goodwin 1963). I will assume that about one minute

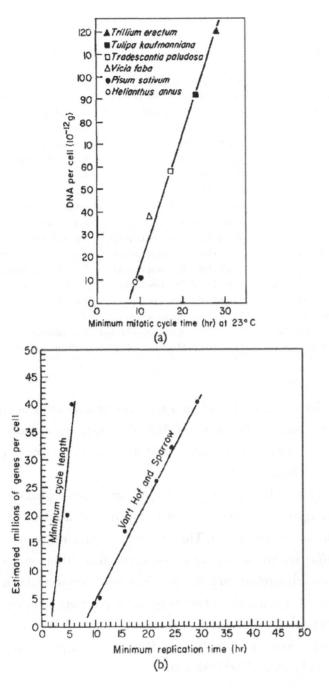

Figure 11. (a) Van't Hof & Sparrow's (1963) Fig. 3 showing minimum cell replication time as a function of the DNA per nucleus for several plant species. (b) Projected cycle time in nets of 2 to 40 million binary genes using all 16 Boolean functions of two input variables, compared to Van't Hof and Sparrow's plot. In the range where Van't Hof and Sparrow report a linear relation, the binary net model predicts values which are nearly linear. Reduction in the number of elements assigned tautology or contradiction should raise expected cycle lengths and shift the nearly linear slope of the theoretical data to correspond closely with Van't Hof and Sparrow's data.

Table 1. Data for Fig. 12

ORGANISM	DNA PER CELL	CELL REPLICATION TIME
Bacteria	Watson (1965)	Altman & Dittmer (1962)
Protozoa	Nanney & Rudzinska (1960)	Altman & Dittmer (1962)
Sea urchin	Sparrow & Evans (1961)	Mazia (1961)
Chicken	Vendrely (1955)	Cleaver (1967)
Mouse	Vendrely (1955)	Cleaver (1967)
Rat	Vendrely (1955)	Cleaver (1967)
Man	Vendrely (1955)	Cleaver (1967)
Rabbit	Vendrely (1955)	Cleaver (1967)
Dog	Vendrely (1955)	Cleaver (1967)
Frog	Vendrely (1955)	Cleaver (1967)
Vicia faba	Van't Hof & Sparrow (1963)	Van't Hof & Sparrow (1963)
Pisum sativum	Van't Hof & Sparrow (1963)	Van't Hof & Sparrow (1963)
Tradescantia paludosa	Van't Hof & Sparrow (1963)	Van't Hof & Sparrow (1963)
Tulipa kaufmanniana	Van't Hof & Sparrow (1963)	Van't Hof & Sparrow (1963)
Helianthus annuus	Van't Hof & Sparrow (1963)	Van't Hof & Sparrow (1963)
Trillium erectum	Van't Hof & Sparrow (1963)	Van't Hof & Sparrow (1962)
Aspergillus nidulans	Horowitz & Metzenberg (1965)	Rosenberger & Kessel (1967)
Saccharomyces cervesiae	Horowitz & Metzenberg (1965)	Williamson (1964)

We now know that the number of genes is not proportional to DNA length as one goes from *E. coli* to humans. This is an over-estimate of the number of genes in humans by two orders of magnitude. In this paper, for purposes of comparing the model with data, Kauffman identified the number of genes determined in this fashion with the parameter N of the model. However, N is the number of regulatory nodes in the network and this identification needs to take into account how that number depends non-trivially upon genome size (see Bornholdt and Kauffman 2019).

suffices for a state transition in a real genetic net. Thus, if the model predicts a state cycle length of 100, the biochemical realization of the model should require about 100 minutes to traverse its cycle of oscillatory chemical concentrations.

In Fig. 12 I have plotted the logarithm of cell replication time in minutes against the logarithm of the estimated number of genes in that cell, for several species. The data include bacteria, protozoa, yeast, *Aspergillus*, sea urchin, chicken, mouse, rat, man, rabbit, dog, frog (and minimum cell replication time for) *Vicia faba*, and several other plants (sec Table 1). The number of genes per cell was estimated by comparison of its DNA per cell with that of *Escherichia coli*, which Watson (1965) has estimated to have about 2000 genes. Based on these procedures, human cells embody about $2,000,000$ genes.

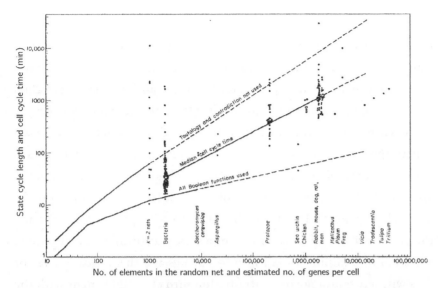

State cycle length and cell cycle time (min)

No. of elements in the random net and estimated no. of genes per cell

This figure represents a courageous leap on the part of Kauffman to connect the model to data. However, later developments have made this connection untenable, because attractor sizes were found to increase with N much faster than depicted in this figure (see marginal note on fig. 4).

Figure 12. Logarithm of cell replication time in minutes plotted against the logarithm of the estimated number of genes per cell for various single cell organisms, and various cell types in several metazoan organisms. The data for the plants, *Vicia faba*, *Pisum*, etc. are the *minimum* replication times described by Van't Hof & Sparrow (1963). The solid line through the biologic data connects the median replication times of bacteria, protozoa, chicken, mouse and dog and rabbit, and man. Data from binary nets of 1024 elements using neither nor contradiction are included for comparison. Median cycle lengths in binary nets with and without tautology and contradiction, as a function of the number of elements in the net, are superimposed on the biologic data. Scale: 2×10^6 genes $= 6 \times 10^{-12}$ g DNA per cell.

The median cellular replication time for bacteria, protozoa[1], chicken, mouse, and man are also shown in Fig. 12. It is apparent that these median replication times fall very nearly on a straight line whose slope on a log / log plot is 0.5. The expected replication time in minutes is therefore about the square root of the estimated number of genes. The square root of N increases rapidly initially, then more slowly.

The behavior of randomly interconnected reaction nets predicts this observed relation between DNA content and replication time. The length of state cycles in random nets increases at almost the same rate

---

[1]Bacteria were assumed to have about the same DNA per cell content and to code for about 2000 genes. In protozoa, the number of genes per cell is difficult to estimate due to the macronucleus. I have treated all protozoa as having about the same number of genes per cell, and estimated this number by dividing the cellular DNA content in *Tetrahymena* by the ratio of macronucleus DNA to micronucleus DNA in *Paramecium*. I assume the DNA per cell in *Aspergillus nidulans* is about equal to that in *Neurospora crassa*. Rosenberger and Kessel (1967) chose growth media to yield disparate replication times in *Aspergillus* (1.4, 1.8, 3.7, 4.7, 7.0, 9.0hr). I assume the first three represent relatively normal values.

as a function of the number of elements, as do cell cycle times as the number of genes increases. Based on the assumption that a state transition requires about one minute, the model, without tautology and contradiction, predicts a cycle time of about 50 minutes in a net of 2000 elements, and 16 hours in a net of $1,000,000$. The rate of increase of cycle lengths in nets with and without tautology and contradiction are shown superimposed on the biologic data of Fig. 12. Cell replication time falls between the two. In nets using neither tautology nor contradiction, the asymptotic slope of the logarithm of the cycle length is about $0.6 \log N$; using all 16 Boolean functions the asymptotic slope is 0.3. Decreasing the estimate of the time required for a state transition in a real genetic net from one minute to 0.5 minute, brings the theoretical curve for nets without tautology or contradiction into close agreement with the observed slope of log median cell replication times against log number of genes.

In the range of DNA per cell where Van't Hof and Sparrow (1963) describe a linear relation between the DNA content per cell and minimum replication time, the relation between net size and cycle length in nets using all 16 Boolean functions is very nearly linear. The two slopes are of the same order of magnitude [see Fig. 11(b)]. Reduction in the number of elements assigned tautology or contradiction should bring the theoretical slope close to the observed.

The model also appears to predict the distribution of replication times in cells with the same number of genes. Bacteria, with about the same number of genes—2000—concentrate their replication times between 12 and 100 minutes, and scatter them up to 2000 rarely. Random nets of 1000 elements, using neither tautology nor contradiction, concentrate their state cycle lengths between 10 and 100 states, and scatter them up to 2000 to 10,000 rarely. In Fig. 12 are several state cycle lengths in nets of 1000 elements. The distribution is similar to that for bacterial replication times. Both distributions are skewed toward short cycle lengths in a linear plot. A more rigorous test of their similarity lies in the fact that both remain skewed toward short cycles in a logarithmic plot, as shown in Fig. 12.

The single hypothesis that living things behave as typical randomly connected switching nets appears to predict moderately well both the rate of increase in the median replication time as the DNA content of cells increases, and also the distribution about that median of replication time.

Is this correspondence coincidental? Replication of the DNA in higher organisms is known to be initiated at many independent sites. Initiation of replication along any small segment of a chromosome is thought to require the activity of a "replicon", and protein synthesis (Mazia 1961). If these replicons form elements in the total metabolic net of the cell, depending for their own initiation upon the previous synthesis of other materials, it would not be unduly surprising hat the periodicity of their activity, the S period, is bound by the periodicity of the entire metabolic net.

Viewing the periodicity of the cell cycle as an expression of state cycles in a randomly connected net may account for the lack of effect upon cell replication time of increasing polyploidy (Van't Hof 1965). Increasing the number of copies of each gene shifts the expression (of the set of copies) of a gene from a binary variable, when there is only one copy, towards a continuous variable, without altering the connections between or function assigned the genes. The set of copies of a gene would now be capable of a graded output depending upon how many product molecules of its input genes were present. Several arguments (Walter, Parker, and Ycas 1967) suggest that if each element (here element = the set of copies of a gene) in a net realizes a continuous, appropriately nonlinear function (e.g. sigmoid) of its inputs, then the net behaves as though it were comprised of binary devices. In this circumstance, cycle lengths should not be greatly changed by increasing polyploidy.

Unorderly nets in which each component directly affects very few others appear to behave with stability as great as that in living things. States on a cycle are similar to each other; only about 15% of the elements change value during a cycle. The remainder emit a constant output. Even more surprising is the stability shown by random nets to random, one unit noise. In these computer simulations a net was often perturbed from any behavior cycle 4000 times or more. Systems perturbed from a cycle return to that cycle with probabilities of about 90%. While there is little data on the stability of a cell's metabolic behavior to infrequent noise, the behavior of random nets seems to demonstrate sufficient stability to qualify as a model of cellular stability in the face of biochemical noise.

8. Cellular Differentiation

The principles underlying cellular differentiation remain among the most enigmatic in biology. We are required to explain the spontaneous generation of a multiplicity of cell types from the single zygote, to deduce a natural tendency of a system to become increasingly heterogeneous, then to stop differentiating.

Among the important characteristics of cell differentiation are: initiation of change; stabilization of change after cessation of stimulus; the efficacy of many substances, exogenous and endogenous, as inductive stimuli; a limit of five or six as the number of cell types which may differentiate directly from any cell type; progressive limitation in the number of developmental pathways open to any small region of the embryo; restricted periods during which a cell is competent to respond to an inductive stimulus; the discreteness of cell types, that is, the mutually exclusive constellations of properties by which cells differ; a requirement for a minimal and preferably heterogeneous cell mass to initiate differentiation in many instances, and to maintain it in some; the occurrence of metaplasia between undifferentiated cell types, or from an undifferentiated type to a specialized type, but the lack of metaplasia (the isolation) between specialized cell types; and the cessation of differentiation (Grobstein 1959).

I believe many aspects of differentiation to be deducible from the typical behavior of randomly built genetic nets.

Cells are thought to differ due to differential expression of, rather than structural loss of, the genes. Differential activity of the genes raises at least two questions which are not always carefully distinguished: the capacity of the genome to behave in more than one mode; and mechanisms which insure the appropriate assignment of these modes to the proper cells. The second presumes the first.

Randomly assembled nets of binary elements behave in a multiplicity of distinct modes. Different state cycles embodied in a net are isolated from each other, for no state may be on two cycles. Thus, a multiplicity

Table 2. Data for Fig. 13

ORGANISM	DNA PER CELL	NUMBER OF CELL TYPES
Man	Vendrely (1955)	Grobstein (1959)
Sponge	Sparrow & Evans (1961)	Estimated from Borradaile, Potts, Eastham, & Saunders (1958)
Jellyfish	Sparrow & Evans (1961)	Estimated from Borradaile, Potts, Eastham, & Saunders (1958)
Cenadidia	Mirsky & Osawa (1961)	Estimated from Borradaile, Potts, Eastham, & Saunders (1958)
Neurospora crassa	Horowitz & Metzenberg (1965)	Baldwin & Rusch (1965)
Saccharomyces cervesiae	Horowitz & Metzenberg (1965)	Baldwin & Rusch (1965)
Algae	Horowitz & Metzenberg (1965)	Baldwin & Rusch (1965)
Hydra[2]	?	Macklin (1968)
Bacteria	Watson (1965)	Macklin (1968)

of state cycles, each a different temporal sequence of genetic activity, is to be expected in randomly constructed genetic nets. It seems reasonable to identify one cell type with one state cycle. To the extent that this binary model, in which the expression of the "gene" is potentially reversible at each clocked moment, is accurate, it demonstrates the common occurrence of multiple modes of behavior in a genetic system.

If this identification is reasonable, the typical number of cycles in a random "genetic" net must be of the same order of magnitude as the number of cell types in organisms with the same number of genes.

Estimates of the number of cell types in an organism are hazardous, but the number in man may be placed at about 100; in annelid worms, at 57; in jellyfish, between 20 and 30; in hydra, between 11 and 17; in sponges, about 12-14; in *Neurospora crassa*, 5; in algae, 5; and in bacteria, 2, vegetative and spore (see Table 2). The logarithm of the values are plotted against the logarithm of the estimated number of genes per cell in each organism, in Fig. 13. A straight line has been drawn through these values; its slope is 0.5.

This is a concrete framing of earlier ideas identifying cell types with the attractors of a dynamical system. This identification is a conceptually unifying theoretical idea that in a single stroke clarifies many observed features of cell types. Kauffman also tells us which dynamical system matters in this context: the genetic regulatory network of the organism. Further, he provides a concrete first-cut model for the genetic regulatory network, namely, the mathematical model in section 2.

This figure was revisited by Bornholdt and Kauffman (2019) after including more recent data on how the numbers of cell types and transcription factors scale with genome size. From their analysis the data required the model exponent α to be about $0.7 (= 0.88/1.26)$. They noted that this was somewhat higher than the value estimated for the model at that time, $\alpha = 0.5$ (see marginal note for fig. 7). Rozum *et al.* (2021), who estimate $\alpha = 0.12 \pm 0.05$, note that the discrepancy is considerably greater. In other words, the model predicts fewer cell types than actually observed.

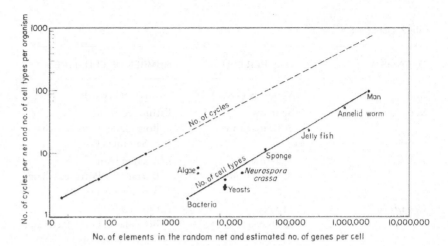

Figure 13. The logarithm of the number of cell types is plotted against the logarithm of the estimated number of genes per cell, and the logarithm of the median number of state cycles is plotted against logarithm N. The observed and theoretical slopes are about 0.5. Scale: 2×10^6 genes per cell $= 6 \times 10^{-12}$ g DNA per cell.

The logarithm of the number of independent cycles in a random net is also about 0.5 logarithm of the number of genes. By projection of the data established in Fig. 7, nets with about $16,000$ genes (comparable to the sponges) should have about 120 cell types, and man, with an assumed $2,000,000$ genes, about 700 cell types. These theoretical predictions are also plotted in Fig. 13.

The rate of increase in the number of cycles in random nets as N increases appears almost identical to the rate of increase in the number of cell types of an organism as the number of genes increases. The theoretical curve is shifted to the left, however, and predicts more cell types than are actually counted. The predictions remain well within an order of magnitude of the biologic data.

Caution is required for several reasons: large nets have not been simulated; these nets use binary elements, nets of greater verisimilitude must be studied; estimates of the number of cell types in an organism, or the number of genes in that organism are only approximate.

The biologic data need not fall on a straight line in order to remain compatible with this model. Account must be taken of the distribution of the number of cycles found in nets of any given size. The distribution of the number of cycles per net is skewed toward few cycles, as shown in Fig. 6.

With these reservations, I think it fair to say that the correspondence between the predicted number of independent modes of behavior in randomly interconnected nets and the observed number of cell types in organisms is good.

Cells differ from one another in the possession of a constellation of properties which do not intergrade. Similarly, cycles in random nets may be compared for the minimum dissimilarity between their states. In nets of 100 elements, the minimum distance between cycles is commonly $0.05N$ to $0.25N$. Like cell types, behavior cycles are generally separated from one another by a constellation of properties. Since no state may lead to two states, hence be on two cycles, state cycles, like cell types, are mutually exclusive.

If the multiplicity of modes of behavior in a random net helps elucidate the capacity of the genome to behave in more than one way, the appropriate segregation of these modes of behavior to the correct cells requires explanation. Biochemical noise may play a very large role in directing that segregation. A theory which assigns to biochemical noise the task of segregation of different modes of genetic behavior to different cells offers great advantages. Biochemical noise is ubiquitous, unavoidable, and therefore reliable. It remains to show that biochemical noise in a randomly cross coupled genetic net can produce orderly sequential segregation of behavior modes to the appropriate cells.

Perturbation of nets, behaving on cycles, by one unit of noise generally had only a transient effect on the systems behavior. With a probability of about 0.9, the system returned to the cycle perturbed. Of the remaining $0.1N$ noisy inputs, these caused the system to shift from any cycle to at most one to six other cycles with probabilities greater than 0.01, and a few more with probabilities below 0.01. It is therefore of considerable interest that, throughout phylogeny, no cell differentiates directly into more than a few other cell types. Restriction in the possible transitions between modes of behavior appears to be characteristic of both random nets and cell types.

The spontaneous generation of a multiplicity of cell types from a single cell type follows explicitly from this model. The occurrence of infrequent noise induces on the cycles of a randomly constructed net the transition probabilities between them which form a Markov chain.

Such a chain *must* have at least one ergodic region—a set of cycles each of which can reach all cycles of that set, but no other cycles. It *may* have transient cycles lying outside the single ergodic set, reaching into, but not reachable, from that set. It also *may* have more than a single ergodic set; each ergodic set must be isolated from all other ergodic sets, however, all may be reachable from some single transient either directly, or via other transients.

In this and the next paragraph, Kauffman notes a limitation of the model in explaining cell types.

Let the net embody only a single ergodic set of cycles. If placed on any cycle in the set and perturbed by noise, the system will "spontaneously" pass from cycle to cycle along the allowed transition pathways. An isolated cell would appear to oscillate among its modes of behavior, driven by external noise. If the net is a replicating cell, the clone will explore the permitted transition pathways between cycles and populate the ergodic set according to the asymptotic transition probabilities between the cycles. Cells will spontaneously start to change, pass down restricted pathways of development, populate the complete set of possible modes of behavior, and settle to some stable distribution. Since the net, by hypothesis, embodies only a single ergodic set, each cycle may reach all; differentiation of any cell cannot be stable, a cell of one type should occasionally "spontaneously" change to become a cell of a different type. Since all types may be reached from any type, deletion of a subset of cell types should create a net movement of cells into the type of cells removed—regeneration should occur.

Stable, irreversible differentiation would require either location in a microenvironment in which the "noise" was sharply biased by the neighboring cell types, or, more fundamentally, a multiplicity of ergodic regions.

Assume a net with more than a single ergodic set. (I have not yet found such a net.) Let there be a transient which reaches, via other transients, into all ergodic sets. Call this transient cycle the zygote. Let it replicate. Then, the zygote is totipotent with respect to all its ergodic regions. We may explain the initiation of differentiation; the zygote is on a Markovian transient cycle in a noisy environment and must eventually leave. We may explain the cessation of differentiation; the system enters an ergodic set and becomes trapped. We have deduced the apparently spontaneous generation of heterogeneity. As the system passes, goaded by noise, from the zygote toward some ergodic set, it must pass branch points to other ergodic sets. Before reaching such a branch point, no noise will move it to that ergodic set; while passing, noise will so move it; after passing, the system will not be competent to respond to noise and reach that ergodic set. Hence we expect the competence of limited duration, the efficacy and reliability of noise as the stimulus for induction, the aid to differentiation provided by contact with heterogeneous tissue as a source of noise; stabilization of change after its induction and the branch point is passed; progressive restriction of developmental pathways as branch points to ergodic sets are passed; limitation in the number of cell types which may arise directly from any cell type; difficulty of metaplastic transformation between specialized cells (in different ergodic sets), and the possibility of metaplastic transformation between undifferentiated (transient) and specialized cell types. Let the net replicate during this perturbation and a particular number will pass down each transition from each cycle, reach each ergodic set, occupy all allowable cycles and distribute themselves according to the asymptotic transition probabilities between cycles and replication rates of each cell type. Grant death to some, and a steady-state population of various cell types arises. Because cells are trapped in separate ergodic regions, overall regeneration is not possible. Within each region, restricted regeneration remains possible. Wounds heal.

Earlier, I alluded to the argument (Walter, Parker, and Ycas 1967) that a set of elements whose outputs are sigmoid functions of their inputs behave as a set of binary devices. If true, this suggests that the results obtained for binary nets, rather than being highly simplified approximations, may approach closely to an accurate solution of the behavior of randomly interconnected, biologically appropriate nonlinear, metabolic nets.

Study of the typical behavior of randomly assembled determinate nets has barely begun. Further research is now needed to extend these results to larger nets; to study the effect of different numbers of inputs per element; to establish firmly the behavior of nets whose elements realize biologically appropriate continuous or probabilistic functions on their inputs; to find the effect of increasing levels of state noise, and more particularly, of "biased" noise due to spatial proximity with other copies of the net behaving on different cycles, and to study the effect of mutation—random alteration in the structure of the net, on its behavior.

While the model has been developed to study cellular control processes, it is formally identical to nerve net models and may find application in other branches of science.

9. Conclusion

A living thing is a richly interconnected net of chemical reactions. One can little doubt that the earliest proto-organisms aggregated their reaction nets at random in the primeval seas; or that mutation continues to modify living metabolic nets in random ways. Evolution, therefore, probably had as its initial substrate the behavior of randomly aggregated reaction nets.

It is a fundamental question whether two billion years of survival pressure have succeeded in selecting from a myriad of unorderly reaction nets those few improbable, that is non-random and ordered, metabolic nets which alone behave with the stability requisite for life; or whether living things are akin to randomly constructed automata whose characteristic behavior reflects their unorderly construction no matter how evolution selected the surviving forms.

The data I have presented suggest: that large, randomly interconnected feedback nets of binary "genes" behave with the stability requisite for life; that they undergo short stable cycles in the states of their constituents; that the time required for these behavior cycles parallels and predicts the time required for cell replication in many phyla; that the number of distinguishable modes of behavior of a randomly constructed net predicts with considerable accuracy the number of cell types in an organism which embodies a genetic net of the same size; that, like cells, a random net is capable of differentiating directly from any one mode of behavior to at most a few of its other modes; and that these restricted transition possibilities between modes of behavior allow us to state a theory of differentiation which deduce the origin, sequence, branching, and cessation of differentiation as the expected behavior of randomly assembled reaction nets.

If original proto-organisms built their reaction nets randomly, it behoves the biologist to build an adequate theory of the behavior of these systems; such a theory should elucidate the problems of biosynthetic organization faced by early living forms. But, if extant biota are also randomly constructed, then an adequate theory of the behavior of randomly assembled reaction nets would constitute an appropriate theory in which to describe the metabolic behavior of nets throughout phylogeny. The correspondence between the behavior of randomly interconnected nets of binary "genes" and the range of biologic data described above, suggest that organisms may indeed form a single population of typical randomly constructed reaction nets. Only if living things do form a single population does a general theory of metabolic behavior seem a reasonable goal for theoretical biology. The consequence of such a theory would be our ability to deduce, not merely describe. metabolic behavior from general propositions about the behavior of any randomly constructed feedback net; and to do so about genetic nets whose exact construction we do not, and may never, know.

A provocative statement, not justified in its stated form, but whose audacity makes you sit up and think.

Large, randomly assembled nets of binary elements behave with simplicity, stability, and order. It seems unlikely that Nature has made no use of such probable and reliable systems, both to initiate evolution and protect its progeny.

Drawing our attention to the unexpected simplicity and order in random Boolean networks is indeed one of the highlights of this paper.

Acknowledgments

This research was supported under USPHS 5 T5 GM 43 – 05 and USPHS 1 – SO – 1 FR 5355 – 04, and partially through the USAEC. A portion of the work was done while a Visiting Scientist at the Research Laboratory of Electronics, M.I.T. from 15th September 1967 to 15th December 1967.

The author wishes to thank Drs Laurel Glass, Sheldon Wolff, Harvey Patt, John Heddle, Creyton Walker, and Warren S. McCulloch for their encouragement and criticism; and Marvin Minsky for making available the use of project MAC computer time while at M.I.T.

REFERENCES

Altman, P. L., and D. S. Dittmer, eds. 1962. *Growth.* Washington, DC: Federation of American Societies for Experimental Biology.

Apter, M. J. 1966. *Cybernetics and Development.* Oxford, UK: Pergamon Press.

Baldwin, H. H., and A. P. Rusch. 1965. "The Chemistry of Differentiation in Lower Organisms." *Annual Review of Biochemistry* 34:565–594.

Bonner, J. F. 1965. *The Molecular Biology of Development.* London, UK: Oxford University Press.

Borradaile, L. A., F. A. Potts, L. E. S. Eastham, and J. T. Saunders. 1955. *The Invertebrata.* 3rd ed. Cambridge, UK: Cambridge University Press.

Bretscher, M. S. 1968. "How Repressor Molecules Function." *Nature* 217:509–511.

Cleaver, J. E. 1967. *Thymidine Metabolism and Cell Kinetics.* Amsterdam, Netherlands: North Holland.

Goodwin, B. C. 1963. *Temporal Organization in Cells.* London, UK: Academic Press.

Grobstein, C. 1959. "Differentiation of Vertebrate Cells." *The Cell* (London, UK) 1.

Horowitz, N. H., and R. L. Metzenberg. 1965. *0* 34:527–564.

Jacob, F., and J. Monod. 1963. "21st Symp. Soc. Study of Development and Growth." London, UK: Academic Press.

Kauffman, S. A. 1967. "Sequential DNA Replication and the Control of Differences in Gene Activity Between Sister Chromatids—A Possible Factor in Cell Differentiation." *Journal of Theoretical Biology* 17:483.

Macklin, M. 1968. "Biological Phase Relationships." *Nature* 217:622–624.

Mazia, D. 1961. "Random Genetic Nets." *The Cell* (New York, NY) 3:467.

Mirsky, A. E., and S. Osawa. 1961. "Academic Press." In *The Cell,* 2:677–770. New York, NY.

Nanney, D. L., and M.A. Rudzinska. 1960. "Protozoa." In *The Cell,* 4:109. New York, NY: Academic Press.

Rosenberger, R. F., and M. Kessel. 1967. "Synchrony of Nuclear Replication in Individual Hyphae of *Aspergillus Nidulans.*" *Journal of Bacteriology* 94:1464.

Rubin, H., and R. Sitgreave. 1954. *Probability Distributions Related to Random Transformations on a Finite Set.* Technical report 19A. Applied Mathematics and Statistics Lab, Stanford University.

Schrödinger, E. 1944. *What is Life?* Cambridge, UK: Cambridge University Press.

Slone, N. J. H. 1967. *Lengths of Cycle Time in Random Neural Networks.* Ithaca, NY: Cornell University Press.

Sparrow, A. H., and H. J. Evans. 1961. "Nuclear Factors Affecting Radio-Sensitivity. II. Dependence on Nuclear and Chromosome Structure and Organization," 14:101–24.

Sugita, M. 1963. "Functional Analysis of Chemical Systems in Vivo Using a Logical Circuit Equivalent. II. The Idea of a Molecular Automaton." *Journal of Theoretical Biology* 4:179.

Van't Hof, J. 1965. "Relationships Between Mitotic Cycle Duration, S-period Duration and the Average Rate of DNA Synthesis in the Root Meristem Cells of Several Plants." *Experimental Cell Research* 39:48–58.

Van't Hof, J., and A. H. Sparrow. 1963. "A Relationship Between DNA Content, Nuclear Volume, and Minimum Mitotic Cycle Time." *Proceedings of the National Academy of Sciences* 49 (6): 897–902.

Vendrely, R. 1955. "The Deoxyribonucleic Acid Content of the Nucleus." (New York, NY) 2:155.

Walker, C. C., and W. R. Ashby. 1966. *On Temporal Characteristics of Behavior in Certain Complex Systems.* 3:100–108.

Walter, C., R. Parker, and M. Ycas. 1967. "A Model for Binary Logic in Biochemical Systems." *Journal of Theoretical Biology* 15:208.

Watson, J. D. 1965. *Molecular Biology of the Gene.* New York, NY: W. A. Benjamin, Inc.

Williamson, D. H. 1964. "Synchrony in Cell Division and Growth." Edited by E. Zeuthen. (New York, NY).

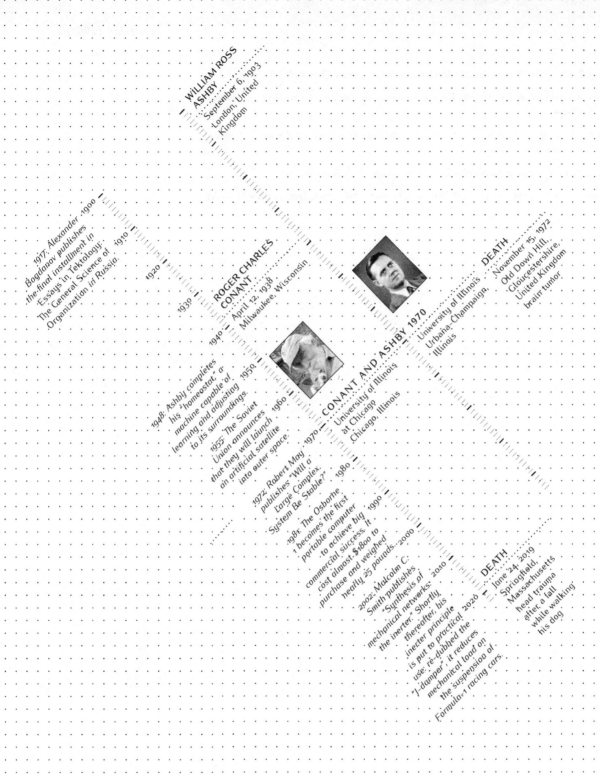

WILLIAM ROSS ASHBY
September 6, 1903
London, United Kingdom

1917: Alexander Bogdanov publishes the final installment in "Essays in Tektology: The General Science of Organization in Russia.

1910 1920 1930

ROGER CHARLES CONANT
April 12, 1938
Milwaukee, Wisconsin

1940

1948: Ashby completes his "homeostat," a machine capable of learning and adjusting to its surroundings.

1950

1955: The Soviet Union announces that they will launch an artificial satellite into outer space.

1960

DEATH
November 15, 1972
Old Down Hill, Gloucestershire, United Kingdom
brain tumor

CONANT AND ASHBY 1970
University of Illinois at Chicago, Chicago, Illinois

University of Illinois, Urbana-Champaign, Illinois

1970

1972: Robert May publishes "Will a Large Complex System Be Stable?"

1980

1981: The Osborne 1 becomes the first portable computer to achieve big commercial success, it cost almost $1,800 to purchase and weighed nearly 25 pounds.

1990

2000

2002: Malcolm C. Smith publishes "Synthesis of mechanical networks: the inerter." Shortly thereafter, his inerter principle is put to practical use; re-dubbed the "J-damper," it reduces mechanical load on the suspension of Formula-1 racing cars.

2010

2020

2026

2050

DEATH
June 24, 2019
Springfield, Massachusetts
head trauma after a fall while walking his dog.

CONANT·AND·ASHBY

[34]

REQUISITE COMPLEXITY—
A CONTEMPORARY VIEW OF CYBERNETIC
CONTROL AND COMMUNICATION

*James P. Crutchfield, University of California at Davis
and Santa Fe Institute*

R. C. Conant and W. R. Ashby,
"Every Good Regulator of a
System Must be a Model of
That System," in *International
Journal of Systems Science* 1
(2), 89–97 (1970).

*Reprinted by permission of
Taylor & Francis Ltd.*

Abstract

This modern perspective on Roger Conant and Ross Ashby's 1970 article
"Every Good Regulator of a System Must be a Model of that System" accounts
for advances in nonlinear dynamics, information theory, and computational
mechanics. In this way, connecting the original historical effort to the modern,
today's complex-systems research can be appreciated as a revival and extension of
Norbert Wiener's cybernetics.

Cybernetic Control and Communication

Much of the interest and, indeed, need for the study of complex systems
derives from the simple fact that our world—both natural and artificial—
is replete with active, dynamic, adaptive entities that themselves interact.
Even more to the point, we humans are enthusiastically changing,
updating, and refining our own immediate environment. As is all too well
appreciated now, this is both good and bad (Crutchfield 2009). Current
impacts and judgments aside, at a minimum there is a need to understand
how complex systems work and how to design them to operate the way
we need and would like them to function. The main lessons of twentieth-
century mathematics and physical theory, though, is that prediction,
mechanistic understanding, and design are inherently difficult. Chaotic
dynamics (Ott 1993) and self-organization (Cross and Greenside 2009)
immediately come to mind as example emergent phenomena that make
complex systems supremely challenging.

This all said, these concerns are not even remotely new. There was a historically fascinating period in the mid-twentieth century when it seems to have suddenly dawned on scientists that complex systems existed and were key to scientific, engineering, and even social progress. The mathematician Norbert Wiener (1948) captured this by coining cybernetics as the study of "control and communication in the animal and the machine."

The following summarizes, in this light, an important contribution from this time—Conant and Ashby's (CA) "Every Good Regulator of a System Must Be a Model of That System." In this we see a wholehearted acknowledgment of complex systems—the objects of study have become "complex dynamic systems." And CA set a style of inquiry that persists to this day to look for broad principles and laws that describe and predict their behaviors. Their title lays out the goal: to demonstrate that for a system to effectively interact with its environment, it must in some sense internalize and then leverage the regularities and randomness of its environment.

From the outset CA zero in on "models," providing an exegesis on their key role: the need, when confronted with a presumed complex system, to express how it behaves and is structured. In many ways, this is quite modern. Today, much of what we think science and engineering must do is build models of the systems we wish to analyze, simulate, and predict. To my mind, CA's highlighting of models is a stand-in for the need to articulate a system's organization.

Their interest is that of design—how to make a complex dynamic system behave in some desired way or to achieve some desired condition. This is the notion of control or, as they frame it, regulation. A commonly used example is homeostasis in the human body. Despite vagaries and variations in the ambient environment, human physiology must maintain an internal temperature that is relatively constant. Otherwise, much of our biochemistry fails to function. That is, regulatory mechanisms monitor the external environment and then modify internal operations to maintain the needed temperature. This is homeostasis—regulation consists of generating a control regime that as closely as possible nullifies and compensates externally imposed variations. Appreciating this regulatory task immediately broaches the question of what mechanisms support such dynamic adaptation. CA offer up an answer in their theorem:

> *Any regulator that is maximally both successful and simple must be isomorphic with the regulated system.*

This is nicely intuitive. Perhaps stating the opposite helps: if the regulator knew nothing about the system—nothing about its accessible configurations and states—it could do no effective control. The regulator could perturb the overall system, but those changes would not be coordinated with the system's moment-by-moment condition. And so the regulator would help as much as it hindered reaching the goal.

However, CA's point contains much more. There must be a rough map (at least an approximate isomorphism) of the system's possible behaviors somewhere in the regulator so that the latter can coordinate and perhaps even anticipate the control signal needed to counteract the system's potential behavior that would lead to missing the desired state. A modern framing would refer instead to the inverse model that gives the model inputs which produce desired system outputs.

Striving for generality, perhaps for an organizational principle even, CA chose to establish the result using Claude Shannon's (1948) communication theory to show that the regulator must compensate the system's behavior by driving the uncertainty (Shannon entropy) of the goal states to zero. Conant (1969), elsewhere, shows that the system (reguland) and regulator must effectively be coupled by a communication channel that shares information.

One use of the generality of the information-theoretic proof is that it applies to various kinds of regulatory mechanisms. CA discuss the more-familiar error-control regulation in which the system's deviation from the goal is fed back into the system in a way to drive it to the goal. The information theory approach, though, allows CA to show that regulation can be achieved under a more general setting—their "cause-controlled regulation."

Finally, to properly place CA's efforts in the setting of modern stochastic processes, it must be pointed out that recent results provide a counterexample to CA's theorem. Note that CA's regulators are predictive models in that they map system histories onto the regulator's states. Ruebeck *et al.* (2018) show that if the system is instead specified by a generative model, the system very easily requires predictors with many more, even infinitely more, states. And so, too, the simplest "successful" regulator will be infinite, falling outside CA's finite framing of regulation.

THERMODYNAMICS OF REQUISITE COMPLEXITY

CA's approach leaves out the energetic costs of regulation. And so, unfortunately, it falls quite short for real-world applications. The good news is that the intervening decades eventually led to a thermodynamics of regulation.

In particular, Boyd, Mandal, and Crutchfield (2016, 2018) introduced the theory of requisite complexity—a contemporary take that commandeers recent results in multivariate information theory, ergodic theory, and far-from-equilibrium statistical mechanics to give a modern interpretation of cybernetic control and communication, as CA laid out.

Key to biological success, Ashby (1960a, 1960b) had earlier identified the requisite variety that confronts an adaptive organism as the set of detectable, accessible, and controllable states in its environment. Boyd, Mandal, and Crutchfield (2017) analyzed the role of requisite variety in the thermodynamic functioning of information-heat engines, identifying the information-processing resources—requisite complexity—needed for operation.

Information engines are a form of autonomous Maxwellian demon (Leff and Rex 2002) capable of exploiting fluctuations in an external information reservoir to harvest useful work from a thermal bath (Boyd, Mandal, and Crutchfield 2016). They obey the information processing second law (IPSL) that determines the amount of thermodynamically useful information in a complex system, which only then can be fully leveraged and harvested via the requisite complexity in the Maxwellian demon. Altogether, this provides a quantitative paradigm for understanding how adaptive agents leverage structured thermal environments, including both positive and negative energy fluctuations, for their own thermodynamic benefit. In short, information engines operate as memoryful communication channels, interacting with their environment sequentially and storing results to an output, while shuttling energy between reservoirs.

Employing computational mechanics' structural view of dynamical processes (Crutchfield 2012) and the new IPSL, Boyd, Mandal, and Crutchfield (2017) analyzed general information engines interacting with structured environments that generate correlated input signals. On the one hand, it demonstrated that an information engine need not have memory to exploit an uncorrelated environment. On the other, and more appropriate to biological adaptation, it showed that an engine must have memory to most effectively leverage structure and correlation in its environment. The lesson is that to optimally harvest work an information engine's memory must reflect the input generator's memory—optimal information engines must model their environment.

Boyd, Mandal, and Crutchfield (2018) also showed how to construct the minimally complex information engine—its ε-machine— and placed bounds on the required thermodynamic resources to operate. In short, complementing CA delineation of the necessary information properties for regulation, the modern results address the energetics and structural complexity of learning and adaptation. For example, achieving good thermodynamic regulation would augment CA's $H[Z] < \varepsilon$ criterion with minimizing the entropy production of R, S, and Z.

Of historical note, the minimality of the optimal ε-machine regulator appears to have been anticipated in CA's comments on needless regulator complexity:

> *the theorem can be interpreted as saying that although not all optimal regulators are models of their regulands, the ones which are not are all unnecessarily complex.*

Note that this use of "model" is CA's rather strict notion of isomorphism as an exact matching, component by component, of regulator and reguland. Rather, one is tempted to say the regulator models the system as long as it regulates independent of the size of its implementation. A needlessly large model, with all its potential redundancy, is still a model.

Conclusion

CA's theorem that a good regulator must informationally capture the reguland's requisite variety is rather intuitive. Nonetheless, it gives important insights into design constraints for implementing controllers of complex adaptive dynamical systems. Beyond engineering, the scientific challenge posed is to recast this seeming obviousness and narrative motivation into a quantitatively predictive theory—hopefully, one that indicates how to experimentally test and how to engineer functional complex dynamical systems. As the theory of requisite complexity so clearly demonstrates, much of early cybernetics, though well-inspired and inspiring, needs to be reworked using modern theoretical tools. Then it may succeed in Wiener's original ambitious goals. 🖝

Further Reading

A fascinating cast of characters inhabits cybernetics' rich history, and many additional insights remain to be harvested from their original works. A selection of historical sources includes:

1. Claude Shannon's "A Mathematical Theory of Communication" (1948).

2. Norbert Wiener's *Cybernetics: Or Control and Communication in the Animal and the Machine* (1948).

3. Wiener's *The Human Use of Human Beings: Cybernetics and Society* (1988).

4. W. Ross Ashby was one of the principle early expositors, who took Wiener's notions seriously. Ashby, as reflected in the article here, thought deeply about a general theory of behavior in complex adaptive natural systems. See Ashby's *An Introduction to Cybernetics* (1960a) and *Design for a Brain* (1960b).

5. Conway and Siegelman's "Dark Hero of the Information Age" (2006) traces Norbert Wiener's colorful life, placing it in the context of the transition from World War II to the Cold War.

Acknowledgments

The author thanks Alec Boyd, Sam Loomis, Kyle Ray, Adam Rupe, and Greg Wimsatt for helpful comments, the Telluride Science Research Center for hospitality during visits, and the participants of the Information Engines Workshops there. This material is based upon work supported by, or in part by, FQXi Grant number FQXi-RFP-IPW-1902, and US Army Research Laboratory and the US Army Research Office under grants W911NF-18-1-0028 and W911NF-21-1-0048.

REFERENCES

Ashby, W. R. 1960a. *An Introduction to Cybernetics.* 2nd. New York, NY: John Wiley & Sons.

———. 1960b. *Design for a Brain: The Origin of Adaptive Behavior.* 2nd. New York, NY: Chapman & Hall.

Boyd, A. B., D. Mandal, and J. P. Crutchfield. 2016. "Identifying Functional Thermodynamics in Autonomous Maxwellian Ratchets." *New Journal of Physics* 18:023049. https://doi.org/10.1088/1367-2630/18/2/023049.

———. 2017. "Leveraging Environmental Correlations: The Thermodynamics of Requisite Variety." *Journal of Statistical Physics* 167 (6): 1555–1585. https://doi.org/10.1007/s10955-017-1776-0.

———. 2018. "Thermodynamics of Modularity: Structural Costs Beyond the Landauer Bound." *Physical Review X* 8 (3): 031036. https://doi.org/10.1103/PhysRevX.8.031036.

Conant, R. C. 1969. "The Information Transfer Required in Regulatory Processes." *IEEE Transactions on System Science and Cybernetics* 5 (4): 334–338. https://doi.org/10.1109/TSSC.1969.300226.

Conway, F., and J. Siegelman. 2006. *Dark Hero of the Information Age: In Search of Norbert Wiener, the Father of Cybernetics.* New York, NY: Basic Books.

Cross, M., and H. Greenside. 2009. *Pattern Formation and Dynamics in Nonequilibrium Systems.* Cambridge, UK: Cambridge University Press.

Crutchfield, J. P. 2009. "The Hidden Fragility of Complex Systems: Consequences of Change, Changing Consequences." In *Cultures of Change / Changing Cultures,* edited by P. Alsina and J. Perello, 98–111. Barcelona, Spain: ACTAR Publishers.

———. 2012. "Between Order and Chaos." *Nature Physics* 8:17–24. https://doi.org/10.1038/nphys2190.

Jaeger, H. 2000. "Observable Operator Models for Discrete Stochastic Time Series." *Neural Computation* 12 (6): 1371–1398. https://doi.org/10.1162/089976600300015411.

Leff, H., and A. Rex. 2002. *Maxwell's Demon 2: Entropy, Classical and Quantum Information, Computing.* New York, NY: Taylor / Francis.

Loomis, S. P., and J. P. Crutchfield. 2020. "Thermal Efficiency of Quantum Memory Compression." *Physical Review Letters* 125 (2–10): 020601. https://doi.org/10.1103/PhysRevLett.125.020601.

Ott, E. 1993. *Chaos in Dynamical Systems.* New York, NY: Cambridge University Press.

Ruebeck, J., R. G. James, J. R. Mahoney, and J. P. Crutchfield. 2018. "Prediction and Generation of Binary Markov Processes: Can a Finite-State Fox Catch a Markov Mouse?" *Chaos: A Journal of Nonlinear Scienece* 28 (1): 013109. https://doi.org/10.1063/1.5003041.

Shannon, C. E. 1948. "A Mathematical Theory of Communication." *Bell Systems Technical Journal* 27:379–423, 623–656. https://doi.org/10.1002/j.1538-7305.1948.tb01338.x.

Upper, D. R. 1997. "Theory and Algorithms for Hidden Markov Models and Generalized Hideen Markov Models." PhD diss., University of California, Berkeley.

Wiener, N. 1948. *Cybernetics: Or Control and Communication in the Animal and the Machine.* Cambridge, MA: MIT Press.

———. 1988. *The Human Use of Human Beings: Cybernetics and Society.* Cambridge, MA: Da Capo Press.

EVERY GOOD REGULATOR OF A SYSTEM MUST BE A MODEL OF THAT SYSTEM

Roger C. Conant, University of Illinois
and W. Ross Ashby, University of Illinois

Abstract

The design of a complex regulator often includes the making of a model of the system to be regulated. The making of such a model has hitherto been regarded as optional, as merely one of many possible ways.

In this paper a theorem is presented which shows, under very broad conditions, that any regulator that is maximally both successful and simple *must* be isomorphic with the system being regulated. (The exact assumptions are given.) Making a model is thus necessary.

The theorem has the interesting corollary that the living brain, so far as it is to be successful and efficient as a regulator for survival, *must* proceed, in learning, by the formation of a model (or models) of its environment[1].

Introduction

Today, as a step towards the control of complex dynamic systems, models are being used ubiquitously. Being modelled, for instance, are the air traffic flow around New York, the endocrine balances of the pregnant sheep, and the flows of money among the banking centres.

So far, these models have been made mostly with the idea that the model might help, but the possibility remained that the cybernetician (or the Sponsor) might think that some other way was better, and that making a model (whether digital, analogue, mathematical, or other) was a waste of time. Recent work (Conant 1969), however, has suggested that the relation between regulation and modelling might be much closer, that modelling might in fact be a *necessary* part of regulation. In this article we address ourselves to this question.

[1] Communicated by Dr. W. Ross Ashby. This work was in part supported by the Air Force office of Scientific Research under Grant AF-OSR 70-1865.

A historically fascinating period in the mid-twentieth century arose around Norbert Wiener's cybernetics, when it dawned on scientists and engineers that complex systems were key to scientific, engineering, and social progress. Conant and Ashby's article made an important contribution, offering up a principle for controlling complex dynamical systems: For a system to effectively interact with its environment, it must internalize and then leverage the regularities and randomness of its environment.

The setting is one of design, that is, engineering the regulation of a complex system. This differs, importantly, from determining if a real-world system is being regulated, from detecting from where the regulation comes, and from identifying how a regulator insinuates its control influence on the regulated system. These discovery aspects, key to the sciences, are markedly more challenging as they subsume many of the engineering aspects, but layer on measurement and inference.

Conant & Ashby (CA) take the bull by the horns right out of the gate: The concept of models is key to complex systems, but can be fraught. Why? First, models stand in for what we can explicitly articulate about a system of interest—what, indeed, makes it complex? Second, however, training in many scientific disciplines leads their researchers to ignore explicitly laying out structural assumptions; these assumptions, being taken to define the subdiscipline, need not be re-examined. CA claim that building models is essential in complex systems, particularly when the task at hand is to control a system. Their sensitivity to this is laudable and still holds value today.

Notable to read this exegesis on models from a twenty-first-century perspective: The issue (even including CA's seeming defensiveness) did not change for over half a century.

The answer is likely to be of interest in several ways. First, there is the would-be designer of a regulator (of traffic round an airport say) who is building, as a first stage, a model of the flows and other events around the airport. If making a model is *necessary*, he may proceed relieved of the nagging fear that at any moment his work will be judged useless. Similarly, before any design is started, the question: How shall we start? may be answered by: A model *will* be needed; let's build one.

Quite another way in which the answer would be of interest is in the brain and its relation to behaviour. The suggestion has been made many times that *perhaps* the brain operates by building a model (or models) of its environment; but the suggestion has (so far as we know) been offered only as a possibility. A proof that model-making is necessary would give neurophysiology a theoretical basis, and would predict modes of brain operation that the experimenter could seek. The proof would tell us what the brain, as a complex regulator for its owner's survival, *must* do. We could have the basis for a theoretical neurology.

The title will already have told this paper's conclusion, but to it some qualifications are essential. To make these clear, and to avoid vaguenesses and ambiguities (only too ready to occur in a paper with our range of subject) we propose to consider exactly what is required for the proof, and just how the general ideas of regulation, model, and system are to be made both rigorous and objective.

Regulation

Several approaches are possible. Perhaps the most general is that given by Sommerhoff (1950) who specifies five variables (each a vector or n-tuple perhaps) that must be identified by the part they play in the whole process.

The immediate task is to set context, done as a kind of architectural nesting and typically visualized with diagrams that connect boxes with arrows. The full meaning of the box-objects is only appreciated in their relationship to each other as highlighted by the arrows.

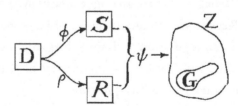

Figure 1.

(1) There is the total set Z of events that may occur, the regulated and the unregulated; e.g. all the possible events at an airport, good and bad. (Set Z in Ashby's (1967) reformulation in terms of set theory.)

(2) The set G, a sub-set of Z, consisting of the 'good' events, those ensured by effective regulation.

(3) The set R of events in the regulator R; (e.g. in the control tower). [We have found clarity helped by distinguishing the regulator as an object from the set of events, the values of the variables that compose the regulator. Here we use italic and Roman capitals respectively.]

(4) The set S of events in the rest of the system S (e.g. positions of aircraft, amounts of fuel left in their tanks) [with italic and Roman capitals similarly].

(5) The set D of primary disturbers (Sommerhoff's 'coenetic' variable); those that, by causing the events in the system S, tend to drive the outcomes out of G; (e.g. snow, varying demands, mechanical emergencies).

(Figure 1 may help to clarify the relations, but the arrows are to be understood for the moment as merely suggestive.) A typical act of regulation would be given by a hunter firing at a pheasant that flies past. D would consist of all those factors that introduce disturbance by the bird's coming sometimes at one angle, sometimes another; by the hunter being, at the moment, in various postures; by the local wind blowing in various directions; by the lighting being from various directions. S consists of all those variables concerned in the dynamics of bird and gun other than those in the hunter's brain. R would be those variables in his brain. G would be the set of events in which shot does hit bird. R is now a 'good regulator' (is achieving 'regulation') if and only if, for all values of D, R is so related to S that their *interaction* gives an event in G.

This formulation has withstood 20 years' scrutiny and undoubtedly covers the great majority of cases of accepted regulation. That it is also

The choice of exposition is telling. It is rather that of mathematics: Give the general setting first and then explain by examples. The pitfall, as seen here, is that we the readers do not yet know what "regulation" is. And so, the first paragraphs risk not conveying fully what CA intend. That said, CA are emphasizing generality by this tactic. The solution for the reader is to re-read and re-read.

This style of modeling, compared to that in the physical sciences, is phenomenological. It highlights desired behavioral and functional roles of the box-objects in terms of events. The stance is more that of a designer or engineer. Physical science would rather start by identifying the various system states, the allowed global configurations; then, consistent with physical law, write down their interactions; and, finally, derive the system's (perhaps-emergent) properties. (This last goal remains largely open. Discovering emergent patterns is an active research endeavor.) The phenomenological approach here risks imputing (hoped-for) behavior and function that might be inconsistent with the system's specified architecture. Overall, the effort is aspirational— "this architecture could work"— as opposed to giving a quantitative theory that predicts it will or will not work.

This section's notation, particularly regarding mappings, is based on the interpretation of a mapping as a relation—a set of pairs of objects. The "set of pairs" interpretation of mappings clarifies the meaning of the equations. Equation (1) says that the relation ρ must only contain (d, r) pairs that "can result in" a good state under the composed relation $(\phi.\psi)$.

Then, the immediately following equation assures that the relation is not trivial. This approach has to do with the '60s-'70s being a heyday of mathematical formalism; see CA's citation of Bourbaki later, which is famous for its high levels of formality. Note that the methods since worked out have both (i) clarified these concepts without the need for such an abstract formalism, but also (ii) grounded the formalism in the context of measure theory and stochastic processes.

This simply nods to the possibility, even commonality, that overall performance or effectiveness can be quantitatively monitored.

A complementary and unaddressed issue goes beyond a regulator's "goodness." This concerns a regulator's structural complexity in terms of internal states and operation costs. Without these considerations, the main result has limited practical applicability.

rigorous may be shown (Ashby 1967) by the fact that if we represent the three mappings by which each value (fig. 1) evokes the next:

$$\phi : D \to S$$

$$\rho : D \to R$$

$$\psi : S \times R \to Z$$

then 'R is a good regulator (for goal G, given D, etc., ϕ and ψ)' is equivalent to

$$\rho \subset [\psi^{-1}(G)] \cdot \phi, \qquad (1)$$

to which we must add the obvious condition that

$$\rho\rho^{-1} \subset 1 \subset \rho^{-1}\rho,$$

to ensure that ρ is an actual mapping, and not, say, the empty set! (We represent composition by adjacency, by a dot, or by parentheses according to which best gives the meaning.)

It should be noticed that in this formulation there is no restriction to linearity, to continuity, or even to the existence of a metric for the sets, though these are in no way excluded. The variables, too, may be partly functions of earlier real time; so the formulation is equally valid for regulations that involve 'memory', provided the sets D, etc., are defined suitably.

Any concept of 'regulation' must include such entities as the regulator R, the regulated system S, and the set of possible outcomes Z. Sometimes, however, the criterion of success is not whether the outcome, after each interaction of S and R, is within a goal-set G, but is whether the outcomes, on some numerical scale, have a root-mean-square sufficiently small.

A third criterion for success is to consider whether the entropy $H(Z)$ is sufficiently small. When Z can be measured on an additive scale they tend to be similar: complete the constancy of outcome $\Leftrightarrow H(Z) = 0 \Leftrightarrow$ r.m.s. $= 0$, (though the mathematician can devise examples to show that they are essentially independent). But the entropy measure of scatter has the advantage that it can be applied when the outcome can only be classified, not measured (e.g. species of fish caught in trawling, amino-acid chain produced by a ribosome.) In this paper we shall use the last

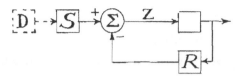

Figure 2.

This box-and-arrow architecture is what is more familiar to the control engineer. With R monitoring output behaviors and providing control signal (error: the difference between desired and observed behavior) through a feedback loop.

measure, $H(Z)$, and we define 'successful regulation' as equivalent to 'H(Z) is minimal'.

Error-, and Cause-, Controlled Regulation

The reader may be wondering why error-controlled regulation has been omitted, but there has been no omission. Everything said so far is equally true of this case; for if the cause-effect linkages are as in fig. 2.

R it is still receiving information about D's values, as in fig. 1, but is receiving it after a coding through S. The matter has been discussed fully by Conant (1969). There he showed that the general formulation of fig. 1 (which represents only that R must receive information from D by *some* route) falls into two essentially distinct classes according to whether the flow of information from D to Z is conserved or lossy. Regulation by error-control is essentially information-conserving, and the entropy of Z cannot fall to zero (there must be some residual variation). When, however, the regulator R draws its information directly from D (the cause of the disturbance) there need be no residual variation: the regulation may, in principle, be made perfect.

Under error-control, if the error vanishes, regulation turns off.

If the regulator directly sees the environment it can continue to apply control, perhaps improving the robustness of staying in good regulation.

The distinction may be illustrated by a simple example. The cow is homeostatic for blood-temperature, and in its brain is an error-controlled centre that, if the blood-temperature falls, increases the generation of heat in the muscles and liver—but the blood-temperature must fall first. If, however, a sensitive temperature-recorder be inserted in the brain and then a stream of ice-cold air driven past the animal, the temperature rises without any preliminary fall. The error-controlled reflex acts, in fact, only as reserve: ordinarily, the nervous system senses, at the skin, that the cause of a fall has occurred, and reacts to regulate before the 'error' actually occurs. Error-controlled regulation is in fact a primitive and demonstrably inferior method of regulation. It is inferior because with it the entropy of the outcomes Z cannot be reduced to zero; its success can only be partial. The regulations used by the higher organisms evolve progressively to types more effective in using information about the causes (at D) as the source and determiner of their regulatory actions. *From here on, in this paper, we shall consider 'regulation' of this more advanced, cause-controlled type* (though much of what we say will still be true of the error-controlled.)

Models

Defining 'regulation', as we have seen, is easy in that one is led rapidly to one of a few forms, closely related and easily distinguished in practical use. The attempt to define a 'model', however, leads to no such focus. We shall obtain a definition suitable for this paper, but first let us notice what happens when one attempts precision. We can start with such an unexceptionable 'model' as a table-top replica of Chartres cathedral. The transformation is of the type, in three dimensions:

$$y_1 = kx_1$$
$$y_2 = kx_2$$
$$y_3 = kx_3$$

with k about 10^{-2}. But this example, so clear and simple, can be modified a little at a time to forms that are very different. A model of Switzerland, for instance, might well have the vertical heights exaggerated (so that the three k's are no longer equal). In two dimensions, a (proportional) photograph from the air may be followed by a Mercator's projection with distortion, that no longer leaves the variables separable. So we can go through a map of a subway system, with only the points of connection valid, to 'maps' of a type describable only mathematically.

In dynamic systems, if the transformation converts the real time t to a model time t' also in real time we have a 'working' model. An unquestionable 'model' here would be a flow of electrons through a net of conducting sheets that accurately models, in real time, the flow of underground water in Arizona. But the model sailing-boat no longer behaves proportionately, so that a complex relation is necessary to relate the model and the full-sized boat. Thus, in the working models, as in the

Note that "dynamic systems" is the term of art in control engineering that typically refers to linear systems. As such, it is rather more circumscribed than the area of mathematics called "dynamical systems" which addresses arbitrary nonlinear, time-dependent systems. This latter area was in full development at the time of this article. It is a question for history why the advances there were not known or used by CA. Perhaps the most telling lack is the existence of inherent dynamic instability now called deterministic chaos, which had been discovered by Poincaré many decades prior to the rise of cybernetics.

Historical note: The specific example of a model here is an analog computing model. Today, we tend to imagine a "model" as something coded in a digital computer.

static, we can readily obtain examples that deviate more and more from the obvious model to the most extreme types of transform, without the appearance of any natural boundary dividing model from non-model.

Can we follow the mathematician and use the concept of 'isomorphism'? It seems that we cannot. The reason is that though the concept of isomorphism is unique in the branch where it started (in the finite groups) its extension to other branches leads to so many new meanings that the unicity is lost.

As example, suppose we attempt to apply it to the universe of binary relations. R, a subset of E×E, and S, a subset of F×F, are naturally regarded as 'isomorphic' if there exists a one-one mapping σ of E onto F such that $S = \sigma R \sigma^{-1}$ (Riguet 1948; Bourbaki 1958). But S and R are still closely related, and able to claim some 'model' relationship if the definition is weakened to

$$\exists \sigma, \tau : S = \sigma R \tau^{-1}$$

(with τ also one-one). Then it can be weakened further by allowing ϕ (and τ) to be a mapping generally or even a binary relation. The sign of equality similarly can be weakened to 'is contained in'. We have now arrived at the relation given earlier (1) under 'regulation'):

$$\rho \subset A \cdot \phi$$

which evidently implies some '-morphic' relation between ρ and ϕ (with A assumed given).

In this paper we shall be concerned chiefly with isomorphism between two dynamic systems (S and R in fig. 1). We can therefore try using the modern abstract definition of 'machine with input' as a rigorous basis.

To discuss iso-, and homo-, morphism of machines, it is convenient first to obtain a standard representation of these ideas in the theory of groups, where they originated. The relation can be stated thus:

Let the two groups be, one of the set E of elements e_i, with group operation (multiplication) δ, so that $\delta(e_i, e_j) = e_k$, and other similarly

The interest here is a way to track similarity of behaviors and of systems. The concern about isomorphism is too limited, though. Dynamical systems theory developed several concepts for similarity: isomorphism is one that it had extended far outside of finite groups; topological and metric conjugacy are others. Each was appropriate to different kinds of similarity and so allowed for more refined notions of similarity and difference.

The relation $S = \sigma R \tau^{-1}$ is familiar from hidden Markov model inference. Its earliest form is found in Upper's (1997) Proposition 4.1.7 and in Jaeger (2000). So, CA's definition of a model as an isomorphism has stood the test of time quite well.

Focusing on groups here is too restrictive when comparing complex systems. Rather one uses the generalization of semigroups. This allows for "noisy" or approximate comparisons. This is essential for real-world systems that are often subject to random perturbations by the environment, such as thermal fluctuations.

of δ' on elements F. Then the second is a homomorph of the first if and only if there exists a mapping h, from E to F, so that, for all $e_i, e_j \in$ E:

$$\delta'[h(e_i), h(e_j)] = h[\delta(e_i, e_j)]. \tag{2}$$

If h is one-one onto F, they are isomorphic. This basic equation form will enable us to relate the other possible definitions.

Hartmanis and Stearns' (1966) definition of machine M′ being a homomorphism of M follows naturally. Let machine M have a set S of internal states, a set I of input-values (symbols), a set O of output-values (symbols), and let it operate according to δ, a mapping of S × I to S, and λ, a mapping of S × I to O. Let machine M′ be represented similarly by S′, I′, O′, δ', λ'. Then M′ is a homomorphism of M if and only if there exist three mappings:

$$h_1, \text{ of S to S}'$$
$$h_2, \text{ of I to I}'$$
$$h_3, \text{ of O to O}'$$

such that, for all $s \in$ S and $i \in$ I:

$$h_1[\delta(s, i)] = \delta'[h_1(s), h_2(i)],$$
$$h_3[\lambda(s, i)] = \lambda'[h_1(s), h_2(i)]. \tag{3}$$

This definition corresponds to the natural case in which corresponding inputs (to the two machines) will lead, through corresponding internal states, to corresponding outputs. But, unfortunately for our present purpose, there are many variations, some trivial and some gross, that also represent some sort of 'similarity'. Thus, a more general form, representing a more complex form of relation, would be given if the mappings

$$h_1, \text{ of S to S}', \text{ and } h_2, \text{ of I to I}',$$

were replaced by one mapping

$$h_4, \text{ of I × S to I}' \times \text{S}'.$$

(More general because h_4 may or may not be separable into h_1 and h_2). Then the criterion would be,

$$\forall i, s : \delta'[h_4(s, i)] = h_4[\delta(s, i)], \tag{4}$$

a form not identical with that at (3).

There are yet more. The 'Black Box' case ignores the internal states S, and treats two Black Boxes as identical if equal inputs give equal outputs. Formally, if μ and μ' are the mappings from input to output, then the second Box is a homomorphism of the first if and only if there exists a mapping h, of I to I', such that:

$$\forall i \in I : \mu'[h(i)] = h[\mu(i)] \tag{5}$$

The Black Box case requires only examining machine behaviors. In this case, a unique minimal stochastic machine is available directly from the behaviors using the Predictive Equivalence Relation of Crutchfield (2012).

Here it should be remembered that equality of outputs is only a special case of correspondence. Also closely related are two Black Boxes such that the second is 'de-coder' to the first: the second, given the first's output, will take this as input and emit the original input:

$$\forall i \in I : \mu'\mu(i) = i. \tag{6}$$

This is an isomorphism. In the homomorphic relation, the input i and the final output $\mu'\mu(i)$ would both be mapped by h to the same class:

$$\forall i \in I : h\mu'\mu(i) = h(i). \tag{7}$$

These examples may be sufficient to show the wide range of abstract 'similarities' that might claim to be 'isomorphisms'. There seem, in short, to be as many definitions possible to isomorphism as to model. It might seem that one could make practically any assertion one likes (such as that in our title) and then ensure its truth simply by adjusting the definitions. We believe, however, that we can mark out one case that is sufficiently a whole to be worth special statement.

We consider the regulatory situation described earlier, in which the set of regulatory events R and the set of events S in the rest of the system (i.e. in the 'reguland' S, which we view as R's opponent) jointly determine, through a mapping ψ, the outcome events Z. By an optimal regulator we will mean a regulator which produces regulatory events in such a way that $H(Z)$ is minimal. Then under very broad conditions stated in the proof below, the following theorem holds:

The setting here analyzes only a single "step" in the overall system's operation: one application of the mappings ρ, σ, and h. It is not a time dependent setting in which R and S are full dynamical systems. CA briefly address this at the bottom of the next page, noting that the result applies to sufficiently slow changes in S.

Theorem: The simplest optimal regulator R of a reguland S produces events R which are related to the events S by a mapping $h : S \rightarrow R$.

Restated somewhat less rigorously, the theorem says that the best regulator of a system is one which is a model of that system in the

The criterion of simplest regulator is notable, as there was little or no reference above to regulator structure. Requiring minimal $H(Z)$, uncertainty in outcomes, does not require a minimal mechanism for the regulator. Thus, appealing to simplicity in the latter is a new result, but one that is not required for concluding that R models S. Physically, though, simplicity of the regulator is important—it has energetic consequences; see Boyd, Mandal, and Crutchfield (2017).

Cognizant of this, a key assumption reasserts itself: That R's control of S does not change S's structure, rather it merely guides S through states allowed by S's structure. The contrast to keep in mind is when one drives a system in which the driving signal adds energy to and so modifies the range of states that S can reach. CA assume this cannot happen. Figure 1's connectivity precludes it.

In effect, S determines R's state.

sense that the regulator's actions are merely the system's actions as seen through a mapping h. The type of isomorphism here is that expressed (in the form used above) by

$$\exists h : \forall i : \rho(i) = h[\sigma(i)] \tag{8}$$

where ρ and σ are the mappings that R and S impose on their common input I. This form is essentially that of (5) above.

Proof: The sets R, S, and Z and the mapping $\psi : R \times S \to Z$ are presumed given. We will assume that over the set S there exists a probability distribution $p(S)$ which gives the relative frequencies of the events in S. We will further assume that the behaviour of any particular regulator R is specified by a conditional distribution $p(R|S)$ giving, for each event in S, a distribution on the regulatory events in R. Now $p(S)$ and $p(R|S)$ jointly determine $p(R, S)$ and hence $p(Z)$ and $H(Z)$, the entropy in the set of outcomes. $(H(Z) \equiv - \sum_{z_k \in Z} p(z_k) \log p(z_k).)$ With $p(S)$ fixed, the class of optimal regulators therefore corresponds to the class of optimal distributions $p(R|S)$ for which $H(Z)$ is minimal. We will call this class of optimal distributions π.

It is possible for there to be very different distributions $p(Z)$ all having the same minimal entropy $H(Z)$. To consider that possibility would merely complicate this proof without affecting it in any essential way, so we will suppose that every $p(R|S)$ in π determines, with $p(S)$ and ψ, the same (unique) $p(Z)$. We now select for examination an arbitrary $p(R|S)$ from π.

The heart of the proof is the following lemma:

Lemma: $\forall s_j \in S$, the set $\{\psi(r_i, s_j) : p(r_i, s_j) > 0\}$ has only one element. That is, for every s_j in S, $p(R|s_j)$ is such that all r_i with positive probability map, with s_j under ψ, to the same z_k in Z.

Proof of lemma: Suppose, to the contrary, that $p(r_1|s_j) > 0$, $p(r_2|s_j) > 0$, $\psi(r_1, s_j) = z_1$, and $\psi(r_2, s_j) = z_2 \neq z_1$. Now $p(r_1, s_j)$ and $p(r_2, s_j)$ contribute to $p(z_1)$ and $p(z_2)$ respectively, and by varying these probabilities (by subtracting Δ from $p(r_1, s_j)$ and adding Δ to $p(r_2, s_j)$) we could vary $p(z_1)$ and $p(z_2)$ and thereby vary $H(Z)$. We could make Δ either positive or negative, whichever would make $p(z_1)$ and $p(z_2)$ more unequal. One of the useful and fundamental properties of the entropy function is that any such increase in imbalance in $p(Z)$ necessarily decreases $H(Z)$. Consequently, we could start with a $p(R|S)$ from the class π, which minimizes $H(Z)$, and produce a new $p(R|S)$ resulting in a lower $H(Z)$; this contradiction proves the lemma.

Returning to the proof of the theorem, we see that for any member of π and any s_j in S, the values of R for which $p(R|s_j)$ is positive all give the same z_k. Without affecting $H(Z)$, we can arbitrarily select one of those values of R and set its conditional probability to unity and the others to zero. When this process is repeated for all s_j in S, the result must be a member of π with $p(R|S)$ consisting entirely of ones and zeroes. In an obvious sense this is the *simplest* optimal $p(R|S)$ since it is in fact a mapping h from S into R. Given the correspondence between optimal distributions $p(R|S)$ and optimal regulators R, this proves the theorem.

The Theorem calls for several comments. First, it leaves open the possibility that there are regulators which are just as successful (just as 'optimal') as the simplest optimal regulator(s) but which are unnecessarily complex. In this regard, the theorem can be interpreted as saying that although not all optimal regulators are models of their regulands, the ones which are not are all unnecessarily complex.

Second, it shows clearly that the search for the best regulator is essentially a search among the mappings from S into R; only regulators for which there is such a mapping need be considered.

Third, the proof of the theorem, by avoiding all mention of the inputs to the regulator R and its opponent S, leaves open the question of how R, S, and Z are interrelated. The theorem applies equally well to the configurations of fig. 1 and fig. 2, the chief difference being that in fig. 2 R is a model of S in the sense that the events R are mapped versions of the events S, whereas in fig. 1 the modelling is stronger; R must be a homo- or isomorph of S (since it has the same input as S and a mapping-related output).

Last, the assumption that $p(S)$ must exist (and be constant) can be weakened; if the statistics of S change slowly with time, the theorem holds over any period throughout which $p(S)$ is essentially constant. As $p(S)$ changes, the mapping h will change appropriately, so that the best regulator in such a situation will still be a model of the reguland,

CA note that R may not be the smallest controller; e.g., that with the minimal number of states. By their identifying modeling with being isomorphic, then R is not a model of S in this case. Since R nonetheless regulates S, it seems too strict to say in this way that R is not modeling S.

In this, CA miss an opportunity to define approximate regulation and noisy regulators. A system should be able to sacrifice regulatory fidelity for cheaper regulation. This surely is important to real-world cybernetic complex systems. The natural extension for this considers smooth entropies that allow balancing memory cost against accuracy; see Loomis and Crutchfield (2020).

CA nod to the fully dynamical setting in which R affects S's accessible states ("events").

but a time-varying model will be needed to regulate the time-varying reguland.

Discussion

CA's main result addresses finite-state, discrete-time behaviors. The modern version that extends to continuous, stochastic dynamical systems is found in Crutchfield (2012). And, indeed, with the latter's broadened definition of optimal model and constructive algorithms for statistical inference, any performative system must model its environment to the extent needed for its survival. That is, there is a mapping, a generalized version of CA's $h(.)$ function, from the system's internal states and behaviors to the relevant subset of the environment's states and behaviors. More to the point, Boyd, Mandal, and Crutchfield (2017) generalizes this to the Principle of Requisite Complexity to account not just for behaviors, but for the use of thermodynamic (energetic and entropic) resources to support those behaviors.

The first effect of this theorem is to change the status of model-making from optional to compulsory. As we said earlier, model-making has hitherto largely been suggested (for regulating complex dynamic systems) as a possibility: the theorem shows that, in a very wide class (specified in the proof of the theorem), success in regulation implies that a sufficiently similar model must have been built, whether it was done explicitly, or simply developed as the regulator was improved. Thus the would-be model-maker now has a rigorous theorem to justify his work.

To those who study the brain, the theorem founds a 'theoretical neurology'. For centuries, the study of the brain has been guided by the idea that as the brain is the organ of thinking, whatever it does is right. But this was the view held two centuries ago about the human heart as a pump; today's hydraulic engineers know too much about pumping to follow the heart's method slavishly: they know what the heart ought to do, and they measure its efficiency. The developing knowledge of regulation, information-processing, and control is building similar criteria for the brain. Now that we know that any regulator (if it conforms to the qualifications given) must model what it regulates, we can proceed to measure how efficiently the brain carries out this process. There can no longer be question about *whether* the brain models its environment: it must.

REFERENCES

Ashby, W. R. 1967. "The Set Theory of Mechanism and Homeostasis." In *Automaton Theory and Learning Systems,* edited by D. J. Stewart, 23–51. Horncastle, United Kingdom: Thompson Book Company.

Bourbaki, N. 1958. *Théorie des Ensembles: Fascicule de Résultats, 3rd edition.* Paris, France: Éditions Hermann.

Conant, R. C. 1969. "The Information Transfer Required in Regulatory Processes." *IEEE Transactions on Systems Science and Cybernetics* 5 (4): 334–338.

Hartmanis, J., and R. E. Stearns. 1966. *Algebraic Structure Theory of Sequential Machines.* New York, NY: Prentice-Hall.

Riguet, J. 1948. "Relations Binaires, Fermetures, Correspondances de Galois." *Bulletin de la Société Mathématique de France* 76:114–155.

Sommerhoff, G. 1950. *Analytical Biology.* Oxford, UK: Oxford University Press.

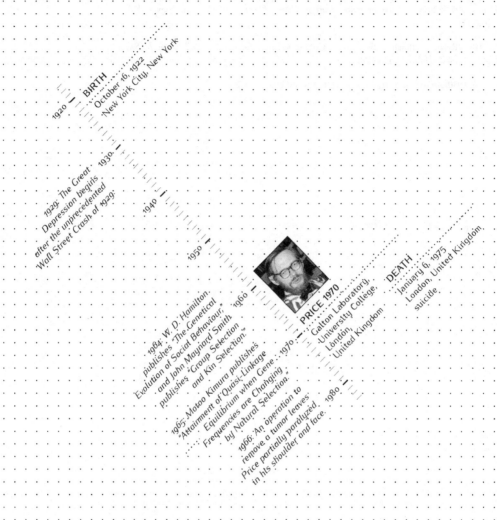

1920 — **BIRTH**
October 16, 1922
New York City, New York

1929: The Great
Depression begins
after the unprecedented
Wall Street Crash of 1929.

1930 —

1940 —

1950 —

1964: W. D. Hamilton
publishes "The Genetical
Evolution of Social Behaviour,"
and John Maynard Smith
publishes "Group Selection
and Kin Selection."

1960 —

1965: Motoo Kimura publishes
"Attainment of Quasi-Linkage
Equilibrium when Gene
Frequencies are Changing
by Natural Selection."

1970 —

PRICE 1970
Galton Laboratory,
University College,
London,
United Kingdom

DEATH
January 6, 1975
London, United Kingdom,
suicide.

1966: An operation to
remove a tumor leaves
Price partially paralyzed
in his shoulder and face.

1980 —

GEORGE · ROBERT · PRICE

[35]

THE PRICE EQUATION:
THE MATHEMATICAL BASIS OF
EVOLUTIONARY THEORY?

Michael Lachmann, Santa Fe Institute

This short paper is both important and controversial. It is a generalization of Fisher's fundamental theorem (1930), and Hamilton's rule (1964). But before we delve into the science, we should learn about the author. George R. Price had his fifteen minutes of national fame when in 1955 he published a paper in the journal *Science* arguing against recent claims of experimental proof of extra-sensory perception (ESP). Swift rebuttals followed in, among others, in *The New York Times*, *Esquire*, and a whole dedicated issue in *Science*. Price then turned to trying to revolutionize the process of design by describing a system that would enable using computers during the design process—his contribution can be seen as an important part in the invention of computer-aided design (CAD). In 1967 Price moved to the United Kingdom, where he worked in evolutionary theory and kin selection, discussing it with W. D. Hamilton, and later with John Maynard Smith on the concept of an evolutionary stable strategy (ESS)—an evolutionary equivalent of the Nash equilibrium. George Price's life ended tragically by suicide in January 1975.[1]

What is the Price equation? The equation itself is similar to the product rule for differentiation:[2] $(u \cdot v)' = u' \cdot v + u \cdot v'$, for arbitrary u and v, except that we apply it to the distribution of some property q in the population p, to get $\int (q \cdot p)' = \int q \cdot p' + \int q' \cdot p$. The change of q can be split into two parts: one part that results from a change of the distribution of q in the population, and a second that part the results of from the change of q

G. R. Price, "Selection and Covariance," *Nature* 227, 520–521 (1970).

Reprinted with permission of Springer Nature.

---

[1] For more on George Price's life and death, see Harman (2010).

[2] See Ay *et al.* (2017), sec. 6.2.1.

itself. This split can be seen in equation (4) of the paper:

$$\Delta Q = \text{Cov}(q, z)/\bar{z} + \sum \Delta q_i z_i / N\bar{z} \qquad (1)$$

The left results from a covariance between the property that we are interested in and how many in the population survive the process or are born, and the right part asks how q changes within the individuals. One example described in the paper involves looking at the change in the average IQ of students between the beginning and end of a college class—though maybe looking at the age of the students could be more insightful. The change in average age results from (1) a covariance between the age of the students and whether they hang on till the end of the year, and (2) the change in the age of each of the surviving students over the school year— normally a change of a few months. Thus, we will end up with an older class if everybody stays, but if mostly older students drop out, the class at the end of the year could have younger average age, even though all students aged over that time.

Similar to the product rule, the importance of the Price equation comes from its simplicity and wide applicability. The Price equation is one way of understanding how evolution leads to a change in a population: the mean value of a character will increase if larger values lead to better survival. A mutation–selection balance will be reached when the increased survival on the left-hand side of the sum is balanced by a decrease in the right-hand side as a result of mutations. We can also look at the link with Fisher's fundamental theorem. It states: "the rate of increase of fitness of any species is equal to the genetic variance in fitness." Just like the Price equation, Fisher's fundamental theorem also purports to explain and quantify the action of selection: selection causes an increase in fitness, and the increase is equal to the variance of the fitness in the population, the variance on which selection acts. Much ink has been spilled on the interpretation and derivation of this theorem. In relation to the Price equation, it is easy to see that if instead of looking at an arbitrary property q, we look at fitness itself, here written as z, and ignore the right-hand term, we get

$$\Delta Z = \text{Cov}(z, z)/\bar{z} = Var(z, z)/\bar{z} \qquad (2)$$

an expression very similar to Fisher's fundamental theorem. Why the right side of the sum, the change that results from a change within individuals, can be dropped is the main reason for the spilled ink. One interpretation is that Fisher was only describing the change resulting from selection itself.

Until now I've explained the Price equation in terms of individuals, but the summation and covariance can be taken over arbitrary groupings of the population. Thus, we can ask if an average property changed as a result of group selection. We split the population into groups, and then ask if there is a covariance between survival of a group and the average property of the group, and, further, whether the property changes within each group. Thus, when talking about the evolution of altruism, the amount of altruism within each group might help the group survive, but within each group altruism might decline, either because individuals within the group switch to being selfish or possibly because altruistic individuals within the groups do not survive. We could also expand the average change within each group again using the Price equation, giving us then selection both within and between groups (Price 1972).

The controversy surrounding the Price equation stems in part from the formulation using covariance. Covariance is often used to talk about the relationship between two random variables in statistics. In the Price equation, however, there is no random variable. We simply rewrite the actual change that occurred in the population. The summation is across individuals or groups rather than across a distribution of random variables. There is no randomness in the Price equation. This use or abuse of covariance in the Price equation caused some confusion and thus controversy. In Price's second paper (1972), he thus wrote, "In this paper we will be concerned with population functions and make no use of sample functions, hence we will not observe notational conventions for distinguishing population and sample variables and functions." Perhaps he was trying to discard problems others saw with his equation. Note that it is possible to write an equation that takes into account both the variation within the population, as Price has done, and the variation across different draws of populations.[3]

We thus see that the Price equation stands at the base of much of evolutionary theory. Together with Fisher's fundamental theorem, it explains how and whether traits change over evolution; it can be applied to

---

[3]See, for example, Rice (2008).

group selection and kin selection. In fact, Hamilton's rule can be derived from it, and it can be applied recursively to groups, groups of groups, genes within individuals, and so on. Price believed that it can be extended to a general theory of selection, a task that he sadly never accomplished. ❧

REFERENCES

Ay, N., J. Jost, H. Vân Lê, and L. Schwachhöfer. 2017. *Information Geometry.* Cham, Switzerland: Springer International Publishing. https://doi.org/10.1007/978-3-319-56478-4.

Fisher, R. A. 1930. *The Genetical Theory of Natural Selection.* Oxford, UK: Clarendon Press.

Hamilton, W. D. 1964. "The Genetical Evolution of Social Behaviour. I." *Journal of Theoretical Biology* 7 (1): 1–16. https://doi.org/10.1016/0022-5193(64)90038-4.

Harman, O. 2010. *The Price of Altruism: George Price and the Search for the Origins of Kindness.* London, UK: Bodley Head.

Harmon, O. 2011. "Birth of the First ESS: George Price, John Maynard Smith, and the Discovery of the Lost 'Antlers' Paper." *Journal of Experimental Zoology Part B: Molecular and Developmental Evolution* 316 (1): 1–9. https://doi.org/10.1002/jez.b.21377.

Maynard Smith, J., and G. R. Price. 1973. "The Logic of Animal Conflict." *Nature* 246 (5427): 15–18. https://doi.org/10.1038/246015a0.

Price, G. R. 1955. "Science and the Supernatural." *Science* 122 (3165): 359–367. https://doi.org/10.1126/science.122.3165.359.

———. 1972. "Extension of Covariance Selection Mathematics." *Annals of Human Genetics* 35 (4): 485–490. https://doi.org/10.1111/j.1469-1809.1957.tb01874.x.

———. 1995. "The Nature of Selection." *Journal of Theoretical Biology* 175 (3): 389–396. https://doi.org/10.1006/jtbi.1995.0149.

Rice, S. H. 2008. "A Stochastic Version of the Price Equation Reveals the Interplay of Deterministic and Stochastic Processes in Evolution." *BMC Evolutionary Biology* 8 (1): 262. https://doi.org/10.1186/1471-2148-8-262.

SELECTION AND COVARIANCE

George R. Price, University College London

This is a preliminary communication describing applications to genetical selection of a new mathematical treatment of selection in general.

Gene frequency change is the basic event in biological evolution. The following equation (notation to be explained), which gives frequency change under selection from one generation to the next for a single gene or for any linear function of any number of genes at any number of loci, holds for any sort of dominance or epistasis, for sexual or asexual reproduction, for random or nonrandom mating, for diploid, haploid or polyploid species, and even for imaginary species with more than two sexes

$$\Delta Q = \text{Cov}(z, q)/\bar{z} \qquad (1)$$

The equation easily translates into regression coefficient (β_{zq}) or correlation coefficient (ρ_{zq}) form

$$\Delta Q = \beta_{zq}\sigma_q^2/\bar{z} = P\rho zq\sigma_z\sigma_q/\bar{z}$$

It thus has great transparency, making it useful as a tool in qualitative evolutionary reasoning. It can also be applied to non-genetic selection. For example, if students' expectations of passing a certain course vary with IQ and if student IQs do not change appreciably during the course, then equation 1 (with its variables suitably redefined) will give the difference in mean IQ between students entering the course and those completing it (and equation 4 below will apply if IQs do change during the course).

Derivation is as follows. Let P_1 and P_2 be populations of a single species, such that P_1 contains all parents of P_2 members and P_2 consists of all offspring of P_1 members. Let the number of P_1 members be N. We label these with identification numbers $i = 1, 2, \ldots, N$, assigned in

Price continued to work on a full and extended version, but was never fully satisfied with the result. He published "some extension" in a 1972 paper in *Annals of Human Genetics*, and his notes were published posthumously in 1995.

any order. Let n_z be the zygotic ploidy of the species for gene A; let g_i be the dose of gene A in individual i (for example, if $n_z = 2, g_i = 0, 1,$ or 2 according to whether i lacks gene A, is heterozygous for A or is homozygous for A); let q_i be the frequency of gene A in individual i, defined by $q_i = g_i/n_z$; and let Q_1 be the frequency of gene A in population P_1

$$Q_1 = \Sigma g_i/n_z N = \Sigma n_z q_i/n_z N = \bar{q} \qquad (2)$$

where the summations are taken over all members of P_1 ($i = 1$ to N) and $\bar{q}$ is the arithmetic mean in population P_1 (that is, $\bar{q}$ is a population variable even though I use sample variable notation).

Now we turn attention to offspring. A gamete from a P_1 member that contributes genes to a P_2 member will be termed a "successful gamete". Let n_G be the gametic ploidy for gene A; let z_i be the number of successful gametes produced by individual i (=the number of i's offspring); let g'_i be the number of A genes in the set of all of i's successful gametes; let q'_i be the frequency of gene A in this set of gametes, defined by $q'_i = g'_i/z_i n_G$ if $z_i \neq 0, q'_i = q_i$ if $z_i = 0$; let $\Delta q_i = q'_i - q_i$; and let Q_2 be the frequency of gene A in population P_2. The following can be seen to hold

$$
\begin{aligned}
Q_2 &= \left(\Sigma g'_i\right)/\Sigma z_i n_G = \left(\Sigma z_i n_G q'_i\right)/\Sigma z_i n_G = \Sigma z_i q'_i/N\bar{z} \\
&= \Sigma z_i q_i/N\bar{z} + \Sigma z_i \Delta q_i/N\bar{z} = [\bar{z}\cdot\bar{q} + \mathrm{Cov}(z,q)]/\bar{z} + \Sigma z_i \Delta q_i/N\bar{z} \\
&= \bar{q} + \mathrm{Cov}(z,q)/\bar{z} + \Sigma z_i \Delta q_i/N\bar{z}
\end{aligned}
$$
$$(3)$$

where the summations are taken over all P_1 members, $\bar{z}$ is the arithmetic mean of z in P_1 and $\mathrm{Cov}(z,q)$ is the covariance (or first order central product moment) of z and q in population P_1. Subtraction of equation 2 from equation 3 gives

$$\Delta Q = Q_2 - Q_1 = \mathrm{Cov}(z,q)/\bar{z} + \Sigma z_i \Delta q_i/N\bar{z} \qquad (4)$$

If meiosis and fertilization are random with respect to gene A, the summation term at the right will be zero except for statistical sampling effects ("random drift"), and these will tend to average out to give equation 1.

This is an important step in the derivation. You have to keep using the indexes of the first generation, even if individuals switch between groups.

Five points about equation 1 will be briefly explained. First, equation 1 in its regression coefficient form can be visualized in terms of a linear regression line fitted to a scatter diagram of z against q. (A linear regression line is the best construction in terms of the population effect ΔQ, even if it gives a poor fit in terms of individual points.) Since the regression line has slope β_{xq}, gene frequency change due to selection is exactly proportional to the slope. Therefore, at any step in constructing hypotheses about evolution through natural selection— for example, about why human canines do not protrude, why deer antlers are annually shed and renewed, why parrots mimic, why dolphins play—one can visualize such a diagram and consider whether the slope really would be appreciably non-zero under the assumptions of the theory. If there is no slope, then there is no frequency change except by Δq effects, and the hypothesis is probably wrong.

Second, equation 1 fails if gene A ploidy is not the same in each P_1 member. Suppose, for example, that the A locus is in X but not Y chromosomes in a species with XX females and XY males. Then Q_1 is redefined as $Q_1 = (\Sigma g_i) / \Sigma n_i$, where n_i is A locus ploidy in individual i (that is, $n_i = 1$ if i is male, or 2 if i is female); and Q_2, q_i, and q_i' are redefined in corresponding ways. If P_1 and P_2 have sex ratios of unity (as is commonly the case at conception), then the following can be derived

$$\Delta Q = \frac{2}{3}\,\text{Cov}(z, q)_F / \bar{z}_F + \frac{1}{3}\,\text{Cov}(z, q)_M / \bar{z}_M \qquad (5)$$

where $\text{Cov}(z, q)_F$ is the z, q covariance and $\bar{z}_F$ is the mean in P_{1F}, the female subset of P_1, and $\text{Cov}(z, q)_M$ and $\bar{z}_M$ apply to the male subset, P_{1M}.

Third, the specifications that were stated for P_1 and P_2 imply a "discrete generations model". This was done solely in order to simplify this preliminary report. Actually equation 1 can be applied to species with overlapping, interbreeding generations, and it is not necessary that P_2 should contain all offspring of P_1 members, nor that P_1 should contain all parents of P_2 members. Departure from the "all parents" condition, however, requires reinterpretation of what ΔQ means, and departure from the "all offspring" condition (meaning all

This is a hint of the ESS theory to come (Maynard Smith and Price 1973). Price was fascinated with deer antlers—not lethal or very well adapted for killing an opponent. He was trying to apply game theory to this problem, and a draft he wrote on the issue later led to his paper with John Maynard Smith on the evolutionarily stable strategy.

zygotes conceived) must be done with insight to avoid introducing post-conceptual selection on P_2 (for post-conceptual selection would require the use of equation 4 instead of equation 1).

Fourth, as an example of how multiple gene functions can be handled, let us suppose that a regression analysis has given the relation

$$\varphi_i \approx 2 \cdot 3 + 1 \cdot 2q_{iA} - 0.7q_{iB} + 0.5q_{ic}$$

for the effects of genes A, B, and C on character φ. Then we may decide to define

$$q_i = 2 \cdot 3 + 1 \cdot 2q_{iA} - 0 \cdot 7q_{iB} + 0 \cdot 5q_{iC}$$
$$\Delta Q = Q_2 - Q_1 = (2 \cdot 3 + 1 \cdot 2Q_{2A} - 0.7Q_{2B} + 0 \cdot 5Q_2C)$$
$$- (2 \cdot 3 + 1 \cdot 2Q_{1A} - 0.7Q_{1B} + 0 \cdot 5Q_1C)$$

and equation 1 will hold for these multiple gene functions or for any other linear function of q and Q for any number of genes, if it holds for each gene separately.

Fifth, it seems surprising that so simple a relation as equation 1 has not (to my knowledge) been recognized before. Probably this is because selection mathematics has largely been limited to genetical selection in diploid species, where covariance takes so simple a form that its implicit presence is hard to recognize (whereas if man were tetraploid, covariance would have been recognized long ago; and because, instead of using subscripts as "names" of individuals (as I have done), the usual practice in gene frequency equations is to use subscripts only as names of gene or genotype types, which makes the mathematics seem quite different. Recognition of covariance (or regression or correlation) is of no advantage for numerical calculation, but of much advantage for evolutionary reasoning and mathematical model building.

Some genetical selection cases (such as group selection) and many forms of non-genetic selection require more complex mathematics than that given here. I plan to discuss these and other matters in papers now in preparation.

Acknowledgments

I thank Professor C. A. B. Smith for help, and the Science Research Council for financial support.

This type of linear regression of the effect can be used to derive from the Price equation Hamilton's rule for kin selection $rB > c$, where r is the relatedness, B is the benefit of the interaction and c is the cost.

In a note added to the proof of the 1972 paper, Price notes that Alan Robertson had used a similar equation, which is why a version of it is sometimes referred to as the Robertson–Price identity.

It is interesting that, though the connection between the Price equation and Fisher's fundamental theorem is clear, Price did not discuss it in this paper.

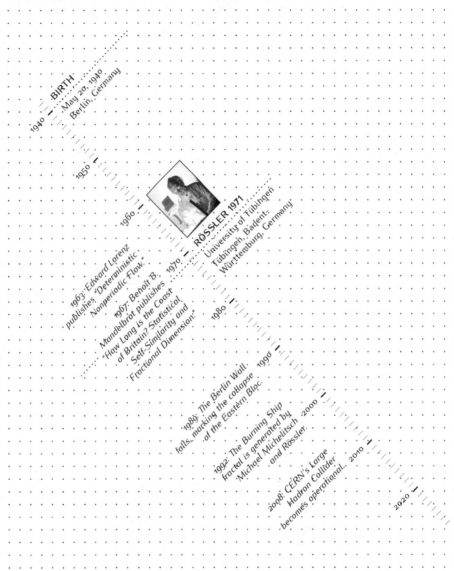

1940

BIRTH
May 20, 1940,
Berlin, Germany

1950

1960

RÖSSLER 1971
University of Tübingen,
Tübingen, Baden-
Württemburg, Germany

1963: Edward Lorenz
publishes "Deterministic
Nonperiodic Flow."

1967: Benoît B.
Mandelbrot publishes
"How Long is the Coast
of Britain? Statistical
Self-Similarity and
Fractional Dimension."

1970

1980

1989: The Berlin Wall
falls, marking the collapse
of the Eastern Bloc.

1990

1992: The Burning Ship
fractal is generated by
Michael Michelitsch
and Rössler.

2000

2008: CERN's Large
Hadron Collider
becomes operational.

2010

2020

OTTO EBERHARD RÖSSLER

[36]

THE WHEELS OF CHEMISTRY

Philipp Honegger, Harvard University, and
Walter Fontana, Harvard University

Otto Rössler's 1971 paper is a landmark in the landscape of systems chemistry that was all but missed, despite developing the consequential idea of generalized autocatalysis, which refers to a system that facilitates its own growth. Rössler is better known for the chaotic attractor named after him (see Rössler 1976) than for the principle of "chemical space" exploration that he outlines in his autocatalysis paper.

One problem with Rössler's paper is obvious: it is written in German. We therefore provide a translation to at least remove that obstacle. Besides language, another factor that might have reduced its visibility was the publication, earlier in the same year, of Manfred Eigen's work on "Selforganization of Matter and the Evolution of Biological Macromolecules," which also deals with autocatalysis. Eigen's paper quickly became a widely acclaimed classic. Again in 1971, Stuart Kauffman started his thread on "autocatalytic sets" in a long appendix piggybacking on his introduction of random Boolean networks. Tibor Gánti was among those who characterized living systems through an abstract chemical model of several interacting autocatalytic subsystems. He published (in Hungarian) his chemical automaton—the "chemoton"—in, you guessed it, 1971 (for an English-language reference, see Gánti 1975). Gánti, however, is less concerned with a process of chemical evolution towards a living state than with the specification of a working model in support of a conceptual and computational exploration of that state. 1971 appears to have been the *annus mirabilis* of autocatalysis.

While vastly differing in the level of detail, the three papers by Eigen, Kauffman, and Rössler constitute mutually opposing corners of a triangle of viewpoints informing the origin of life. Rössler begins

O. E. Rössler, "Ein systemtheoretisches Modell zur Biogenese," in *Zeitschrif für Naturforschung* 26B: 741–746 (1971), translated into English for this volume by Philipp Honegger and Walter Fontana.

Reprinted with permission from Walter de Gruyter Gmbh.

with the discussion of emergent phenomena in chemistry, specifically catalysis. The traditional view of a catalyzed reaction considers a molecule that forms short-lived intermediates with reactants to open up a more favorable path on the free energy surface of their chemical transformation into products. In the process, the catalytic molecule is returned to its original chemical state and therefore shows up as the same entity on both sides of the overall reaction, $A + B + C \rightarrow D + E + C$. The catalyst C cannot be canceled, since the reaction mechanism depends on its presence. Catalysis, however, can also be achieved by constructing a cycle of consecutive noncatalyzed reactions, as in figure 1 of Rössler's paper:

$$A + B \rightarrow C + D \qquad (1)$$

$$D + E \rightarrow F + G \qquad (2)$$

$$G + H \rightarrow I + A \qquad (3)$$

Rössler calls this phenomenon "generalized catalysis" (today we would say "network catalysis") and refers to the traditional version as "true" catalysis.

In generalized catalysis, the catalyst is not a single molecule, but a set of molecules {A,D,G} that are cyclically transformed into each other while converting input substances {B,E,H} into output substances {C,F,I}. At a fine-enough grain of temporal resolution a cyclical scheme must also hold for the process of "true" catalysis by a single molecule, or that molecule would not be restored. Yet, time scales matter: If intermediates are long-lived rather than short-lived, that is, if they are stable molecules, they can participate in a network of additional reactions. This becomes especially consequential if one of the outputs of the cycle leads through a distinct sequence of reactions back to another member of the cycle (for example, if reaction (3) directly produced D instead of I or if I reacted further to eventually produce D). In that case, all intermediates can be amplified exponentially until input substances are exhausted. Rössler encourages chemists to think like engineers who construct complex machinery by combining simple building blocks. For example, adding E and H as starting materials to the reaction mixture (1) unlocks (2) and (3) and, hence, network catalytic or autocatalytic behavior.

Eigen's 1971 paper deals mainly with autocatalysis as direct self-replication, like in a reaction of the form A + X → 2X + B, which in Rössler's terminology is "true" autocatalysis. Eigen's model emphasizes macromolecules, such as nucleic acid sequences, that contain *information* for their own replication. The decoding of that information by actual means of chemical production is abstracted away, yielding an appearance of "true" autocatalysis with associated phenomenological equations. Some of the popularity of Eigen's approach might be due to being firmly situated in a familiar Darwinian framework: Sequences are individualized entities and copying implements imperfect inheritance by descent. In contrast, a network (auto)catalyst is not an individualized entity—we cannot count discrete instances of a chemical cycle, only instances of its components. Network autocatalysis is an emergent organizational pattern, which is why Rössler refers to it as *ordinary autonomous growth*.

Eigen briefly considers network autocatalysis, but in the specific context of polypeptides that catalyze the joining of other polypeptides, which, given reasonable assumptions, can yield cyclical reaction patterns of the catalytic and autocatalytic kind. This scenario, however, is dismissed, because the mechanism is too unspecific to be capable of inheritance by descent and hence of capturing selective advantages that might arise from variation. Kauffman entertains the same idea as Eigen—networks of polypeptides mutually catalyzing their ligation—but approaches it through the lens of a random Boolean network, in which a reaction is a Boolean function (go/no-go of the ligation) controlled by a Boolean input (presence/absence of a suitable polypeptide catalyst). Like Eigen, Kauffman concludes that autocatalytic closure has a meaningful probability of occurrence, but unlike Eigen, Kauffman has no urge to quickly reach the Darwinian shoreline. He seeks to explain patterns of functional order as originating through a process of self-organization distinct from the process through which selection acts upon these patterns to shape surviving forms.

Like for Kauffman, Rössler's objective is an appreciation of what can be reasonably expected to occur without, and hence prior to, Darwinian selection. But distinct from Eigen and Kauffman, Rössler's contribution is an analysis of what the other two take for granted—

catalysis—which leads him to *emergent catalysis* as a cyclical closure of non-catalyzed reactions invoking generic chemistry without appeal to macromolecules. Note that the "autocatalytic set" of Kauffman requires more than cyclical closure; it requires that the catalysts of each reaction be themselves products of the reaction network. By taking as basic components non-catalyzed reactions, Rössler's networks are more primitive and might play a more plausible role in the early stages of chemical evolution on a planet.

The concept of a catalytic cycle has long been known through the discoveries of the Krebs cycle or the Calvin cycle in the 1930s and 1950s. Although the reactions of these evolved biological cycles are themselves catalyzed, the notion that the cyclical arrangement is also catalytic on its own was well appreciated. At a more basic level, Rössler points out that it was the Soviet chemist Nikolai Semenov who discovered in the 1930s "isothermal chemical explosions" that keep going by virtue of supply feedback from chemical reactions rather than heat, which is the usual autocatalyst in many *physical* explosions.

Rössler considers a chemistry that is abstract, that is, whose molecules are represented by placeholder variables (such as A, B, etc.) devoid of chemical structure. This is in stark contrast to approaches based on specific flavors of chemistry, such as polypeptides, polynucleotides, iron-sulfur chemistry, lipid or sugar chemistry (Smith and Morowitz 2016). While the lack of chemical detail requires making assumptions that can be debated, it permits the formulation of a broad *principle* of chemical evolution.

Central to his framework is a purely conceptual *network of spontaneously possible reactions*, which we abbreviate as NSPR. It is of unfathomable extension, as it consists of all molecules and their reactions provided the latter are both thermodynamically possible (i.e., associated with a decrease in free energy) and kinetically feasible (i.e., having a free energy barrier that can be crossed with possibly low but still meaningful probability). Rössler argues that the NSPR contains a very large number of catalytic and autocatalytic cycles.

Assume some tiny set of spontaneously reacting molecules that are initially available in large supply; call them the "starting set." The starting set spontaneously initiates an exploration of chemical space.

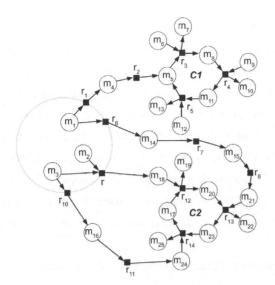

Figure 1. The schematic represents a reaction network in which black squares are reaction nodes and open circles are molecular species. The network contains two catalytic cycles C1 and C2 coupled to the starting set (molecules m_1, m_2, and m_3). In C1, only a member of the catalytic cycle can be produced from the starting set. If all substrates were available, this would suffice to start the cycle, but they are not, because they are not in the starting set. In C2, only the substrate molecules of the cycle can be produced from the starting set. For a catalytic cycle to operate efficiently, both of these conditions must be met. For autocatalytic cycles, the second condition is the most important; it also is the harder one to achieve.

The majority of reactions among the molecules in the starting set are likely to be very slow, causing the exploration to advance initially by single-molecule amounts. This is a regime that mandates a stochastic description, in which a rate constant is the parameter of a probability distribution of time delays to the next reaction event. High free energy barriers mean low rate constants and hence long average time delays. Molecular species that are produced by a sequence of reactions from the starting set become available for further reactions. After a long time lag, this exploratory process may (or may not) discover one of the great many autocatalytic cycles embedded in the NSPR. Rössler emphasizes that the challenge is not the discovery of one member of a cycle by a sequence of reactions from the starting set, but rather the discovery of a cycle for which all substrates can be provided in sufficient concentrations. This point is illustrated schematically in figure 1.

Suppose that, after a possibly long delay, an autocatalytic cycle is actually discovered. This cycle will concentrate mass into its members and its immediate products, which become available in abundances comparable to those of the original starting set. This effectively enlarges the starting set, if it is continuously supplied. The number of possible spontaneous reactions within reach of the exploratory process increases nonlinearly with the diversity of molecular species (a network effect) and so does the probability of discovering a further cycle. But any further cycle contributes to increasing that diversity. Hence there must be a threshold number of discovered cycles beyond which the probability of discovering another cycle approaches 1. From then on, the process of discovering autocatalytic cycles has itself become autocatalytic. Rössler calls this behavior *second-order autonomous growth*.

This, then, is the thread through Rössler's paper:

(i) Catalysis without catalysis: emergent catalysis by cyclic arrangement of non-catalyzed reactions.

(ii) First-order autonomous growth: generalized autocatalysis through positive chemical feedback when a cycle directly or indirectly generates one of its members with stoichiometry greater than 1.

(iii) Turning the wheels: the discovery of an autocatalytic cycle enables the further exploration of chemical space by effectively extending the reservoir of starting substances.

(iv) Second-order autonomous growth: positive feedback on the likelihood of discovering a further cycle with each discovered cycle.

Whether chemistry is a Rösslerian system for discovering systems depends on many assumptions. Assessing these assumptions using abstract models informed by empirical data whips up many open questions. What is required for an abstract NSPR to be "chemical"? Must every reaction be individually "thermodynamically possible," or should the NSPR include energy transduction? What can we say about the density of cycles in a chemical NSPR? Is the cycle density uniform or does it depend dramatically on specific flavors of chemistry? What are the kinetic requirements that support a given extent of chemical space exploration? In particular, what is required for an autocatalytic cycle to persist in a scenario of open chemical space exploration? A constructively cautionary note by Leslie Orgel (2008) is also worth heeding.

Chemistry is a bridgehead to life. Rössler suggests that to jump start a biology, his process of chemical exploration must discover an autocatalytic system from which further discovery proceeds in less blind a fashion. Gánti's chemoton comes to mind as a possible specification of a point at which Rössler hands over to Darwin and life becomes a *controlled* isothermal chemical explosion. ❦

REFERENCES

Eigen, M. 1971. "Selforganization of Matter and the Evolution of Biological Macromolecules." *Naturwissenschaften* 58:465–523. https://doi.org/10.1007/BF00623322.

Gánti, T. 1971. *Az Élet Princípiuma*. Budapest, Hungary: Gondolat.

———. 1975. "Organization of Chemical Reactions into Dividing and Metabolizing Units: The Chemotons." *Biosystems* 7 (1): 15–21. https://doi.org/10.1016/0303-2647(75)90038-6.

Kauffman, S. A. 1971. "Cellular Homeostasis, Epigenesis, and Replication in Randomly Aggregated Macromolecular Systems." *Journal of Cybernetics* 1 (1): 71–96. https://doi.org/10.1080/01969727108545830.

Orgel, L. E. 2008. "The Implausibility of Metabolic Cycles on the Prebiotic Earth." *PLoS Biology* 6 (1): e18. https://doi.org/10.1371/journal.pbio.0060018.

Rössler, O. E. 1976. "Chaotic Behavior in Simple Reaction Systems." *Zeitschrift für Naturforschung A* 31 (3–4): 259–264. https://doi.org/10.1515/zna-1976-3-408.

Semenov, N. N. 1959. *Some Problems of Chemical Kinetics and Reactivity*. Translated by J. E. S. Bradley. Vol. 2. Princeton, NJ: Princeton University Press. https://doi.org/10.1016/C2013-0-05256-5.

Smith, E., and H. J. Morowitz. 2016. *The Origin and Nature of Life on Earth: The Emergence of the Fourth Geosphere*. Cambridge, UK: Cambridge University Press.

A SYSTEM-THEORETIC MODEL OF BIOGENESIS

Otto E. Rössler°

Abstract

Three types of abstract chemical reaction systems are described:

1. The generalized catalytic system,
2. the generalized autocatalytic system,
3. a spontaneously evolving chemical system.

The significance of the second and third system for a very early phase of pre-biological evolution is discussed.

We will be concerned not with a system-theoretic process that can explain the origin of the first living system, but only with a process that can explain the origin of an autonomously growing chemical system sharing a certain property with a living system. That property consists in the capacity to become, through a mechanism of stepwise modification, the "ancestor" of an almost unlimited multitude of diverse, autonomously growing chemical systems.

Such a process is of interest only if it is simple, i.e., if it is based on a single easily describable principle, and if it does not require extraordinary chemical preconditions.

This demand is not necessarily unrealistic. In technology it is customary to synthesize systems with rather extraordinary properties using simple building blocks while following simple principles. By analogy, the combination of simple chemical reactions can result in chemical systems with properties that are new and unusual compared to those of their components. It is even possible for chemical systems of this kind to form spontaneously.

°Translated from German by Philipp Honegger, Harvard Medical School, and Walter Fontana, Harvard Medical School.

This fundamental possibility shall first be demonstrated using an illustrative model. The properties of that system, in particular those of an important special case, will subsequently be needed in specifying the system proper.

AN EXAMPLE

It is known that under certain conditions some chemical substances can, upon addition of another substance, spontaneously react with it to generate one or more new substances. This is represented schematically as $A + B \rightarrow C + D$, or equivalently:

(We assume irreversibility for the sake of simplicity.) Sometimes, the product will spontaneously give rise to further products:

$$B \smile D$$
$$A \smile C \longrightarrow E \longrightarrow F \ldots$$

However, one might also add a new substance E to the product C of the first reaction, causing the spontaneous formation of further products, and so on:

$$B \quad D \quad E \quad G$$
$$A \longrightarrow C \longrightarrow F \ldots$$

Thus, there are many degrees of freedom in the design of reaction sequences. In some sequences a subset of atoms from the initial substance A is conserved over many steps, while in others none of the downstream products (that are being considered) has a single atom in common with upstream reactants. Because of these degrees of freedom, it is fundamentally possible to find sequences that form a cycle after a few (say n) steps (fig. 2).

In the simplest case, following the principles of stoichiometry, a new molecule of A is generated after n steps for each molecule of A consumed in the cycle to form C. Thus, in final analysis, the substance

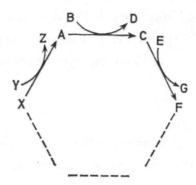

Figure 2. Kinetic scheme of a generalized catalytic reaction (principle).

By "catalysis in a narrow sense" Rössler means a net reaction that proceeds by a catalytic mechanism: A + C → B + C. In contrast, "catalysis without catalyst" refers to a combination of non-catalytic net reactions whose overall effect is catalytic, such as A + B → C, C → D, D → A + E, which consumes B and produces E. This is known today as *network catalysis*.

A is not depleted by its reaction with B to form C—a reaction enabled by the very presence of A—but rather behaves like a catalyst that is continuously regenerated. The same is true for substances C, F, ..., X. The reaction system in figure 2 can therefore be called a *"generalized catalytic reaction."* Substances D, G, ..., Z constitute the "products of catalysis" in this reaction. The "substrate" from which these products are generated consists of the externally added substances B, E, ..., Y. The set of these substances cannot be empty, or the cycle would only consist of pure follow-up reactions, but must include at least one food substance. Each of the "generalized catalysts" C, F, ..., X is equivalent. A single one of them, when added to the set of food substances, is sufficient to generate all products. Indeed, from its mass all other generalized catalysts that participate in the cycle are formed.

This is an example for how very simple chemical prerequisites can result in an unexpected (systemic) effect: *Catalysis without the presence of a catalyst* (understood in a narrow sense). It seems possible to assemble reaction sequences of this kind artificially. If all that matters is the creation of a particular product, many degrees of freedom exist to achieve the eventual regeneration of the substance initiating the reaction sequence. Most importantly, the generalized catalytic reaction is an example for how a reactive system with nontrivial behavior can emerge "by itself" under suitable conditions.

A SPECIAL CASE OF GENERALIZED CATALYSIS

A particular case of the scheme in figure 2 deserves special attention: Once the stoichiometric coefficient of the net reaction A → A (and C → C, etc.) becomes greater than 1, that is, a more than complete "regeneration" of the substances participating in the cycle occurs, the system-theoretic phenomenon of autonomous growth can ensue. As shown in figure 3, this excess regeneration occurs already if the stoichiometric coefficient of 2 occurs in just one of the reaction steps (A+B → C+C+D), that is, when forming two equal groups of atoms. The phenomenon of "generalized autocatalysis" occurs as long as the molecules produced in excess encounter the same reaction conditions as their predecessors. (Note that this proof does not rely on specific kinetic arguments, but on general relational ones. However, consideration of the details in each case permits additional, more specific assertions. The type of reaction and the rate constants in the forward and reverse direction determine the particular growth function, the rate of growth and the range of growth; allowing for inhomogeneous conditions enables spatial differentiation; etc.[1])

The additional instance of C does not have to be produced in the same step.

One difference between true "autocatalysis" and the more easily realizable so-called cross-catalysis (two catalysts that mutually produce each other) is that no catalyst in the narrow sense is needed. Nonetheless, the case of autocatalysis is covered as a special case in the scheme of figure 3 (by using two reaction steps and just one input substance) if one assumes a simple Michaelis–Menten-type reaction mechanism. Cross-catalysis and cyclic catalyses of higher order yielding autonomous growth are also included as special cases, if one considers that the cycle may contain additional cross-links.

Just as with generalized catalysis, the cycle can again be reconstituted in the presence of the food substances from a single substance of those that constitute the cycle. In this case, however, a single molecule suffices

---

[1] R. Rosen. 1970. *Dynamical System Theory in Biology.* New York, NY: Wiley-Interscience.

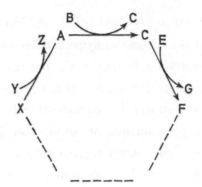

Figure 3. Kinetic scheme of a generalized autocatalytic reaction (principle).

in principle.[2] Thus, the generalized autocatalytic reaction system demonstrates the principles stipulated at the outset with particular clarity.

TWO CONCLUDING REMARKS ON THE TOPIC OF GENERALIZED AUTOCATALYSIS

It must be mentioned that the system shown in figure 3 is by no means unknown in the literature. It has been discussed in the context of "isothermal chain reactions"[3] and was mentioned repeatedly in a purely theoretical context.[4] However, it has not yet been expressed as an abstract principle of relevance to the artificial and spontaneous synthesis of systems. Finally, as always in a systems-theoretic context of chemistry, we must discuss the thermodynamic "admissibility" of a proposed "kinetics." A proof for the admissibility of "autocatalysis" in the general sense of a substance promoting its own formation has already been provided within the framework of the thermodynamics of irreversible processes (extended to strongly nonlinear dependencies between fluxes and forces).[5]

---

[2] For reversible reaction steps more than one molecule may be necessary. In practice, the presence of trace impurities able to react with cycle species necessitates using enough starting concentrations or pressures to saturate these impurities.

[3] N. N. Semjonow. 1961. *Einige Probleme der chemischen Kinetik und Reaktionsfähigkeit: Freie Radikale und Kettenreaktionen*. Berlin, Germany: Akademie-Verlag.

[4] H. J. Morowitz. 1967. "Biological Self-Replication Systems." *Progress in Theoretical Biology* 1:35–58.

[5] P. Glansdorff and I. Prigogine. 1964. "On a General Evolution Criterion in Macroscopic Physics." *Physica* 30 (2): 351–374.

Assumptions of the Model

The behavior of autonomous growth derived in the previous example belongs to the simplest patterns of systemic behavior producible by a proper *interconnection* of simple reactions. One can expect to also find examples that do not require catalysts in the narrow sense for the other well-known behavior patterns in reaction systems (such as oscillations and multi-stability). However, in the present context the issue is another one.

The plugging together of systems of a certain type into "systems of higher-order" is a common construction principle in technology. The subsystems maintain thereby a certain level of autonomy. The same principle is also found in biology. It is not far fetched to hypothesize that chemical systems of higher order are possible as well.

This is the case for the process of a systemic chemical evolution that will be described next. It can be characterized as "second-order autonomous growth". The difference to ordinary autonomous growth consists in the autocatalytic generation not of the number of molecules but the number of systems. An aspect in common with ordinary autonomous growth consists in the spontaneous emergence of such behavior.

The preconditions for such a process are simple. They are included in the assumptions made for terrestrial "chemical evolution",[6] but they are so general that they could be satisfied by completely different chemical conditions. The most essential of these preconditions is identical to the principle at the basis of organic chemistry. It is the fact that with carbon it is possible to generate an almost unlimited number of distinct products using a small number of suitable starting materials.[7] It is conceivable, however, that under different physical conditions other kinds of starting materials (without carbon) also possess the capability

Indeed, autocatalytic networks (*sensu* Rössler) can exhibit all of these behaviors, as was shown experimentally.

---

[6] M. Calvin. 1967. "Chemical Evolution." In *Progress in Theoretical Biology*, edited by F. M. Snell, 1:1–34. Cambridge, MA: Academic Press.

[7] The number of possible derivates is smaller than the number of macromolecular combinations producible by permutation of the starting materials. However, some larger units are almost completely freely permutable. This means that the set of all possible products can be compared to a "small universal library". Following Kurd Lasswitz, an universal library is the set of all books producible by permutation of a given alphabet with a given (in this case small) length.

of constructing a universal library of products, for instance by forming alternating chains.

The derivation of further preconditions is best approached through the concept of a network of possible reactions. This is the set of all reactions that become possible by positing a few types of substances. This network is very large if by "possible" we mean the energetically (thermodynamically) feasible reactions. For instance, just the two substances CO_2 and H_2O yield together with an energy source (in the simplest case: light quanta of a particular energy) at atmospheric pressure and room temperature a universal library of energetically possible products and their associated reactions.

The network of energetically possible reactions is a very theoretical concept. It includes the more interesting network of *spontaneously* possible reactions, that is, those reactions that are not only possible energetically (due to a gradient in free enthalpy) but also "kinetically" because the activation energies required to form transition states of the Eyring type are sufficiently low at the given temperature. This second network is usually much smaller (as in the example just mentioned). However, a connection between these two concepts will be shown next.

The network of reactions that are energetically but not necessarily kinetically possible contains a very large number of cyclic reaction systems of the kind shown in Fig. 3. The reasons are twofold: First, a product of the nth reaction step does not need to be more similar to the starting substance than any arbitrary substance.[8] Second, the probability that a substance picked randomly from the network can react with any other substance in the network is, on average, constant. (This changes only if more is known about one of the substances, for example that it is energy-rich, or if both substances are specified). The principle of a random wiring of the network of energetically possible reactions follows from the possibility of a molecule containing the most varied atom groups capable of the most varied reaction possibilities.

Among the very large number of cyclical reaction systems contained in the network of energetically but not necessarily kinetically possible

Lacking any chemical detail in the specification, the reaction network is treated as more or less uniform. In reality, chemical networks are anisotropic as they consist of highly reactive molecules, moderately reactive and relatively inert ones. Groups of atoms that often occur together in molecules (i.e., functional groups) entertain specific relations of reactivity that can lead to dense subnetworks (e.g., formose chemistry) and sparse ones (e.g., noble gases).

---

[8] F. F. Seelig. 1971. "Activated Enzyme Catalysis as a Possible Realization of the Stable Linear Chemical Oscillator Model." *Journal of Theoretical Biology* 30 (3): 497–514.

reactions there is a still very large number of cycles all of whose steps are also kinetically possible. Although these cycles are connected to the starting substances by energetically feasible reactions (that is, reactions with a nonzero rate constant), none of them can self-start within an arbitrarily large amount of time [even] when the starting substances are connected to an inexhaustible reservoir. The reason is the small magnitude of the rate constants of the reaction steps leading to these cycles.

This statement contradicts the assumption of a continuum kinetics. Under that assumption, a cycle of the kind described would start up already with infinitesimally small concentrations. Moreover, due to the small rate constants, the whole reaction system would be coupled to an extent that makes it meaningless to speak of individual subsystems. Yet, the above statement follows from the fact that, say, a production rate of 10^{-12} molecules per liter and minute in a reaction volume of 1 liter does *not* mean that the hypothetical 10–12 molecules produced after a minute are instantly available to react with other molecules. Concentrations below 1 molecule (relative to the total homogeneous reaction volume) have the same effect as the introduction of a *time delay* in an otherwise continuous dynamical system.[9] This fact is one of the basic tenets of any process of chemical evolution.

To start up one of the possible spontaneous cycles in the network requires an uninterrupted chain of possible spontaneous reactions leading to each of the substrates on which the cycle depends. This requirement seems more easily satisfiable for one of the generalized catalysts than for the entirety of input substrates. Furthermore, the latter require a continuous supply. The same set of input substrates, however, is often sufficient to support an entire universal library of autonomously growing systems. Therefore, a very large number of more or less equivalent sets of input substrates exist that make the requirement for the spontaneous formation of a single one of them no longer that unrealistic.

Rössler makes the case for stochastic chemical kinetics. When the number of molecules is large, the height of a barrier determines the rate at which molecules flow over it. When the number of molecules is small, flow rates must be replaced with transition probabilities; low probabilities (high barriers) imply longer average waiting times to a crossing event.

While an uninterrupted reaction sequence is required for each substrate feeding into a cycle, only one is required for the cycle itself.

This harks back to the idealization of a uniform reaction network three paragraphs ago.

---

[9] When creating a series of several reactions of this type, the time delay does not increase in an additive order, but in a multiplicative one.

The System-Theoretical Model

Having specified the essential preconditions, assume next that a small number of starting materials, which are kept at constant concentration, fulfill the requirements for spontaneously setting off a single simple cycle. By virtue of its catalytic function, this cycle then produces a whole series of substances, to wit, in addition to the other catalysts in the cycle, also all products of the cycle (C, G, ..., Z in Fig. 3), which can further react with one another and with the starting materials. At the end of the growth phase of the cycle, the primary products are available at steady-state concentrations, that is, they will also be replenished at concentrations comparable to those of the given starting substances.

Thus, the special case that all requirements for the realization of one cycle are satisfied has the same effect as if a larger set of starting substances had been provided (some of them at constant concentration). Since the probability of jump starting one of the many possible spontaneous cycles in the network of possible reactions increases stronger than linear (in fact combinatorially) in the number of substances present, the starting of one cycle facilitates the occurrence of a second one, which in turn facilitates the occurrence of a third, and so on, to an ever increasing extent. This evidently points at the existence of a threshold: After starting up a critical number of cycles, the probability of kicking off at least one further cycle, and from there on ever more cycles, suddenly becomes almost 1.

The same statement can be represented in simple formal terms thus:

$$n = f_1(N)$$
$$N = f_2(n), \tag{4}$$

where n is the number of substances present in the reaction network, N is the number of already active cycles, and f_1 and f_2 are two functions increasing monotonically with N and n, respectively. This positive feedback becomes "super-critical" only if the product of f_1 and f_2 exceeds 1.

The value of the threshold depends on special conditions other than on n_0 (the number of externally added substances kept partially at constant concentration). If, for example, the initial mixture contains by chance, in addition to the substances needed for a universal library,

While Rössler's argument of an increasing occupation of chemical space has merit, it neglects that reaction branches can peter out in inactive materials. Autocatalysis is "self-healing" as long as its growth rate outpaces its decay rate (Blackmond 2009).

Network autocatalysis increases the number of replenished molecular species and, typically, the number of reactions increases more than linearly with the number of molecular species in a network.

other materials that possess a small yet broad catalytic activity, such as metal ions, then the threshold would be lowered considerably.

With this, the process sought has been found. One could call this behavior, which, after crossing a threshold, spontaneously generates ever more autonomously growing systems an "autonomous growth of second order". It produces not only ever more autonomously growing systems, but also systems whose immediate spontaneous formation is increasingly unlikely. While simple autocatalytic systems, such as depicted in figure 3, are the only ones growing at first, they are soon joined by interconnected ones and others that contain "true" catalysts. Finally, autonomously growing systems of very high complexity can become activated.

Where the threshold resides in each specific case, and whether it can be overcome within a natural system of reactions under natural conditions and on a natural time scale, is a question that needs to be studied separately. Likewise, one has to reckon with the emergence of other systemic behaviors of the second order. The behavior described here is only valid as long as the coupling of individual unstable systems is weak. It seems as if the inclusion of diffusion could delay the phase of a general interconnection to an arbitrary extent. The description of the processes following the "explosive phase" is, however, of secondary interest, much as in the case of the first example.[10]

So far the emphasis was on the explosion-like aspect of the behavior. Another, equally important, aspect is the automatic "screening" of a universal library. This behavior is also known from biology, where it relates to the far more special universal library of possible nucleic acid sequences. Summing up, the hypothesis proposed here consists in positing that the general process just described is suited to start a specific, for example a biological, one. This would be the case if among the screened systems there was one that could become the starting point of an explosion of the second-order functioning no longer blindly, but in accordance with a principle of descent (and thus under certain additional conditions far more effective).

"True" here refers to single-molecule as opposed to network catalysis.

Rössler's general argument is based on statistical properties of a roughly uniform reaction network. Without further details it is difficult to assess its suitability as a model of biogenesis. But the idea that in some corner of chemistry the process laid out here can occur is intriguing.

---

[10]In the purely well-mixed case, the final state of the full system could be characterized by oscillations of the Volterra-Kerner type (Kerner 1957).

Discussion

The two essential results that were achieved are 1. the specification of the structure of a generalized autocatalytic system and 2. the structure of a "second-order autocatalytic system" representing an example of chemical evolution.

Both results were not achieved with kinetic or dynamic methods. Rather, the derivation followed from simple relational schemes (in the first case: from A follows B, stoichiometry, relations of consumption. In the second case: cycle, network, wiring). The restriction to this general level loses a great deal of specific information. Yet, it allows certain law-like regularities to become visible. For example, the proof that all chemical systems of the type shown in figure 3 are unstable cannot be achieved by kinetic methods, that is, using the theory of dynamical systems. Even when limiting the analysis to the special case of linear reaction systems described by first-order ordinary differential equations, the proof that such systems exhibit autonomous growth, that is, that they possess a critical point at the origin of phase space or, equivalently, a positive eigenvalue of their characteristic polynomial, presents considerable difficulty. This is even more the case for chemical systems of this type that must be described by nonlinear and partial differential equations. Likewise, the principle of second-order instability cannot be derived in general at the level of an explicit dynamic description.

The results achieved thus suffer from the disadvantage that they do not completely describe any specific case. However, they enable specific quantitative models that could not be constructed otherwise. For instance, it is possible to model the unstable system of the second kind at the level of cycles as a system of switches with conditional connections and weak initial conditions (that is, as a nonlinear finite automaton). A simulation at the level of substances is also possible, either also in terms of switches (as a rough qualitative model) or more finely grained by using system of functional differential equations with a weakly inhomogeneous initial condition. The most complicated case would be represented by a dynamical model consisting of partial functional differential equations. With the help of quantitative models

This statement seems puzzling, if interpreted from the vantage point of deterministic dynamics. However, at very low concentrations, the discrete nature of particles requires a stochastic description. The system can die out by fluctuations even if particle numbers are positive, despite increasing expectation values. The zero point is therefore at best a conditionally unstable point.

an assessment can be made about the extent to which natural reaction systems fulfill the conditions of the model.

In conclusion it is important to note that the described model, which represents a very general form of a chemical evolutionary theory, can be of significance for terrestrial biogenesis, if certain minimal requirements regarding the functional complexity of the biological "ancestral system" must be made.[11]

I'm grateful to the Deutsche Forschungsgemeinschaft for supporting this work. ☙

REFERENCES

Blackmond, D. G. 2009. "An Examination of the Role of Autocatalytic Cycles in the Chemistry of Proposed Primordial Reactions." *Angewandte Chemie International Edition* 48 (2): 386–390.

Calvin, M. 1967. "Chemical Evolution." In *Progress in Theoretical Biology,* edited by F. M. Snell, 1:1–34. Cambridge, MA: Academic Press.

Glansdorff, P., and I. Prigogine. 1964. "On a General Evolution Criterion in Macroscopic Physics." *Physica* 30 (2): 351–374.

Kaplan, R. W. 1968. "Molekularbiologische Probleme der Lebensentstehung." *Naturwissenschaften* 55 (3): 97–104.

Kerner, E. H. 1957. "A Statistical Mechanics of Interacting Biological Species." *Bulletin of Mathematical Biophysics* 19 (2): 121–146.

Morowitz, H. J. 1967. "Biological Self-Replication Systems." *Progress in Theoretical Biology* 1:35–58.

Rosen, R. 1970. *Dynamical System Theory in Biology.* New York, NY: Wiley-Interscience.

Seelig, F. F. 1971. "Activated Enzyme Catalysis as a Possible Realization of the Stable Linear Chemical Oscillator Model." *Journal of Theoretical Biology* 30 (3): 497–514.

Semjonow, N. N. 1961. *Einige Probleme der chemischen Kinetik und Reaktionsfähigkeit: Freie Radikale und Kettenreaktionen.* Berlin, Germany: Akademie-Verlag.

---

[11]R. W. Kaplan. 1968. "Molekularbiologische Probleme der Lebensentstehung." *Naturwissenschaften* 55 (3): 97–104.

1920

BIRTH
April 14, 1921
Oakland,
California

1928: John von
Neumann
publishes
*On the Theory of
Games of Strategy.*

1930

1940

1950

1948: President Truman
signs off on The Marshall
Plan, authorizing $5
billion in aid to sixteen
nations in Europe.

1958: Morton Grodzins
publishes *The
Metropolitan Area as
a Racial Problem.*

1960

SCHELLING 1971
Harvard,
Cambridge,
Massachusetts

1964: Stanley Kubrick's
*"Dr. Strangelove or:
How I Learned to Stop
Worrying and Love
the Bomb* premieres.

1970

1980

1990

1994: W. Brian Arthur
publishes *"Inductive
Reasoning and
Bounded Rationality."*

2000

2005: Schelling shares
the Sveriges-Riksbank
Nobel Prize in Economics
with Robert Aumann.

2010

DEATH
December 13, 2016
Bethesda,
Maryland,
complications
following a
fractured hip.

THOMAS CROMBIE SCHELLING

[37]

TIPPING POINTS: SCHELLING'S ACCOUNT OF SORTING AND SEGREGATION

H. Peyton Young, University of Oxford
and London School of Economics and Political Science

In a remarkable but not very well-known article, the philosopher and polymath Michael Polanyi distinguished between two kinds of order: planned and spontaneous. A planned order is constructed and designed from the top down; its components are placed into specific positions and constrained to act in particular ways by a central authority. A spontaneous order, by contrast, is an ordered arrangement resulting from the "spontaneous mutual adjustment of its elements."[1]

This concept has deep roots in the social sciences—indeed, it played a central role in the writings of David Hume, Adam Smith, and other members of the Scottish Enlightenment. They argued that many social institutions, including legal systems and markets, could be understood as forms of spontaneous order, and furthermore that such systems are often superior to those that have been deliberately designed to achieve some goal. Much later, this point of view was revived by members of the Austrian school of economics, including Carl Menger and Friedrich Hayek. Nevertheless, in spite of these distinguished antecedents, in Thomas Schelling's day the evolutionary point of view had been largely sidelined: the reigning paradigm in economics was expressed in terms of optimization, high rationality, and equilibrium.

Schelling's 1971 article represents a major departure from this way of thinking. Indeed, it represents one of the clearest expressions of the notion of spontaneous order and how it can be applied

T. C. Schelling, "Dynamic Models of Segregation," in *Journal of Mathematical Sociology* 1: 143–186 (1971).

Reprinted by permission of Taylor & Francis Ltd.

---

[1]See Polanyi (1941). He was the younger brother of the economic historian Karl Polanyi, best known for his work *The Great Transformation*. Michael Polanyi attributes the notion of spontaneous or dynamic order to the distinguished gestalt psychologist Wolfgang Koehler.

to a contemporary matter of practical significance, namely, racial segregation. The article is also one of the earliest examples of what has come to be known as agent-based modeling, this in spite of the fact that Schelling uses only the most primitive computational methods to illustrate his points.

Schelling proposes several different models of segregation that are conceptually related but focus on different aspects of the problem. In one formulation, people choose to live in a particular area or belong to a particular organization depending on how many others like themselves are already there. The focus is on *ex ante* diversity in people's preferences, and how individual decisions about joining and leaving lead dynamically to different types of equilibrium outcomes, including those that are decidedly not diverse. The analysis is carried out using simple vector field diagrams indicating the direction of flow in each part of the state space. The analysis illustrates how different degrees of segregation can arise depending on initial conditions and the shape of the preference distributions. It also highlights the importance of "tipping points": critical thresholds beyond which the dynamics cascade into a segregated state. This terminology had been used in prior studies of segregation by urban sociologists, but Schelling was the first to give a precise analytical formulation of this idea, and tipping points have since become very much associated with his name.

Schelling begins, however, with another model of segregation that focuses on the *spatial dynamics* of the process. The setup is deceptively simple: Schelling asks us to arrange stars and zeros in arbitrary fashion on a checkerboard, leaving some spaces empty. He then asks us to imagine that these symbols represent agents with different characteristics (such as race, religion, or language), and that they have preferences over the mix of agents in their immediate neighborhood—specifically the nearest eight squares on the board (the Moore neighborhood). Finally, he invites us to choose one agent at a time and ask whether the agent under consideration would prefer to relocate to some empty space. As he shows by example, the resulting sequence of adjustments often leads to a spatial configuration or pattern that is highly segregated. The outcome is "spontaneous" in the sense that no one intended or planned it; rather, a mostly segregated pattern coalesces from the actions of many dispersed individuals acting purely in their own immediate interest.

As previously noted, this style of argument has distinguished antecedents in economics, with Adam Smith's invisible hand being one of the best-known expressions of it. As in Smith's account, agents only act in their immediate self-interest; they do not need to know much about the system as a whole or the details of other agents' preferences. Second, the protagonists can be highly heterogeneous in their preferences; indeed, this is what makes the outcome interesting. Nevertheless, there are striking differences between Schelling's model and the neoclassical account of market equilibrium. A key difference is that Schelling is primarily interested in the dynamics that lead to equilibrium, rather than the equilibrium per se. Furthermore, the dynamics are specified in minute detail at the level of each agent: they are truly bottom-up. This stands in contrast to neoclassical accounts, such as Walras's auctioneer, which is fundamentally a top-down story.

A second difference between Schelling's account and the neoclassical economic paradigm is to demonstrate that people with perfectly reasonable preferences, who would like to avoid being in the minority but would be happy to live in a somewhat mixed neighborhood, may end up in a configuration that appears to be driven by extreme racial prejudice. This stands in contrast to the standard account of competitive markets, where selfish individual motives give rise to beneficial social outcomes. In short, spontaneous order need not be a good thing. Schelling's point is more subtle, however: it is that bad social outcomes need not be an indication of bad motives on the part of individuals. While acknowledging that segregation can result from deliberate actions by institutions (such as red-lining) and from strong racial prejudice (white flight), he shows that it also can arise *purely spontaneously* even in the absence of such forces.

A pioneering feature of Schelling's article is that it is one of the earliest examples of what today would be called agent-based modeling.[2]

---

[2]Schelling's framework has spawned a large literature on agent-based models in the social sciences. For overviews of this approach and its various applications see Epstein and Axtell (1996), Epstein (2006), and Helbing (2012).

In general such a model has the following characteristics: First, there is no centralized or coordinated control over individual behavior. Second, agents are described quite specifically in terms of their location, endowments, preferences, and the like. Third, their rules of interaction are decentralized and uncoordinated. Typically they interact locally and make decisions based on partial and fragmentary information. Fourth, they usually exhibit some form of bounded rationality. This does not rule out the possibility that they may try to anticipate the behavior of others; indeed, Schelling considers just this possibility when he observes that agents who flee a neighborhood may do so in anticipation that others are going to flee. Nevertheless, agents in these models are not assumed to have great powers of rational calculation or to base their decisions on knowledge of the evolutionary process as a whole.

Finally, the main object of study in agent-based modeling is the dynamics of adjustment. It is, of course, useful to know whether the process eventually equilibrates, and which equilibria (if any) are most likely to be selected. Of even greater interest, however, is the evolutionary path taken, that is, the look and feel of the adjustment process itself. This stands in striking contrast to much of modern economic theory, which focuses on the properties of equilibrium rather than the process by which such equilibria come about; indeed, the latter is often not specified at all. The great majority of Schelling's article is devoted to studying in detail the dynamics that result from different specifications of his model. There are no overarching theorems that say which equilibria are most likely to be realized under different conditions (although he makes some very good guesses). Above all, Schelling adopts a hands-on approach in which he invites readers to undertake their own simulations. This is a distinctive feature of the agent-based modeling approach.

It could be said that one limitation of Schelling's analysis, and of agent-based modeling in general, is that it relies rather heavily on simulations in lieu of provable results about the likelihood of different outcomes. In recent years, however, a general framework has been developed for addressing this issue. The essential idea is to consider a dynamic adjustment process in which individual behaviors are driven *mainly* by some plausible heuristic, such as best response to local information, but there are occasional deviations from this process that result from mistakes, experimentation, unobserved utility shocks, and the like. The result is a stochastic dynamical system that may exhibit quite different long-run behavior from the corresponding deterministic process. The advantage of such systems is that not only are they more realistic descriptions of real-world behavior, but they permit one to compute the long-run probability of being in different states using the theory of large deviations.

One of the simplest and most versatile models of this type is to suppose that deviations from best response have a probability that decreases exponentially with the prospective loss in utility. This assumption leads to an ergodic process whose stationary distribution can be calculated analytically. Applying this framework to Schelling's spatial model, one can characterize the neighborhood patterns that have the highest probability of being realized when the probability of deviations is small. In particular one can identify conditions that lead with high probability to completely segregated states.[3]

None of this is to detract from Schelling's contribution; it merely underlines the potential richness of his framework. It also needs to be emphasized that when he wrote this article in the 1970s, it was a strikingly novel departure from the usual style of analysis in economics, where equilibrium was presumed, not derived, and models tended to be populated by abstract, perfectly rational agents—sometimes only a single "representative" agent. Heterogeneity, bounded rationality, and out-of-equilibrium dynamics were ideas that only came into their own much later.

It should also be emphasized that Schelling's style is highly original and distinctive. The models he proposes are simple, even minimalist, but he takes pains to enumerate the numerous factors that are *not* included in the model and are clearly germane to the problem at hand:

> *At least two main processes of segregation are omitted. One is organized action-legal or illegal, coercive or merely exclusionary, subtle or flagrant, overt or covert, kindly or malicious, moralistic or pragmatic. The other is the process,*

---

[3]See Young (1998, chapter 3) and Zhang (2004).

> *largely but not entirely economic, by which the poor get separated from the rich, the less educated from the more educated, the unskilled from the skilled, the poorly dressed from the well dressed, in where they work and live and eat and play, in whom they know and whom they date and whom they go to school with. Evidently color is correlated with income, and income with residence; so even if residential choices were color-blind and unconstrained by organized discrimination, whites and blacks would not be randomly distributed among residences.*

In other words, the models he proposes are incomplete. Nevertheless, they are highly informative, and they gain in explanatory power precisely because their ingredients are so simple and clearly specified. ⸙

REFERENCES

Epstein, J. 2006. *Generative Social Science: Studies in Agent-Based Computational Modeling*. Princeton, NJ: Princeton University Press.

Epstein, J. M., and R. L. Axtell. 1996. *Growing Artificial Societies: Social Science from the Bottom Up*. Cambridge, MA: MIT Press.

Helbing, D., ed. 2012. *Social Self-Organization: Agent-Based Simulations and Experiments to Study Emergent Social Behavior*. Zurich, Switzerland: Springer.

Polanyi, M. 1941. "The Growth of Thought in Society." *Economica* 8 (32): 428–456. https://doi.org/10.2307/2550108.

Young, H. P. 1993. "The Evolution of Conventions." *Econometrica* 61 (1): 57–84. https://doi.org/0012-9682(199301)61:1<57:TEOC>2.0.CO;2-W.

———. 1998. *Individual Strategy and Social Structure: An Evolutionary Theory of Institutions*. Princeton, NJ: Princeton University Press.

Zhang, J. 2004. "A Dynamic Model of Residential Segregation." *Journal of Mathematical Sociology* 28 (3): 147–170. https://doi.org/10.1080/00222500490480202.

DYNAMIC MODELS OF SEGREGATION[†]

Thomas C. Schelling, Harvard University

Abstract

Some segregation results from the practices of organizations, some from specialized communication systems, some from correlation with a variable that is non-random; and some results from the interplay of individual choices. This is an abstract study of the interactive dynamics of discriminatory individual choices. One model is a simulation in which individual members of two recognizable groups distribute themselves in neighborhoods defined by reference to their own locations. A second model is analytic and deals with compartmented space. A final section applies the analytics to 'neighborhood tipping.' The systemic effects are found to be overwhelming: there is no simple correspondence of individual incentive to collective results. Exaggerated separation and patterning result from the dynamics of movement. Inferences about individual motives can usually not be drawn from aggregate patterns. Some unexpected phenomena, like density and vacancy, are generated. A general theory of 'tipping' begins to emerge.

This is not the first use of the term "tipping" in the context of neighborhood segregation, but Schelling gave it general currency. See also Malcolm Gladwell's *The Tipping Point* (Little Brown, 2000).

People get separated along many lines and in many ways. There is segregation by sex, age, income, language, religion, color, taste, comparative advantage and the accidents of historical location. Some segregation results from the practices of organizations; some is deliberately organized; and some results from the interplay of individual choices that discriminate. Some of it results from specialized communication systems, like different languages. And some segregation is a corollary of other modes of segregation: residence is correlated with job location and transport.

If blacks exclude whites from their church, or whites exclude blacks, the segregation is organized, and it may be reciprocal or one-sided. If blacks just happen to be Baptists and whites Methodists, the two colors will be segregated Sunday morning whether they intend to be or not. If blacks join a black church because they are more comfortable among their own color, and whites a white church for the same

[†]This study was sponsored by The RAND Corporation with funds set aside for research in areas of special interest, and was issued as RM-6014-RC in May 1969. The views expressed are not necessarily those of RAND or its sponsors.

reason, undirected individual choice can lead to segregation. And if the church bulletin board is where people advertise rooms for rent, blacks will rent rooms from blacks and whites from whites because of a communication system that is correlated with churches that are correlated with color.

Some of the same mechanisms segregate college professors. The college may own some housing, from which all but college staff are excluded. Professors choose housing commensurate with their incomes, and houses are clustered by price while professors are clustered by income. Some professors prefer an academic neighborhood; any differential in professorial density will cause them to converge and increase the local density. And house-hunting professors learn about available housing from other professors and their wives, and the houses they learn about are the ones in neighborhoods where professors already live.

The similarity ends there, and nobody is about to propose a commission to desegregate academics. Professors are not much missed by those they escape from in their residential choices. They are not much noticed by those they live among, and, though proportionately concentrated, are usually a minority in their neighborhood. While indeed they escape classes of people they would not care to live among, they are more conscious of where they do live than of where they don't, and the active choice is more like congregation than segregation, though the result may not be so different.

This article is about the kinds of segregation—or separation, or sorting—that can result from discriminatory individual behavior. By 'discriminatory' I mean reflecting an awareness, conscious or unconscious, of sex or age or religion or color or whatever the basis of segregation is, an awareness that influences decisions on where to live, whom to sit by, what occupation to join or to avoid, whom to play with or whom to talk to. The paper examines some of the individual incentives, and perceptions of difference, that can lead collectively to segregation. The paper also examines the extent to which inferences can be drawn, from the phenomenon of collective segregation, about the preferences of individuals, the strengths of those preferences, and the facilities for exercising them.

The ultimate concern is segregation by 'color' in the United States. The analysis, though, is so abstract that any twofold distinction could constitute an interpretation—whites and blacks, boys and girls, officers and enlisted men, students and faculty, teenagers and grownups. The only requirement of the analysis is that the distinction be twofold, exhaustive, and recognizable.

At least two main processes of segregation are omitted. One is organized action—legal or illegal, coercive or merely exclusionary, subtle or flagrant, open or covert, kindly or malicious, moralistic or pragmatic. The other is the process, largely but not entirely economic, by which the poor get separated from the rich, the less educated from the more educated, the unskilled from the skilled, the poorly dressed from the well dressed, in where they work and live and eat and play, in whom they know and whom they date and whom they go to school with. Evidently color is correlated with income, and income with residence; so even if residential choices were color-blind and unconstrained by organized discrimination, whites and blacks would not be randomly distributed among residences.[†]

This is not to claim that the organized discrimination or the economically induced segregation is less powerful, or less important, or less a matter of social concern, than the segregation that results from individual action. Indeed, aside from the question of which mechanism may account for the greater part of observed separation by color, the organized segregation involves civil rights; and the economically determined segregation raises questions of social equity. On those grounds alone the subject of this paper might be put in third place. Still, in a matter as important as racial segregation in the United States, even third place deserves attention.

It is not easy, though, to draw the lines separating 'individually motivated' segregation, the more organized kind, and the economically induced kind. Habit and tradition are substitutes for organization. Fear of sanctions can coerce behavior whether or not the fear is justified, and whether the sanctions are consensual, conspiratorial or dictated.

[†] A comprehensive treatment of socioeconomic differentials between whites and nonwhites, in relation to residential patterns, is in Pascal (1967).

Common expectations can lead to concerted behavior. ('Guilt by association,' when sanctioned by ostracism, is often self-enforcing.)

The economically induced separation is also intermixed with discrimination. To choose a neighborhood is to choose neighbors. To pick a neighborhood with good schools is to pick a neighborhood of people who appreciate schools (or of people who want to be with the kind of people who appreciate schools). People may furthermore rely, even in making economic choices, on information that is itself color-discriminating; believing that darker-skinned people are on the average poorer than lighter-skinned, one may consciously or unconsciously rely on color as an index of poverty (or, believing that others rely on color as an index, adopt their signals and indices in order to coincide with them). And if the process goes far enough, alienation, strangeness, fear, hostility, and sheer habit can accentuate the tendency toward avoidance. If the sentiment is reciprocated, positive feedback will amplify the segregating tendencies of both groups.

Economic segregation might statistically explain some initial degree of segregation; if that degree were enough to cause color-consciousness, a superstructure of pure discrimination could complete the job. Eliminating the economic differentials entirely might not cause the collapse of the segregated system that it had already generated.

For all these reasons the lines dividing the individually motivated, the collectively enforced, and the economically induced segregation are not clear lines at all. They are furthermore not the only mechanisms of segregation. (Separate or specialized communication systems—especially distinct languages—can have a strong segregating influence that, though interacting with the three processes mentioned, is nevertheless a different mechanism.) Still, they are very different mechanisms and have to be separately understood.

This paper, then, is about those mechanisms that translate unorganized individual behavior into collective results.

INDIVIDUAL INCENTIVES AND COLLECTIVE RESULTS

Economists are familiar with systems that lead to aggregate results that the individual neither intends nor needs to be aware of, results that sometimes have no recognizable counterpart at the level of the

This account of motivations and mechanisms that support segregation is very rich. Although the article is best known for its analytical models, this qualitative account is very informative. The article is unusual because it combines two complementary styles of analysis.

individual. The creation of money by a commercial banking system is one; the way savings decisions cause depressions or inflations is another.

Similarly, biological evolution is responsible for a lot of sorting and separating, but the little creatures that mate and reproduce and forage for food would be amazed to know that they were bringing about separation of species, territorial sorting, or the extinction of species. Among social examples, the coexistence or extinction of second languages is a phenomenon that, though affected by decrees and school curricula, is a massive 'free market' activity with results that correspond to no conscious collective choice.

Choice of second language is a brilliant example of a coordination game played by large populations.

Romance and marriage are exceedingly individual and private activities, at least in this country, but their genetic consequences are altogether aggregate. The law and the church may constrain us in our choices, and some traditions of segregation are enormously coercive; but outside of royal families there are few marriages that are part of a genetic plan. When a short boy marries a tall girl, or a blonde a brunette, it is no part of the individual's purpose to increase genetic randomization or to change some frequency distribution within the population.

In some cases small incentives, almost imperceptible differentials, can lead to strikingly polarized results. Gresham's Law is a good example. Some traditions, furthermore, are sternly self-enforcing: passing to the right of an oncoming car. Some collective actions have almost the appearance of being organized—fads in clothing, dancing and car styles.

Some of the phenomena of segregation may be similarly complex in relation to the dynamics of individual choice. One might even be tempted to suppose that some 'unseen hand' separates people in a manner that, though foreseen and intended by no one, corresponds to some consensus or collective preference or popular will. But in economics we know a great many macro-phenomena, like depression and inflation, that do not reflect any universal desire for lower incomes or higher prices. Similarly with bank failures and market crashes. What goes on in the 'hearts and minds' of small savers has little to do with whether or not they cause a depression. The hearts and minds and motives and habits of millions of people who participate in a segregated society may or may not bear close correspondence with the massive results that collectively they can generate.

We also know that people who would not support the government with private donations may vote a system of mandatory taxes to finance public goods. The worth of a new turnpike may depend on keeping traffic below the level of congestion that would just equalize its attractiveness with that of alternative routes. 'Freedom of choice' is sometimes nothing more than the lack of enforceable contract. Thus unregulated behavior does not necessarily reflect preferences about its results. People acting individually are often unable to affect the results; they can only affect their own positions within the overall results.

Evolutionary processes may lead to typewriter keyboards, weights and measures and the pitches of screws, systems of coinage, and lefthand or righthand automobile drive that are self-perpetuating in spite of inefficiency until a heroic effort can bring about concerted change. Yet, also, some massive concerted changes can occasionally be brought about by some simple manipulation, as when daylight saving goes into effect or when a round table replaces a rectangular one in a highly stratified conference room.

A special reason for doubting any social efficiency in aggregate segregation is that the range of choice is often so meager. The demographic map of almost any American metropolitan area suggests that it is easy to find residential areas that are all white or nearly so and areas that are all black or nearly so but hard to find localities in which neither whites nor nonwhites are more than, say, three-quarters of the total. And, comparing decennial maps, it is nearly impossible to find an area that, if integrated within that range, will remain integrated long enough for a man to get his house paid for or his children through school. The distribution is so U-shaped that it is virtually a choice of two extremes.

SOME QUANTITATIVE CONSTRAINTS

Counting blacks and whites in a residential block or on a baseball team will not tell how they get along. But it tells something, especially if numbers and ratios matter to the people who are moving in or out of the block or being recruited for the team. And with quantitative analysis

In a single sentence Schelling calls attention to a wide range of positive feedback processes that inspired much subsequent work. The overarching point is that these bottom-up, unregulated processes do not necessarily lead to socially efficient outcomes (unlike Adam Smith's invisible hand).

there are usually a few logical constraints, somewhat analogous to the balance-sheet identities in economics. Being logical constraints, they contain no news unless one just never thought of them before.

The simplest constraint on dichotomous mixing is that, within a given set of boundaries, not both groups (colors, sexes) can enjoy numerical superiority. Within the population as a whole, the numerical ratio is determined at any given time; but locally, in a city or a neighborhood, a church or a school, either blacks or whites can be a majority. But if each insists on being a *local* majority, there is only one mixture that will satisfy them—complete segregation.

Relaxing the condition, if whites want to be at least three-fourths and blacks at least one-third, it won't work. If whites want to be at least two-thirds and blacks no fewer than one-fifth, there is a small range of mixtures that meet the conditions. And not everybody can be in the mixtures if the aggregate ratio is outside the range.

Other constraints have to do with small numbers. A classroom can be mixed but the teacher is one color; mixed marriages can occur only in the ratio of one to one; a three-man team cannot represent both colors equally, and even in a two-man team each member has company exclusively of one color.

In spatial arrangements, like a neighborhood or a hospital ward, everybody is next to somebody. A neighborhood may be 10% black or white; but if you have a neighbor on either side, the minimum nonzero percentage of opposite color is 50. If people draw their boundaries differently we can have everybody in a minority: at dinner, with men and women seated alternately, everyone is outnumbered two to one locally by the opposite sex but can join a three-fifths majority if he extends his horizon to the next person on either side. If blacks occupy one-sixth of the beds in a hospital and there are four beds to a room, at least 40% of the whites will be in all-white rooms.

Transitions involve the usual relations among numbers and their derivatives. A college that wants suddenly to have 10% of its students black will have to admit 40% black freshmen, only to discover that it must then pass three classes before accepting more. Professions, occupations and residences are constrained by these numerical relations, whether it is color, sex, nationality, age or degree status that is involved.

SEPARATING MECHANISMS

The simple mathematics of ratios and mixtures tells us something about what outcomes are logically possible, but tells us little about the behavior that leads to, or that leads away from, particular outcomes. To understand what kinds of segregation or integration may result from individual choice, we have to look at the processes by which various mixtures and separations are brought about. We have to look at the incentives and the behavior that the incentives motivate, and particularly the way that different individuals comprising the society impinge on each other's choices and react to each other's presence.

There are many different incentives or criteria by which blacks and whites, or boys and girls, become separated. Whites may simply prefer to be among whites and blacks among blacks. Alternatively, whites may merely avoid or escape blacks and blacks avoid or escape whites. Whites may prefer the company of whites, while the blacks don't care. Whites may prefer to be among whites and blacks also prefer to be among whites, but if the whites can afford to live or to eat or to belong where the blacks cannot afford to follow, separation can occur.

Whites and blacks may not mind each other's presence, may even prefer integration, but may nevertheless wish to avoid minority status. Except for a mixture at exactly 50:50, no mixture will then be self-sustaining because there is none without a minority, and if the minority evacuates, complete segregation occurs. If both blacks and whites can tolerate minority status but there is a limit to how small a minority the members of either color are willing to be—for example, a 25% minority—initial mixtures ranging from 25% to 75% will survive but initial mixtures more extreme than that will lose their minority members and become all of one color. And if those who leave move to where they constitute a majority, they will increase the majority there and may cause the other color to evacuate.

Evidently if there are lower limits to the minority status that either color can tolerate, and if complete segregation obtains initially, no individual will move to an area dominated by the other color. Complete segregation is then a stable equilibrium. The concerted movement of blacks into a white area or whites into a black area could achieve some minimum percentage; but in the absence of concert, somebody has to move first and nobody will.

What follows is an abstract exploration of some of the quantitative dynamics of segregating behavior. The first section is a spatial model in which people—actually, not 'people' but items or counters or units of some sort—distribute themselves along a line or within an area in accordance with preferences about the composition of their surrounding neighborhoods. In this model there are no objective neighborhood boundaries; everybody defines his neighborhood by reference to his own location. An individual moves if he is not content with the color mixture of his neighborhood, moving to where the color mixture does meet his demands. For simplicity, everyone of a given color has the same preferences regarding the color mixture of his own neighbors.

In the next model space is compartmented. People are either in or out of a common neighborhood; those in it all belong to the same neighborhood irrespective of their particular locations within it. What matters to everybody is the color ratio within the whole neighborhood. In that model we allow variation in the preferences of individuals, some being more tolerant than others, some perhaps having a preference for integration. We look there at the question, what distribution of preferences or tolerances among the individuals of a given color may be compatible or not compatible with dynamically stable mixtures, what effect the initial conditions and the dynamics of movement will have on the outcome, and what kinds of numerical constraints may alter the results.

In the final section we look at neighborhoods with a limited capacity, like real residential neighborhoods with some fixed number of houses or schools with a limit on pupils.

Spatial Proximity Model

The results of this section are experimental. They are crude and abstract but have the advantage that anyone can reproduce them using materials that are readily available.

I assume a population exhaustively divided into two groups; everyone's membership is permanent and recognizable. Everybody is assumed to care about the color of the people he lives among and able to observe the number of blacks and whites that occupy a piece of territory. Everybody has a particular location at any moment; and everybody is capable of moving if he is dissatisfied with the color mixture where he is. The numbers of blacks and whites, their color preferences, and the sizes of 'neighborhoods' will be manipulated.

I am going to put my population into a stylized two-dimensional area. But the general idea is vividly displayed by distributing individuals along a line. There is some fascination in the process as it emerges in the linear model; furthermore, the linear experiment can be replicated by any reader in five minutes; variants can readily be devised, and any reader with a spare half hour can change the hypotheses to suit himself.

Schelling invites the reader to experiment with different arrangements and adjustment rules. The focus is on the "look and feel" of the dynamics, rather than on overarching theorems about convergence. This approach is a hallmark of agent-based modeling.

LINEAR DISTRIBUTION

The line of stars and zeros in Figure 1 corresponds to the odd and even digits in a column of random numbers. It turns out that there are 35 stars and 35 zeros, and they look reasonably 'random.' (There is no need to test for oddities and regularities; it is easier to replicate numbers.) We interpret these stars and zeros to be people spread out in a line, each concerned about whether his neighbors are stars or zeros.

We expect the stars and zeros to be evenly distributed in the large but unevenly in the small. If stars and zeros are content to live together in a ratio of about 50:50, each finds himself in a satisfactorily mixed neighborhood if he defines his neighborhood as a long enough stretch of the line. If instead everybody defines 'his neighborhood' as his own house and the two neighbors next to him, a quarter of the stars and zeros are going to be 'surrounded' by neighbors of opposite color. Satisfaction depends on how far one's 'neighborhood' extends.

```
 .   ..  . . ..    .  .      .   ..  ..  . .     ...  . . .  . ..
0+000++0+00++00+++0++0++00++00++00++0+0+00+++0++00000+++000+00++0+0++0
```

Figure 1.

Suppose, now, that everybody wants at least half his neighbors to be like himself, and that everyone defines 'his neighborhood' to include the four nearest neighbors on either side of him. A star wants at least four of his eight nearest neighbors to be stars; a zero wants at least four of his eight nearest neighbors to be zeros. Including himself, this means that he wants a bare majority, five out of the nine. (For those near the end of the line the rule is that, of the four neighbors on the side toward the center plus the one, two or three outboard neighbors, half must be like oneself.)

I have put a dot over each individual whose neighborhood does not meet his demands. Twelve stars and 14 zeros are dissatisfied with their neighborhoods. (The expected number is just under 13.)

Now we need a rule about how they move. Let me specify that a dissatisfied member moves to the nearest point that meets his minimum demand—the nearest point at which half his neighbors will be like himself at the time he arrives there. 'Nearest' means the point reached by passing the smallest number of neighbors on the way; and he merely intrudes himself between two others when he gets there. We also need an order of moving; arbitrarily let the discontented members move in turn, counting from left to right. The star second from the left moves first, the star sixth from the end moves second, and so forth.

Two things happen as they move. Some who were content will become discontent, because like members move out of their neighborhoods or opposite members move in. And some who were discontent become content, as opposite neighbors move away or like neighbors move close. The rule will be that any originally discontented member who is content when his turn comes will not move after all, and anyone who becomes discontent in the process will have his turn after the 26 original discontents have had their innings. The definition of the neighborhood is the four nearest neighbors on either side at the moment one decides to move or to stay; if someone moves in between a man and his next neighbor, the fourth neighbor away ceases to be a neighbor because he is now fifth.

Nobody in this model anticipates the movements of others. When it is his turn to move, he moves if his neighborhood demands are not met where he is and stays if they are, without regard to what he could anticipate if he studied the prospective decisions of others whose turns come later.

Applying these rules, the first discontented man on the left (the star located second from the end) moves to the right, passing six neighbors, and inserts himself between the zero who was eighth from the end and the

Game theory (and much of modern economic theory) insists that agents anticipate the moves of others. Here Schelling dispenses with anticipatory behavior, although later in the article he will briefly consider its effects.

star who was ninth. He now has two stars among the four neighbors to the left of him and two among the four to the right. The next to move is the star who used to be fifth from the end; he moves over to the right of the star that moved first and is followed by the star who was to his right, who moves over to the right of him. Next the discontented zero moves, and he moves to the left, passing four stars along the way. (Rightwards he would have had to move a greater distance.)

And so forth. The result is the top line of Figure 2, containing eight newly discontent individuals. We now give them their turn: and they rearrange themselves to form the bottom line in Figure 2, in which everybody is content. (There is no guarantee that two rounds will put everybody in equilibrium. One round may do it, more than two may be required.)

The result is six clusters of like individuals, containing 8, 15, 10, 15, 16 and 6 members respectively, averaging 12 members.

If we count the like and opposite neighbors among the eight belonging to each of the 70 individuals, we find that 440 out of 540 neighbors are of the same color, or 81.5%. Counting himself as the ninth member of his neighborhood, everyone lives in a neighborhood in which his own color predominates by an average ratio somewhat greater than five to one. This resulted from individuals' *seeking* a ratio not less than five to four.

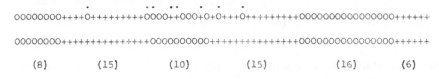

| (8) | (15) | (10) | (15) | (16) | (6) |

Figure 2.

We knew in advance that, if there were an equilibrium, everyone would get to live in a neighborhood at least five-ninths his own color. We knew, or could easily have discovered, that equilibria existed. We could have surmised that our rules of movement would lead to equilibria, because each person's search for others of like color raises the likelihood that people of like color will stay in the place he moves to and those of opposite color will leave it. We got a more striking result.

Notice that regular alternation of stars and zeros would satisfy everybody with exactly half his neighbors of like color. So would alternating pairs: two zeros, two stars, two more zeros, etc. Alternating groups of three or four would not meet the condition; but any groups of five or more in alternation meet it. We got groups of about twelve.

If people, though not wanting to be in the minority, prefer mixed neighborhoods, only 40 of the 70 managed it at all. Thirty have no neighbors of opposite color. Furthermore, those who would like some neighbors of opposite color but are unwilling themselves to be in a neighborhood minority can move nearer to the boundary of their own color group, but will never go beyond the boundary; if everybody wants two or three neighbors of opposite color, there will be turmoil within each group as people continually move to within a couple of spaces of the color boundary; none of this affects the grouping itself.

Another example, taken from another column in the same table of random digits, is presented in Figure 3. Initially, out of 72 members, there are 30 discontents; one round of moving leads to the second line in that figure, and again we have six groups and the same resulting neighborhood statistics as in the first case.

Some tabletop experimentation suggests that, with everything else the same, different random sequences yield from about five groupings with an average of 14 members to seven or eight groupings with an average of 9 or 10, six being the modal number of groups and 12 the modal size. Similar experimentation suggests that the order of moves makes little difference unless we allow our people to anticipate outcomes and seek either to maximize or to minimize group sizes. (It also appears that the 70 people who fit within the margins of a typewriter are a large enough linear sample if stars and zeros are about equal in number.)

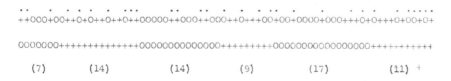

Figure 3.

VARIATIONS OF THE LINEAR MODEL

Our model has five elements that are readily varied: neighborhood size, demanded percentage of one's own color, ratio of stars to zeros in the total population, rules governing movement, and original configuration.

If we reduce neighborhood size, we get the same general pattern of alternating clusters (which we could call 'alternating homogeneous neighborhoods' except that they do not correspond to 'neighborhoods' as the members define them). Testing with the two random sequences that we have already used, defining the neighborhood as three people on either side of a resident, we find 37 initial discontents in the first case, 5 new discontents after the first round of moving, and an end result of ten groups with an average size of 7. The second sequence generates 29 discontents, 3 new ones after the first round, with an end result of seven clusters averaging 10 per cluster. Further experiment suggests a mean of 7 or 8 per cluster, or approximately twice the minimum size of cluster that meets the demand (alternating clusters of 4) and with the average person's neighborhood 75% to 80% his own color.[†]

To illustrate what happens if we have unequal totals of zeros and stars, I have eliminated 17 of the 35 zeros in our first sequence (from Figure 1), letting a roll of the die determine the fate of each zero. Different rolls of the die will get you different reduced sequences; Figure 31 shows the one that I got.

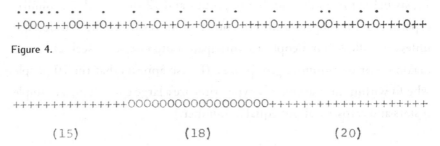

+OOO+++OO++O+++O++O++O++OO++O++++O+++++OO+++O+O+++O++

Figure 4.

++++++++++++++++OOOOOOOOOOOOOOOOOOOO++++++++++++++++++++++

      (15)   (18)   (20)

Figure 5.

[†] A curious property of this six-neighbor neighborhood is that, short of clusters of four or more, the only pattern that meets the demand for half one's neighbors like himself is . . . O O + O + + O O + O + + ... Even this one is unstable at the ends: it must run indefinitely in both directions or form a closed curve, else it unravels completely into clusters.

All the zeros are now discontent, and three of the stars, with neighborhood defined again as the four on either side. Using the familiar rules of movement, all the zeros congregate in the first round, as in Figure 5.

Again rolling dice to eliminate about half the zeros from our second sequence (that of Figure 3), yielding again a ratio of about two stars for every zero, I found 18 of 20 zeros discontent and 2 of the stars. After a round of moving there were still 4 discontented members, and after a second round, 2. After the third round, the top line of Figure 6 was obtained. Using the same original sequence, but another random deletion, and again another random deletion from the same original, the other two lines of Figure 6 were obtained as end results.

```
+++++++++++OOOOOOOOOO+++++++++++OOOOO+++++++++++OOOOO

+++++++++++OOOOOOOOOO++++++++++++OOOOOOOOOOO++++++++++

+++++++++++++OOOOOOOOOOOOOOOOO+++++++++++++++++++++++
```

Figure 6.

As the numerical inequality of majority and minority becomes more extreme, one expects the segregation (or 'segregatedness') of the majority to become more extreme—there aren't enough of the minority to go around. If stars outnumber zeros by four to one, even a regular distribution will give stars an average of but one-fifth neighbors of opposite color. Furthermore, since the minimum size of segregated cluster that will satisfy the minority's demands for one-half neighbors of like color is 5, the minimum clustering among the majority that would satisfy the minority is 4×5, or 20.

What is less immediately apparent, but becomes apparent on reflection, is that the minority itself tends to become more segregated from the majority, as its relative size diminishes. That is, the minority clusters become absolutely larger as the minority itself becomes smaller. Or, to put it differently, as the relative size of the minority is diminished, the number (frequency) of minority clusters diminishes more than proportionately.

The reason is not too obscure: as the randomly distributed minority diminishes in proportion to the total population, the likelihood of four or more members of the minority among any eight consecutive individuals diminishes more than proportionately; so the number of potentially stable clusters ('growth nodes') declines relative to the minority population. Since everybody, under our rules of movement, travels to a place where at least four of eight individuals are his own color, they all end up together at places where at least four out of eight originally coincided by chance. Even demanding but three neighbors of like color, a 10% minority will form clusters averaging about twice the size of those obtained in Figures 2 and 3. Demanding half, the mean cluster of a 10% minority will contain upwards of 100 if the aggregate population is large enough to sustain any growth nodes at all!

RESTRICTED MOVEMENT

A related point is interesting. Suppose the minority becomes relatively small, say 20% or 10%, still with initial random distribution, and we impose a limit on travel distance. Some, probably many, perhaps all, will become unable to move to where their demands are satisfied. We then modify the rule: if a neighborhood half your own color does not occur within the allowed radius of travel, move to the nearest place where three out of eight occur. The result is that everybody achieves his desired neighborhood, half or more his own color, without traveling as far as if he and the others had been free to travel! The limitation on travel channels them into the smaller, more frequently occurring, potential clusters ('growth nodes'), which proceed to grow into clusters that more than satisfy them.

Thus travel restrictions imposed on individual movement can be a substitute for *concerted* movement. It can also be a substitute for *anticipatory* movement, in which a person stops among three fellows of like color knowing, as he makes it four, that a fifth will soon arrive and stay.

All of this is too abstract and artificial to be a motion picture of whites and blacks or boys and girls choosing houses along a road or even stools along a counter, but it is suggestive of a segregating process and

Here again Schelling acknowledges the possibility of anticipatory behavior without making it a centerpiece of the model.

illustrates some of the dynamics that could be present in individually motivated segregation.

AREA DISTRIBUTION

A convenience of the linear model was that, when we moved a person (or a counter) from a spot between two neighbors to a spot between two other neighbors, everybody could just move over to make room or to close up the vacant space, and the linear order was preserved. To do the same in two dimensions is not so easy; we need a rule about who moves over in which direction to make room for the newcomer or to close up a vacated space. A convenient way to meet the problem is to deal with absolute space rather than relative position: divide the area into a fixed number of spaces, leaving some vacant; a person can move only into a vacant space, and when he moves he leaves a space vacant. 'Neighborhood' is defined in terms of neighboring spaces.

To be specific: divide the area into squares like a checkerboard (but without any alternating colors) and distribute colored chips at random among the squares, leaving some squares blank. One chip occupies one square, and a 'neighborhood' is defined by reference to the surrounding squares; each square on a checkerboard has eight immediate neighbors, so a convenient minimum-sized neighborhood for an individual is his own square plus the eight surrounding; larger 'neighborhoods' can be considered by including the 24 surrounding squares in a 5 × 5 area, etc. An actual board, in contrast to a conceptually infinite expanse, has sides and corners; but, then, so probably do most natural areas, and this may be no disadvantage. Along the edge of the board a square has only five neighboring squares, and in a corner but three. The whole area need not itself be square; convenience may dictate some other shape, and if one wants to study the influence of natural boundaries a long and narrow checkerboard six squares wide and twenty long will have a higher proportion of residents on the edge than a square one.

In order that people be able to move there must be some vacant spaces; in order that they have significant choice of where to move there must be quite a few. While it is interesting to study what happens if the supply of vacant spaces is restricted, unless one is actually studying the influence of restricted supply the vacancies need to be a reasonably high proportion of the total. It turns out that 25% to 30% vacancies allows fair freedom of movement without making the board too empty.

The rule of movement, then, is that an individual discontent with his own neighborhood moves to the nearest vacant spot that surrounds him with a neighborhood that meets his demands. In most of what I'm going to show you, 'neighborhood' has been defined as the eight surrounding squares that, together with one's own square, form a 3×3 square. Color preferences with respect to one's neighborhood can be defined either in absolute terms—the number of one's own color within the eight surrounding squares—or in relative terms— the ratio of neighbors of one's own color to opposite color among the eight surrounding squares. If all squares were occupied, every absolute number would correspond to a ratio; but because one may have anywhere from zero up to eight neighbors, there are eight denominators and therefore eight numerators to specify in describing one's neighborhood demands.

As in the linear model, I make an initial distribution at random. It might make sense to distribute the blank spaces evenly, but I let them be determined at random, too. (It makes some difference.) In some cases I use equal numbers of blacks and whites, in others a ratio of two to one or larger. I then specify for each of the colors what its neighborhood demands are. I specify the rule for moving, which is usually to move to the nearest satisfactory square, with 'nearest' measured by the number of squares one traverses horizontally and vertically. And we need a rule to specify the order in which they move; this part is more complicated than in the linear model. In some cases the order of move was determined merely by position on the board, such as working generally from left to right; it is also interesting to see what happens if all of one color completes its moves before the other color moves. It is possible, of course, to test the sensitivity of the results with respect to the order of moves. Because what is reported here has all been done by hand and eye, no exact rule for the order of moves has been adhered to strictly.

As a start, we can use some of the same parameters as in our first linear model: equal numbers of stars and zeros distributed at random among the squares, with a suitable fraction left blank for ease of movement; 'neighborhood' defined as the eight surrounding squares; and a universal demand that no fewer than half of one's neighbors be of the same color, the discontent moving to the nearest satisfactory vacant square.

Figure 7.

Figure 7 shows an initial random distribution. There are 13 rows, 16 columns, 208 squares (for reasons of convenience that I won't go into here). It might seem unnecessary to reproduce an actual picture of randomly distributed stars and zeros and blank squares; but some of the results are going to be judged impressionistically, and it is worthwhile to get some idea of the kind of picture or pattern that emerges from a random distribution. If one insists on finding 'homogeneous neighborhoods' in this random distribution, he can certainly do so. *Randomness* is not *regularity*. If we are going to look at 'segregated areas' and try to form an impression of how segregated they are, or an impression of how segregated they *look*, we may want a little practice at drawing neighborhood boundaries in random patterns.

Patterns, though, can be deceptive, and it is useful to have some measures of segregation or concentration or clustering or sorting. One possible measure is the average proportion of neighbors of like or opposite color. If we count neighbors of like color and opposite color for each of the 138 randomly distributed stars and zeros in Figure 7, we find that zeros on the average have 53% of their neighbors of the same color, stars 46%. (The percentages can differ because stars and zeros can have different numbers of blank neighboring spaces.)

There are, of course, many regular patterns that would yield everybody a set of neighbors half his own color and half the opposite color. Neglecting blank spaces for the moment, a checkerboard pattern will do it; alternate diagonal lines of stars and zeros will do it; dividing the board into 2×2 squares of four cells each, and forming a checkerboard out of these four-cell squares, will also yield everybody four neighbors of like color and four of opposite. And so forth. *Patterning* is evidently related to, but distinct from, any measures of neighborhood homogeneity that we may work out.[†]

Now play the game of solitaire. Identify the discontents—there are 25 stars and 18 zeros in Figure 7 whose neighbors are less than half of like color—and, in some order, move them to where they are content, continuing to move the newly discontent until the entire board is in equilibrium. (There is no guarantee that everybody can find a blank space that suits him, but with the numbers we are using now it usually turns out that he can.) The *particular* outcome will depend very much on the order in which discontented stars and zeros are moved, the *character* of the outcome not very much. The reader can check this for himself in about ten minutes if he has a roll of pennies, a roll of nickels, and a sheet of paper big enough for 16 columns of one-inch squares.

Working generally from the upper left corner downward and to the right, an equilibrium was achieved as shown in Figure 8. Working from the center outwards, the same initial distribution led to the equilibrium of Figure 9. The 'segregation' in Figure 8 is too striking to need comment. In Figure 9 it is also striking, though more fragmented. The pattern in Figure 9 stands out more if we draw some boundaries; this may be cheating a little, in making an apparent pattern stand out, but that is why I first presented it without the boundaries and also why I suggested scrutinizing the random distribution to see that some 'segregated patterns' emerged even there. Figure 10 is Figure 9 with some boundaries drawn in.

[†] Patterning—departure from randomness—will prove to be characteristic of integration, as well as of segregation, if the integration results from choice and not chance.

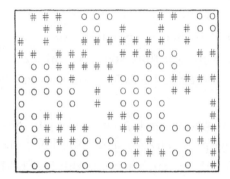

Figure 8.

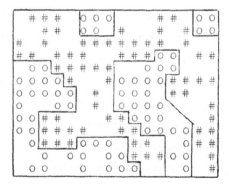

Figure 9.

Figure 10.

    Though the patterns are impressionistic, the neighbor count is not. Originally, it will be recalled, the average percentage of like neighbors that the zeros had was 53, and stars 46. On the average, both colors were virtually at their minimum demands (as they were bound to be with equal numbers in total). But after the discontent have adjusted, and the newly discontent have then adjusted, and so on to equilibrium as in Figure 9, zeros on the average have neighbors who are five-sixths zeros, stars have neighbors who are four-fifths stars. On the average each zero has five neighbors, of whom (not quite) one is a star. Including himself, there are thus six people in the average zero's neighborhood, five his own color and one opposite. In the average star's neighborhood there are about four and a half neighbors, one of whom is a zero; including himself, there are thus five and a half residents of his neighborhood, one of whom is of opposite color.

Another statistic is the percentage of the population that has no neighbors of opposite color at all. In the random distribution of Figure 7 the number is 13 (which corresponds exactly to the expected value in an 11×16 matrix with one-third stars, one-third zeros, and one-third blanks). In Figure 9 the number is 54, or approximately 40% compared with 10% .[†]

The figures are even more lopsided for Figure 8, where, counting himself, the average person lives in a neighborhood that is 90% his own color (89 for zeros, 91 for stars), and two-thirds of both colors have no neighbors of opposite color.

Now we can vary some parameters to see what we get. I shall not show any more initial distributions; they all involve the same 13 rows and 16 columns, blank spaces usually equal to about 30% of the total, and a random distribution of the two colors. We can vary the ratio of stars to zeros, the fraction or number of own color that stars and zeros demand, and in a few cases the size of the 'neighborhood.' We look, too, at the consequences of an actual preference for integration.

My samples have been too small, so far, to allow serious generalizations, so I shall formulate hypotheses suggested by what I have

---

[†] It may be helpful to compare the pattern of stars and zeros in Figure 9 with those of some standard reference pattern, such as rectangular blocks of stars and zeros on an unbounded checkerboard. The neighbor count of Figure 9 turns out to be identical with that obtained if stars and zeros occur in 7×7 squares of 49 each. (It should be kept in mind that 2×2 squares yield the same neighbor count, one to one, as expected in the random distribution.) Similarly, 3×3 squares are the smallest homogeneous groups in which someone has no neighbors of opposite color, the percentage for 3×3 being 11%, almost exactly that expected in a random distribution of the size and shape of Figure 7; the 39% without neighbors of opposite color in Figure 9 correspond to mono-colored 5×6 groupings on an unbounded surface (12 out of 30, or 40%).

done. Quantitative measures, of course, refer exclusively to an artificial checkerboard and are unlikely to have any quantitative analogue in the living world. *Comparisons* among them, however, such as the effect of reducing or enlarging the size of a minority, may be capable of some extension to that world.

INTENSITY OF DEMAND FOR LIKE NEIGHBORS

If the two colors are equal in number, if neighborhoods are defined as the eight surrounding squares, and if both colors have the same demands for neighbors like themselves, the segregation that results is slight when the demand is for about one-third of one's neighbors like oneself and striking when the demand is as high as one-half.

This result is both impressionistic and quantitative: the results are visually striking in the one case and not in the other, and the resulting ratios of like neighbors to opposite neighbors is upwards of four to one for demands of one-half or more, and less than 1.5 for demands of about one-third. See Figure 11, in which the demands are for about one-third.[†]

```
  O   O O O O # O   O O O O   O
O   O O   O # # O   O O   O O  
O O # # O O   O # # O     O   O
# # #   O   O O # # O O   O # O
#   # # # #   #     # #       #
  O O #     # #   # O #       #
# O O O #       # O O O #     #
O # # # #   # # # O O   # # # #
O #   # O       O O   O O O   #
O # #   O O # #   O O   O O O  
  O # # # O O # # O O   # O # #
  O O #   # O   # # O # #   #  
O O   # #   # #     # #   # #  
```

Figure 11.

An increase in the demand for like neighbors does three things. First, it increases the number that will be initially discontent. Second, it increases the like-color density that results from each movement: each

† Since the number of neighbors is a small integer, the fractions demanded for different numbers of neighbors have to differ. In Figure 11, the demands are for one like neighbor out of four or fewer, two out of five neighbors or more. The average number of neighbors in the initial distribution is five and one-half, the average number when equilibrium is reached is about four and one-half; the average effective preference is therefore in the neighborhood of one-third.

individual that moves not only *acquires* more neighbors of like color the more he demands, but *becomes* a like neighbor to more neighbors the more he acquires. And, third, the greater the demands the more movement is induced by those that move on the part of those that were originally content. These three effects compound together to make the resulting segregation a rapidly rising function of demands in the range from about 35% to 50%.

When the demands of both colors are for 50%, their sum is of course 100%. Evidently for neighborhoods with fixed boundaries, no coexistence is possible if the demands of the two colors add up to more than one. In the present model there are not fixed boundaries, so it is possible to have mixed areas with everybody in the majority in his own neighborhood. But the degree of flexibility is not great. Therefore we should expect that demands summing to more than one should result in extreme segregation, as apparently they do.

UNEQUAL DEMANDS

If stars and zeros are about equal in number but one is more demanding than the other, the more demanding end up with a higher proportion of like neighbors, but not much higher. An illustration is Figure 12, in which the zeros (77) and the stars (72) are about equal in number but the zeros are less demanding. Zeros demand that one out of four or fewer be their own color, two out of five or more; stars demand two their own color if they have three to five neighbors, three if they have six or seven neighbors, and four out of eight. Zeros end up with a ratio of 2:1 of neighbors their own color; stars, who are nearly twice as demanding, show the somewhat higher ratio of 2:5.

Evidently he means 2.5:1, not 2:5.

If one forgets momentarily the logical constraints, there is surprise in this. Shouldn't the more separatist of the two colors get more separated? No, separation is a reciprocal thing: for every white with a black neighbor there is exactly one black with a white neighbor, if 'neighbors' are consistently defined. Ratios for the two colors can differ only if stars have more or fewer stars as neighbors than zeros have zeros. The ratios differ, that is, only by different mean population densities in the neighborhoods of the two colors. Such a difference does occur but is limited, among other things, by the number of blank spaces on

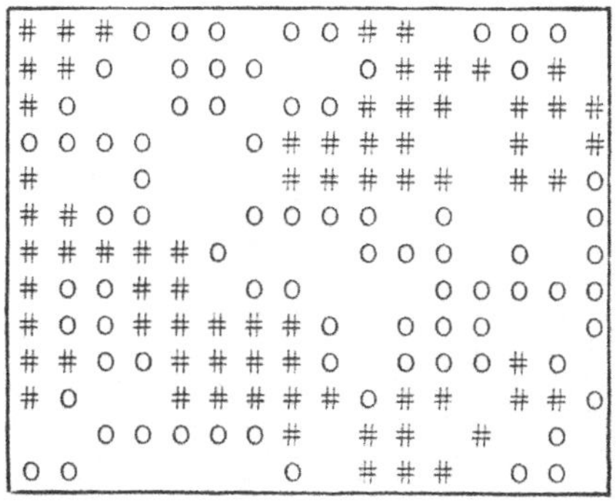

Figure 12.

the board. With no blank spaces, the like-neighbor ratios for the two colors would be mathematically constrained to equality if the two colors were equal in number, and for unequal numbers would differ strictly as a function of their numerical ratios. (The percentage of neighbors of opposite color for the majority would be equal to that for the minority multiplied by the numerical ratio of the minority to the majority.)

In Figure 12 the stars are noticeably more compacted than the zeros; the latter are spaced out more. This is a result to be regularly expected— but only after one has learned to expect it.

UNEQUAL NUMBERS, EQUAL DEMANDS

If we put one of the two colors in minority status, letting it be outnumbered two to one or four to one, greater segregation occurs than with equal numbers, for any given set of demands on the part of the two colors. When one of the colors numbers only half the other, demands for about one-third neighbors of like color lead to ratios close to two to one for the minority (and, necessarily, still higher for the majority).

Figure 13 illustrates this effect. Stars outnumber zeros about two to one; demands are identical—a minimum of two neighbors of like color. The effective 'demand' averages about 35%. The zeros, whose ratio of like to unlike neighbors in a random distribution is about 1:2, end up with the ratio reversed, 2:1, a fourfold increase in ratio. Stars went from an initial ratio of 2:1 to ratio of 4:1.

With extreme color ratios, like five to one or more, the minority tends to display a phenomenon related to its absolute density rather

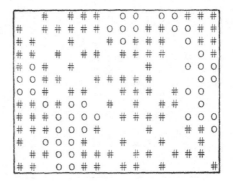

Figure 13.

than its relative density. We observed this earlier in the linear model. The proportion of initially satisfied individuals is so small that nearly everybody in the minority moves. Everybody, furthermore, moves toward whatever cluster of like-colored individuals he can find; and the number of such clusters declines disproportionately as the minority becomes smaller. The result is that the minority forms larger clusters, large enough to cause even a tolerant majority to become locally dissatisfied.

An extreme case of this absolute-number principle is easily envisioned by supposing an area populated initially by one color alone, into which newcomers of opposite color enter one by one. The first is located at random and has no place to go; the best the second can do is to join the first; the third, wherever he lands, if he wants any like neighbors at all, joins the first two, and similarly with the fourth and fifth and all who follow. In the end all the newcomers are together. Each has the choice between joining the only cluster or remaining entirely alone. If the available blank spaces permit them to achieve a significant density, the color initially resident will begin to vacate the locality of the cluster, and the result will be a solid neighborhood of the new color. This result will be independent of the moderateness of the color demands of the newcomers.

The process is illustrated in Figure 14, one part of which is an initial random scatter in which the stars outnumber the zeroes by five to one. Neighborhoods were defined as the 24 surrounding squares. The zeros were given a very moderate demand—an absolute number of but two zeros in the entire 24 surrounding squares—and stars the somewhat immoderate demand that zeros be no more than one-third of the population in the 24 surrounding squares. In the random distribution only a single star is dissatisfied, the one nearest to the lower right corner. The pattern that results from movement is somewhat sensitive to the precise order of movement imputed to the various dissatisfied zeros, of whom there are 11 out of the 15 individuals. Two results obtained from different moving orders are shown in Figure 14. The like-neighbor ratio for zeros can be computed on the basis of either 24 neighboring spaces or, for comparability with earlier results, 8. In the larger neighborhoods, zeros (in the two results) achieve not quite one-half neighbors of like color; computed for the 8-neighbor neighborhoods, they achieve almost three-quarters.

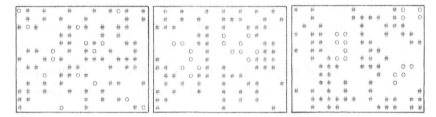

Figure 14.

POPULATION DENSITIES

An unexpected result that undoubtedly has ecological significance in some context is in what the sorting does to the population densities of the individual neighborhoods. It will be recalled that with equal numbers of the two colors but different demands, the more demanding color ended with a higher ratio of like to opposite neighbors. This was possible because of a discrepancy in the average number of like neighbors acquired in the process by the two colors. That the more demanding ends up in more homogeneous clusters is mathematically equivalent to the result that the more demanding ends up with more neighbors, in more densely populated neighborhoods. This result was recognized as a mathematical consequence of what appeared to be a discrepancy in the 'segregatedness' between the more and the less demanding of the two colors.

An extension of Schelling's model would incorporate the price of housing into people's preferences. One could assume, for example, that the local price of housing decreases as the local vacancy rate increases. See Zhang (2004).

Attention was called earlier to Figure 12 because stars had a somewhat higher ratio of like to opposite neighbors than zeros did, a ratio of 2.5 compared with 2.0. The same figure illustrates the density phenomenon. Stars on the average, in that figure, have 5.35 neighbors, zeros 4.55. Stars and zeros occupy similar numbers of border positions, so the difference is not due to a discrepancy in the number of neighboring spaces.

Actually the impression one gets in Figure 12 is that zeros are even more dispersed, and stars more compacted, than those numbers suggest. The reason is that many blank spaces are 'neighbors' of other blank spaces, yet occur within territories that clearly 'belong' to the zeros. Our 'neighbor count,' computed from the squares adjacent to stars and zeros, misses this phenomenon. The neighbor count is based on individual neighborhoods, not on any 'collective neighborhoods' that we might identify. The pattern in Figure 12, however, tempts us to draw territorial boundaries, identifying regions occupied exclusively by zeros and regions occupied exclusively by stars. When the segregation is quite incomplete, it is by no means easy to do this; and alternative rules for drawing boundaries may lead to quite different results; but in Figure 12 the segregation is sufficiently marked to leave little to discretion. We can easily draw neat boundaries that completely separate stars from zeros, and we can furthermore impute blank spaces almost unambiguously to star territories and zero territories. If we do this we find the following. Splitting the blank spaces that might plausibly be imputed either to star territory or to zero territory, the 59 blanks divide into about 14 that we can impute to 'star territory' and about 45 that we can impute to zeros. (Ten ambiguous blanks were divided five each in this calculation.) Including blank spaces 'belonging' to them, the 72 stars occupy territory comprising 86 spaces altogether, and a population density of .83 within that territory. The 77 zeros occupy territory comprising 122 spaces altogether, with a population density of .63. 'Zero territory' is 37% vacant, 'star territory' only 17%.

Figure 12 may display the density phenomenon to more than average degree, but it usefully introduces a notion of 'collective territory,' that appears to be a necessary supplement to the 'individual neighborhood' in describing the outcome, even though it enters no one's motivation.

Population densities were then examined for the case of equal demands and unequal numbers, and an equally striking difference in population density showed up. The minority tends to accumulate in denser neighborhoods than the majority. Figure 13 displays the greater compactness of the minority. The mean number of neighbors per zero is 6.0, per star it is just under 5.0. And again one can draw rather unambiguous boundaries dividing stars from zeros—or 'star territory' from 'zero territory'—and find that zero territory has an occupancy rate of about 83%, star territory of about 64%. The vacancy rate in star territory is just over twice that in zero territory. (Four somewhat ambiguous blank spaces, in the fourth column from righthand side, were allocated two each to star and zero territory.)

A more extreme result is obtained when one group is both smaller in numbers and more demanding as to neighbors. In Figure 15 the ratio of stars to zeros is almost four to one; stars demand one star out of four or fewer neighbors, two out of five or more, while zeros demand two out of five or fewer, three out of six or seven, four out of eight. In addition to rather striking separation of the two colors, there is virtually complete occupancy of 'zero territory' amidst a quite dispersed star population. Stars average 5.1 neighbors apiece; zeros average 6.8, and, given their locations, 7.0 is the maximum.

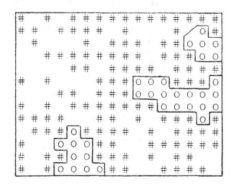

Figure 15.

This density phenomenon is suggestive but not easily related to residential patterns. Our model not only uses a stylized form of empty space—uniform squares—but, most important, makes no provision for other factors that are bound to have a strong influence on residential density—incomes, family sizes, and the cost of space. (If surfers at a public beach like to be by themselves but swimmers have an even stronger incentive to avoid surfboards, our model suggests they will become separated into groups but the surfers will enjoy more acreage per capita!)

SIZE OF NEIGHBORHOOD

Enlarging the area within which a person counts his neighbors attenuates the tendency to segregate, at least for moderate demands and near-equal numbers of the two colors. This observation may not stand up when less tolerant demands, and greater differentials in initial numbers, are put into the larger neighborhoods.

CONGREGATIONIST PREFERENCES

The reader might try to guess what neighborhood demands generated the pattern shown in Figure 16. The degree of 'segregation' compares with that of Figure 10. For the two colors together, like neighbors are just over 75%; and among the two colors, 38% have no neighbors of opposite color. Careful inspection would show a few individuals in Figure 16 who are more 'integrated' than in Figure 10.

O	O	O	O			#	#		#	#		#			
O		O	O		#	#	O	#	#		#	#		#	#
	O		O		#	O	O	O		O	#	#	#		#
#	O	O	O		#	O	O	#	O	O	O		#	#	
#	#	O	O	#	#		#	#	#	O	O	#	#	#	
#	#	#	#	#	#			#		O	O	#	#	#	#
	O	#	#	#	#	O	O	O			O	O	#	#	#
O	O	O		O	O		O	O	#	#	O	O	#	#	#
	O	O	O		O	O	O		#	#	O		#	#	#
O		O	O		O	O		#	#	O	O		O	#	
	O		O	O	O	#	#	#	#	O	O	O	O	O	O
O		O			#	#	#	#	#		O	O		O	O
	O				#	#	#	#	#	#					O

Figure 16.

It might appear that the demanded ratios in Figure 16 were slightly—only slightly—less than in Figure 10. But in fact there are no demanded ratios in this case. Each individual was assumed to want three neighbors like himself out of eight surrounding spaces (or two out of five, along the edge), and to be indifferent to the presence of the opposite color. That is, opposite neighbors were equivalent to blank spaces in the evaluation of neighborhoods. Everyone's demands leave room for up to five opposite neighbors out of eight; but in achieving an absolute figure of three out of eight like himself—in 'congregating' with his own color—he separates from the others just as if he had demanded majority status.

INTEGRATIONIST PREFERENCES

The foregoing results all assume that members of both colors have certain minimum demands for neighbors of like color, but no maximum demands. We can experiment with a demand for 'integration' either by supposing some preferred ratio, or by supposing that there is an upper as well as lower bound to the fraction of neighbors of like color that one wants. Figure 17 shows results from two different 'integrationist' preference schedules.

In both cases zeros are just over half the number of stars. In the left panel there is, for both stars and zeros, an upper as well as a lower limit to the number of like neighbors demanded: among eight neighbors, at least three and at most six like oneself; among seven, at least three and at most five; among six, at least three and at most four; among five, at least two and at most four; among four, either two or three; among three, either one or two; and one out of two. In the right panel there is a scale of preferences rather than upper and lower limits: out of eight neighbors, five like oneself is the preferred number but, if the board offers no such choice, then four and six are equally preferred as second choice; failing that, three and seven are equally attractive, with two and eight tied for next place, then one and finally none. Similarly with other numbers of neighbors: half for odd numbers, just over half for even, with second and third choices pairing numbers both above and below the preferred number.

Tentative experimentation suggests three phenomena that are not present in the case of purely 'separatist' demands:

1. Integration requires more complex patterning than separation; equilibrium is achieved only with a much larger number of moves; and a larger number of individuals move. More individuals may be incapable of being satisfied. And there are problems of the consistency of the

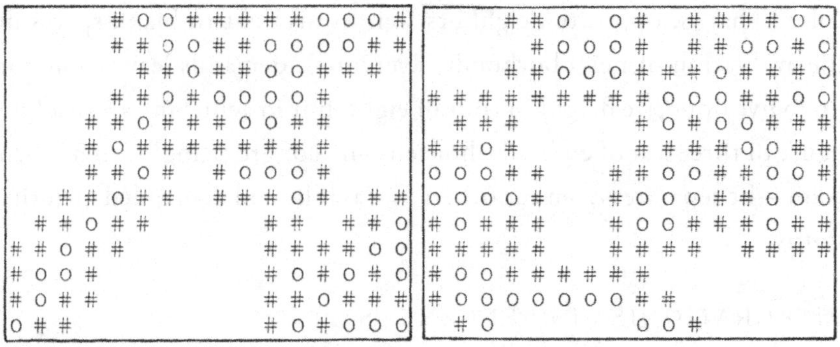

Figure 17.

integrationist demands, not only of the two colors but of each of them with the overall color ratio in the population.

2. If one of the colors is a minority, the two colors have to pattern themselves in such a way that the minority is 'rationed.' That is, the patterns have to be 'efficient' in the way members of the majority can share minority neighbors. The result may look just as non-random as the segregated results achieved earlier; the patterns are as striking, but they are different patterns. The minority, for example, may be spread out in conspicuous lines rather than clustered in conspicuously convex areas, as in Figure 17.

3. The process of moving produces 'dead spaces.' An area densely settled by either color will be evacuated in its center; neither color will then move into the area, but the boundary is stable because it has contact with the opposite color. The result is that the blank spaces form their own 'clusters' in the final equilibrium, giving an appearance quite different from that produced by purely separatist motives.

Bounded-Neighborhood Model

We turn now to a different model, with a changed definition of 'neighborhood.' Instead of everyone's defining his neighborhood by reference to his own location, there is a common definition of the neighborhood and its boundaries. A person is either inside it or outside it. Everyone is concerned about the color ratio within the neighborhood but not with any configuration of the colors within the neighborhood. 'Residence' in this model can therefore just as well, perhaps even better, be interpreted as membership or participation in a job, an office, a university, a church, a voting bloc, a club, a restaurant, or a hospital.

In this model there is one particular bounded area that everybody, black or white, prefers to its alternatives. He will reside in it unless the percentage of residents of opposite color exceeds some limit. Each person, black or white, has his own limit. ('Tolerance,' we shall occasionally call it.) If a person's limit is exceeded in this area he will go someplace else-a place, presumably, where his own color predominates or where color does not matter.

'Tolerance,' it should be noticed, is a *comparative* measure, and it is specific to this location. Whites who appear, in this location, to be *less tolerant of blacks* than other whites may be merely *more tolerant of the alternative locations.*

The higher the limits, the more blacks and whites would be content to live together in the area. Evidently the upper bounds must be compatible for some blacks and some whites—as percentages they must add to at least 100—or no contented mixture of any whites and blacks is possible. Evidently, too, if nobody can tolerate extreme ratios, an area initially occupied by one color alone would remain so. There may be some number among the other color that, if *concerted* entry were achieved, would remain; but, acting individually, nobody would be the first.

We can experiment with frequency distributions of 'tolerance' to see what results they lead to. We cannot discover realistic distributions because they depend on the area in question; and the area in the model is unnamed. What we can do is to look at the *process* by which the area becomes occupied, or remains occupied, by blacks or whites or a mixture of both, and look for some general principles that relate outcomes to the shapes of the curves, the initial positions, and the dynamics of movement.

We assume that all preferences go in the same direction: a person need not care, but if he does his concern takes the form of an upper limit to the other color that can occur in this area without his choosing to go elsewhere. There is no lower limit: there are no minority-seeking individuals, nor any who will leave if the area is not suitably integrated. Absolute numbers do not matter, only ratios; there are no economies of

Here Schelling does away with the assumption that agents have specific spatial locations in order to focus on the effect of heterogeneity in their preferences. In an expanded version of the model, agents could differ in their preferences as well as their locations. This situation can be analyzed by techniques in stochastic dynamical systems theory, but to my knowledge it has not been done in any generality.

scale in being among one's own color. There are no individual positions within the mix: nobody is near the center or near the boundary, nobody has a 'next neighbor.'

To study the dynamics we shall assume that people both leave and return. (This is restrictive: if the preference for this locality were due merely to the fact that some people were already here and the cost of leaving were high, that cost would not be recovered by returning.) People in the area move out if the ratio is not within their color limit; people outside move in if they see that it meets their requirements.

Information is perfect: everybody knows the color ratio within the area at the moment he makes his choice. People do not, however, know the intentions of others and do not project future turnover.

As to the dynamics of motion, we need not stipulate in advance whether whites move in or out more rapidly than blacks do. Their relative speeds of reaction will sometimes matter, and in our analysis we can watch and see how they matter. We need, though, the somewhat plausible assumption that, as between two whites dissatisfied with the ratio of white to black, the more dissatisfied leaves first—the one with the lesser tolerance. Then, as a result of sorting, the whites within the locality at any given time will all have higher tolerance of blacks than any of the whites outside, and similarly for blacks inside and outside. It is the least tolerant whites that move out first, and the most tolerant that move in first, and similarly for blacks.

Our initial data are represented by a cumulative frequency distribution of 'tolerance' of the members of each color group. We can experiment with various hypothetical schedules of tolerance, but for the initial experiment we begin with a straight line.

AN ILLUSTRATIVE STRAIGHT-LINE DISTRIBUTION OF 'TOLERANCE'

For the whites, the horizontal axis measures the number of whites, the vertical axis measures the ratio of blacks to whites representing the upper limits of their tolerances. We can take the total of whites to be 100. Suppose that the median white is willing to live with blacks in equal numbers, so that 50 among our 100 whites will abide a ratio of black to white of 1.0 or greater. The most tolerant white can abide a black-white

Here again Schelling avoids the assumption that agents anticipate the moves of others. An interesting extension of the model would be to assume that agents are forward-looking with different rates of time preference.

ratio of two to one, that is, is willing to be in a one-third minority; and the least tolerant white cannot stand the presence of any blacks. The cumulative distribution of tolerances for a white population will then appear as in the top of Figure 18. It is a straight line with intercept at a ratio of 2.0 on the vertical axis and intercept on the horizontal axis at the 100 whites who comprise the white population.

Suppose that blacks have an identical distribution of tolerance for whites, the median tolerance being a ratio of one to one, and that the number of blacks is half the number of whites, 50.

It is evident without further analysis that there are at least some whites and some blacks who could contentedly coexist. Fifty of the whites would be willing to live with all the blacks, though not all 50 blacks would be willing to live with 50 whites; but a mixture of 25 blacks and 25 whites, consisting of the more tolerant 25 blacks and 25 of the more tolerant 50 whites, would be content together. There are 10 blacks who could tolerate a ratio of 1.6 to 1, or 16 whites; and any 16 among the 80 or so whites who will tolerate a black-white ratio of 10:16 would be content to join them. To explore all the combinations that might form a contented mix, but especially to study the dynamics of entry and departure, it is useful to translate both our schedules from ratios to absolute numbers, and put them on the same diagram.

TRANSLATION OF THE SCHEDULES

This is done in the bottom of Figure 18. The curve labeled W is a translation of the white tolerance schedule. For each number of whites along the horizontal axis the number of blacks whose presence they will tolerate is equal to their own number times the corresponding ratio on the schedule of tolerance. Thus 50 whites can tolerate an equal number of blacks, or 50. Seventy-five can tolerate half their number, 37.5; 25 can tolerate 1.5 times their number, or 37.5. Ninety can tolerate but one-fifth their number, 18; 20 can tolerate 36, and so forth.

In this fashion the straight-line tolerance schedule translates into a parabolic curve showing the absolute numbers that correspond to the limits of tolerance of alternative numbers of whites. (Economists will recognize that the cumulative frequency distribution translates into this absolute-numbers curve in the same way that a demand curve translates into a total revenue curve.) Similar arithmetic converts the blacks' schedule of tolerance into the smaller parabolic dish that opens toward the vertical axis in Figure 18.

This vector field diagram, illustrating the notion of basins of attraction, is common in the physical sciences but much less so in economics when Schelling wrote this article.

☞

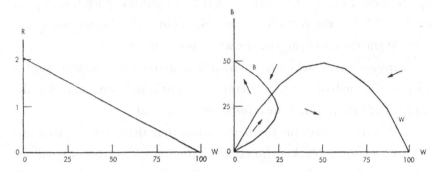

Figure 18.

STATIC VIABILITY

Any point in Figure 18 that lies within both parabolas (the area of overlap) denotes a *statically* viable combination of blacks and whites. There are that many whites who will abide the presence of that many blacks, and there are that many blacks who will abide the presence of that many whites. Any point on the diagram that is beneath the whites' curve but to the right of the blacks' curve represents a mixture of whites and blacks such that all the whites are contented but not all the blacks. Some of the blacks may be content, but not all those present. And a point on the diagram that lies outside both curves—the region to the upper right—denotes a mixture of whites and blacks at which neither all the whites nor all the blacks could be satisfied; some of both colors would be dissatisfied.

DYNAMICS OF MOVEMENT

It is the dynamics of motion, though, that determine what color mix will ultimately occupy the area. The simplest dynamics are as follows: if all whites present in the area are content, and some outside would be content if they were inside, the former will stay and the latter will enter; and whites will continue to enter as long as all those present are content and some outside would be content if present. If not all whites present are content, some will leave; they will leave in order of their discontent, so that those remaining are the most tolerant; and when their number in relation to the number of blacks is such that the whites remaining are all content, no more of them leave. A similar rule governs entry and departure of blacks.

We can now plot, for every point on the diagram, the vector of population change within this area. Within the overlapping portion of the two curves, the numbers of blacks and whites present will both be increasing. Within the white curve but outside the black curve, whites will be coming into the area and blacks departing; the direction of motion on the diagram will be toward the lower right, and nothing stops that motion until all blacks have departed and all whites have come in. To the upper left, within the black curve but beyond the white curve, blacks will be entering and whites departing; and the process can terminate only when all the whites have left and all the blacks have come in. Mixtures denoted by points outside both curves, to the upper right, will be characterized by the departure of both colors; and when one of the colors is reduced to where it is within its own curve, continued departure of the other color will improve the ratio for the color within its own curve; those who left will begin to return, and the other color will evacuate completely.

There are only two stable equilibria. One consists of all the blacks and no whites, the other all the whites and no blacks. Which of the two will occur depends on how the process starts and, perhaps, the relative speeds of white and black movement. If initially one color predominates it will move toward complete occupancy. If initially some of both are present, in 'statically viable' numbers, relative speeds of black and white entry will determine which of the two eventually turns discontent and evacuates. If both are initially present in large numbers, relative speeds of exit will determine which eventually becomes content with the ratio, reverses movement, and occupies the territory.

There are, then, compatible mixes of the two colors—any mixture denoted by the overlap of the two curves. The difficulty is that any such mixture attracts outsiders, more of one color or both colors, eventually more of just one color, so that one color begins to dominate numerically. A few individuals of the opposite color then leave; as they do, they further reduce the numerical status of those of their own color who stay behind. A few more are dissatisfied, and they leave; the minority becomes even smaller, and cumulatively the process causes evacuation of them all.

ALTERNATIVE SCHEDULES

This is, of course, not the only result. The outcome depends on the shapes we attribute to the tolerance schedules, and to the sizes of the white and black populations. With steeper straight-line schedules and equal numbers of blacks and whites we can produce a stable mixture with a large number of blacks and whites.

Specifically, suppose that the median white can tolerate a ratio of 2.5 blacks per white, i.e., will inhabit this area even if whites are a minority of 25% to 30%. Suppose the most tolerant white can accept a ratio of five to one and the least tolerant will not stay with any blacks. The tolerance schedule will be a straight line with a vertical intercept at 5.0. If the blacks are equal in number and have an identical distribution of tolerance for the presence of whites, the two schedules will translate into identical parabolas as shown in Figure 19.

Here, in addition to the two stable equilibria at 100 blacks and no whites and at 100 whites and no blacks, there is a stable mixture at 80 blacks and 80 whites. In fact, over a wide range of initial conditions it is this mixed equilibrium that will be approached through the movement of blacks and whites. As long as half or more of both colors are present— actually, slightly over 40% of both colors—the dynamics of entry and departure will lead to the stable mixture of 80 blacks and 80 whites. Even for very small numbers of both colors present, if the initial ratios are within the slopes of the two curves (which allow somewhat more than four to one of either color) and if neither color tends to enter much more rapidly than the other, the two colors will converge on the 80 − 80 mixture. Still, if the area were initially occupied by either color, it would require the concerted entry of more than 25% of the other color to lead to this stable mixture. Thus each of the three equilibria—the all-white, the all-black, and the 80 − 80 mixture—is stable against fairly large perturbations.

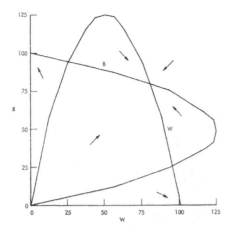

Figure 19.

ALTERNATIVE NUMBERS

The stable equilibrium generated in Figure 19 disappears if the total number of blacks exceeds that of whites or whites exceed blacks by, say, two to one. In that case one curve lies within the other curve, rather than intersecting it, as shown in Figure 20. Alternatively, leaving total numbers of blacks and whites equal, the stable equilibrium disappears if the straight-line tolerance schedules are made less steep; with the schedules that underlie Figure 18, equal numbers result in Figure 21. (For straight-line tolerance schedules and equal numbers of the two colors, there is no stable intersection of the two parabolas unless the tolerance schedules have vertical intercepts of 3.0, with median tolerance of 1.5.)

LIMITING NUMBERS

Limiting the numbers allowed to be present can sometimes produce a stable mixture. If the number of whites in the preferred area is limited to 40 and if the most tolerant 40 are always the first to enter and the last to leave, the curves of Figure 20 are replaced by those of Figure 22, with a stable mixture at 40 whites and a comparable number of blacks.

With the curves of Figure 18, however, the numbers of *both* colors would have to be restricted to yield the stable intersection shown in Figure 23. If the *total* number present can be restricted, but not the numbers of the two colors separately, we get a kind of neutral

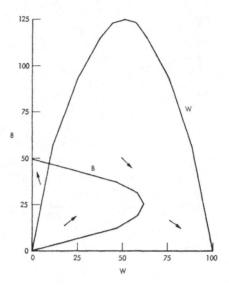

Figure 20.

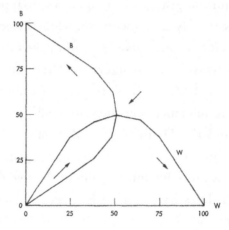

Figure 21.

equilibrium along the overlapped portion of the 45-degree line shown in Figure 24. If there is 'turnover' of the population, the mixture may drift toward a higher ratio of whites to blacks or a higher ratio of blacks to whites. If it goes outside the overlapping portion of the two curves to the lower right, the black minority will evacuate.

It is interesting that the limitation on the number of whites that may be present has the same effect in our model as if the whites in excess of that number had no tolerance for any blacks at all. Whether they are excluded, or merely exclude themselves, it is their *absence* that keeps the

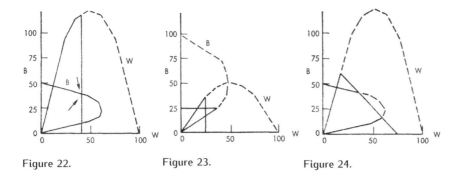

Figure 22.   Figure 23.   Figure 24.

whites from overwhelming the blacks by their numbers and makes the stable mixture possible.

VARYING 'TOLERANCE'

Thus it is not the case that 'greater tolerance' increases the likelihood of a stable mixture—at least, not if 'greater tolerance' means that within a given population some members are statistically replaced by others more tolerant. On the contrary, replacing the two-thirds least tolerant whites in Figure 22 by even less tolerant whites keeps the whites from overwhelming the blacks by their numbers.

This would not happen if we made *all* whites less tolerant. If we make the tolerance schedule of the whites merely less steep, thus shortening the whites' parabola in Figure 22, we do not get our stable intersection of curves. What is required, as we manipulate the tolerance schedule in search of a stable equilibrium, is that at our dividing point of 40% or so of the whites the more tolerant whites just within that percentage figure remain as tolerant as they were and the less tolerant just beyond that figure become even less tolerant. (What happens to the very most tolerant and the very least tolerant makes little difference so long as they do not drastically change.) The broken line shown in Figure 25 is the kind that will produce the stable mixture when the blacks are outnumbered two to one with the curve of Figure 20.

VARIETIES OF RESULTS

Evidently there is a wide variety of shapes of tolerance schedules that we could experiment with and different assumed aggregate ratios of blacks and whites. While there is no room here for a large number of combinations, the method is easy and the reader can pursue by himself the cases that most interest him. There are a few results that deserve to be summarized even though the analysis will not be shown.

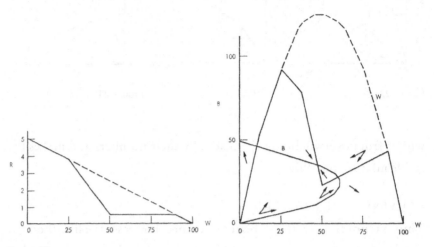

Figure 25.

1. The only logical restriction on the shape of a 'tolerance schedule' is that it slope downward to the right; the only ensuing logical restriction on the shape of the absolute-numbers curves is that a ray from the origin intersect such a curve only once. Within this restriction it is possible to have curves that provide a single stable equilibrium, two stable equilibria, three or four or even more. The single one may be with one color exclusively present or with both colors present; two stable equilibria may be all-white and all-black, or one mixture and one consisting of a single color, or two mixtures. Three stable equilibria can be one mixture plus two extremes, one extreme plus two mixtures, or actually even three mixtures, and so forth. The occurrence of several mixed-color stable equilibria is usually sensitive, though, to small changes in the shapes and positions of the curves. It is the extreme one-color stable equilibria that tend to be least disturbed by shifts in the tolerance schedules or changes in the aggregate numbers; and the occurrence of a *single* mixed stable equilibrium may be fairly immune to shifts in the curves.

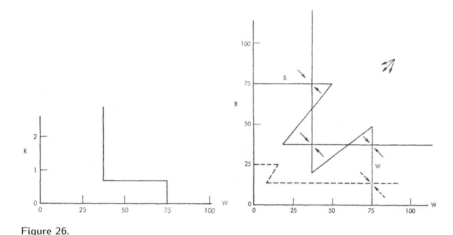

Figure 26.

Figures 26 and 27 illustrate a few interesting possibilities. In Figure 26 the whites divide into three parts—those that have unlimited tolerance, those that have (the same) limited tolerance, and those that have no tolerance for the presence of blacks. If blacks are equal in number and similarly divided the solid curve for blacks is obtained; there are three stable equilibria, each containing the whites and blacks of unlimited tolerance, one containing them only, and the others containing as well the whites of limited tolerance or, alternatively, the blacks. If blacks are half the number of whites, the dotted line replaces the solid line and there is the single equilibrium. If instead the blacks' curve is the parabola of Figure 20, it may intersect the vertical part of the whites' curve to produce a stable mixture, together with another stable all-white equilibrium.

Figure 27 illustrates two extreme cases. One tolerance schedule is a rectangular hyperbola, $RN = .9$, where R is the opposite-own color ratio and N the number, for both blacks and whites in equal numbers. The other is the horizontal line, $R = 1.1$, all whites having the same tolerance. The latter lies almost entirely within the former and appears much less 'tolerant' in the aggregate, but provides a precarious stable equilibrium with all blacks and all whites present—precarious because it is stable only against small perturbations. Evidently a great variety of shapes can be

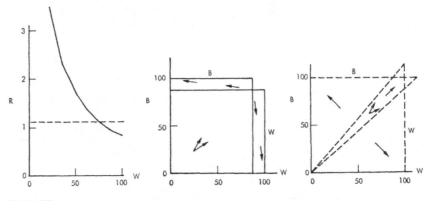

Figure 27.

fitted beneath the rectangular hyperbola, being 'dominated' by it as far as tolerance is concerned—i.e., being unambiguously less tolerant throughout—yet capable of producing one or more stable mixtures. The rectangular hyperbola for whites is compatible with the black schedule of Figure 20 (yielding the parabolic reaction curve) if black numbers are sufficient to make the curve protrude through the 'ceiling' at 100 whites.

2. To make possible a stable mixed equilibrium it is sometimes sufficient to limit the number of one color that may be present; it is sometimes necessary to limit the number of both colors that may be present; and if the curves do not overlap at all there is no numbers limitation that will bring about a stable mixture.

3. Limiting the *ratio* of black to white or white to black that may be present, by restricting the further entry of the color that exceeds the limiting ratio, may or may not provide a stable equilibrium according to the shapes and positions of the two curves. Furthermore, limiting the ratio may exclude one or more stable equilibria and thus bring about the particular color combination corresponding to a particular stable equilibrium. Two possibilities are shown in Figures 28 and 29. The interpretation of the ratio limit, in both these figures, is that when the ratio of white to black is at or beyond its limit no more whites may enter (though blacks are free to leave, causing the ratio

to increase further), and similarly for the limiting ratio of black to white. In Figure 28 no stable equilibrium is produced by the ratio limits; the stable equilibria are all-white and all-black but without all the whites or all the blacks. In Figure 29 a stable equilibrium is produced at the white/black upper limit where it intersects the blacks' reaction curve.

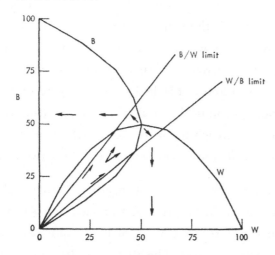

Figure 28.

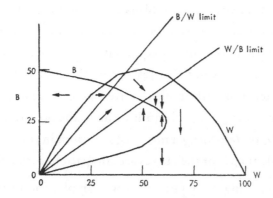

Figure 29.

4. A limitation on total occupancy can provide a neutral equilibrium that may be wide or narrow according to the shapes of the curves, as in Figure 24.

5. If the two colors have similar tolerance schedules for each other, the likelihood of a stable mixed equilibrium is greater, the more

nearly equal are the numbers of the two colors. That is, the greater the disparity in total numbers of blacks and whites, the fewer are the tolerance schedules for the two colors that will lead to a stable equilibrium.

6. In general, for a stable mixture, the minority must be the more tolerant of the two groups. Either the mixed equilibrium will be one in which the majority group outnumbers the minority group, or else it will be one in which a larger percentage of the majority absents itself than of the minority. That is to say, if whites outnumber blacks in the aggregate by five to one, a mixed population in the local area requires either that blacks be outnumbered by whites or that four-fifths or more of the whites be incapable of abiding equal numbers of the two colors.

7. If there are only two locations altogether, one of which is preferred by both colors, the alternative to mixed living in the preferred location is not that members of both colors can go elsewhere and live by themselves. The alternative location is bound to be occupied by one of the two colors only, since any difference in the ratios in the two places would make the color with the most adverse ratio in the alternative location doubly motivated to move into the preferred area; and at equal ratios both colors would prefer to move. It turns out that restricting the alternatives to a single area, where not both colors can live segregated, can have the effect (*a*) of *providing* a mixed equilibrium in the preferred area, or the effect (*b*) of *destroying* a mixed equilibrium in the preferred area. Plausible shapes of the curves are compatible with either result.

Superimposing on Figure 20, for example, the restriction of a single alternative location occupied by all those blacks and whites that do not live in the preferred location, we obtain a mixed stable equilibrium consisting of all the blacks and some of the whites in the preferred area (as well as two stable segregated equilibria). Superimposing the same restriction on Figure 19, however, spoils the possibility of a stable mixture and only the two segregated extremes are dynamically stable.

If both blacks and whites are divided in their preferences for the two areas, some of both colors preferring one area, some the other, there may be stable mixtures in both areas, a stable mixture in one with part of one color exclusively in the other, or stable segregated occupancy of the two areas, depending on the shapes of the curves and the initial conditions.

INTEGRATIONIST PREFERENCES

Surprisingly, the results generated by this analysis do not depend upon each color's having a preference for living separately. They do not even depend on a preference for being in the majority!

For simplicity of exposition it has been supposed that each individual is limited in his 'tolerance' for the other color and will go elsewhere, to live among his own color, if the ratio in his preferred place becomes too extreme. And this was indeed the hypothesis under study when the results were originally worked out. The question then presented itself, suppose these blacks and whites actually prefer mixed neighborhoods: what must we do to capture this neighborhood preference in a model of the general sort already developed?

On reflection it appeared that the analysis was already finished and the same model represented both hypotheses. More than that, the same *results* flowed from the two alternative hypotheses.

We postulate a preference for mixed living and simply *reinterpret* the same schedules of tolerance to denote merely the upper limits to the ratios at which people's *preference for integrated residence* is outweighed by their extreme minority status (or by their inadequately majority status).

The same model fits both interpretations. The results are as pertinent to the study of preferences for *integration* as to the study of preferences for *separation*. (The only asymmetry is that we did not postulate a lower limit to the acceptable proportion of opposite color, i.e., an upper limit to the proportion of like color in the neighborhood.)

POLICIES AND INSTRUMENTS

The analysis is pertinent to the study of the way that *numerical quotas* or *ratio quotas* or *limits on total numbers* may affect the likelihood of a mixed stable equilibrium. It is equally pertinent to the study of the role of *concerted action*. The occurrence of an intersection of the two curves could constitute a stable equilibrium but does not usually guarantee that that equilibrium will result; it usually competes with extreme mono-colored stable equilibria. When there are two or more potential stable equilibria, *initial conditions* and *rates of movement* determine which one will result.

Getting 'over the hump' from one stable equilibrium to another often requires either a large perturbation or concerted action. Acting in concert, people can achieve an alternative stable equilibrium. (Blacks and whites cannot both successfully concert in opposition to each other; either color, by concerted action, may overwhelm the other, but not both simultaneously.)

The difficulty of transiting between equilibria can be formalized by the notion of resistance in the evolutionary games literature. See Young (1993).

The model as described is limited in the phenomena it can handle because it makes no allowance for *speculative behavior*, for *time lags* in behavior, for *organized action*, or for *misperception*. It also involves a single area rather than many areas simultaneously affected, each of which is one of the 'alternatives' that we have in mind when we study another. The model can, however, be enlarged to accommodate some of these enrichments.

Tipping

The foregoing analysis can be used to explore the phenomenon of 'neighborhood tipping.' 'Tipping' is said to occur when a recognizable new minority enters a neighborhood in sufficient numbers to cause the earlier residents to begin evacuating. The phenomenon has been discussed by Morton Grodzins (1957), who says that 'for the vast majority of white Americans a tipping point exists,' and cites 20% Negroes as a commonly estimated upper limit in some Eastern cities. He states as an empirical generalization that, once an urban area begins to swing from mainly white to mainly Negro, the change is rarely reversed. (This could mean either that tipping is nearly universal and irreversible, or alternatively that tipping, when it occurs, accelerates a process that is inevitable and irreversible anyway.) A study of Chicago (Duncan and Duncan 1957) found no instance between 1940 and 1950 of a mixed neighborhood (25% to 75% white) in which succession from white to Negro occupancy was arrested or reversed.

The 'tipping phenomenon' was observed closely by A. J. Mayer (1960) in a well-defined neighborhood of about 700 single-family homes, surrounded by racially mixed neighborhoods. A few houses were sold to Negroes in 1955. 'The selling of the third house convinced everyone that the neighborhood was destined to become mixed.' A year later 40 houses had been sold to Negroes; everyone defined the neighborhood as 'mixed'; and opinion varied on whether the neighborhood would become completely Negro. In another two years the percentage had gone above 50%, and the end result was no longer questioned.

The same or a similar phenomenon has occasionally been observed for ethnic groups other than Negroes, also for clubs, schools, occupations, and apartment buildings, sometimes with males and females rather than ethnic groups, and sometimes with age groups. (An ice cream parlor in Lexington, Massachusetts 'tipped' to a teenage clientele; lady shoppers and mothers of small children ceased coming, and it closed.)

Some crucial characteristics of any model of this alleged phenomenon are whether the neighborhood has a fixed and well-recognized boundary, whether the new entrants (the 'minority') are clearly recognizable as a separate group, what the normal rate of turnover is, how many potential entrants there are compared with the size of the neighborhood and at what rate their number increases, what alternative neighborhoods are available for those who evacuate and what alternatives there are for the 'minority' that seeks entrance.

This is evidently the kind of process our analysis has been dealing with. Specifically, this is a phenomenon that is alleged to occur in a well-defined neighborhood when something disturbs the original equilibrium at 100% white.

Assuming that this is a neighborhood of houses, rather than a blank space available for settlement, there is a rather inflexible capacity limit on the combined total of both colors that can be accommodated. Entry is limited either by the normal turnover of housing or by the rate at which the initial residents can evacuate. There is a primary role of the white population (or initial population, whatever its defining characteristic) that already resides in the area, but an important additional interest in the potential new white entrants who would represent the inflow under normal turnover in the absence of any tipping phenomenon. If the process takes time, the potential population would keep changing in composition, as today's home-hunters settle elsewhere and new ones arise in the general area. We can sometimes assume that whites already resident have somewhat more tolerance than outsiders, relative to their preference for living in this area, simply because it takes a stronger inducement to make a family move out than to make a family merely decide not to move in.

The black population may be small or large relative to the neighborhood. Or it could be small in the short run but cumulatively large with the passage of time.

A number of possibilities are illustrated in Figures 30, ??, and 32. In few if any of these figures is it clear just what we might want to call the 'tipping point.' There are several points at which something discontinuous happens or some cumulative process begins. Furthermore, it is interesting that *in none of the cases shown does any important discontinuity necessarily occur at the modal or typical tolerance value.* If 'most Americans can tolerate about 20 percent blacks in their community,' any tipping point or tipping points will tend to occur at quite different percentage figures!

Among the figures shown, an important difference is between those in which the blacks have an 'in-tipping' point and those in which they do not. When the black reaction curve encloses the lower righthand point of all-white occupancy, as in the upper left panel of Figure 30, there are blacks ready to move in as rapidly as houses become available; when it does not enclose that point, there is an initial all-white stable equilibrium that has to be overcome by some event or process. That process could be concerted entry, erroneous entry by a few, organized introduction of a few, redefinition of the neighborhood boundary so that some who were not inside become 'inside,' or something of the sort.

A possibility is that the number of blacks willing to live as a small minority in this white neighborhood is not zero but is too small to attract other blacks, but nevertheless reaches a large cumulative total over time, so that a slow process of black entry may gradually bring the black--white ratio up to where more blacks are attracted and, by entering, attract still more, and so on in the cumulative process analyzed earlier. At the point where the black reaction curve cuts the 45-degree line denoting the capacity of the neighborhood, we might say that 'tipping-in' has begun. This is the point at which blacks will surge in if houses are available, rather than merely show up from time to time.

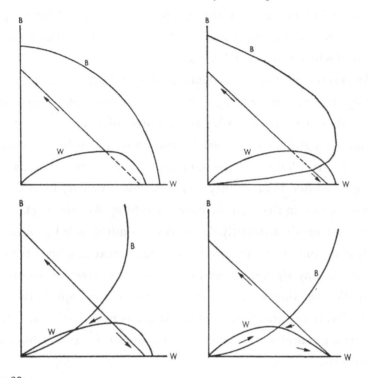

Figure 30.

Another important difference is between the cases (Figure 30) in which there are enough blacks to fill the neighborhood and the cases (Figure ??) in which there are not. One possibility is that there are enough blacks seeking entry to cause the whites to evacuate but not enough to fill the neighborhood, so that the neighborhood becomes all black and partly vacant, as in the middle panel of Figure ??. Another is that there are not enough blacks to cause all the whites to evacuate, but the whites who remain in the mixed population are too few in number, together with the blacks, to fill the area, as in the lower panel of Figure ??, so that a mixed equilibrium occurs with excess capacity. (As the price of housing falls in the face of excess capacity, more blacks may be attracted, but possibly more whites will also.)

Still another case is shown in Figure 32. Here the presence of a few Negroes will cause whites to evacuate in appreciable numbers but, because the white tolerance schedule becomes inelastic, the white reaction curve becomes steep and cuts the 45-degree line, so that white evacuation ceases and more blacks can move in only as vacancies occur from normal turnover. (If or when the population mix reaches the point where the reaction curve again cuts the 45-degree line, the cumulative process of white evacuation begins again.)

An entering minority may define a subneighborhood as the relevant territory. If blacks are willing to be 30% of a subneighborhood of 50 houses, they may 'tip in' after the number of black homes reaches 15, even though in a larger neighborhood of 1,000 houses they are only $1\frac{1}{2}$%. An alternative phenomenon is that whites evacuate the subneighborhood because they count the black density locally, on an adjacency basis; in that case we have something like our checkerboard analysis to consult. Evidently the process is limited only by evacuation speeds if no one in the majority can abide a next neighbor from the minority or any significant number across the street or around the corner. The 'proximity model' of stars and zeros may apply in the small, and the 'bounded area model' in the large, as next neighbors react to immediate proximity while more distant ones react to neighborhood proportions.

Speculation has been adduced as an aggravating factor. Whites may respond not to the number or percentage of blacks currently present, but to the anticipated increase in the number. They may, that is,

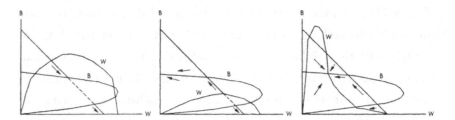

Figure 31.

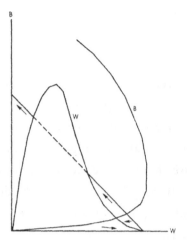

Figure 32.

anticipate the process.[†] Evidently if whites believe that the percentage of blacks will become intolerable and are prepared to leave in anticipation once they believe it, the number of blacks required to cause 'out-tipping' is not the number that begins a cumulative process in our analysis but rather the number that induces this belief. There will still be a cumulative process: those whites who evacuate in anticipation may enhance the belief of other whites in the inevitability of the process.

Speculative departure, though, requires that there be some penalty on late departure or some premium on early departure. Anticipated financial loss or anticipated delay in the departure could cause people to leave early; otherwise people could wait and see. Such things as lease and ownership arrangements would be relevant here.

The partitioning of territory into well-defined neighborhoods may contribute to a 'channeling' process. It may lead blacks to concentrate on one area rather than several; it may lead whites to believe that the blacks will concentrate on one area rather than several. It may lead to experience that tends to confirm the tipping hypothesis, so

---

[†] In the Russell Woods example, mentioned earlier, the residents certainly expected large numbers of Negroes on the basis of the first three or so, and at 40% Negro nearly everybody took an ultimate 100% for granted. Just knowing that he is bound to move in a year or two may make a person move at the first convenient opportunity; otherwise only risk of financial loss, or of being 'locked in' beyond one's own 'static tipping point,' would cause speculative evacuation.

that if speculative departure is relevant, the beliefs conducive to departure will be reinforced. And it can lead to a concentration of real estate sales activity on a 'target neighborhood.' If lending and sales agencies have been reluctant to sell houses or lend on them to Negroes in all-white neighborhoods, the inhibitions may dissolve upon entry of a few Negroes into a particular neighborhood, causing a differential ease of entry and serving as a further signal that Negro demand, blocked elsewhere, will concentrate on this neighborhood. Thus 'neighborhood tipping,' in contrast to the domino effect of very local proximity avoidance, depends on comparatively small and well-defined neighborhoods.

An interesting and important question is whether an entire metropolitan area might 'tip.' There is also the question whether some major nonresidential unit, say the U.S. Army, could tip. City school systems evidently lend themselves to the phenomenon.

The process, if it occurs, is too complex to be treated comprehensively here. But evidently analysis of 'tipping' phenomena wherever it occurs—in neighborhoods, jobs, restaurants, universities or voting blocs—and whether it involves blacks and whites, men and women, French-speaking and English-speaking, officers and enlisted men, young and old, faculty and students, or any other dichotomy, requires explicit attention to the dynamic relationship between individual behavior and collective results. Even to recognize it when it occurs requires knowing what it would look like in relation to the differential motives or decision rules of individuals.[†]

This is an example of Schelling's distinctive style: in a single sentence he dramatically enlarges the scope of his analysis without going into details.

[†] For further discussion see Schelling (1969). See also Morrill (1965) for a random-movement model that generates, by selective resistance at the boundary, a ghetto-expansion process that can be compared with city maps.

REFERENCES

Duncan, O. D., and B. Duncan. 1957. *The Negro Population of Chicago*. Chicago, IL: University of Chicago Press.

Grodzins, M. 1957. *Metropolitan Segregation*. Chicago, IL: University of Chicago Press.

Mayer, A. J. 1960. "Russell Woods: Change Without Conflict." In *Studies in Housing & Minority Groups*, edited by N. Glazer and D. McEntire. Berkeley, CA: University of California Press.

Morrill, R. L. 1965. "The Negro Ghetto: Problems and Alternatives." *The Geographical Review* 55:339–361.

Pascal, A. H. 1967. *The Economics of Housing Segregation*. Technical report RM-5510-RC. Santa Monica, CA: The RAND Corporation, November.

Schelling, T. C. 1969. *Neighborhood Tipping*. Technical report Discussion Paper No. 100. Harvard Institute of Economic Research, December.

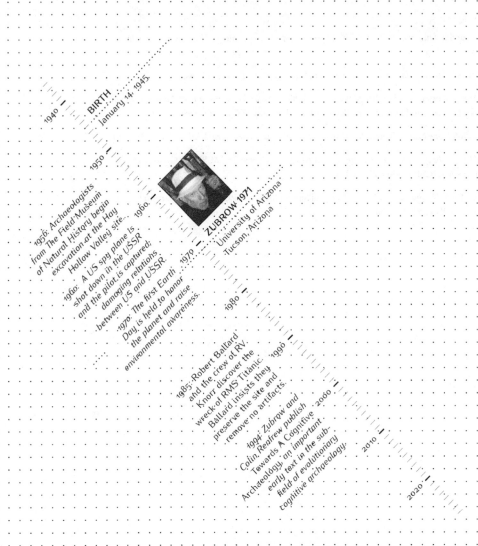

1940

BIRTH
January 14, 1945.

1950

*1956: Archaeologists
from The Field Museum
of Natural History begin
excavation at the Hay
Hollow Valley site.* 1960.

*1960: A US spy plane is
shot down in the USSR
and the pilot is captured,
damaging relations
between US and USSR.*

1970: The first Earth 1970
*Day is held to honor
the planet and raise
environmental awareness.*

ZUBROW 1971
University of Arizona
Tucson, Arizona

1985: Robert Ballard 1980
*and the crew of RV.
Knorr discover the
wreck of RMS Titanic.
Ballard insists they
preserve the site and
remove no artifacts.*

1994: Zubrow and 1990
*Colin Renfrew publish
Towards A Cognitive
Archaeology, an important
early text in the sub-
field of evolutionary
cognitive archaeology.* 2000

2010

2020

EZRA B.W. ZUBROW

[38]

PREHISTORY IN THE LAND OF MALTHUS

*Timothy A. Kohler, Washington State University
and Santa Fe Institute*

Archaeologists attempting to understand our non-literate ancestors often disagree on the appropriate sets of constraints to impute on ancient societies. Why, for example, don't we see farming, cities, writing, and other complex technologies earlier than we do? (Or later, for that matter?) Of course for pre–*Homo sapiens sapiens*, where cognitive constraints must also be considered, the task is more daunting still, but even when we are considering just the last 50,000 years, where it's safe to endow our predecessors with modern cognitive and linguistic abilities, what really sets the limits on what people could accomplish and how they organized themselves? For example, is it mainly ecological constraints such as climate and how people harvest energy and materials from their environment that set limits on population size (with downstream effects on everything else), or is it a specific failure to accumulate and effectively transmit knowledge, skills, and technology that regulates the rate by which human societies increased in size and complexity?

Of course a reasonable position is that there is a co-evolution among how we make our livings, the technologies available, the knowledge and skills applied by members of a society, and how we organize ourselves. Specialized technologies that are highly effective for specific tasks require accumulated skills and depend on divisions of labor, all of which require larger group sizes and low-friction ways of passing the fruits of one's labor to other group members in exchange for their outputs from applying different specialized technologies. This morass of dependencies is not easy to analyze over the long term, where each variable is both subject to evolutionary change but also constrained by its socio-ecological matrix.

E. B. W. Zubrow, "Carrying Capacity and Dynamic Equilibrium in the Prehistoric Southwest," in *American Antiquity* 36 (2): 127–138 (1971).

Reproduced with permission of Cambridge University Press and American Antiquity.

Breaking into this system has required choosing relatively limited chunks of time and space in which most variables (technologies, skills, accumulated knowledge, and perhaps social structure) do not change very much, and then finding frameworks allowing those variables that do change to be fruitfully analyzed. In "Carrying Capacity and Dynamic Equilibrium in the Prehistoric Southwest," Ezra Zubrow analyzes how human population size changed over some 1,400 years of late pre-European-contact history across several ecological zones in a relatively small but intensely studied portion of east-central Arizona.

In 1971 Zubrow was just finishing his dissertation at the University of Arizona and was on his way to a position at Stanford. His emphasis on quantification and particularly his proposal that growth was strongly limited by carrying capacity were relatively novel in archaeology but squarely in line with the priorities of the "new archaeology." In his suggestion that an optimal zone would get settled up to the point where more marginal zones provide equal returns, Zubrow foreshadows a huge literature using optimality as an analytical tool in the historical social sciences (for examples from human behavioral ecology, see Smith and Winterhalder 1992). This paper also roots a phylogeny of archaeological research on resource and population dynamics that today has differentiated into many subspecies, including analyses of ideal free (Winterhalder *et al.* 2010) and despotic (Prufer *et al.* 2017) settlement distributions.

Zubrow defined carrying capacity as the sustainable dynamic equilibrium between population and resources. He recognized that climatic variability could alter resource abundance, affecting carrying capacity; that economic or technological innovations such as agriculture could raise carrying capacity; and that standards of living, degree of population aggregation (e.g., settlement size), and other factors potentially recoverable by archaeologists could be affected by the distance between population size and carrying capacity, and whether that distance is positive or negative. In general, the societies Zubrow studied were growing rapidly precisely because they were undergoing their agricultural (or Neolithic) demographic transition (Kohler and Reese 2014), which substantially raised the carrying capacity of their environment relative to the low ceiling experienced by foragers.

What, then, caused the severe local population decline in the Hay Hollow Valley in the fourteenth century CE? Zubrow makes a case that declining resource productivity as proxied by decreases in relative frequency of pinyon pine pollen (often considered an index for precipitation) is part of the explanation. But he couldn't push this hypothesis very far because he did not have a model for maize productivity in the valley. Faced with similar problems in understanding why Pueblo populations decline and then leave the central Mesa Verde region in the 1200s CE—where we have the advantage of annual estimates for maize productivity—it appears that declining local productivity in comparison with attractive areas to the southeast is a major part of the explanation (Bocinsky and Kohler 2014; Scheffer *et al.* 2021). But various local problems, including increased violence, degradation of slowly renewable resources such as deer and forests, and perhaps even raiding by nomadic ancestors of the Diné from the north, played key supporting roles (Kohler, Bocinsky, and Bird 2022; Scheffer *et al.* 2021).

The general picture Zubrow painted of Southwestern farming societies approaching their Malthusian limits, and then encountering difficulties as resource productivity fluctuated, remains essentially correct as a high-level overview (Schwindt *et al.* 2016). Fifty years after this paper, though, we could (rather unfairly!) fault Zubrow for failing to put this local sequence into a larger regional framework. In the 1300s large portions of the (non-desert) Southwest witnessed growth of large settlements in the context of spatial contraction of farming populations and extensive changes in their religious and economic practices and social organization. While Zubrow mostly ignores these changes rather than trying to unravel what is cause and what is effect, his approach might be read to indicate that he thinks population pushing against resource limits leads the way to these other changes. From a complexity perspective, this would be a huge oversimplification, since it would ignore how the possible paths societies may take are constrained by the forms that are known, or that are technologically and socially reachable. It is also surprising that he doesn't engage Boserup's theory of agricultural intensification, published a few years before this essay.

Limits to growth weighed on many minds in the early 1970s. The first Earth Day was celebrated the year before Zubrow's article appeared, and the year after his paper, Donella Meadows and her MIT colleagues published their famous model-based treatment of world economic history and futures, underscoring the problems of exponential growth (1972). Today, of course, we realize that our outputs of atmosphere-warming gases may be as dangerous as the shortfalls in food and raw materials that most concerned the MIT modelers (Steffen *et al.* 2018). In the long run, it may be the systems thinking implicit in Zubrow's approach (better developed in his 1975 monograph) that will have the greatest beneficial impact in helping us envisage and build a positive future. ✴

REFERENCES

Bocinsky, R. K., and T. A. Kohler. 2014. "A 2,000-Year Reconstruction of the Rain-Fed Maize Agricultural Niche in the US Southwest." *Nature Communications* 5:5618. https : / / doi . org / 10 . 1038 / ncomms6618.

d'Alpoim Guedes, J., S. A. Crabtree, R. K. Bocinsky, and T. A. Kohler. 2016. "21st-Century Approaches to Ancient Problems: Climate and Society." *Proceedings of the National Academy of Sciences* 113 (51): 14483–14491. https://doi.org/10.1073/pnas.1616188113.

Diachenko, A., and E. B. W. Zubrow. 2015. "Stabilization Points in Carrying Capacity: Population Growth and Migrations." *Journal of Neolithic Archaeology* 17:1–15. https://doi.org/10.12766/jna.2015.1.

Fretwell, S. D., and H. L. Lucas, Jr. 1969. "On Territorial Behavior and Other Factors Influencing Habitat Distribution in Birds." *Acta Biotheoretica* 19 (1): 45–52. https://doi.org/10.1007/BF01601953.

Kohler, T. A., R. K. Bocinsky, and D. Bird. 2022. "Fluctuat nec mergitur: Seven Centuries of Pueblo Crisis and Resilience." In *Multidisciplinary Perspectives on Historical Collapse,* edited by M. A. Centeno, P. W. Callahan, P. Larcey, and T. Patterson, 146–166. New York, NY: Routledge.

Kohler, T. A., and K. M. Reese. 2014. "Long and Spatially Variable Neolithic Demographic Transition in the North American Southwest." *Proceedings of the National Academy of Sciences* 111 (28): 10101–10106. https://doi.org/10.1073/pnas.140436711.

Meadows, D. H., D. L. Meadows, J. Randers, and W. W. Behrens III. 1972. *The Limits to Growth: A Report for the Club of Rome's Project on the Predicament of Mankind.* New York, NY: Universe Books.

Prufer, K. M., A. E. Thompson, C. R. Meredith, B. J. Culleton, J. M. Jordan, C. E. Ebert, B. Winterhalder, and D. J. Kennett. 2017. "The Classic Period Maya Transition from an Ideal Free to an Ideal Despotic Settlement System at the Polity of Uxbenká." *Journal of Anthropological Archaeology* 45:53–68. https: //doi.org/10.1016/j.jaa.2016.11.003.

Scheffer, M., E. H. van Nes, D. Bird, R. K. Bocinsky, and T. A. Kohler. 2021. "Loss of Resilience Preceded Transformation of Prehispanic Pueblo Societies." *Proceedings of the National Academy of Sciences* 118 (18): e2024397118. https://doi.org/10.1073/pnas.2024397118.

Schwindt, D. M., R. K. Bocinsky, S. G. Ortman, D. M. Glowacki, M. D. Varien, and T. A. Kohler. 2016. "The Social Consequences of Climate Change in the Central Mesa Verde Region." *American Antiquity* 81 (1): 74–96. https://doi.org/10.7183/0002-7316.81.1.74.

Smith, E. A., and B. Winterhalder, eds. 1992. *Evolutionary Ecology and Human Behavior.* Hawthorne, NY: Aldine de Gruyer.

Steffen, W., J. Rockström, K. Richardson, T. M. Lenton, C. Folke, D. Liverman, C. P. Summerhayes, *et al.* 2018. "Trajectories of the Earth System in the Anthropocene." *Proceedings of the National Academy of Sciences* 115 (33): 8252–8259. https://doi.org/10.1073/pnas.1810141115.

Winterhalder, B., D. J. Kennett, M. N. Grote, and J. Bartruff. 2010. "Ideal Free Settlement of California's Northern Channel Islands." *Journal of Anthropological Archaeology* 29 (4): 469–490. https://doi.org/10.1016/j.jaa.2010.07.001.

Zubrow, E. B. W. 1975. "Prehistoric Carrying Capacity: A Model." (Menlo Park, CA).

CARRYING CAPACITY AND DYNAMIC EQUILIBRIUM IN THE PREHISTORIC SOUTHWEST

Ezra B. W. Zubrow

Abstract

A model of carrying capacity as a dynamic equilibrium system is generated and made operational in order to test a series of hypotheses relating population and settlement patterns. The development of populations in marginal resource zones is shown to be a function of optimal zone exploitation in the Hay Hollow Valley. MacArthur's deviation amplifying model is presented as an alternative to the model's diminishing resource curves as a possible explanation of the extinction of Hay Hollow population by A.D. 1400. Finally, the effects of population excess disequilibriums as defined by the model are examined in relationship to the settlement pattern variables of population aggregation, spatial aggregation and residential area.

This paper is one specific result of an examination of the implications of a general model of carrying capacity as a dynamic equilibrium system (Zubrow 1969). The model is used to account for archaeological data from the Hay Hollow Valley in eastern Arizona. Before considering the model, I wish to make my general assumption base explicit. First, I am assuming the validity of a neo-Malthusian approach. Malthus' major argument which first appeared in the *Essay on Population* has been encapsulated by an anonymous writer in the following limerick.

> *To get land's fruit in quantity,*
> *Takes jolts of labor ever more*
> *Hence food will grow like one, two, three,*
> *While numbers grow like one, two, four.*

(Samuelson 1961, 16)

Since its original publication in 1798, there have been many criticisms of the *Essay*. First and most trivial, his ratios have been shown to be in error. Second, Malthus hypothesized that each advance in technology is absorbed by an increase in population which prevents any increase in the standard of living. This was disproved by the industrial revolution. As an empirical generalization, it was valid for most of the pre-industrial world prior to 1760. However, as a general law, it fell due to the fallacious assumption that increases in production could never exceed increases in population.

The neo-Malthusians such as Boulding and Peacock feel that the general Malthusian model applies where the industrial revolution has not changed the potential for production by several quantum leaps. In these labor intensive economies, population is a major factor in determining the production function and the law of diminishing returns eventually limits production. Although Malthus' stability of the standard of living is rejected, the conclusion that population growth is a correlate of technological change is viable. Thus, in the neo-Malthusian model the ratios are replaced by population pressure in a series of organized, spatially differentiated eco-systems, each with its own level of consumption expectations based on food chains with internal and external ecological connections.

My second assumption is that it is possible to measure prehistoric populations and resources through indirect indices. Archaeological surveys have traditionally served two functions. First, they provide the archaeologist with an approximation of the unexcavated material remains. Second, they may be used to provide an estimate of population. It is a crude estimate, perhaps, of absolute population but it is less crude for estimating relative population size. The more intensively an area is surveyed and the more systematically it is sampled, the more refined is the estimate. An effective indirect index for monitoring the changes in prehistoric resource systems is pollen analysis.

With this background, it is possible to turn to the model of carrying capacity as a dynamic equilibrium system. Carrying capacity is the maximum number of organisms or amounts of biomass which can maintain itself indefinitely in an area, in other words, a homeostatic equilibrium point. It is a homeostatic equilibrium in that there is a tendency toward the maintenance of a state of balance between opposite forces or processes which result in a diminishing net change or a stable constant. It is dynamic in that the point at which the state of balance exists may change over time and space.

It may be surprising for non-archaeologists to learn that prior to the 1970s many archaeologists were extremely reluctant to hazard population estimates. The new archaeology required such estimates to move forward on its other goals.

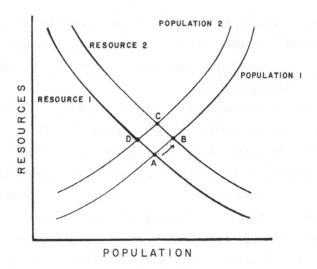

Figure 1. Carrying capacity as a dynamic equilibrium system. *Note*: Resource 1 and Resource 2 refer to iso-resource curves (or resource levels) in which resources plus population equal an energy or biomass constant.

What are the two opposing forces which determine the equilibrium? On the one hand, Liebig's extended law (Boughey 1968, 2) states population size is determined by maxima and minima of specific resources. On the other hand, the "prime dynamic mover" appears to be reproduction. A population will tend to keep reproducing and growing in size until an ultimate limit is reached which is determined by the supply of nutrients and energy. When there is a change in the supply of nutrients and energy, a change in the carrying capacity results, and there is a consequent growth or decrease of the biomass until a new equilibrium is reached. Letter A of Fig. 1 denotes a carrying capacity equilibrium point. If a change in the resource curves takes place from Resource 1 to Resource 2, there results a disequilibrium with resources being greater than population. We would expect the biomass or population to grow along the population curve until a new equilibrium point B is reached. Similarly, one may predict what would happen in the other cases—a decrease in the resource curve or an increase or decrease in the population curve.

Neo-Malthusian models such as the one just described have both advantages and disadvantages. The primary advantages are first, given the initial conditions, one may predict the expected consequences, and second, one may quantify both the initial conditions and the expected results. The primary disadvantage of this type of neo-Malthusian model building is that contemporary demographic and ecological data do not lend themselves to testing the model. This is because the time span for which data exists is too short in relation to long term ecological processes. Secondarily, modern technological development with its concomitant diversity of resources, complex trade patterns, and ease of mobility, complicate the data to the point that it is necessary to utilize factor and discriminant analyses to remove the masking data patterns and variables.

Archaeology is thus in a unique position to evaluate this type of model. Its data span long time periods and some of the societies it considers have not developed the complex resource networks, trade systems, and technologies which distinguish our modern industrial nation states. As presented initially, the model is oversimplified. It does not take into account the spatial differentiation or temporal change in resource patterns. First, let us examine the implications of the spatial differentiation of resources holding the temporal changes in the resource base constant. One may imagine a complex heterogeneous resource pattern as exemplified by Fig. 2 where there are four distinct resources. If we divide this complex pattern into a set of homogeneous resource spaces (which I shall call for the rest of this paper resource zones), it will be easier to build the more generalized model. Our simplified model presented in Fig. 1 accounts for one resource zone. In order to account for the heterogeneous pattern, we need only to sum the models of the individual resource zones. This is exemplified in Fig. 2 where the total carrying capacity for the heterogeneous area will be the sum of the individual resource zone carrying capacities denoted on the diagram by E being equal to $A + B + C + D$.

Now adding the temporal variable, we may note that external conditions such as climate, may cause different resource curves to exist at different points in the chronology. Thus, over time there might be changes in the individual resource zone curves, as well as in the summation curves. These changes need not be uniform.

With this more or less general introduction to the model now completed, one may turn to the specific problem. It has often been noted

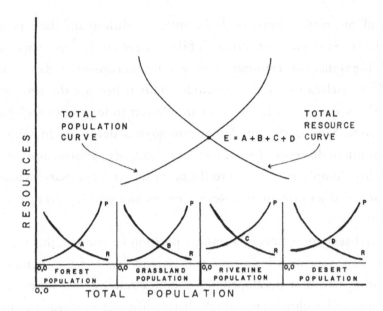

Figure 2. Heterogeneous resource model. The summation of homogeneous resource zones.

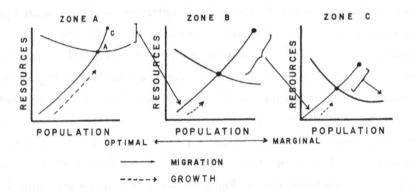

Figure 3. Migration pattern from model.

that the distribution of settlements follows a definite pattern through time which is partially dependent upon the spatial distribution of resources (Kroeber 1939; Haggett 1966). The hypothesis to be examined is that the development of populations in marginal resource zones is a function of optimal zone exploitation. In order to operationalize this hypothesis in terms of the model, we must set up a series of resource zones with consecutively diminishing resource curves as in Fig. 3.

It is easy to define at this point what is meant by optimal and marginal resource zones. By optimal, we mean the resource zone with the highest resource curve. All the other zones are marginal. The lower the resource curve the more marginal the resource zone.

One may predict on the basis of the model what will happen as a population starts to grow in the optimal resource zone (Fig. 3). If the population is less than the carrying capacity, it will increase until it reaches the carrying capacity. If the population overshoots the carrying capacity as a result of simple population growth or as a result of population growth combined with immigration, then the population surplus (the distance C to A in Fig. 3) has two choices— gradual extinction or out-migration to the next zone which is more marginal. In the more marginal zone the process would repeat itself. But each time one moves from zone to more marginal zone it takes less population to reach carrying capacity. If there is no change in the resource curves over time, we would expect the following sequence of events. First, a population filling up the optimal zone to carrying capacity, then a little later a second zone filling up to a smaller carrying capacity, and then a little later a third zone filling up, etc. There are indications, however, discussed by Birdsell (1957), Stott (1969), and Isard (1960) that the out-migration process might slowly begin shortly before carrying capacity is reached for population pressure would be beginning to be felt. On the basis of our model, the predicted population curves by zone would look similar to Fig. 4.

However, one must remember that we have been holding our resource curves constant through time. If they should begin to drop, the resulting carrying capacity decrease would result in larger out migration. This possibility is diagrammed in Fig. 5.

To what extent does the data support the first hypothesis? I have made two tests. The first utilizes the archaeological population indices from the Hay Hollow Valley while the second simulates actual carrying capacity values. The results of both must be compared to the model's predictions.

Topographic zones were defined at the Hay Hollow Valley which show some ecological differentiation. Zone 1 is a mesa top with juniper-pinyon vegetation and basaltic soils. Zone 2 is the side of the mesa. Zone 3 is upper saltbush grassland. Zone 4 is the upper highland terrace with juniper-pinyon vegetation. Zone 5 is the lower highland terrace and

Zubrow appears to have been unaware that two years earlier Fretwell and Lukas (1969) had published a formal model for this same situation, though among birds. They defined what Zubrow will describe in this paragraph as the "ideal free distribution."

Since there are no constraints on entering these new habitats, Zubrow describes populations approximating an ideal free distribution. If existing populations in these new habitats constrained dispersal, for example by territorial behavior, the result might instead approximate an ideal despotic distribution.

Zubrow was in the vanguard in opening up archaeology to research in biology, ecology, and geography.

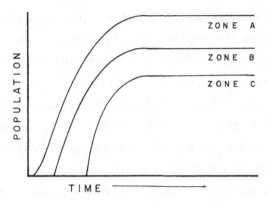

Figure 4. Population predictions by zones from heterogeneous model without change in resource curves.

Zone 7 the lower grass bottomlands. Zone 6 has no habitation sites and is thus excluded.

Survey data have been collected in three samples which when combined cover intensively an area of 18.4 square miles. There are two samples in which 25% of the area has been surveyed and one sample in which 100% of the land has been covered. The survey technique consisted of setting up grids and then having 5-10 people spaced 10 yards apart walking back and forth across a grid square searching for sites until the entire grid was covered. On the basis of these surveys, Fred Plog and Michael Schiffer have made room and population estimates based on surface evidence and by regression analysis. There have been minor corrections of the data on the basis of my excavations of seven sites that had been previously surveyed. Paul S. Martin and David Gregory have established the chronology of the sites. This chronology has been partially cross checked with radiocarbon dates.

The only evidence of seasonal occupation of sites in the Hay Hollow Valley is in a study of Basketmaker III subsistence by Vernon Grubisich (1969). On the basis of pollen analysis, he found, after considering a large sample of sites, that only three were seasonally occupied. Thus, the calculations are based primarily upon year long occupation. Further analysis of different time periods, however, may reveal significant seasonal occupation.

Solely on the basis of the density of the present flora and the proximity to water resources, one would expect the resource curve of Zone 7 to be the highest with diminishing carrying capacity potential in the other zones during the agricultural period. Fig. 6 shows the number of habitation rooms by zone in the 100% sample. The detailed data upon which all of the graphical compilations are based will appear in my dissertation. The similarity between Figs. 4, 5, and 6 are clear. If one uses the total number of sites as an index of population, then Fig. 6 clearly shows a greater similarity to Fig. 5 than to Fig. 4. It should be noted that these results indicate a decrease in the resource curves after A.D. 1150. This decrease has been explained in an article by Schoenwetter and Dittert (1968) as the result of differences in effective moisture caused by a change in the seasonal rainfall pattern at approximately this date. Hevly (1970) explains this decrease in resources with multiple factors including (1) a change in rainfall pattern from summer to winter dominant or to a biseasonal pattern, and (2) a change in the temperature pattern from warm to cool.

It is clear, however, that the changing resource curves should be verified independently of the model and the population indices for the valley. A series of pollen analyses were undertaken by Hevly. The clearest indicator of climatic change, particularly of moisture and temperature, was the pinyon pollen. This correlated positively with changes of both agricultural and gathered economic pollens to a high degree. In order not to confuse cause with effect nor to take into account the cultural filter on the potential resource curves, we will use the changes in pinyon pollen as a relative index of the change in the resource curves. Given the above, the bar graph section of Fig. 10 (the pinyon pollen curve) shows independently that there is a drop in the resource curves after A.D. 1150.

The role of cultigens in the successive economies has been studied by Burkenroad (1968) and Hevly (1970). Utilizing several indices drawn from tool assemblages, Burkenroad calculates that agriculture begins to predominate over gathering at approximately A.D. 650. This is supported by Hevly's pollen data. If one may use the relative proportions of domesticated and non-domesticated economic pollen calculated as a percentage of total pollen as an index of the role of cultigens, one finds at A.D. 700 that domesticates at 7% are greater than non-domesticates at 5%. The maximum post A.D. 700 cultigen non-cultigen ratio is reached at A.D. 1275 when domesticates are 12% and non-domesticates are 5%. After that the ratio decreases.

Many new approaches to this problem have been developed in the last two decades (e.g., d'Alpoim Guedes *et al.* 2016).

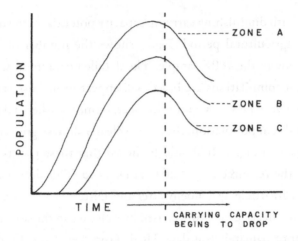

Figure 5. Population predictions by zones from heterogeneous model with change in resource curves.

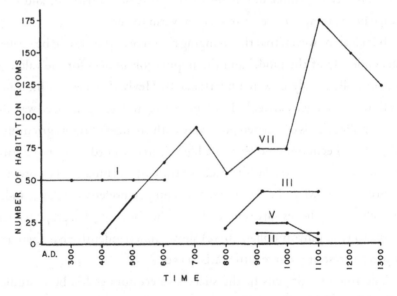

Figure 6. Number of habitation rooms per zone based on 52 sites. The 100% sample.

Actual quantification of the model for maximal carrying capacity values is shown in Table 1. The area of each ecological zone is calculated from aerial photographs and maps. Somewhat arbitrarily, the amounts of dry grams of biomass produced are taken from Odum's values for agriculture and arid areas, and it is assumed on the basis of the U.N. world sample that 2500 kilocalories per day are necessary and sufficient to maintain an average individual in the population. The 5% consumption

Table 1. Maximal carrying capacity calculations.

Zone:	VII	V	III	IV	II	I
Area: Square miles	9.92	2.84	.92	1.43	2.15	1.17
Biomass grams per square meter per day	2.0	1.0	.5	.4	.2	.3
Kilocalories per gram of biomass	4.0	4.0	4.0	4.0	4.0	4.0
Kilocalories	20×10^7	15×10^7	9×10^7	6×10^7	4×10^7	3×10^7
At 5% consumption rate the number of people at carrying capacity	4110	290	190	120	80	70

figure of total produced biomass is also an arbitrary but reasonable estimate. Examining Table 1, one would expect the population size to decrease by zone in the following order: Zone 7 with the largest population, Zone 5, Zone 3, Zone 4, Zone 2, and finally Zone 1 with the smallest population.

Since these area figures (Table 1) include both land covered in the 100% and 25% samples, one must utilize Fig. 7 to test the validity of the simulated zone ordering. Turning to Fig. 7 then, one gets the following actual distribution of sites through time by zone: Zones 7, 2, 5, 3, 4, 1. Only one zone is out of the expected sequence.

There are several possible reasons for this which will also point out some of the simplifying assumptions in this preliminary simulation. First, I have assumed that the sites are located in the zone that they utilize. Second, I have assumed that the geographic size of the zones remain constant over time. Third, I have not attempted to define multiple zone utilization per site. These assumptions however are not insurmountable. For example, one should be able to use the actual location of each site in comparison to the zonal boundaries to determine a function which would predict multiple zonal use of resources for each site.

On the basis of the two tests, it would appear that the data generally supports the hypothesis that the development of populations in marginal resource zones is a function of optimal zone exploitation. The model

At the time, Zubrow was criticized for including in this figure biomass that people couldn't eat; such criticisms eventually led to the development of agricultural paleoproductivity models.

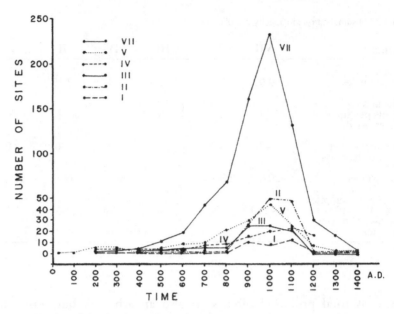

Figure 7. Number of sites by time and zone based on 100% and two 25% samples.

not only allows one to use heuristically the hypothesis but suggests the interaction of the underlying variables.

Human populations are not simply mechanistic. Two factors should be noted. First, they do not grow exactly to the carrying capacity point and then have an intrinsic growth rate of zero. Instead, they will sometimes overshoot the carrying capacity point and with the resulting disequilibrium there will be an increase in the mortality rate and out-migration as previously shown. When this occurs, there is a certain amount of leeway, for the standard of living acts as a buffer. Survival may result for a population above carrying capacity at the expense of lowering the standard of living. However, if the intrinsic growth rate is still positive the standard of living decrease is only a delaying action and eventually the Malthusian checks will catch up. Second, human populations do not grow continuously. Instead, the reality of generations results in a time lag. These two factors, the buffering of the standard of living and the time lag make the more careful examination of the homeostatic mechanism and the conditions under which it functions necessary.

Utilizing our graphical model, the population's homeostatic adjustment would be presented as a decreasing oscillation on the

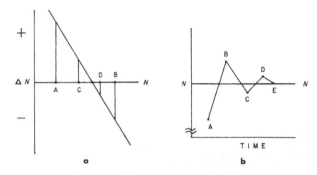

Figure 8. *a*. Homeostatic population adjustment showing the process of successive changes in population size (from MacArthur and Connell 1966, 137). *b*. Homeostatic population adjustment showing the change in population size as a time plot (from MacArthur and Connell 1966, 137).

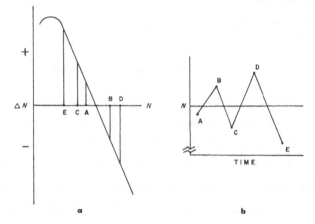

Figure 9. *a*. Deviation amplifying mechanism showing the process of successive changes in population size (from MacArthur and Connell 1966, 137). *b*. Deviation amplifying mechanism showing the change in population size as a time plot (from MacArthur and Connell 1966, 138).

population curve around the carrying capacity point. Alternatively, MacArthur (MacArthur and Connell 1966) has shown the oscillation in terms of the size of the change of population. Thus, in Fig. 8 *a*, a population of initial size A, will successively be of sizes B, C, D, etc. Note B is placed so that the distance from A to B equals the perpendicular of the line segment above A. This may be replotted across time as in Fig. 8 *b*. As MacArthur points out, if the population grew continuously there need not have been a time lag nor an oscillation. His graphs do not show the buffering effect of the standard of living. If a lower standard of living is tolerable, the horizontal axis N (Fig. 8 *a*) is lowered, which results in a higher equilibrium point for N (Fig. 8 *b*) in the time curve plot. It should

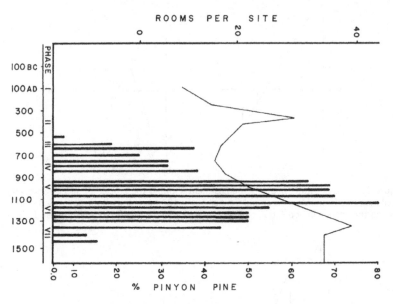

Figure 10. Population aggregation and resource index in the Hay Hollow Valley.

be noted that this may take place after the oscillation process has begun which would result in an asymmetrical oscillation and is the essence of the population dynamics in Geertz' involution concept (Geertz 1968).

MacArthur notes that if the slope of the line of $\triangle N/N$ is greater than $63°$ the oscillations become more violent through time. They increase rather than decrease and instead of a homeostatic process one has a deviation amplifying process such as discussed by Maruyama (1968) (Figs. 8 *a*, 8 *b*). The graphical model of carrying capacity as a dynamic equilibrium system would suggest that population extinction such as seen in the Hay Hollow Valley about A.D. 1400 could result solely from a decrease in the resource curves to the point that no population could be supported. MacArthur's model provides in the deviation amplifying process alternative explanation to this resource depletion as a cause for extinction. Possibly both processes are involved.

Up to this point, we have been relating population size and zonal distribution to resources, but we have not related settlement pattern variables such as population aggregation, spatial aggregation, or residential area to the resources. If the population is above the carrying capacity point or at carrying capacity when the resource curves begin to drop, and if access to resources is related to population size, then one

Since Zubrow does not attempt to quantify whether in fact these deviations were decreasing or increasing through time, this alternative hypothesis is not very compelling. Some years later he published a method to estimate carrying capacity without a resource productvity model (Diachenko and Zubrow (2015).

would expect the smaller villages to be depopulated first. For example, let us imagine three villages, one with a population of 100, one with a population of 40, and one with a population of 20. If there is a 50% decrease in resources which causes a loss of population of 50%, the three villages would have populations of 50, 20, and 10. If there were another 50% decrease, the three villages would be 25, 10, and 5. The smallest village would no longer have sufficient manpower to continue its functions as a village including its subsistence, religious, and political activities. Thus, the smallest population would migrate either to one of the other villages or out of the area of study. If the population migrated to another village there would be an average of 20 people per village; if they migrated out of the area, there would be an average of $17\frac{1}{2}$ people per site and if the smallest village somehow continued to exist there would be 13 people per site. The point to be noted here is that if small villages continue to exist, the average number of persons per village is smaller than if they do not. One might suggest that during periods of resource depletion there will be population aggregation. In other words, as resources decrease there will be fewer sites but *relatively* more people living in each site as the small villages become extinct. Utilizing the 100% survey data the results may be seen in Fig. 10. The bar graphs are the pinyon pollen indirect index of resources as discussed previously. The line is the average number of rooms per site which is taken to be an index of population aggregation. During the major period of resource depletion, from A.D. 1150 on, the number of rooms per site remains quite high. This indicates that during this period there is population aggregation since the smaller sites which would have lowered the average number of rooms per site are not having that effect.

At the same periods of time that we note population aggregation, we would expect spatial aggregation. This is the result of the increasing necessity for the population to utilize areas of optimal resource production during periods of resource depletion. If one examines the data in Fig. 11, this relationship may be seen graphically. The bar graphs are the resource indices which are the same as in the previous graph. The line calculated by Gregory is the measurement of the nearest neighbor statistic between sites. This is an index of the continuum between perfect spatial dispersion and aggregation. Perfect hexagonal dispersion

This is too simplistic, and in fact exactly the opposite effect has been documented elsewhere. A more complete explanation of aggregation would consider at least the volume and diversity of goods exchanged among households within a settlement, and among settlements, the structure of production, and degree of hostility on the landscape.

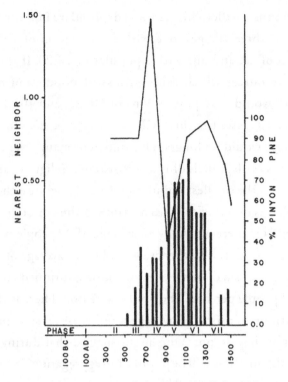

Figure 11. Spatial aggregation and resource index in the Hay Hollow Valley.

is 2.15 and complete aggregation is 0.0. Fig. 11 demonstrates that after A.D. 700 the spatial relationship between sites was one of aggregation whenever the pinyon pollen index was below 50%.

The third variable, residential area, should also decrease during periods of resource depletion. Whenever the population is above the resource curve, there are insufficient resources to meet the demand. As a result, a set of resource priorities will need to be established. For example, under these conditions, a village should allocate more of its labor force to subsistence tasks than to building of large residential structures. Thus, we would expect that residential area will decrease during resource depletion due to the priority of subsistence expenditure of resources. The data in Fig. 12 represents a sample of the 100% survey chosen by time and ecological zone. The resource curve is the same as in the two previous diagrams. There is a close correlation between residential area as measured by average room size and the resource curve. The results show a clear decrease in residential area as resources decrease.

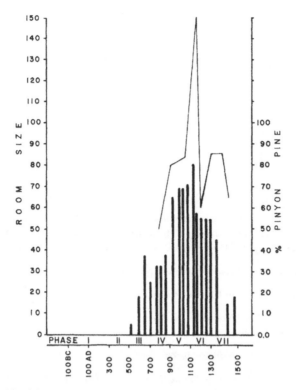

Figure 12. Residential area and resource index in the Hay Hollow Valley.

In conclusion, this paper has:

1. Built a model of carrying capacity as a dynamic equilibrium system.

2. Operationalized the model in order to test the hypothesis that the development of populations in marginal resource zones is a function of optimal zone exploitation.

3. Presented data supporting the above hypothesis from the Hay Hollow Valley of Arizona.

4. Presented MacArthur's homeostatic and deviation amplifying model as an alternative to diminishing resource curves to explain the extinction of the Hay Hollow population in A.D. 1450.

5. Examined the effects of population excess disequilibriums as defined by the model on settlement pattern variables of population aggregation, spatial aggregation, and residential area. ✔

REFERENCES

Birdsell, J. B. 1957. "Some Population Problems Involving Pleistocene Man." In *Population Studies: Animal Ecology and Demography*, edited by K. B. Warren, 22:47–70. Cold Spring Harbor Symposia on Quantitative Biology. Cold Spring Harbor, NY: Long Island Biological Laboratory.

Boughey, S. 1968. *Ecology of Populations*. New York, NY: Macmillan.

Burkenroad, D. 1968. "Population Growth and Economic Change."

Geertz, C. 1968. *Agricultural Involution: The Process of Ecological Change in Indonesia*. Berkeley, CA: University of California Press.

Grubisich, V. J. 1969. "An Examination of Basketmaker Subsistence."

Haggett, P. 1966. *Locational Analysis in Human Geography*. New York, NY: St. Martin's Press.

Hevly, R. 1970. "Paleoecology of Archaeological Sites From East Central Arizona."

Isard, W. 1960. *Methods of Regional Analysis: An Introduction to Regional Science*. New York, NY: John Wiley & Sons.

Kroeber, A. L. 1939. *Culture and Natural Areas of Native North America*. Berkeley, CA: University of California Press.

MacArthur, R. H., and J. H. Connell. 1966. *Biology of Populations*. New York, NY: John Wiley & Sons.

Maruyama, M. 1968. "The Second Cybernetics: Deviation Amplifying Mutual Causal Processes." In *Modern Systems Research For the Behavioral Scientist*, edited by W. Buckley, 304–313. Chicago, IL: Aldine.

Samuelson, P. A. 1961. *Economics: an Introductory Analysis*. New York, NY: McGraw-Hill.

Schoenwetter, J., and A. E. Jr. Dittert. 1968. "An Ecological Interpretation of Anasazi Settlement Patterns." In *Anthropological Archaeology in the Americas,* edited by B. J. Meggers, 41–66. Washington, DC: Anthropological Society of Washington.

Stott, D. H. 1969. "Cultural and Natural Checks on Population Growth." In *Environment and Cultural Behavior,* edited by A. P. Vayda, 90–120. Garden City, NY: Natural History Press.

Zubrow, E. B. W. 1969. "Population, Contact, and Climate in the New Mexican Pueblos." Master's thesis, Department of Anthropology, University of Arizona.

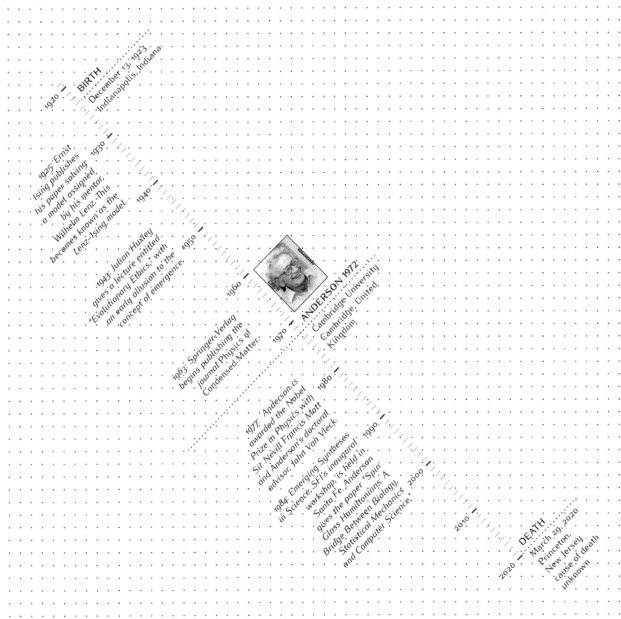

1920

BIRTH
December 13, 1923
Indianapolis, Indiana.

1925: Ernst Ising publishes his paper solving a model assigned by his mentor, Wilhelm Lenz. This becomes known as the Lenz–Ising model.

1930

1940

1943: Julian Huxley gives a lecture entitled "Evolutionary Ethics," with an early allusion to the concept of emergence.

1950

1960

1963: Springer-Verlag begins publishing the journal Physics of Condensed Matter.

ANDERSON 1972:
Cambridge University, Cambridge, United Kingdom.

1970

1977: Anderson is awarded the Nobel Prize in Physics with Sir Nevill Francis Mott and Anderson's doctoral advisor, John Van Vleck.

1980

1984: Emerging Syntheses in Science, SFI's inaugural workshop, is held in Santa Fe. Anderson gives the paper "Spin Glass Hamiltonians: A Bridge Between Biology, Statistical Mechanics, and Computer Science."

1990.

2000

2010

DEATH
March 29, 2020
Princeton, New Jersey,
cause of death unknown

2020

PHILIP·WARREN·ANDERSON

[39]

RISE OF COMPLEXITY SCIENCES IN A REDUCTIONIST WORLD

*Tanmoy Bhattacharya, Los Alamos National Laboratory
and Santa Fe Institute*

P. W. Anderson, "More is Different: Broken Symmetry and the Nature of the Hierarchical Structure of Science," in *Science* 177 (4047): 393–396 (1972).

Reprinted with permission from AAAS.

Introduction

The human mind has, for ever, reduced the entirety of its perceived regularities into a small number of comprehensible theories. For most of history, these theories have stayed distinct, with their unique aims, epistemology, and vocabulary. The scientific revolutions of the last millennium, however, would not let this be: the same reductionist principle that led to the invention of the individual sciences now felt the need to coalesce all such knowledge into one connected framework (Stein 1958). And, this framework was naturally structured by attempting to explain the less understood—usually more complex—sciences "mechanistically" in terms of the better understood ones (Sarkar 1989). As a result, today, one can arrange the sciences in a rough linear hierarchy—such as of particle physics, solid state or many-body physics, chemistry, molecular biology, cell biology, ..., physiology, psychology, social sciences—where the phenomena described at each successive stage can be described mechanistically in terms of the former, as in Philip Anderson's foundational 1972 paper. But, should this methodological (Ruse 2005) reductionist view also entail a replacement of a theory by its reduction?

In fact, fifty years back, when Anderson was writing this piece, there was a belief that the "most fundamental" of these sciences, the one that dealt with the cleanest of the natural systems, that of the motion of isolated particles and composites of a few of these, was all that was worthy of intensive (Weisskopf 1967) study, of induction of yet more fundamental laws, and everything else was merely deduction of extensive results from this. The high scientists working in these fundamental disciplines often disparagingly described the rest as "mere" engineering, or even "stamp collecting" (Bernal 1939). And, yet, it was intuitively clear that it could not be so: the allometric scaling laws (Schmidt-Nielsen 1984) existed without reference to the chemistry that certainly drove metabolism, the laws of evolutionary biology existed almost independent of the laws of the chemistry of the nucleic acids that encode heredity, and one did not need quantum electrodynamics to understand the chemical bonds that drove all of organic chemistry, and hence life.

It is at this juncture that Anderson is writing the piece in defense of emergence. As we study complex systems within any science, we discover "new laws, concepts, and generalization" that, though constrained by the same laws as those governing simpler systems, are, nevertheless, independent of them, demand their own internal logical consistency, and need the same inductive principles, or creativity, in their discovery. In fact, it is often the case that these laws have their own universal character, not caring about the details of the microscopic laws from which they surely emerge. Anderson in this seminal paper studies how this shift comes about: what ought to be merely a quantitative difference in the complexity leads to a qualitative difference in the concepts that are useful.

In this, he identifies a common principle: that of broken symmetry. In every science, there are factors that matter, and there are factors that don't: these translate to the concept of the science having a certain symmetry, at least approximately, that manifestly controls regularities at this scale. Thus, for example, the laws of physics at the scale of atoms and molecules don't care much about left versus right—when a certain phenomenon exists, with a few irrelevant exceptions, the mirror image is possible with almost equal strength. Not only that, but for simple systems it is not worthwhile considering asymmetric configurations. They are not stable and rapidly flip around, so that on average they become symmetric.

But, this changes for more complex systems: the time-scale over which it "symmetrizes" grows rapidly with complexity, and soon we reach the opposite regime, where asymmetry is the norm, and the symmetry plays very little role. More importantly, the symmetry only applies to the whole system; each part of the system lends an asymmetric reference frame for the rest of the system. Inasmuch as a complex system is interesting precisely because of the interactions between the parts, the symmetry of the whole system is uninteresting at this scale. In this regime, then, the emergent regularities—which arise as the complexity itself averages and washes out many details of the underlying theory— are now explained by a completely different set of symmetries. The original symmetry is "broken" and new unrelated ones arise in its stead.

Of course, one can object that the breaking of the old symmetries and the rise of the new ones never happens for finite systems, which all real systems are. But, symmetries do not need to be exact for them to be useful. As the system gets larger and more complex, the phenomena of interest in it can be thought of as small modifications— or perturbations—of our expectations of an infinitely large system. For such effectively infinite systems, most of the phenomena at the scale of the constituents truly average out and are unimportant. What survive are a few anomalous ones that then define the focus of the science at the new scale. And, how many and what these emergent "degrees of freedom" are, is often determined by consistency relations at the new scale. In this sense, the emergent theory is, then, as fundamental as the one from which it derives, and the one it replaces.

Anderson's exposition ends with speculations of how this general idea of symmetry breaking applies to the connection between the living and nonliving worlds as well. Though there has been some recent work on viewing the origin of life through the lens of phase transitions (Mathis, Bhattacharya, and Walker 2017), many of these concepts haven't yet been fully elucidated—this work is still driving research fifty years since its publication.

Influential works in science often clarify and distill how two apparently distinct concepts can coexist. Darwin's theory thus made possible for causal dynamics to be teleological (Darwin 1859). Dennett's work showed how one can attribute intention to deterministic dynamics

(Dennett 1987). In this paper, we see a similar resolution of an apparent conflict: how emergence can coexist with reductionism within a consistent framework of understanding. ᕬ

REFERENCES

Bernal, J. D. 1939. *The Social Function of Science.* Cambridge, MA: MIT Press. https://books.google.com/books?id=uxaDAAAAIAAJ.

Darwin, C. 1859. *On the Origin of Species by Means of Natural Selection, or the Preservation of Favoured Races in the Struggle for Life.* London, UK: John Murray.

Dennett, D. C. 1987. *The Intentional Stance.* Cambridge, MA: MIT Press.

Mathis, C., T. Bhattacharya, and S. I. Walker. 2017. "The Emergence of Life as a First-Order Phase Transition." *Astrobiology* 17 (3): 266–276. https://doi.org/10.1089/ast.2016.1481.

Ruse, M. 2005. "Reductionism." In *The Oxford Companion to Philosophy,* 2nd, edited by T. Honderich, 793. https://doi.org/10.1093/acref/9780199264797.001.0001.

Sarkar, S. 1989. "Reductionism and Molecular Biology: A Reappraisal." PhD diss., University of Chicago.

Schmidt-Nielsen, K. 1984. *Scaling: Why Is Animal Size So Important?* New York, NY: Cambridge University Press.

Stein, H. 1958. "Some Phiosophical Aspects of Natural Science." PhD diss., University of Chicago.

Weisskopf, V. F. 1967. "Nuclear Structure and Modern Research." *Physics Today* 20 (5): 23–26. https://doi.org/10.1063/1.3034302.

MORE IS DIFFERENT

P. W. Anderson, Bell Laboratories

The reductionist hypothesis may still be a topic for controversy among philosophers, but among the great majority of active scientists I think it is accepted without question. The workings of our minds and bodies, and of all the animate or inanimate matter of which we have any detailed knowledge, are assumed to be controlled by the same set of fundamental laws, which except under certain extreme conditions we feel we know pretty well.[1]

It seems inevitable to go on uncritically to what appears at first sight to be an obvious corollary of reductionism: that if everything obeys the same fundamental laws, then the only scientists who are studying anything really fundamental are those who are working on those laws. In practice, that amounts to some astrophysicists, some elementary particle physicists, some logicians and other mathematicians, and few others. This point of view, which it is the main purpose of this article to oppose, is expressed in a rather well-known passage by Weisskopf (1965):

> *Looking at the development of science in the Twentieth Century one can distinguish two trends, which I will call "intensive" and "extensive" research, lacking a better terminology. In short: intensive research goes for the fundamental laws, extensive research goes for the explanation of phenomena in terms of known fundamental laws. As always, distinctions of this kind are not unambiguous, but they are clear in most cases. Solid state physics, plasma physics, and perhaps also biology are extensive. High energy physics and a good part of nuclear physics are intensive. There is always much less intensive research going on*

It is important to acknowledge at the outset that methodological reductionism is at the core of the modern scientific revolution, and there is no attempt here to replace it. What this article will argue is that emergence in no way contradicts this bedrock principle.

Methodological reductionism only implies a connection between theories, where the terms of one theory arise out of the terms of another. To some scientists, this implies—falsely, according to this work—that the emergent theory cannot be studied in isolation without reference to the underlying one, or, at the very least, there is no advantage to studying it in this fashion.

---

[1] The author is a member of the technical staff of the Bell Telephone Laboratories, Murray Hill, New Jersey 07974, and visiting professor of theoretical physics at Cavendish Laboratory, Cambridge, England. This article is an expanded version of a Regents' Lecture given in 1967 at the University of California, La Jolla.

than extensive. Once new fundamental laws are discovered, a large and ever increasing activity begins in order to apply the discoveries to hitherto unexplained phenomena. Thus, there are two dimensions to basic research. The frontier of science extends all along a long line from the newest and most modern intensive research, over the extensive research recently spawned by the intensive research of yesterday, to the broad and well developed web of extensive research activities based on intensive research of past decades.

The effectiveness of this message may be indicated by the fact that I heard it quoted recently by a leader in the field of materials science, who urged the participants at a meeting dedicated to "fundamental problems in condensed matter physics" to accept that there were few or no such problems and that nothing was left but extensive science, which he seemed to equate with device engineering.

The main fallacy in this kind of thinking is that the reductionist hypothesis does not by any means imply a "constructionist" one: The ability to reduce everything to simple fundamental laws does not imply the ability to start from those laws and reconstruct the universe. In fact, the more the elementary particle physicists tell us about the nature of the fundamental laws, the less relevance they seem to have to the very real problems of the rest of science, much less to those of society.

The constructionist hypothesis breaks down when confronted with the twin difficulties of scale and complexity. The behavior of large and complex aggregates of elementary particles, it turns out, is not to be understood in terms of a simple extrapolation of the properties of a few particles. Instead, at each level of complexity entirely new properties appear, and the understanding of the new behaviors requires research which I think is as fundamental in its nature as any other. That is, it seems to me that one may array the sciences roughly linearly in a hierarchy, according to the idea: The elementary entities of science X obey the laws of science Y.

Here is the crux of the matter. Reductionism means that the emergent laws can be accounted for by the laws at the constituent level. In reality, it is almost never true that such laws are a good way of describing science at an emergent scale.

The breakdown of the constructionist approach has two aspects to it. One, which is trivial and being discussed here, is that it is practically impossible to carry it out, owing to the enormous computational resources it requires as the scale and complexity of the problem increases.

X	Y
solid state or many-body physics	elementary particle physics
chemistry	many-body physics
molecular biology	chemistry
cell biology	molecular biology
.	.
.	.
.	.
psychology	physiology
social sciences	psychology

But this hierarchy does not imply that science X is "just applied Y." At each stage entirely new laws, concepts, and generalizations are necessary, requiring inspiration and creativity to just as great a degree as in the previous one. Psychology is not applied biology, nor is biology applied chemistry.

In my own field of many-body physics, we are, perhaps, closer to our fundamental, intensive underpinnings than in any other science in which nontrivial complexities occur, and as a result we have begun to formulate a general theory of just how this shift from quantitative to qualitative differentiation takes place. This formulation, called the theory of "broken symmetry," may be of help in making more generally clear the breakdown of the constructionist converse of reductionism. I will give an elementary and incomplete explanation of these ideas, and then go on to some more general speculative comments about analogies at other levels and about similar phenomena.

Before beginning this I wish to sort out two possible sources of misunderstanding. First, when I speak of scale change causing fundamental change I do not mean the rather well-understood idea that phenomena at a new scale may obey actually different fundamental laws—as, for example, general relativity is required on the cosmological scale and quantum mechanics on the atomic. I think it will be accepted that all ordinary matter obeys simple electrodynamics and quantum theory, and that really covers most of what I shall discuss. (As I said, we must all start with reductionism, which I fully accept.) A second source of confusion may be the fact that the concept of broken symmetry has been borrowed by the elementary particle physicists, but their use of the term is strictly an analogy, whether a deep or a specious one remaining to be understood.

The fundamental failure of the constructionist approach is contrasted with the emergent view. Most of the work in the constructionist approach goes towards calculating quantities of no relevance to the emergent level, which deals with vanishingly few, difficult to calculate, aggregate concepts from the constituent level.

These concepts have their own consistency requirements, giving rise to laws and generalization that often make no reference to the underlying layer and are sometimes independent of the microscopic details.

Anderson points out a common confusion: some effects may lose relevance because of an approximation. Gravity being very weak, its nonlinear effects are irrelevant when not dealing with enormous scales. To the extent that these do not change the terms of reference in the discussion, these have little to do with emergence. The latter primarily concerns complexity, the former scale. Since the two are often related, pure examples are difficult to come by and the examples adduced here can be criticized.

Let me then start my discussion with an example on the simplest possible level, a natural one for me because I worked with it when I was a graduate student: the ammonia molecule. At that time everyone knew about ammonia and used it to calibrate his theory or his apparatus, and I was no exception. The chemists will tell you that ammonia "is" a triangular pyramid

with the nitrogen negatively charged and the hydrogens positively charged, so that it has an electric dipole moment (μ), negative toward the apex of the pyramid. Now this seemed very strange to me, because I was just being taught that nothing has an electric dipole moment. The professor was really proving that no nucleus has a dipole moment, because he was teaching nuclear physics, but as his arguments were based on the symmetry of space and time they should have been correct in general.

I soon learned that, in fact, they were correct (or perhaps it would be more accurate to say not incorrect) because he had been careful to say that no stationary state of a system (that is, one which does not change in time) has an electric dipole moment. If ammonia starts out from the above unsymmetrical state, it will not stay in it very long. By means of quantum mechanical tunneling, the nitrogen can leak through the triangle of hydrogens to the other side, turning the pyramid inside out, and, in fact, it can do so very rapidly. This is the so-called "inversion," which occurs at a frequency of about 3×10^{10} per second. A truly stationary state can only be an equal superposition of the unsymmetrical pyramid and its inverse. That mixture does not have a dipole moment. (I warn the reader again that I am greatly oversimplifying and refer him to the textbooks for details.)

I will not go through the proof, but the result is that the state of the system, if it is to be stationary, must always have the same symmetry as the laws of motion which govern it. A reason may be put very

Strictly speaking, this statement is not true as a mathematical theorem, but the conditions that need to be attached to make it true do not change the ensuing discussion.

simply: In quantum mechanics there is always a way, unless symmetry forbids, to get from one state to another. Thus, if we start from any one unsymmetrical state, the system will make transitions to others, so only by adding up all the possible unsymmetrical states in a symmetrical way can we get a stationary state. The symmetry involved in the case of ammonia is parity, the equivalence of left- and right-handed ways of looking at things. (The elementary particle experimentalists' discovery of certain violations of parity is not relevant to this question; those effects are too weak to affect ordinary matter.)

Having seen how the ammonia molecule satisfies our theorem that there is no dipole moment, we may look into other cases and, in particular, study progressively bigger systems to see whether the state and the symmetry are always related. There are other similar pyramidal molecules, made of heavier atoms. Hydrogen phosphide, PH_3, which is twice as heavy as ammonia, inverts, but at one-tenth the ammonia frequency. Phosphorus trifluoride, PF_3, in which the much heavier fluorine is substituted for hydrogen, is not observed to invert at a measurable rate, although theoretically one can be sure that a state prepared in one orientation would invert in a reasonable time.

We may then go on to more complicated molecules, such as sugar, with about 40 atoms. For these it no longer makes any sense to expect the molecule to invert itself. Every sugar molecule made by a living organism is spiral in the same sense, and they never invert, either by quantum mechanical tunneling or even under thermal agitation at normal temperatures. At this point we must forget about the possibility of inversion and ignore the parity symmetry: the symmetry laws have been, not repealed, but broken.

If, on the other hand, we synthesize our sugar molecules by a chemical reaction more or less in thermal equilibrium, we will find that there are not, on the average, more left- than right-handed ones or vice versa. In the absence of anything more complicated than a collection of free molecules, the symmetry laws are never broken, on the average. We needed living matter to produce an actual unsymmetry in the populations.

In really large, but still inanimate, aggregates of atoms, quite a different kind of broken symmetry can occur, again leading to

This is an example of the scale issue brought up earlier. Parity violation is important in particle physics, and may give rise to electric dipole moments of nuclei, atoms, and molecules expected to by "symmetric," but the phenomena of asymmetric molecules does not depend on such parity violations, nor are they affected by it for all practical purposes.

Living matter is an example of a system that breaks the underlying symmetry. The original symmetry now only implies that left chiral life is as probable as right chiral life: but still admits that any one instance of a connected web of life is most likely to lack this underlying symmetry. This is a classic example of symmetry breaking.

a net dipole moment or to a net optical rotating power, or both. Many crystals have a net dipole moment in each elementary unit cell (pyroelectricity), and in some this moment can be reversed by an electric field (ferroelectricity). This asymmetry is a spontaneous effect of the crystal's seeking its lowest energy state. Of course, the state with the opposite moment also exists and has, by symmetry, just the same energy, but the system is so large that no thermal or quantum mechanical force can cause a conversion of one to the other in a finite time compared to, say, the age of the universe.

There are at least three inferences to be drawn from this. One is that symmetry is of great importance in physics. By symmetry we mean the existence of different viewpoints from which the system appears the same. It is only slightly overstating the case to say that physics is the study of symmetry. The first demonstration of the power of this idea may have been by Newton, who may have asked himself the question: What if the matter here in my hand obeys the same laws as that up in the sky—that is, what if space and matter are homogeneous and isotropic?

The second inference is that the internal structure of a piece of matter need not be symmetrical even if the total state of it is. I would challenge you to start from the fundamental laws of quantum mechanics and predict the ammonia inversion and its easily observable properties without going through the stage of using the unsymmetrical pyramidal structure, even though no "state" ever has that structure. It is fascinating that it was not until a couple of decades ago (Bohr and Mottelson 1953) that nuclear physicists stopped thinking of the nucleus as a featureless, symmetrical little ball and realized that while it really never has a dipole moment, it can become football-shaped or plate-shaped. This has observable consequences in the reactions and excitation spectra that are studied in nuclear physics, even though it is much more difficult to demonstrate directly than the ammonia inversion. In my opinion, whether or not one calls this intensive research, it is as fundamental in nature as many things one might so label. But it needed no new knowledge of fundamental laws and would have been extremely difficult to derive synthetically from those laws; it was simply an inspiration, based, to be sure, on everyday intuition, which suddenly fitted everything together.

It is interesting to note that emergence, at every level, reinforces this primacy of symmetry. In fact, the new concepts at each emergent level are controlled by their own symmetries, which are often distinct from the symmetries at the constituent level.

This is a very fundamental issue of what symmetry breaking means: complexity is about *relations*, not about *aggregation*. The symmetry of the constituents merely states a property of invariance for the aggregate, which is not of importance at the emergent level. What is important are the properties of one part relative to the other, and the underlying symmetry does not constrain it.

The basic reason why this result would have been difficult to derive is an important one for our further thinking. If the nucleus is sufficiently small there is no real way to define its shape rigorously: Three or four or ten particles whirling about each other do not define a rotating "plate" or "football." It is only as the nucleus is considered to be a many-body system—in what is often called the $N \to \infty$ limit—that such behavior is rigorously definable. We say to ourselves: A macroscopic body of that shape would have such-and-such a spectrum of rotational and vibrational excitations, completely different in nature from those which would characterize a featureless system. When we see such a spectrum, even not so separated, and somewhat imperfect, we recognize that the nucleus is, after all, not macroscopic; it is merely approaching macroscopic behavior. Starting with the fundamental laws and a computer, we would have to do two impossible things—solve a problem with infinitely many bodies, and then apply the result to a finite system—before we synthesized this behavior.

A third insight is that the state of a really big system does not at all have to have the symmetry of the laws which govern it; in fact, it usually has less symmetry. The outstanding example of this is the crystal: Built from a substrate of atoms and space according to laws which express the perfect homogeneity of space, the crystal suddenly and unpredictably displays an entirely new and very beautiful symmetry. The general rule, however, even in the case of the crystal, is that the large system is less symmetrical than the underlying structure would suggest: Symmetrical as it is, a crystal is less symmetrical than perfect homogeneity.

Perhaps in the case of crystals this appears to be merely an exercise in confusion. The regularity of crystals could be deduced semiempirically in the mid-19th century without any complicated reasoning at all. But sometimes, as in the case of superconductivity, the new symmetry—now called broken symmetry because the original symmetry is no longer evident—may be of an entirely unexpected kind and extremely difficult to visualize. In the case of superconductivity, 30 years elapsed between the time when physicists were in possession of every fundamental law necessary for explaining it and the time when it was actually done.

The phenomenon of superconductivity is the most spectacular example of the broken symmetries which ordinary macroscopic bodies

This is the argument made at the beginning: the terms of reference for the emergent system become explicit as the system becomes infinite. A "first-principles" calculation would, therefore, have to take a limit of the system becoming infinite, discover the few relevant concepts that retain at that limit, and then back off to study the same for finite systems. Without the framework of an emergent theory, this is practically impossible, and, arguably, even theoretically so.

The reason, of course, is that the symmetry of the aggregate predicted by the symmetry of the constituents is unimportant even when it exists—and for truly infinite systems, it may not even exist. What governs the focus at the emergent scale are new concepts.

What happens here is that for really large systems, dynamics of the aggregate as a whole slows down to become imperceptible. Thus, many states appear to be stationary, even when their finite analogues are not so. These states, individually, do not carry the symmetries of the underlying theory.

This is the emergence of new concepts. Most concepts do not have an interesting limit as the system size becomes large: in a sense, they average out when looked at the emergent scale. Instead new aggregate concepts arise that are now the focus of the emergent scale.

In these situations, the broad outlines argued before are still true. But, the details of the behavior are different, and the language of phase transitions may not be appropriate.

undergo, but it is of course not the only one. Antiferromagnets, ferroelectrics, liquid crystals, and matter in many other states obey a certain rather general scheme of rules and ideas, which some many-body theorists refer to under the general heading of broken symmetry. I shall not further discuss the history, but give a bibliography at the end of this article (Landau 1937).[2]

The essential idea is that in the so-called $N \rightarrow \infty$ limit of large systems (on our own, macroscopic scale) it is not only convenient but essential to realize that matter will undergo mathematically sharp, singular "phase transitions" to states in which the microscopic symmetries, and even the microscopic equations of motion, are in a sense violated. The symmetry leaves behind as its expression only certain characteristic behaviors, for instance, long-wavelength vibrations, of which the familiar example is sound waves; or the unusual macroscopic conduction phenomena of the superconductor; or, in a very deep analogy, the very rigidity of crystal lattices, and thus of most solid matter. There is, of course, no question of the system's really violating, as opposed to breaking, the symmetry of space and time, but because its parts find it energetically more favorable to maintain certain fixed relationships with each other, the symmetry allows only the body as a whole to respond to external forces.

This leads to a "rigidity," which is also an apt description of superconductivity and superfluidity in spite of their apparent "fluid" behavior. [In the former case, London noted this aspect very early (London 1950).] Actually, for a hypothetical gaseous but intelligent citizen of Jupiter or of a hydrogen cloud somewhere in the galactic center, the properties of ordinary crystals might well be a more baffling and intriguing puzzle than those of superfluid helium.

I do not mean to give the impression that all is settled. For instance, I think there are still fascinating questions of principle about glasses and

---

[2]Eds: Broken symmetry and collective motion, general: J. Goldstone, A. Salam, S. Weinberg, *Phys. Rev.* 127, 965 (1962); P. W. Anderson, *Concepts in Solids* (Benjamin, New York, 1963), pp. 175-182; B. D. Josephson, thesis, Trinity College, Cambridge University (1962). Special cases: antiferromagnetism, P. W. Anderson, *Phys. Rev.* 86, 694 (1952); superconductivity, *ibid.* 110, 827 (1958); ibid. 112, 1900 (1958); Y. Nambu, *ibid.* 117, 648 (1960).

other amorphous phases, which may reveal even more complex types of behavior. Nevertheless, the role of this type of broken symmetry in the properties of inert but macroscopic material bodies is now understood, at least in principle. In this case we can see how the whole becomes not only more than but very different from the sum of its parts.

The next order of business logically is to ask whether an even more complete destruction of the fundamental symmetries of space and time is possible and whether new phenomena then arise, intrinsically different from the "simple" phase transition representing a condensation into a less symmetric state.

We have already excluded the apparently unsymmetric cases of liquids, gases, and glasses. (In any real sense they are more symmetric.) It seems to me that the next stage is to consider the system which is regular but contains information. That is, it is regular in space in some sense so that it can be "read out," but it contains elements which can be varied from one "cell" to the next. An obvious example is DNA; in everyday life, a line of type or a movie film have the same structure. This type of "information-bearing crystallinity" seems to be essential to life. Whether the development of life requires any further breaking of symmetry is by no means clear.

Keeping on with the attempt to characterize types of broken symmetry which occur in living things, I find that at least one further phenomenon seems to be identifiable and either universal or remarkably common, namely, ordering (regularity or periodicity) in the time dimension. A number of theories of life processes have appeared in which regular pulsing in time plays an important role: theories of development, of growth and growth limitation, and of the memory. Temporal regularity is very commonly observed in living objects. It plays at least two kinds of roles. First, most methods of extracting energy from the environment in order to set up a continuing, quasi-stable process involve time-periodic machines, such as oscillators and generators, and the processes of life work in the same way. Second, temporal regularity is a means of handling information, similar to information-bearing spatial regularity. Human spoken language is an example, and it is noteworthy that all computing machines use temporal pulsing. A possible third role is suggested in some of the theories mentioned above: the use of phase

In fact, this view of life as a phase transition of information units is an avenue of active research.

Persistent time periodicity is a standard feature in nonequilibrium systems, and life is fundamentally a nonequilibrium system.

It is not clear yet how general the requirement of time periodicity is. In biological situations, the periodicity often renders robustness, but a general theory is lacking yet. And, temporal regularity is the basis of robust digital manipulation, but its necessity has not yet been fully studied.

Temporal pulsing is ubiquitous in biological systems, and phase relations are a standard means of calibrating one signal against another.

Functional structure is development of an organization that allows a goal directed behavior.

In other words, every level will bring in its own set of concepts that need to be studied. The constituent may constrain what is possible, but the laws are emergent and not merely a construction.

This is to reiterate that reductionism is not dead, far from it! It may be argued that the reductionist approach provides useful constraints. Broken symmetry often manifests itself in remnants that are important at the emergent level.

relationships of temporal pulses to handle information and control the growth and development of cells and organisms (Cohen and Robertson 1971).

In some sense, structure—functional structure in a teleological sense, as opposed to mere crystalline shape—must also be considered a stage, possibly intermediate between crystallinity and information strings, in the hierarchy of broken symmetries.

To pile speculation on speculation, I would say that the next stage could be hierarchy or specialization of function, or both. At some point we have to stop talking about decreasing symmetry and start calling it increasing complication. Thus, with increasing complication at each stage, we go on up the hierarchy of the sciences. We expect to encounter fascinating and, I believe, very fundamental questions at each stage in fitting together less complicated pieces into the more complicated system and understanding the basically new types of behavior which can result.

There may well be no useful parallel to be drawn between the way in which complexity appears in the simplest cases of many-body theory and chemistry and the way it appears in the truly complex cultural and biological ones, except perhaps to say that, in general, the relationship between the system and its parts is intellectually a one-way street. Synthesis is expected to be all but impossible; analysis, on the other hand, may be not only possible but fruitful in all kinds of ways: Without an understanding of the broken symmetry in superconductivity, for instance, Josephson would probably not have discovered his effect. [Another name for the Josephson effect is "macroscopic quantum-interference phenomena": interference effects observed between macroscopic wave functions of electrons in superconductors, or of helium atoms in superfluid liquid helium. These phenomena have already enormously extended the accuracy of electromagnetic measurements, and can be expected to play a great role in future computers, among other possibilities, so that in the long run they may lead to some of the major technological achievements of this decade (Clarke 1969).] For another example, biology has certainly taken on a whole new aspect from the reduction of genetics to biochemistry and biophysics, which will have untold consequences. So it is not true, as a recent article would have it (Pippard 1972), that we each should "cultivate our own valley, and not attempt to build roads over the mountain ranges . . . between the sciences." Rather, we should recognize that such roads, while often the quickest shortcut to another part of our own science, are not visible from the viewpoint of one science alone.

The arrogance of the particle physicist and his intensive research may be behind us (the discoverer of the positron said "the rest is chemistry"), but we have yet to recover from that of some molecular biologists, who seem determined to try to reduce everything about the human organism to "only" chemistry, from the common cold and all mental disease to the religious instinct. Surely there are more levels of organization between human ethology and DNA than there are between DNA and quantum electrodynamics, and each level can require a whole new conceptual structure.

In closing, I offer two examples from economics of what I hope to have said. Marx said that quantitative differences become qualitative ones, but a dialogue in Paris in the 1920s sums it up even more clearly:

FITZGERALD: The rich are different from us.

HEMINGWAY: Yes, they have more money. 🖎

The importance of reductionism is these connections between scales. Pure data-driven analysis suffers from ambiguities in the terms of its reference that can often be resolved in a multi-scale approach.

This is the core of emergence: when quantitative differences are large, the very questions of interest change!

REFERENCES

Bohr, A., and B. R. Mottelson. 1953. "Collective and Individual-Particle Aspects of Nuclear Structure." *Mat. Fys. Medd. Dan. Vid. Selsk* 27 (16).

Clarke, J. 1969. "The Josephson Effect and e/h." Anderson, P. W. 1970. "How Josephson Discovered His Effect." *Physics Today* 23 (11): 23. *American Journal of Physics* 38:1071–1092.

Cohen, M. H., and A. Robertson. 1971. "Wave Propagation in the Early Stages of Aggregation of Cellular Slime Molds." *Journal of Theoretical Biology* 31 (1): 101–118.

Landau, L. D. 1937. "Theory of Phase Transformations. I." *Phys. Z. Sowjetunion* 11:26.

London, F. 1950. *Superfluids.* Vol. 1. New York, NY: Wiley.

Pippard, A. B. 1972. *Reconciling Physics with Reality.* London, UK: Cambridge University Press.

Weisskopf, V. F. 1965. In *The Nature of Matter: Purposes of High-Energy Physics,* edited by L. C. L. Yuan. Also see *Nuovo Cimento Suppl., Ser. 1* 4, 465 (1966); *Physics Today* 20 (No. 5), 23 (1967). Upton, NY: Brookhaven National Laboratory Publication 888 T-360.

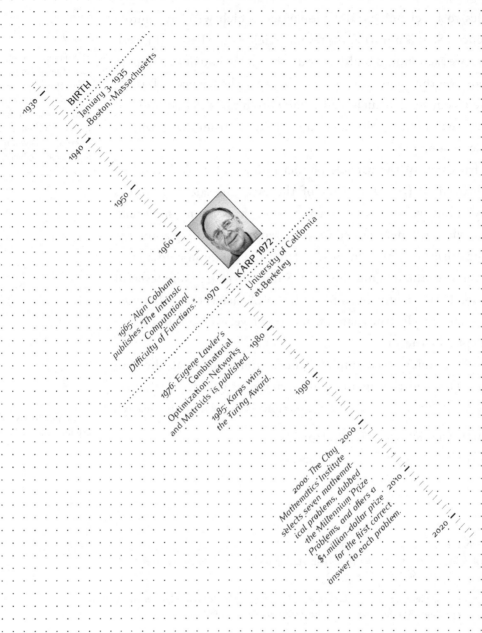

BIRTH
January 3, 1935
Boston, Massachusetts

1930

1940

1950

1960

1965: Alan Cobham publishes "The Intrinsic Computational Difficulty of Functions."

1970

KARP 1972:
University of California at Berkeley

1976: Eugene Lawler's Combinatorial Optimization: Networks and Matroids is published.

1980

1985: Karps wins the Turing Award.

1990

2000

2000: The Clay Mathematics Institute selects seven mathematical problems, dubbed the Millennium Prize Problems, and offers a $1 million-dollar prize for the first correct answer to each problem.

2010

2020

RICHARD MANNING KARP

[40]

GARDENS OF FORKING PATHS: EXPONENTIAL HARDNESS AND EXHAUSTIVE SEARCH

Cristopher Moore, Santa Fe Institute

Which problems are easy, and which are hard? And what is it about their structure that makes them so?

There are many ways to think about this question, but one of the most mathematically well-developed is computational complexity theory. Here we regard a problem as easy if there is an algorithm that solves it efficiently: that quickly finds a solution or quickly determines whether a solution exists. If there is no such algorithm—if our only recourse is to methodically search a vast landscape of possible solutions—then the problem is hard.

Many real-world problems certainly seem hard. Can we arrange a supply chain to produce a product by a certain date? How can we design a power grid that stores and delivers energy at the times and to the places it is needed? Which groups of people should we vaccinate or test most urgently to halt the spread of an epidemic? Problems like these are hard partly because there are many possible strategies for solving them and partly because of our uncertainty about the world. Our solutions may founder because we don't understand how a disease spreads, or how electricity demand will change, or whether vital materials and techniques will be available. Even worse, we may not even agree on our values—the "objective function" or "fitness function" that we are trying to optimize.

The goal of computational complexity theory is to understand the part of hardness that comes from the mathematical structure of a problem: the part that remains hard even if we agree on what our options are and on how to quantify the costs and benefits of each possible strategy. The hardness comes not from the fact that we

R. M. Karp, "Reducibility Among Combinatorial Problems," in *Complexity of Computer Computations*, ed. R. E. Miller and J. W. Thatcher, New York, NY: Plenum Press, 85–103 (1972).

Reprinted with permission from Springer Nature.

have competing interests (although there are wonderful computational complexity results in game theory and economics) but from the vastness of the space of possible strategies and our lack of a map or compass to navigate it.

So suppose that we all agree on what problem we want to solve. Then we can ask how how much computation we need to solve it—say, how much time or memory the best possible method requires—and how these computational resources scale with the problem's size.

As we saw earlier in this volume, in the mid-1960s computer scientists and mathematicians focused on *polynomial time*. An algorithm runs in polynomial time if it can solve examples of size n— a network with n nodes, a game board with n pieces, a genome of n base pairs, and so on—in an amount of time that scales as n raised to some constant, like n, n^2, or n^3. Many of our favorite problems have algorithms with this property. We can align two genomes of length n, matching common subsequences so that just a few mutations, insertions, and deletions change one to the other, in n^2 time. In a map with n locations, we can find the shortest paths from everywhere to everywhere else in n^3 time. If n is one thousand, then n^2 is one million and n^3 is one billion, but computers can do a billion things before breakfast. We call the class of problems for which such algorithms exist P for "polynomial," and we consider them relatively easy.

But many other problems seem to lack such algorithms. The traveling salesman problem asks, given a map with n cities, whether we can visit each city exactly once with a tour whose total length is at most, say, 1,000 miles. Planning such a tour seems much harder than simply finding the shortest path from A to B. If we pursue a naive strategy, we might get stuck in a local optimum, following a chain of nearby cities only to realize that we missed one and now it's too far away to visit. We can retrace our steps and try a different tour. But this backtracking could force us to explore an exponentially branching tree of possibilities—a garden of forking paths—before we find a tour that works.

Or consider the classic four-color-map theorem. It tells us that we can color the countries of any map with four colors so that no two with the same color share a border. But while four colors are always sufficient, they are not always necessary: For some maps, three colors are enough.

But how can we tell whether a given map needs three or four?[1] As the reader can check using a map of Ireland, if we color County Laois red, we can color Kildare, Carlow, Offaly, and Tipperary blue and green—but then no color is left for Kilkenny. It's easy to avoid local conflicts, but conflicts that are subtle and global might not show up until late in our search, when almost all the countries are colored. The solution, if it exists, might require a large rearrangement, forcing us to undo much of our work.

So what makes these problems hard? If there are n countries and each can be red, blue, or green, then *a priori* the number of possible colorings is $3 \times 3 \times \cdots \times 3 = 3^n$, growing exponentially in n. The number of possible orders in which we can visit n cities grows even faster, as $n! = 1 \times 2 \times 3 \cdots \times n$, an enormous number of possible solutions.

The issue is not the sheer size of the landscape but its structure. For some problems, we can bypass this exhaustive search. There is an exponential number of possible alignments of two genomes, but we can use a clever technique called dynamic programming to guide our choices, reducing the original problem to a small number of subproblems that we can solve more easily, and thus find the optimum solution in polynomial time. This strategy is possible, roughly speaking, because aligning the left halves of the genomes is nearly independent from aligning their right halves—they interact only through a small number of choices in the middle.

For many other problems, their variables are too entangled with each other to break them down into independently solvable parts. Each algorithmic strategy we know of—like dynamic programming, convex optimization, and linear algebra—has a special kind of structure it can take advantage of and yields polynomial-time algorithms for problems with this structure. But for the most generic problems, these strategies all fail, leaving us no option we know of but exhaustive search.

If the landscape is "rugged" or "glassy," a searcher almost always gets stuck in a local optimum—a peak or valley where any small change makes things worse. They have to cross a barrier, a deep valley, or a high mountain pass, to escape it in the hope of finding a better solution later

---

[1] Exercise for the reader: telling whether two colors suffice is easy!

on. This landscape picture—the energy landscape of a spin glass, the fitness landscape of an evolving species, or the strategy landscape of a game player or economic actor—is one of the founding metaphors in complex systems. We can certainly try to search more intelligently, using ideas from physics like simulated annealing or ideas from biology like genetic algorithms. But except for special cases, these rugged landscapes seem to have an irreducible complexity—no rhyme or reason that lets us zoom in on the best solution.

This is the essence of the famous P vs. NP question. NP is the class of problems where, given a proposed solution, we can easily evaluate it and see if it works; P is the class of problems for which we can quickly find such a solution (or establish that none exists). In the landscape metaphor, NP problems are those where we can measure the altitude at our current location, and P problems are those for which we can quickly find the highest point. Intuitively, these two classes seem different, and NP seems much larger than P.[2] It is a simple matter to check if a proposed tour visits every city and has a total length less than 1,000 miles, or if a proposed coloring of a map distinguishes all pairs of countries with a border, but it doesn't seem easy to find tours or colorings. These problems seem to have a needle-in-a-haystack quality: You know when you've found a needle, but that doesn't make it easy to find.

But, as in Cobham's earlier foundational paper, it's not clear how to *prove* that these problems are hard—that there is no algorithmic shortcut that lets us skip an exhaustive search. To prove that a problem is in P, all we have to do is find a fast algorithm for it and prove that it works. But to prove that some NP problem is outside P, and thus that P ≠ NP, we have to somehow eliminate *all possible* algorithms—a much more challenging task.

In the early 1970s, a powerful new idea appeared. Consider two problems, L and M, and suppose that we can easily (i.e., in polynomial

---

[2]A common misconception is that NP stands for "non-polynomial," and that NP consists of everything outside of P. In fact P is a subset of NP, and there are yet harder problems outside both. For instance, if I propose a chess strategy and claim it always leads to a win for the first player, it is not clear how you could easily check this claim. If you have to try all possible games created by the other player's choices, then even the checking process could take exponential time.

time) translate any example of L to an example of M. This translation, which computer scientists call a "reduction," means that M is at least as hard as L. To see this, suppose there is a fast algorithm for M. Then there is also a fast algorithm for L: Just translate your L example into M-form and use M's algorithm to solve it. Thus, if M is easy, then L is easy too; and in the other direction, if L is hard, then M is also hard.

Now suppose that a problem L is in NP, and that it has the marvelous property that *any* problem in NP can be translated to it. In that case, it is among the hardest problems in NP. Now there are two possibilities. If there is a fast algorithm for L, then there is one for every problem in NP, and P = NP. On the other hand, if P ≠ NP—if there is even one problem in NP that requires exponential time—then L requires exponential time as well. We call such problems NP-*complete*. As the reader may have guessed, both the traveling salesman and map-coloring problems turn out to be NP-complete, and there are hundreds of others.

Theoretical computer science has not yet advanced to the point where we can exclude the possibility that P = NP. But the only way that could happen is if there were a miraculous polynomial-time algorithm that worked simultaneously for all problems in NP. This would mean that anything that is easy to check is also easy to find—tours, colorings, secret keys for secret codes, elegant proofs in mathematics, and perhaps even scientific theories (as long as we can check them by looking at experimental data). While we cannot rule this out, it is very hard to imagine such an algorithm. Thus, to this day, NP-completeness remains one of the most powerful arguments we have that a problem is exponentially hard.

So how can a problem be NP-complete? It sounds quite mysterious. Since map coloring is NP-complete, for instance, there must be some simple way of translating traveling salesman problems into maps, such that there is a tour of less than 1,000 miles if and only if the corresponding map can be colored with three colors—and a similar translation to maps from any search and optimization problem for which proposed solutions are easy to evaluate. This seems absurd. These problems seem very different from each other. How in the world can one of them express all the others? In what sense could they all have the same underlying structure?

The short answer is: because we can build computers out of many different things. The first NP-complete problem was found by Stephen Cook in his groundbreaking 1971 paper, "The Complexity of Theorem-Proving Procedures." He showed that the problem of telling whether logical formulas are satisfiable—that is, if they are ever true, for at least one setting of their variables—is NP-complete. While he phrased his proof in terms of Turing machines, we can illustrate it as follows. Consider the formula

$$(x \text{ is false or } y \text{ is true}$$
$$\text{and } (x \text{ is false or } z \text{ is true})$$
$$\text{and } (x \text{ is true, or } y \text{ is false, or } z \text{ is false}).$$

This formula demands that these three "clauses" or constraints be satisfied simultaneously. It appears to be a peculiar, and static, relationship for x, y, and z to have. But in fact it is equivalent to the following, as you might enjoy checking:

If y and z are both true, then x must be true.

If either y or z is false, then x must be false.

Now this sounds more dynamic—more like a line of code, "set x to AND(y, z)." Or it could represent an "AND gate" on a microchip, a circuit made of a couple of transistors whose output x is true if and only if its inputs y and z are both true.

This AND gate is one of the basic building blocks of computation. By wiring together such building blocks—which we can do by stringing together a long series of logical clauses—we can carry out any computational process we desire. This means that if we have a program that checks whether its input corresponds to a short tour of some set of cities or a good coloring of some map, we can translate this program into a logical formula. Then the question of whether there is some input the program would accept—for instance, a short tour or a valid coloring with three colors—becomes the question of whether it is possible to make this formula true.[3] Thus the satisfiability problem, which asks

---

[3] It turns out that finding a tour or coloring is not much harder than the yes-or-no question of whether one exists. This is why Karp talks about "languages": the language

whether a logical formula of this form can be made true by some setting of its variables, is NP-complete.

In this paper, Richard Karp takes Cook's insight further, by showing that many other problems are NP-complete as well. Just as logical clauses can simulate computation, colorings and tours can simulate logical clauses. If we choose meanings for our colors, like red is true and blue is false, there are "gadgets" we can build into our map that act like ANDs and ORs, thus translating satisfiable formulas into colorable maps. In a traveling salesman problem, we could represent a logical variable with a chain of cities, and let traversing this chain in one direction or the other represent whether this variable is true or false. We can then build simulations on top of simulations, creating a family tree of NP-complete problems, the first few branches of which are shown on page 1222. This family tree has since grown to include hundreds of problems in algebra, automata, machine learning, statistical physics, calculus, and virtually any other system in which complexity can live.

From this point of view, NP-completeness seems almost inevitable. Just as we can build computers out of transistors, gears, water pipes, or DNA, any search problem whose variables and constraints are versatile enough to represent logical relationships will be NP-complete. This suggests that efficient algorithms and easy problems are the exception, rather than the norm.

It's worth noting, however, that NP-completeness is a pessimistic picture of the world. As I commented in my introduction to Cobham's paper on polynomial time, theoretical computer science usually demands that an algorithm work in every case, and therefore in the worst case. If a problem is NP-complete, that means that it *can* be hard: that there exist hard examples of it. But these hard examples may be very rare. When we use a reduction to prove hardness, we imagine an adversary cleverly constructing an example of one problem in order to encode the variables and constraints of another.

---

corresponding to a problem is the set of examples for which the answer is "yes," such as the set of maps for which three colors suffice. The problem is then to tell whether a given map, encoded as a string of characters, is in this language or not.

This pessimism makes sense when our problems really do come from an adversary—such as during World War II, when Alan Turing and his compatriots worked to crack the Nazi Enigma code. But when problems are posed by nature or simply by chance, we might be forgiven for hoping that they will not be the hardest possible. Protein folding, finding the minimum-energy configuration of an amino acid sequence, is NP-complete in the worst case. If our genome were designed by an adversary, so that the energy landscape of our proteins included a host of misfolded local optima, we would promptly die. But most of our proteins have evolved to fold quickly and reliably into their correct conformations, sometimes with the help of enzymatic chaperones that have co-evolved with them. Nature's examples of hard problems are, mercifully, often easier than we deserve. ✴

REFERENCES

Babai, L. 2015. "Graph Isomorphism in Polynomial Time." *arXiv* 1512.03547 [cs.DS]. https://doi.org/10.48550/arXiv.1512.03547.

Cook, S. A. 1971. "The Complexity of Theorem-Proving Procedures." In *STOC '71: Proceedings of the Third Annual ACM Symposium on Theory of Computing*, 151–158. New York, NY: Association for Computing Machinery.

Khachiyan, L. G. 1979. "A Polynomial Algorithm in Linear Programming." Translated in *Soviet Mathematics Doklady* 20, 191–194, 1979, *Doklady Akademii Nauk SSSR* 244:1093–1096.

Nash, J., and National Security Agency. 1955 [2012]. *Correspondences Regarding Cryptography between John Nash and the NSA*. Declassified by the NSA. https://www.nsa.gov/Portals/70/documents/news-features/press-room/press-releases/2012/nash-exhibit/nash_letters1.pdf.

REDUCIBILITY AMONG COMBINATORIAL PROBLEMS[†]

Richard M. Karp, University of California, Berkeley

Abstract

A large class of computational problems involve the determination of properties of graphs, digraphs, integers, arrays of integers, finite families of finite sets, boolean formulas and elements of other countable domains. Through simple encodings from such domains into the set of words over a finite alphabet these problems can be converted into language recognition problems, and we can inquire into their computational complexity. It is reasonable to consider such a problem satisfactorily solved when an algorithm for its solution is found which terminates within a number of steps bounded by a polynomial in the length of the input. We show that a large number of classic unsolved problems of covering, matching, packing, routing, assignment and sequencing are equivalent, in the sense that either each of them possesses a polynomial-bounded algorithm or none of them does.

1. Introduction

All the general methods presently known for computing the chromatic number of a graph, deciding whether a graph has a Hamilton circuit, or solving a system of linear inequalities in which the variables are constrained to be 0 or 1, require a combinatorial search for which the worst case time requirement grows exponentially with the length of the input. In this paper we give theorems which strongly suggest, but do not imply, that these problems, as well as many others, will remain intractable perpetually.

We are specifically interested in the existence of algorithms that are guaranteed to terminate in a number of steps bounded by a polynomial in the length of the input. We exhibit a class of well-known combinatorial problems, including those mentioned above, which are equivalent, in the sense that a polynomial-bounded algorithm for any one of them would effectively yield a polynomial-bounded algorithm for

The question of polynomial vs. exponential time is one of the most fundamental distinctions in computer science. Early hints of this question appeared in a 1955 letter from John Nash to the US National Security Agency, where Nash conjectured that for sufficiently complex cryptosystems a codebreaker cannot find the secret key in polynomial time; and a 1956 letter from Kurt Gödel to John von Neumann, where Gödel asks if mathematical proofs of length ℓ can be found in time just ℓ^2, in which case human mathematicians could be largely replaced by machines. Along with Cook and Levin, Karp showed showed that a huge variety of search and optimization problems have a similar structure, and that each can express all the others. As a result, if any of these problems require an exponential search, they all do. Showing that a problem is NP-complete remains one of our most powerful arguments that it is exponentially hard.

[†]This research was partially supported by National Science Foundation Grant GJ-474.

all. We also show that, if these problems do possess polynomial-bounded algorithms then all the problems in an unexpectedly wide class (roughly speaking, the class of problems solvable by polynomial-depth backtrack search) possess polynomial-bounded algorithms.

The following is a brief summary of the contents of the paper. For the sake of definiteness our technical development is carried out in terms of the recognition of languages by one-tape Turing machines, but any of a wide variety of other abstract models of computation would yield the same theory. Let Σ^* be the set of all finite strings of 0's and 1's. A subset of Σ^* is called a *language*. Let $\mathcal{P}$ be the class of languages recognizable in polynomial time by one-tape deterministic Turing machines, and let $\mathcal{NP}$ be the class of languages recognizable in polynomial time by one-tape nondeterministic Turing machines. Let Π be the class of functions from Σ^* into Σ^* computable in polynomial time by one-tape Turing machines. Let L and M be languages. We say that L $\propto$ M (L *is reducible to* M) if there is a function f $\in \Pi$ such that f(x) $\in$ M $\Leftrightarrow$ x $\in$ L. If M $\in \mathcal{P}$ and L $\propto$ M then L $\in \mathcal{P}$. We call L and M equivalent if L $\propto$ M and M $\propto$ L. Call L (*polynomial*) *complete* if L $\in \mathcal{NP}$ and every language in $\mathcal{NP}$ is reducible to L. Either all complete languages are in $\mathcal{P}$, or none of them are. The former alternative holds if and only if $\mathcal{P} = \mathcal{NP}$.

The main contribution of this paper is the demonstration that a large number of classic difficult computational problems, arising in fields such as mathematical programming, graph theory, combinatorics, computational logic and switching theory, are complete (and hence equivalent) when expressed in a natural way as language recognition problems.

This paper was stimulated by the work of Stephen Cook (1971), and rests on an important theorem which appears in his paper. The author also wishes to acknowledge the substantial contributions of Eugene Lawler and Robert Tarjan.

2. The Class *P*

There is a large class of important computational problems which involve the determination of properties of graphs, digraphs, integers, finite families of finite sets, boolean formulas and elements of other

This formalizes the notion that a problem L can be be reduced or "translated" to another language M. An example x of L can be converted to an example $f(x)$ of M, so that the yes-or-no answer to x and $f(x)$ are the same: if x is in L's "language" of examples where a solution exists, then $f(x)$ is in M's language too, and vice versa. Moreover, the translation f can be carried out in polynomial time. The astonishing thing is there are problems L to which a vast array of search and optimization problems—every problem in the class NP—can be reduced. Karp called these "polynomial complete," but the terminology NP-complete was adopted shortly afterward.

Cook was the first to recognize that specific problems can be NP-complete. Many of Cook's and Karp's results were obtained independently by Leonid Levin in the Soviet Union, and the NP-completeness of satisfiability is often called the Cook–Levin Theorem.

countable domains. It is a reasonable working hypothesis, championed originally by Jack Edmonds (1965) in connection with problems in graph theory and integer programming, and by now widely accepted, that such a problem can be regarded as tractable if and only if there is an algorithm for its solution whose running time is bounded by a polynomial in the size of the input. In this section we introduce and begin to investigate the class of problems solvable in polynomial time.

The class P of polynomial-time problems was proposed as a model of "tractable" or efficiently solvable problems by Cobham (see Chapter 23) as well as Edmonds (1965).

We begin by giving an extremely general definition of "deterministic algorithm", computing a function from a countable domain D into a countable range R.

For any finite alphabet A, let A^* be the set of finite strings of elements of A; for $x \in A^*$, let $\lg(x)$ denote the length of x.

A *deterministic algorithm* $\mathcal{A}$ is specified by:

> a countable set D (the *domain*)
> a countable set R (the *range*)
> a finite alphabet Δ such that $\Delta^* \wedge R = \phi$
> an *encoding function* E: $D \to \Delta^*$
> a *transition function* τ: $\Delta^* \to \Delta^* \cup_R$.

The *computation* of $\mathcal{A}$ on input $x \in D$ is the unique sequence $y_1, y_2, \ldots$ such that $y_1 = E(x)$, $y_{i+1} = \tau(y_i)$ for all i and, if the sequence is finite and ends with y_k, then $y_k \in R$. Any string occurring as an element of a computation is called an *instantaneous description*. If the computation of $\mathcal{A}$ on input x is finite and of length t(x), then t(x) is the *running time* of $\mathcal{A}$ on input x. $\mathcal{A}$ is *terminating* if all its computations are finite. A terminating algorithm $\mathcal{A}$ computes the function $f_{\mathcal{A}} : D \to R$ such that $f_{\mathcal{A}}(x)$ is the last element of the computation of $\mathcal{A}$ on x.

If $R = \{\text{ACCEPT, REJECT}\}$ then A is called a *recognition algorithm*. A recognition algorithm in which $D = \Sigma^*$ is called a *string recognition algorithm*. If $\mathcal{A}$ is a string recognition algorithm then the *language recognized by* $\mathcal{A}$ is $\{x \in \Sigma^* \mid f_{\mathcal{A}}(x) = \text{ACCEPT}\}$. If $D = R = \Sigma^*$ then $\mathcal{A}$ is called a *string mapping algorithm*. A terminating algorithm $\mathcal{A}$ with domain $D = \Sigma^*$ *operates in polynomial time* if there is a polynomial $p(\cdot)$ such that, for every $x \in \Sigma^*$, $t(x) \leq p(\lg(x))$.

We say an algorithm ACCEPTS an input if the answer is yes, and REJECTS if the answer is no.

To discuss algorithms in any practical context we must specialize the concept of deterministic algorithm. Various well known classes of string recognition algorithms (Markov algorithms, one-tape Turing machines, multitape and multihead Turing machines, random access machines, etc.) are delineated by restricting the functions E and τ to be of certain very simple types. These definitions are standard (Hopcraft and Ullman 1969) and will not be repeated here. It is by now commonplace to observe that many such classes are equivalent in their capability to recognize languages; for each such class of algorithms, the class of languages recognized is the class of recursive languages. This invariance under changes in definition is part of the evidence that recursiveness is the correct technical formulation of the concept of decidability.

The class of languages recognizable by string recognition algorithms which operate in polynomial time is also invariant under a wide range of changes in the class of algorithms. For example, any language recognizable in time p ($\cdot$) by a multihead or multitape Turing machine is recognizable in time $p^2(\cdot)$ by a one-tape Turing machine. Thus the class of languages recognizable in polynomial time by one-tape Turing machines is the same as the class recognizable by the ostensibly more powerful multihead or multitape Turing machines. Similar remarks apply to random access machines.

Definition 1. $\mathcal{P}$ is the class of languages recognizable by one-tape Turing machines which operate in polynomial time.

Definition 2. Π is the class of functions from Σ^* into Σ^* defined by one-tape Turing machines which operate in polynomial time.

The reader will not go wrong by identifying $\mathcal{P}$ with the class of languages recognizable by digital computers (with unbounded backup storage) which operate in polynomial time and Π with the class of string mappings performed in polynomial time by such computers.

Remark. If $f : \Sigma^* \to \Sigma^*$ is in Π then there is a polynomial p($\cdot$) such that $\lg(f(x)) < p(\lg(x))$.

We next introduce a concept of reducibility which is of central importance in this paper.

Definition 3. Let L and M be languages. Then L $\propto$ M (L *is reducible to* M) if there is a function $f \in \Pi$ such that $f(x) \in M \Leftrightarrow x \in L$.

As Cobham said in Chapter 23, while it is mathematically convenient to use a particular model of computation such as a Turing machine, the details of our computing hardware do not change which problems we can solve in polynomial time.

We can define $\mathcal{P}$ perfectly well in terms of what real computers, programmed in our favorite language, can do in polynomial time—as long as we give them all the memory they need. In the age of big data, memory is sometimes the limiting factor in computation, but in search and optimization problems we are usually more concerned with time.

Lemma 1. If $L \propto M$ and $M \in P$ then $L \in P$.

Proof. The following is a polynomial-time bounded algorithm to decide if $x \in L$: compute $f(x)$; then test in polynomial time whether $f(x) \in M$.

We will be interested in the difficulty of recognizing subsets of countable domains other than Σ^*. Given such a domain D, there is usually a natural one-one encoding $e: D \rightarrow \Sigma^*$. For example we can represent a positive integer by the string of 0's and 1's comprising its binary representation, a 1-dimensional integer array as a list of integers, a matrix as a list of 1-dimensional arrays, etc.; and there are standard techniques for encoding lists into strings over a finite alphabet, and strings over an arbitrary finite alphabet as strings of 0's and 1's. Given such an encoding $e: D \rightarrow \Sigma^*$, we say that a set $T \subseteq D$ is *recognizable in polynomial time* if $e(T) \in \mathcal{P}$. Also, given sets $T \subseteq D$ and $U \subseteq D'$, and encoding functions $e: D \rightarrow \Sigma^*$ and $e': D' \rightarrow \Sigma^*$ we say $T \propto U$ if $e(T) \propto e' U$.

As a rule several natural encodings of a given domain are possible. For instance a graph can be represented by its adjacency matrix, by its incidence matrix, or by a list of unordered pairs of nodes, corresponding to the arcs. Given one of these representations, there remain a number of arbitrary decisions as to format and punctuation. Fortunately, it is almost always obvious that any two "reasonable" encodings e_0 and e_1 of a given problem are equivalent; i.e., $e_0(S) \in P \Leftrightarrow e_1(S) \in P$. One important exception concerns the representation of positive integers; we stipulate that a positive integer is encoded in a binary, rather than unary, representation. In view of the invariance of recognizability in polynomial time and reducibility under reasonable encodings, we discuss problems in terms of their original domains, without specifying an encoding into Σ^*.

We complete this section by listing a sampling of problems which are solvable in polynomial time. In the next section we examine a number of close relatives of these problems which are not known to be solvable in polynomial time. Appendix 1 establishes our notation.

Each problem is specified by giving (under the heading "INPUT") a generic element of its domain of definition and (under the heading "PROPERTY") the property which causes an input to be accepted.

If M is easy and L can be reduced to M, then L is easy too: just translate an example of L to the corresponding example of M, and solve it using your efficient algorithm for M. Turning that around, if L is hard then M is also hard.

Numbers, matrices, words, and so on can all be represented as strings of bits. As Ada Lovelace pointed out, the same is true even for musical compositions.

There are multiple ways of representing a network in a computer, such as a list of neighbors for each node, or a matrix of 0s and 1s showing which pairs are connected. These are easily translated to each other.

Each of these problems is known to be in $\mathcal{P}$ because some algorithmic strategy lets us avoid an exhaustive search. We can find minimum spanning trees using a greedy algorithm, find shortest paths using dynamic programming, find matchings and cuts by iteratively improving the flow in a network, and solve systems of linear equations using Gaussian elimination. But each of these strategies seems limited in what problems it can solve.

SATISFIABILITY WITH AT MOST 2 LITERALS PER CLAUSE (Cook 1971)

INPUT: Clauses $C_1, C_2, \ldots, C_p$, each containing at most 2 literals

PROPERTY: The conjunction of the given clauses is satisfiable; i.e., there is a set $S \subseteq \{x_1, x_2, \ldots, x_n, \bar{x}_1, \bar{x}_2, \ldots, \bar{x}_n\}$ such that

    a) S does not contain a complementary pair of literals and

    b) $S \cap C_k \neq \phi, \quad k = 1, 2, \ldots, p.$

☞

These optimization problems (and their yes-or-no versions) are in P because they have simple landscapes in which a local algorithm can quickly find the best possible solution. Minimum Spanning Tree is inspired by early electrical grids, where we want to connect cities with a network of power lines. Shortest Path is the classic routing problem of finding the shortest (or fastest, or cheapest) path from s to t. Minimum Cut asks whether we can divide a network in two so that s and t can no longer reach each other, by breaking a small number of edges. During the Cold War, each side asked whether they could disrupt the other's supply lines by destroying just a few links in their rail network.

MINIMUM SPANNING TREE (Kruskal 1956)

INPUT: G, w, W

PROPERTY: There exists a spanning tree of weight $\leq W$.

SHORTEST PATH (Dijkstra 1959)

INPUT: G, w, W, s, t

PROPERTY: There is a path between s and t of weight $\leq W$.

MINIMUM CUT (Edmonds and Karp 1972)

INPUT: G, w, W, s, t

PROPERTY: There is an s,t cut of weight $\leq W$.

ARC COVER (Edmonds 1965)

INPUT: G, k

PROPERTY: There is a set $Y \subseteq A$ such that $|Y| \leq k$ and every node is incident with an arc in Y.

ARC DELETION

INPUT: G, k

PROPERTY: There is a set of k arcs whose deletion breaks all cycles.

BIPARTITE MATCHING (Hall, Jr. 1948)

INPUT: $S \subseteq Z_p \times Z_p$

PROPERTY: There are p elements of S, no two of which are equal in either component.

SEQUENCING WITH DEADLINES

INPUT: $(T_1, \ldots, T_n) \in Z^n, \quad (D_1, \ldots, D_n) \in Z^n, k$

PROPERTY: Starting at time 0, one can execute jobs $1, 2, \ldots, n$, with execution times T_i and deadlines D_i, in some order such that not more than k jobs miss their deadlines.

SOLVABILITY OF LINEAR EQUATIONS

INPUT: (c_{ij}), (a_i)

PROPERTY: There exists a vector (y_j) such that, for each i, $\sum_j c_{ij} y_j = a_i$.

3. Nondeterministic Algorithms and Cook's Theorem

In this section we state an important theorem due to Cook (1971) which asserts that any language in a certain wide class $\mathcal{NP}$ is reducible to a specific set S, which corresponds to the problem of deciding whether a Boolean formula in conjunctive normal form is satisfiable.

Let $\mathcal{P}^{(2)}$ denote the class of subsets of $\Sigma^* \times \Sigma^*$ which are recognizable in polynomial time. Given $L^{(2)} \in \mathcal{P}^{(2)}$ and a polynomial p, we define a language L as follows:

$$L = \{ x \mid \text{ there exists y such that } \langle x, y \rangle \in L^{(2)} \text{ and } \lg(y) \leq p(\lg(x)) \}.$$

We refer to L as the language derived from $L^{(2)}$ by p-bounded existential quantification.

Definition 4. $\mathcal{NP}$ is the set of languages derived from elements of $\mathcal{P}^{(2)}$ by polynomial-bounded existential quantification.

There is an alternative characterization of $\mathcal{NP}$ in terms of nondeterministic Turing machines. A *nondeterministic recognition algorithm* $\mathcal{A}$ is specified by:

    a countable set D (the *domain*)

    a finite alphabet Δ such that $\Delta^* \cap \{\text{ACCEPT, REJECT}\} = \phi$

    an *encoding function* E: $D \to \Delta^*$

    a *transition relation* $\tau \subseteq \Delta^* \times (\Delta^* \cup \{\text{ACCEPT, REJECT}\})$

such that, for every $y_0 \in \Delta^*$, the set $\{ \langle y_0, y \rangle \mid \langle y_0, y \rangle \in \tau \}$ has fewer than $k_{\mathcal{A}}$ elements, where $k_{\mathcal{A}}$ is a constant. A *computation* of $\mathcal{A}$ on input $x \in D$ is a sequence $y_1, y_2, \ldots$ such that $y_1 = E(x)$, $\langle y_i, y_{i+1} \rangle \in \tau$ for all i, and, if the sequence is finite and ends with y_k, then $y_k \in \{\text{ACCEPT, REJECT}\}$. A string $y \in \Delta^*$ which occurs in some computation is an *instantaneous description*. A finite computation ending in ACCEPT is an *accepting computation*. Input x is *accepted* if there is an accepting computation for x. If $D = \Sigma^*$ then $\mathcal{A}$ is a *nondeterministic string recognition algorithm* and we say that $\mathcal{A}$ *operates in polynomial time* if there is a polynomial $p(\cdot)$ such that, whenever $\mathcal{A}$ accepts x, there is an accepting computation for x of length $\leq p(\lg(x))$.

This formalizes the "checkability" of problems in $\mathcal{NP}$. Given a pair (example, solution) we can check in polynomial time whether that solution works for that example. For instance, given both a map and a coloring with three colors, it's easy to check whether that coloring is valid for that map. Then we can define the set or "language" of examples for which some valid (example, solution) pair exists: for instance, the set of maps for which there is a valid coloring with three colors. Adding "there exists" in this way is called existential quantification, and it raises the complexity from $\mathcal{P}$ to $\mathcal{NP}$.

Another way to define $\mathcal{NP}$ is to imagine a "nondeterministic" computer that can pursue exponentially many possible solutions simultaneously, and count it as "accepting" if any of these solutions succeeds. (This is where the $\mathcal{N}$ in $\mathcal{NP}$ comes from.) Such a computer is completely fictional—even quantum computers can't do this kind of search in parallel—but it is another way to formalize exhaustively searching a landscape.

A nondeterministic algorithm can be regarded as a process which, when confronted with a choice between (say) two alternatives, can create two copies of itself, and follow up the consequences of both courses of action. Repeated splitting may lead to an exponentially growing number of copies; the input is accepted if any sequence of choices leads to acceptance.

The nondeterministic 1-tape Turing machines, multitape Turing machines, random-access machines, etc. define classes of nondeterministic string recognition algorithms by restricting the encoding function E and transition relation τ to particularly simple forms. All these classes of algorithms, restricted to operate in polynomial time, define the same class of languages. Moreover, this class is $\mathcal{NP}$.

Theorem 1. $L \in \mathcal{NP}$ if and only if L is accepted by a nondeterministic Turing machine which operates in polynomial time.

Proof. $\Rightarrow$ Suppose $L \in \mathcal{NP}$. Then, for some $L^{(2)} \in P^{(2)}$ and some polynomial p, L is obtained from $L^{(2)}$ by p-bounded existential quantification. We can construct a nondeterministic machine which first guesses the successive digits of a string y of length $\leq p(\lg(y))$ and then tests whether $\langle x, y \rangle \in L^{(2)}$. Such a machine clearly recognizes L in polynomial time.

$\Leftarrow$ Suppose L is accepted by a nondeterministic Turing machine T which operates in time p. Assume without loss of generality that, for any instantaneous description Z, there are at most two instantaneous descriptions that may follow Z (i.e., at most two primitive transitions are applicable). Then the sequence of choices of instantaneous descriptions made by T in a given computation can be encoded as a string y of 0's and 1's, such that $\lg(y) \leq p(\lg(x))$.

Thus we can construct a deterministic Turing machine T', with $\Sigma^* \times \Sigma^*$ as its domain of inputs, which, on input $\langle x, y \rangle$, simulates the action of T on input x with the sequence of choices y. Clearly T' operates in polynomial time, and L is obtained by polynomial bounded existential quantification from the set of pairs of strings accepted by T'.

The class $\mathcal{NP}$ is very extensive. Loosely, a recognition problem is in $\mathcal{NP}$ if and only if it can be solved by a backtrack search of polynomial bounded depth. A wide range of important computational problems which are not known to be in $\mathcal{P}$ are obviously in $\mathcal{NP}$. For example, consider the problem of determining whether the nodes of a graph G can be colored with k colors so that no two adjacent nodes have the same color. A nondeterministic algorithm can simply guess an assignment of colors to the nodes and then check (in polynomial time) whether all pairs of adjacent nodes have distinct colors.

In view of the wide extent of $\mathcal{NP}$, the following theorem due to Cook is remarkable. We define the satisfiability problem as follows:

In a backtracking search, we try making some choices, like coloring some of the countries on a map or taking the first few steps in a traveling salesman tour. If these choices lead to a dead end or a contradiction, we backtrack to the last place we had a choice, and try a different path. In this way we can explore the entire landscape of solutions, pursuing a branching tree of possibilities—but this typically takes exponential time. $\mathcal{NP}$ is the class of problems where we can tell if and when our search has succeeded.

SATISFIABILITY

INPUT: Clauses $C_1, C_2, \ldots, C_p$

PROPERTY: The conjunction of the given clauses is satisfiable; i.e., there is a set $S \subseteq \{x_1, x_2, \ldots, x_n; \bar{x}_1, \bar{x}_2, \ldots, \bar{x}_n\}$ such that

    a) S does not contain a complementary pair of literals

and b) $S \cap C_k \neq \phi, \quad k = 1, 2, \ldots, p$.

Theorem 2 (Cook). If $L \in \mathcal{NP}$ then $L \propto$ SATISFIABILITY.

The theorem stated by Cook (1971) uses a weaker notion of reducibility than the one used here, but Cook's proof supports the present statement.

Corollary 1. $\mathcal{P} = \mathcal{NP} \Leftrightarrow$ SATISFIABILITY $\in \mathcal{P}$.

Proof. If SATISFIABILITY $\in \mathcal{P}$ then, for each $L \in \mathcal{NP}$, $L \in \mathcal{P}$, since $L \propto$ SATISFIABILITY. If SATISFIABILITY $\notin \mathcal{P}$, then, since clearly SATISFIABILITY $\in \mathcal{NP}$, $\mathcal{P} \neq \mathcal{NP}$.

Remark. If $\mathcal{P} = \mathcal{NP}$ then $\mathcal{NP}$ is closed under complementation and polynomial-bounded existential quantification. Hence it is also closed under polynomial-bounded universal quantification. It follows that a polynomial-bounded analogue of Kleene's Arithmetic Hierarchy (Rogers, Jr. 1967) becomes trivial if $\mathcal{P} = \mathcal{NP}$.

Theorem 2 shows that, if there were a polynomial-time algorithm to decide membership in SATISFIABILITY then every problem solvable by a polynomial-depth backtrack search would also be solvable by a

The satisfiability problem asks whether a set of logical constraints or "clauses" can be simultaneously satisfied by some setting of their variables. As described in the introduction to this chapter, Cook proved that satisfiability is NP-complete, by using these clauses as building blocks of computation (in his case, steps of a Turing machine) to simulate any program that checks potential solutions to a problem. Thus while satisfiability looks like a specific problem about logical formulas, it actually has a very general expressive power.

polynomial-time algorithm. This is strong circumstantial evidence that SATISFIABILITY $\notin \mathcal{P}$.

4. Complete Problems

The main object of this paper is to establish that a large number of important computational problems can play the role of SATISFIABILITY in Cook's theorem. Such problems will be called complete.

Definition 5. The language L is (polynomial) complete if

a) $L \in \mathcal{NP}$

and   b) SATISFIABILITY $\propto$ L.

Theorem 3. Either all complete languages are in $\mathcal{P}$, or none of them are. The former alternative holds if and only if $\mathcal{P} = \mathcal{NP}$.

We can extend the concept of completeness to problems defined over countable domains other than Σ^*.

Definition 6. Let D be a countable domain, e a "standard" one-one encoding $e : D \to \Sigma^*$ and T a subset of D. Then T is *complete* if and only if e (D) is complete.

Lemma 2. Let D and D$'$ be countable domains, with one-one encoding functions e and e$'$. Let $T \subseteq D$ and $T' \subseteq D'$. Then $T \propto T'$ if there is a function $F : D \to D'$ such that

a) $F(x) \in T' \Leftrightarrow x \in T$

and   b) there is a function $f \in \Pi$ such that $f(x) = e' \left(F \left(e^{-1}(x) \right) \right)$

     whenever $e' \left(F \left(e^{-1}(x) \right) \right)$ is defined.

The rest of the paper is mainly devoted to the proof of the following theorem.

Main Theorem. All the problems on the following list are complete.

1. **SATISFIABILITY**

     COMMENT: By duality, this problem is equivalent to determining whether a disjunctive normal form expression is a tautology.

2. **0-1 INTEGER PROGRAMMING**

     INPUT: integer matrix C and integer vector d

     PROPERTY: There exists a $0 - 1$ vector x such that $Cx = d$.

Since satisfiability has this universal expressive power, if we could solve it in polynomial time, we could do the same for any problem in $\mathcal{NP}$—but then $\mathcal{P}$ and $\mathcal{NP}$ would be equal. This would violate our strong intuition that even if solutions are easy to check, they can be hard to find.

A problem is complete if it is general enough, and has enough expressive power, to encode any problem in $\mathcal{NP}$. Informally, this means we can build a computer out of its variables and interactions.

Many of these problems are familiar challenges in logic, optimization, and network theory.

3. CLIQUE

INPUT: graph G, positive integer k

PROPERTY: G has a set of k mutually adjacent nodes.

Clique asks for the largest set of nodes in a network that are all connected to each other. If we switch links and non-links, it becomes Independent Set, which asks for the largest set of nodes with no links between them. This is closely related to "hard sphere" models in physics, where particles have a repulsive force between them that prevents them from being too close to each other.

4. SET PACKING

INPUT: Family of sets $\{S_j\}$, positive integer ℓ

PROPERTY: $\{S_j\}$ contains ℓ mutually disjoint sets.

5. NODE COVER

INPUT: graph G', positive integer ℓ

PROPERTY: There is a set $R \subseteq N'$ such that $|R| \leq \ell$ and every arc is incident with some node in R.

6. SET COVERING

INPUT: finite family of finite sets $\{S_j\}$, positive integer k

PROPERTY: There is a subfamily $\{T_h\} \subseteq \{S_j\}$ containing $\leq k$ sets such that $\cup_{T_h} = \cup_{S_j}$.

Named after William Rowan Hamilton, who also invented quaternions, and for whom the Hamiltonian operator of classical and quantum mechanics is named, Hamilton circuit is a simplification of the traveling-salesman problem. It asks whether there is a tour along the links in a network that visits every node once and returns to its starting place.

7. FEEDBACK NODE SET

INPUT: digraph H, positive integer k

PROPERTY: There is a set $R \subseteq V$ such that every (directed) cycle of H contains a node in R.

8. FEEDBACK ARC SET

INPUT: digraph H, positive integer k

PROPERTY: There is a set $S \subseteq E$ such that every (directed) cycle of H contains an arc in S.

9. DIRECTED HAMILTON CIRCUIT

INPUT: digraph H

PROPERTY: H has a directed cycle which includes each node exactly once.

10. UNDIRECTED HAMILTON CIRCUIT

INPUT: graph G

PROPERTY: G has a cycle which includes each node exactly once.

11. **SATISFIABILITY WITH AT MOST 3 LITERALS PER CLAUSE**

INPUT: Clauses $D_1, D_2, \ldots, D_r$, each consisting of at most 3 literals from the set $\{u_1, u_2, \ldots, u_m\} \cup \{\bar{u}_1, \bar{u}_2, \ldots, \bar{u}_m\}$

PROPERTY: The set $\{D_1, D_2, \ldots, D_r\}$ is satisfiable.

This is a generalization of the map-coloring problem. The chromatic number of a graph or network is the smallest number of colors we need to color the nodes so that any linked pair have different colors. The four-color map theorem says that if a graph is planar, i.e., if it can be drawn in two dimensions without its edges crossing, its chromatic number is at most four. But telling whether a planar graph has chromatic number three, i.e., whether three colors suffice to color it, is $\mathcal{NP}$-complete.

Exact cover includes puzzles where a set of pieces have to fit together to fill a space with no gaps or overlaps.

12. **CHROMATIC NUMBER**

INPUT: graph G, positive integer k

PROPERTY: There is a function $\phi : N \to Z_k$ such that, if u and v are adjacent, then $\phi(u) \neq \phi(v)$.

13. **CLIQUE COVER**

INPUT: graph G', positive integer ℓ

PROPERTY: N' is the union of ℓ or fewer cliques.

14. **EXACT COVER**

INPUT: family $\{S_j\}$ of subsets of a set $\{u_i, i = 1, 2, \ldots, t\}$

PROPERTY: There is a subfamily $\{T_h\} \subseteq \{S_j\}$ such that the sets T_h are disjoint and $\cup T_h = \cup S_j = \{u_i, i = 1, 2, \ldots, t\}$.

15. **HITTING SET**

INPUT: family $\{U_i\}$ of subsets of $\{s_j, j = 1, 2, \ldots, r\}$

PROPERTY: There is a set W such that, for each i, $|W \cap U_i| = 1$.

16. **STEINER TREE**

INPUT: graph G, $R \subseteq N$, weighting function $w : A \to Z$, positive integer k

PROPERTY: G has a subtree of weight $\leq k$ containing the set of nodes in R.

17. **3-DIMENSIONAL MATCHING**

INPUT: set $U \subseteq T \times T \times T$, where T is a finite set

PROPERTY: There is a set $W \subseteq U$ such that $|W| = |T|$ and no two elements of W agree in any coordinate.

18. **KNAPSACK**

INPUT: $(a_1, a_2, \ldots, a_r, b) \in Z^{n+1}$

PROPERTY: $\sum a_j x_j = b$ has a $0 - 1$ solution.

19. JOB SEQUENCING

INPUT: "execution time vector" $(T_1, \ldots, T_p) \in Z^p$,

"deadline vector" $(D_1, \ldots, D_p) \in Z^p$

"penalty vector" $(P_1, \ldots, P_p) \in Z^p$

positive integer k

PROPERTY: There is a permutation π of $\{1, 2, \ldots, p\}$ such that

$$\left(\sum_{j=1}^{p} \left[\text{ if } T_{\pi(1)} + \cdots + T_{\pi(j)} > D_{\pi(j)} \text{ then } P_{\pi(j)} \text{ else } 0 \right] \right) \leq k.$$

20. PARTITION

INPUT: $(c_1, c_2, \ldots, c_s) \in Z^s$

PROPERTY: There is a set $I \subseteq \{1, 2, \ldots, s\}$ such that $\sum_{h \in I} c_h = \sum_{h \notin I} c_h$.

21. MAX CUT

INPUT: graph G, weighting function $w : A \to Z$, positive integer W

PROPERTY: There is a set $S \subseteq N$ such that

$$\sum_{\substack{\{u,v\} \in A \\ u \in S \\ v \notin S}} w(\{u, v\}) \geq W.$$

It is clear that these problems (or, more precisely, their encodings into Σ^*), are all in $\mathcal{NP}$. We proceed to give a series of explicit reductions, showing that SATISFIABILITY is reducible to each of the problems listed. Figure 1 shows the structure of the set of reductions. Each line in the figure indicates a reduction of the upper problem to the lower one.

To exhibit a reduction of a set $T \subseteq D$ to a set $T' \subseteq D'$, we specify a function $F : D \to D'$ which satisfies the conditions of Lemma 2. In each case, the reader should have little difficulty in verifying that F does satisfy these conditions.

MAX CUT asks how we can divide the nodes of a network into two groups that maximize the number of edges crossing from one group to the other. In physics terms, it asks for the ground state of an antiferromagnet, a material where neighboring atoms prefer to have opposite spins. This is closely related to the problem of finding communities in networks: for instance, MIN BISECTION asks how to divide the nodes into two equal groups with the smallest possible number of links between them.

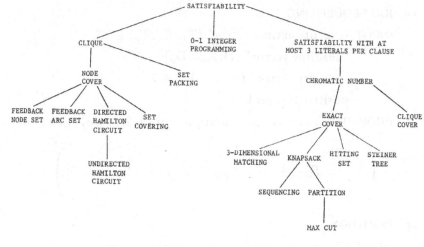

Reductions can be chained together, making a transitive relation: if K can be reduced to L and L can be reduced to M, then K can be reduced to M. This lets us build a family tree of $\mathcal{NP}$-complete problems, starting with the seed of satisfiability planted by Cook. Any one of these problems can simulate all the others. Therefore, either they can all be solved in polynomial time, or none of them can.

Figure 1. Complete Problems.

These proofs are written formally and compactly, and sadly without pictures. But each of these terse lines describes a "gadget" by which one problem can simulate or encode another.

SATISFIABILITY ∝ 0-1 INTEGER PROGRAMMING

$$c_{ij} = \begin{cases} 1 & \text{if } x_j \in C_i \\ -1 & \text{if } \bar{x}_j \in C_i \quad i = 1, 2, \ldots, p \\ 0 & \text{otherwise} \quad j = 1, 2, \ldots, n \end{cases}$$

$b_i = 1 - (\text{the number of complemented variables in } C_i)$,

$i = 1, 2, \ldots, p.$

SATISFIABILITY ∝ CLIQUE

$N = \{\langle \sigma, i \rangle \mid \sigma \text{ is a literal and occurs in } C_i\}$

$A = \{\{\langle \sigma, i \rangle, \langle \delta, j \rangle\} \mid i \neq j \text{ and } \sigma \neq \bar{\delta}\}$

$k = p$, the number of clauses.

CLIQUE ∝ SET PACKING

Assume $N = \{1, 2, \ldots, n\}$. The elements of the sets $S_1, S_2, \ldots, S_n$ are those two-element sets of nodes $\{i, j\}$ not in A.

$S_i = \{\{i, j\} \mid \{i, j\} \notin A\}, \quad i = 1, 2, \ldots, n$

$\ell = k.$

CLIQUE ∝ NODE COVER

G' is the complement of G.

$\ell = |N| - k$

NODE COVER $\propto$ SET COVERING

Assume $N' = \{1, 2, \ldots, n\}$. The elements are the arcs of G'. S_j is the set of arcs incident with node j. $k = \ell$.

NODE COVER $\propto$ FEEDBACK NODE SET

$$V = N'$$
$$E = \big\{\langle u, v \rangle \mid \{u, v\} \in A'\big\}$$
$$k = \ell$$

NODE COVER $\propto$ FEEDBACK ARC SET

$$V = N' \times \{0, 1\}$$
$$E = \big\{\langle\langle u, 0\rangle, \langle u, 1\rangle\rangle \mid u \in N'\big\} \cup \big\{\langle\langle u, 1\rangle, \langle v, 0\rangle\rangle \mid \{u, v\} \in A'\big\}$$
$$k = \ell$$

NODE COVER $\propto$ DIRECTED HAMILTON CIRCUIT

Without loss of generality assume $A' = Z_m$.

$$V = \{a_1, a_2, \ldots, a_\ell\} \cup \{\langle u, i, \alpha\rangle \mid u \in N' \text{ is incident with } i \in A'$$
$$\text{and } \alpha \in \{0, 1\}\}$$

$$E = \{\langle\langle u, i, 0\rangle, \langle u, i, 1\rangle\rangle \mid \langle u, i, 0\rangle \in V\}$$
$$\cup\{\langle\langle u, i, \alpha\rangle, \langle v, i, \alpha\rangle\rangle \mid i \in A', u \text{ and } v \text{ are incident with } i,$$
$$\alpha \in \{0, 1\}\}$$
$$\cup\{\langle\langle u, i, 1\rangle, \langle u, j, 0\rangle\rangle \mid u \text{ is incident with } i \text{ and } j \text{ and } \nexists\, h,$$
$$i < h < j, \text{ such that } u \text{ is incident}$$
$$\text{with } h\}$$
$$\cup\{\langle\langle u, i, 1\rangle, a_f\rangle \mid 1 \leq f \leq \ell \text{ and } \nexists h > i \text{ such that } u \text{ is incident}$$
$$\text{with } h\}$$
$$\cup\{\langle a_f, \langle u, i, 0\rangle\rangle \mid 1 \leq f \leq \ell \text{ and } \nexists h < i \text{ such that } u \text{ is incident}$$
$$\text{with } h\}.$$

DIRECTED HAMILTON CIRCUIT $\propto$ UNDIRECTED HAMILTON CIRCUIT

$$N = V \times \{0, 1, 2\}$$
$$A = \{\{\langle u, 0\rangle, \langle u, 1\rangle\}, \{\langle u, 1\rangle, \langle u, 2\rangle\} \mid u \in V\}$$
$$\cup \{\{\langle u, 2\rangle, \langle v, 0\rangle\} \mid \langle u, v\rangle \in E\}$$

SATISFIABILITY $\propto$ SATISFIABILITY WITH AT MOST 3 LITERALS PER CLAUSE

Replace a clause $\sigma_1 \cup \sigma_2 \cup \ldots \cup \sigma_m$, where the σ_i are literals and $m > 3$, by

$$(\sigma_1 \cup \sigma_2 \cup u_1)(\sigma_3 \cup \cdots \cup \sigma_m \cup \bar{u}_1)(\bar{\sigma}_3 \cup u_1) \cdots (\bar{\sigma}_m \cup u_1),$$

where u_1 is a new variable. Repeat this transformation until no clause has more than three literals.

SATISFIABILITY WITH AT MOST 3 LITERALS PER CLAUSE
$\propto$ CHROMATIC NUMBER

Assume without loss of generality that $m \geq 4$.

$N = \{u_1, u_2, \ldots, u_m\} \cup \{\bar{u}_1, \bar{u}_2, \ldots, \bar{u}_m\} \cup \{v_1, v_2, \ldots, v_m\}$
$\qquad \cup \{D_1, D_2, \ldots, D_r\}$

$A = \{\{u_i, \bar{u}_i\} \mid i = 1, 2, \ldots, n\} \cup \{\{v_i, v_j\} \mid i \neq j\} \cup \{\{v_i, x_j\} \mid i \neq j\}$
$\qquad \cup \{\{v_i, \bar{x}_j\} \mid i \neq j\} \cup \{\{u_i, D_f\} \mid u_i \notin D_f\} \cup \{\{\bar{u}_i, D_f\} \mid \bar{u}_i \in D_f\}$

$k = r + 1$

CHROMATIC NUMBER $\propto$ CLIQUE COVER

G' is the complement of G

$\ell = k$.

CHROMATIC NUMBER $\propto$ EXACT COVER

The set of elements is

$\qquad N \cup A \cup \{\langle u, e, f \rangle \mid u$ is incident with e and $1 \leq f \leq k\}$.

The sets S_j are the following:

$\qquad$ for each $f, 1 \leq f \leq k$, and each $u \in N$,

$\qquad \{u\} \cup \{\langle u, e, f \rangle \mid e$ is incident with $u\}$;

$\qquad$ for each $e \in A$ and each pair f_1, f_2 such that

$\qquad 1 \leq f_1 \leq k, \quad 1 \leq f_2 \leq k$ and $f_1 \neq f_2$

$\qquad \{e\} \cup \{\langle u, e, f \rangle, f \neq f_1\} \cup \{\langle v, e, g \rangle \mid g \neq f_2\}$,

where u and v are the two nodes incident with e.

EXACT COVER $\propto$ HITTING SET

The hitting set problem has sets U_i and elements s_j, such that $s_j \in U_i \Leftrightarrow u_i \in S_j$.

EXACT COVER $\propto$ STEINER TREE

$$N = \{n_0\} \cup \{S_j\} \cup \{u_i\}$$
$$R = \{n_0\} \cup \{u_i\}$$
$$A = \{\{n_0, S_j\}\} \{\{S_j, u_i\} \mid u_i \in S_j\}$$
$$w\left(\{n_0, S_j\}\right) = |S_j|$$
$$w\left(\{S_j, u_i\}\right) = 0$$
$$k = |\{u_i\}|$$

EXACT COVER $\propto$ 3-DIMENSIONAL MATCHING

Without loss of generality assume $|S_j| \geq 2$ for each j.
Let $T = \{\langle i, j \rangle \mid u_i \in S_j\}$. Let α be an arbitrary one-one function from $\{u_i\}$ into T. Let $\pi : T \to T$ be a permutation such that, for each fixed j, $\{\langle i, j \rangle \mid u_i \in S_j\}$ is a cycle of π.

$$U = \{\langle \alpha\left(u_i\right), \langle i, j \rangle, \langle i, j \rangle \rangle | \langle i, j \rangle \in T\}$$
$$\cup \{\langle \beta, \sigma, \pi(\sigma) \rangle | \text{ for all } i, \beta \neq \alpha\left(u_i\right)\} .$$

EXACT COVER $\propto$ KNAPSACK

Let $d = |\{S_j\}| + 1$. Let $\epsilon_{ji} = \begin{cases} 1 & \text{if } u_i \in s_j \\ 0 & \text{if } u_i \notin s_j \end{cases}$. Let
$r = |\{S_j\}|, \quad a_j = \sum \epsilon_{ji} d^{i-1} \quad \text{and} \quad b = \frac{d^t - 1}{d - 1}$.

KNAPSACK $\propto$ SEQUENCING

$$p = r, \quad T_i = P_i = a_i, \quad D_i = b.$$

KNAPSACK $\propto$ PARTITION

$$s = r + 2$$
$$c_i = a_i, \quad i = 1, 2, \ldots, r$$
$$c_{r+1} = b + 1$$
$$c_{r+2} = \left(\sum_{i=1}^{r} a_i\right) + 1 - b$$

PARTITION $\propto$ MAX CUT

$$N = \{1, 2, \ldots, s\}$$
$$A = \{\{i, j\} \mid i \in N, j \in N, i \neq j\}$$
$$w(\{i, j\} = c_i \cdot c_j$$
$$W = \left\lceil \frac{1}{4} \sum c_i^2 \right\rceil$$

Some of the reductions exhibited here did not originate with the present writer. (Cook 1971) showed that SATISFIABILITY $\propto$ SATISFIABILITY WITH AT MOST 3 LITERALS PER CLAUSE. The reduction

SATISFIABILITY $\propto$ CLIQUE

is implicit in Cook (1970), and was also known to Raymond Reiter. The reduction

NODE COVER $\propto$ FEEDBACK NODE SET

was found by the Algorithms Seminar at the Cornell University Computer Science Department. The reduction

NODE COVER $\propto$ FEEDBACK ARC SET

was found by Lawler and the writer, and Lawler discovered the reduction

EXACT COVER $\propto$ 3-DIMENSIONAL MATCHING

The writer discovered that the exact cover problem was reducible to the directed traveling-salesman problem on a digraph in which the arcs have weight zero or one. Using refinements of the technique used in this construction, Tarjan showed that

EXACT COVER $\propto$ DIRECTED HAMILTON CIRCUIT

and, independently, Lawler showed that

NODE COVER $\propto$ DIRECTED HAMILTON CIRCUIT

The reduction

DIRECTED HAMILTON CIRCUIT $\propto$ UNDIRECTED HAMILTON CIRCUIT

was pointed out by Tarjan.

Below we list three problems in automata theory and language theory to which every complete problem is reducible. These problems are not known to be complete, since their membership in NP is presently in doubt. The reader unacquainted with automata and language theory can find the necessary definitions in Hopcraft and Ullman (1969).

EQUIVALENCE OF REGULAR EXPRESSIONS
INPUT: A pair of regular expressions over the alphabet $\{0, 1\}$
PROPERTY: The two expressions define the same language.

EQUIVALENCE OF NONDETERMINISTIC FINITE AUTOMATA
INPUT: A pair of nondeterministic finite automata with input alphabet $\{0, 1\}$
PROPERTY: The two automata define the same language.

CONTEXT-SENSITIVE RECOGNITION
INPUT: A context-sensitive grammar Γ and a string x
PROPERTY: x is in the language generated by Γ.

First we show that

SATISFIABILITY WITH AT MOST 3 LITERALS PER CLAUSE $\propto$ EQUIVALENCE OF REGULAR EXPRESSIONS

The reduction is made in two stages. In the first stage we construct a pair of regular expressions over an alphabet $\Delta = \{u_1, u_2, \ldots, u_n, \bar{u}_1, \bar{u}_2, \ldots, \bar{u}_n\}$. We then convert these regular expressions to regular expressions over $\{0, 1\}$.

The first regular expression is $\Delta^n \Delta^*$ (more exactly, Δ is written out as $(u_1 + u_2 + \cdots + u_n + \bar{u}_1 + \cdots + \bar{u}_n)$, and Δ^n represents n copies

These problems are at least as hard as any problem in NP, and are probably much harder. The structures they talk about—regular expressions, finite automata, and context-sensitive grammars—can "unfold" into computations that are much longer than their descriptions. As a result, they don't have short solutions that are easily checked, and thus they seem to outside NP. In fact they are complete for PSPACE, the class of problems solvable with a polynomial amount of memory (and perhaps exponential time). For many two-player games, including checkers, the Hawaiian game of Kōnane, and some versions of Go, finding a winning strategy from a given board position is PSPACE-complete. We believe that PSPACE is far above NP in the complexity hierarchy.

of the expression for Δ concatenated together). The second regular expression is

$$\Delta^n \Delta^* \cup \cup \sum_{i=1}^{n} \left(\Delta^* u_i \Delta^* \bar{u}_i \Delta^* \cup \Delta^* \bar{u}_i \Delta^* u_i \Delta^* \right) \cup \cup \sum_{h=1}^{r} \theta \left(D_h \right)$$

where

$$\theta \left(D_h \right) = \begin{cases} \Delta^* \bar{\sigma}_1 \Delta^* & \text{if} \quad D_h = \sigma_1 \\ \Delta^* \bar{\sigma}_1 \Delta^* \bar{\sigma}_2 \Delta^* \cup \Delta^* \bar{\sigma}_2 \Delta^* \bar{\sigma}_1 \Delta^* & \text{if} \quad D_h = \sigma_1 \cup \sigma_2 \\ \Delta^* \bar{\sigma}_1 \Delta^* \bar{\sigma}_2 \Delta^* \bar{\sigma}_3 \Delta^* \cup \Delta^* \bar{\sigma}_1 \Delta^* \bar{\sigma}_3 \Delta^* \bar{\sigma}_2 \Delta^* \\ \quad \cup \Delta^* \bar{\sigma}_2 \Delta^* \bar{\sigma}_1 \Delta^* \bar{\sigma}_3 \Delta^* \cup \Delta^* \bar{\sigma}_2 \Delta^* \bar{\sigma}_3 \Delta^* \bar{\sigma}_1 \Delta^* \\ \quad \cup \Delta^* \bar{\sigma}_3 \Delta^* \bar{\sigma}_1 \Delta^* \bar{\sigma}_2 \Delta^* \cup \Delta^* \bar{\sigma}_3 \Delta^* \bar{\sigma}_2 \Delta^* \bar{\sigma}_1^* \Delta^* \\ \qquad\qquad\qquad\qquad \text{if} \quad D_h = \sigma_1 \cup \sigma_2 \cup \sigma_3. \end{cases}$$

Now let m be the least positive integer $\geq \log_2 |\Delta|$, and let ϕ be a 1-1 function from Δ into $\{0,1\}^m$. Replace[2] each regular expression by a regular expression over $\{0,1\}$, by making the substitution $a \to \phi(a)$ for each occurrence of each element of Δ.

EQUIVALENCE OF REGULAR EXPRESSIONS $\propto$ EQUIVALENCE OF NONDETERMINISTIC FINITE AUTOMATA

There are standard polynomial-time algorithms (Salomaa 1969) to convert a regular expression to an equivalent nondeterministic automaton. Finally, we show that, for any $L \in \mathcal{NP}$,

L $\propto$ CONTEXT-SENSITIVE RECOGNITION

Suppose L is recognized in time p( ) by a nondeterministic Turing machine. Then the following language $\tilde{L}$ over the alphabet $\{0, 1, \#\}$ is accepted by a nondeterministic linear bounded automaton which simulates the Turing machine:

$$\tilde{L} = \left\{ \#^{p(\lg(x))} x \#^{p(\lg(x))} \mid x \in L \right\}.$$

Hence $\tilde{L}$ is context-sensitive and has a context-sensitive grammar $\tilde{\Gamma}$. Thus $x \in L$ iff

$$\tilde{\Gamma}, \#^{p(lg(x))} x \#^{p(lg(x))}$$

is an acceptable input to CONTEXT-SENSITIVE RECOGNITION.

We conclude by listing the following important problems in NP which are not known to be complete.

GRAPH ISOMORPHISM

INPUT: graphs G and G′

PROPERTY: G is isomorphic to G′.

NONPRIMES

INPUT: positive integer k

PROPERTY: k is composite.

LINEAR INEQUALITIES

INPUT: integer matrix C, integer vector d

PROPERTY: Cx ≥ d has a rational solution. ✎

Each of these problems existed in limbo between $\mathcal{P}$ and $\mathcal{NP}$-completeness for many years. Linear inequalities, more commonly known as linear programming and a fundamental problem in economics, was shown to be in $\mathcal{P}$ by Khachiyan in 1979 using methods which extended to many other optimization problems. Primality was shown to be in $\mathcal{P}$ by Agrawal, Kayal, and Saxena in 2002. Graph isomorphism asks whether two networks are identical up to a relabeling of their nodes. Polynomial-time algorithms are known for many special cases, and in 2015 Babai showed that it is at worst "just outside" of $\mathcal{P}$ by giving an algorithm which runs in time n^c where c grows slowly with n. Whether it is in P in all cases remains open.

REFERENCES

Cook, S. A. 1971. "The Complexity of Theorem-Proving Procedures." In *STOC '71: Proceedings of the Third Annual ACM Symposium on Theory of Computing*, 151–158. New York, NY: Association for Computing Machinery.

Dijkstra, E. W. 1959. "A Note on Two Problems in Connexion with Graphs." *Numerische Mathematik* 2 (3): 269–271.

Edmonds, J. 1965. "Paths, Trees, and Flowers." *Canadian Journal of Mathematics* 17:449–467.

Edmonds, J., and R. M. Karp. 1972. "Theoretical Improvements in Algorithmic Efficiency for Network Flow Problems." *Journal of the ACM* 19 (2): 248–264.

Hall, Jr., M. 1948. "Distinct Representatives of Subsets." *Bulletin of the American Mathematical Society* 54:922–926.

Hopcraft, J. E., and J. D. Ullman. 1969. *Formal Languages and Their Relation to Automata*. Boston, MA: Addison–Wesley.

Kruskal, J. B. 1956. "On the Shortest Spanning Subtree of a Graph and the Traveling Salesman Problem." *Proceedings of the American Mathematical Society* 7 (1): 48–50.

Rogers, Jr., H. 1967. *Theory of Recursive Functions and Effective Computability*. Maidenhead, UK: McGraw-Hill.

Salomaa, A. 1969. *Theory of Automata*. New York, NY: Pergamon Press.

APPENDIX I

Notation and Terminology Used in Problem Specification

PROPOSITIONAL CALCULUS

$x_1, x_2, \ldots, x_n$	$u_1, u_2, \ldots, u_m$	propositional variables
$\bar{x}_1, \bar{x}_2, \ldots, \bar{x}_n$	$\bar{u}_1, \bar{u}_2, \ldots, \bar{u}_m$	complements of propositional variables
σ, σ_i		literals
$C_1, C_2, \ldots, C_p$	$D_1, D_2, \ldots, D_r$	clauses

$$C_k \subseteq \{x_1, x_2, \ldots, x_n, \bar{x}_1, \bar{x}_2, \ldots, \bar{x}_n\}$$
$$D_\ell \subseteq \{u_1, u_2, \ldots, u_m, \bar{u}_1, \bar{u}_2, \ldots, \bar{u}_m\}$$

A clause contains no complementary pair of literals.

SCALARS, VECTORS, MATRICES

Z	the positive integers
Z^p	the set of p-tuples of positive integers
Z_p	the set $\{0, 1, \ldots, p - 1\}$
$\langle x, y \rangle$	the ordered pair $\langle x, y \rangle$
$(a_i)\ (y_j)$ d	vectors with nonnegative integer components
(c_{ij}) C	matrices with integer components

GRAPHS AND DIGRAPHS

$G = (N, A)$ $G' = (N', A')$	finite graphs
N, N' sets of nodes A, A' sets of arcs	
s, t, u, v nodes $e, \{u, v\}$ arcs	
$(X, \bar{X}) = \{\{u, v\} \mid u \in X \text{ and } v \in \bar{X}\}$	cut
If $s \in X$ and $t \in \bar{X}$, $(X, \bar{X})$ is a s-t cut.	
$w: A \to Z$ $w': A' \to Z$	weight functions

The weight of a subgraph is the sum of the weights of its arcs.

$H = (V, E)$ digraph V set of nodes, E set of arcs	
$e, \langle u, v \rangle$ arcs	

SETS

ϕ	the empty set
$\mid S \mid$	the number of elements in the finite set S
$\{S_j\}$ $\{T_h\}$ $\{U_i\}$	finite families of finite sets

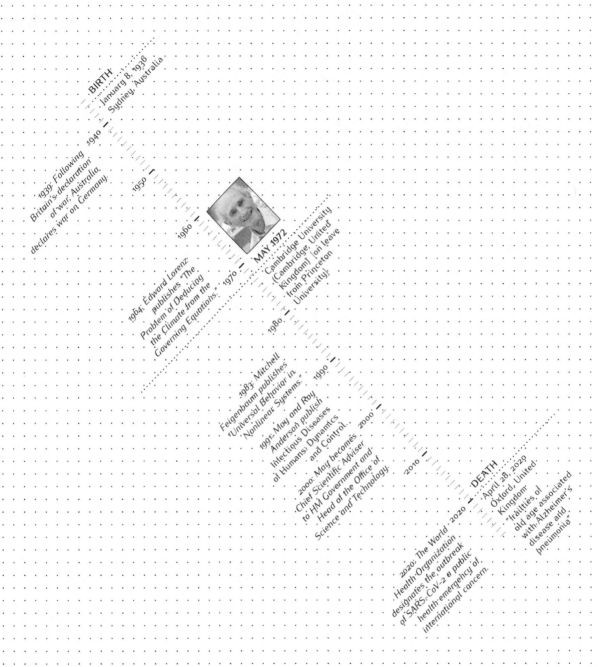

BIRTH
January 8, 1936
Sydney, Australia

1939: Following Britain's declaration of war, Australia declares war on Germany.

1964: Edward Lorenz publishes "The Problem of Deducing the Climate from the Governing Equations."

MAY 1972
Cambridge University (Cambridge, United Kingdom) [on leave from Princeton University].

1983: Mitchell Feigenbaum publishes "Universal Behavior in Nonlinear Systems."

1991: May and Roy Anderson publish Infectious Diseases of Humans: Dynamics and Control.

2000: May becomes Chief Scientific Adviser to HM Government and Head of the Office of Science and Technology.

2020: The World Health Organization designates the outbreak of SARS-CoV-2 a public health emergency of international concern.

DEATH
April 28, 2020
Oxford, United Kingdom
"frailties of old age associated with Alzheimer's disease and pneumonia."

ROBERT MCCREDIE MAY

[41]

DIVERSITY/COMPLEXITY/STABILITY

Jennifer A. Dunne, Santa Fe Institute

In this deceptively short 1972 paper, Robert ("Bob") May set a new foundation for how researchers understood and explored the relationships between diversity, complexity, and stability in large, dynamic systems composed of interacting components. That modest paper and a related monograph published the following year had implications that challenged and transformed understanding at the time and whose impact, influence, and inspiration continue to reverberate today.

R. M. May, "Will a Large Complex System Be Stable?" *Nature* 236, 413–414 (1972).

Reprinted with permission of Springer Nature.

May, a physicist by training and profession, had reached a critical transition in his career in the late 1960s when he became interested in ecological research, in part due to his concern for the social responsibility of science. Two key features of ecology at that time set the stage for his 1972 paper: 1) most ecologists were unconvinced of the value of mathematical approaches, which were thus vastly underutilized; and 2) conventional wisdom suggested that "complexity begets stability" in ecosystems, a longstanding notion that dated back at least to the origins of ecology as a distinct area of research (e.g., Forbes 1880).

The most prominent ecologists of the mid-twentieth century, including Charles Elton, Eugene Odum, G. Evelyn Hutchinson, and Robert MacArthur, elevated the idea that complex, diverse ecosystems are more stable than simple ones to the level of paradigm, in some cases putting a quantitative gloss on it. For example, MacArthur (1955), borrowing heuristics from information theory, suggested that "a large number of paths through each species is necessary to reduce the effects of overpopulation of one species." He concluded that "stability increases as the number of links increases" and that stability is easier to achieve in more diverse assemblages of species.[1]

---

[1] It was MacArthur who encouraged May to write the 1973 monograph during conversations they had while May spent the second half of a 1970–1971 sabbatical at

Separate from the ecological concerns of the era, Mark Gardner and W. Ross Ashby published a brief paper in *Nature* in 1970, "Connectance of Large Dynamic (Cybernetic) Systems: Critical Values for Stability." Their framing was about "dynamic, large, and complex" systems generally, such as airport traffic, slums, and the human brain. Interested in augmenting the "meagre" theoretical understanding of stability in large systems, their innovation was to examine randomly, partially connected matrices, a (slightly) more realistic depiction of interactions in real world systems than the fully connected matrices studied previously. Using simulations to assess the local stability of linearized dynamic systems with $n = 4, 7$, and 10 elements as a function of increasing connectance C (the percentage of possible connections that are non-zero), Gardner and Ashby demonstrated that as systems grew larger, small increases in connectance resulted in increasingly rapid drops to zero probability of stability. In other words, increasing diversity (n) and connectance (C) result in unstable systems at relatively low critical values.

May's subsequent paper, which explicitly drew on their approach, provided two important steps forward. First, while Gardner and Ashby reported computational results for a few small systems, May translated that into an analytical framework, assisted by heuristics, for large systems in the limit of $n \gg 1$. May assessed the local stability of randomly assembled, linearized, deterministic differential equation systems as a function of n, C, and s (the average strength of interaction between pairs of nodes). For May, the "complexity" of his 1972 title referred to the combination of connectance and average interaction strength. His proposed stability criterion, known as the May–Wigner theorem, showed that such community matrices near equilibrium will tend to be stable if $s(nC)^{1/2} < 1$. As he explained in his 1973 monograph (p. 65; note: he switched notation n to m),

> *The central feature of these results for large systems is the sharp*
> *transition from stable to unstable behavior as either the number*

---

the Institute for Advanced Study. MacArthur, the pre-eminent US theoretical ecologist at the time, also encouraged May to become his successor at Princeton, as he was dying of cancer. May initially demurred, but ultimately did take over the chair in 1973. (See the 2008 interview by Professor Robyn Williams of "Lord Robert May, Physicist and Ecologist," published by the Australian Academy of Science).

of species m, or the connectance C, or the average interaction strength s, exceed a critical value.

May's 1972 paper and 1973 monograph thus generalized and provided mathematical rigor to Gardner and Ashby's findings on the stability of idealized and simplified dynamic complex systems composed of interacting parts.

Second, May firmly rooted his mathematical explorations of system stability in an ecological context. May used his results to explicitly challenge the prevailing notion in ecology that diverse, complex ecosystems are more likely to be stable than simpler ones. As he wrote towards the end of his monograph (p. 174),

> *In short, there is no comfortable theorem assuring that increasing diversity and complexity beget enhanced community stability; rather, as a mathematical generality, the opposite is true. The task, therefore, is to elucidate the devious strategies which make for stability in enduring natural systems.*

In one fell swoop, May toppled a treasured ecological canard; demonstrated the power and utility of simple mathematical formulations and theoretical frameworks for ecology; and provided a convenient target for dissent as well as inspiration for elaborations that continue today.

Large swathes of ecological research over the last half-century represent attempts to "elucidate" those "devious strategies." For example, there is a direct lineage from May's work to the now vast literature on food webs and other ecological networks. Such research, which employs theoretical, computational, empirical, and experimental approaches, has proliferated as researchers investigate the relationships among many types of stability (e.g., robustness, persistence, resilience), multiple ways of measuring diversity, and various characterizations of the complexity of interactions. Methodologically, more sophisticated ways to document and analyze the nuances of non-random network structure and to model non-linear dynamics have emerged. There has also been rich cross-fertilization with research on other kinds of networks, for example, more recent work by May and others on "Systemic Risk in Banking Systems" (Haldane and May 2011).

May's work has also provided a backdrop for high-profile areas of research such as "biodiversity and ecosystem function" (BEF) and tipping points. BEF uses experiments and observations to unravel the relationship, if any, between the diversity of species and the functioning of ecosystems, for example as measured by primary productivity. The tipping-point literature incorporates both empirical and theoretical analyses of potentially irreversible critical transitions in ecosystems, for example, in response to climate change, with applications to many other kinds of complex systems.

Amazingly, May made two other foundational contributions to complexity science. First, he was one of the pioneers of chaos theory through insights gained from his work on models of insect population dynamics. One of the simplest population models ecologists were using when May turned his attention to ecology was a first-order difference equation suitable for exploring the dynamics of species with discrete, non-overlapping generations. In a series of papers in *Science* (1974) and *Nature* (1975, 1976), May showed that slight changes in the initial conditions of these very simple deterministic equations produce a "surprising array of dynamical behavior" that ranges from stable points to damped or undamped oscillations to chaotic fluctuations (May 1976). This provided both an early exploration of chaos emerging in simple mathematical systems and an important set of insights for ecology. It highlighted the challenge and necessity of differentiating random from deterministic behavior in ecological (or other complex system) dynamics, and it tossed a lightning bolt into the long-running debate over the relative importance of density dependence versus density independence for ecological outcomes.

Second, also in the early 1970s, May began to use his mathematical expertise to explore the dynamics of host-parasitoid and epidemiological systems, culminating in the 1992 magnum opus *Infectious Diseases of Humans: Dynamics and Control* with Roy Anderson. They wrote, "The primary aim of this book is to show how simple mathematical models of the transmission of infectious agents within human communities can help to interpret observed epidemiological trends, to guide the collection of data towards further understanding, and to design programmes for the control of infection and disease." Understanding the spread and control of HIV became an early, successful application of their framework, among many other examples.

The defining characteristics of May's work, whether on stability and complexity, deterministic chaos, host–disease systems, or myriad other topics, was to distill the relevant simplicity from apparently complex problems, define and explore a useful, testable mathematical framework, and suggest how it pointed to new directions of inquiry for everything from theoretical to applied research. His approach and his contributions continue to provide an important touchstone for a broad array of research on complex systems today. ❦

REFERENCES

Anderson, R. M., and R. M. May. 1992. *Infectious Diseases of Humans: Dynamics and Control.* Oxford, UK: Oxford University Press.

Forbes, S. A. 1880. "On Some Interactions of Organisms." *Bulletin of the Illinois State Laboratory of Natural History* 1 (3): 3–17.

Gardner, M. R., and W. R. Ashby. 1970. "Connectance of Large Dynamic (Cybernetic) Systems: Critical Values for Stability." *Nature* 228:784. https://doi.org/10.1038/228784a0.

Haldane, A. G., and R. M. May. 2011. "Systemic Risk in Banking Ecosystems." *Nature* 469:351–355. https://doi.org/10.1038/nature09659.

MacArthur, R. 1955. "Fluctuations of Animal Populations, and a Measure of Community Stability." *Ecology* 36:533–536. https://doi.org/10.2307/1929601.

May, R. M. 1972. "Will a Large Complex System Be Stable?" *Nature* 238:413–414. https://doi.org/10.1038/238413a0.

———. 1973. *Stability and Complexity in Model Ecosystems.* 1st. Princeton, NJ: Princeton University Press.

———. 1974. "Biological Populations with Nonoverlapping Generations: Stable Points, Stable Cycles, and Chaos." *Science* 186:645–647. https://doi.org/10.1126/science.186.4164.645.

———. 1975. "Deterministic Models with Chaotic Dynamics." *Nature* 256:165–166. https://doi.org/10.1038/256165a0.

———. 1976. "Simple Mathematical Models with Very Complicated Dynamics." *Nature* 261:459–467. https://doi.org/10.1038/261459a0.

WILL A LARGE COMPLEX SYSTEM
BE STABLE?

Robert M. May, Institute for Advanced Study

Robert M. May, Institute for Advanced Study

May acknowledges the general nature of his mathematical exploration, but here he frames his analysis specifically as an investigation of ecosystems, reflecting his interest in doing socially relevant science. Hence the elements of the matrix are species populations, the connections between them are trophic (feeding) interactions, and those interactions have a strength (the magnitude of the effect of species k on species j). This represents an analysis of idealized, simplified food webs. The title of his follow-up 1973 monograph reflects May's commitment to bringing mathematical frameworks suitable for complex systems to ecology.

Gardner and Ashby (1970) have suggested that large complex systems which are assembled (connected) at random may be expected to be stable up to a certain critical level of connectance, and then, as this increases, to suddenly become unstable. Their conclusions were based on the trend of computer studies of systems with 4, 7 and 10 variables.

Here I complement Gardner and Ashby's work with an analytical investigation of such systems in the limit when the number of variables is large. The sharp transition from stability to instability which was the essential feature of their paper is confirmed, and I go further to see how this critical transition point scales with the number of variables n in the system, and with the average connectance C and interaction magnitude α between the various variables. The object is to clarify the relation between stability and complexity in ecological systems with many interacting species, and some conclusions bearing on this question are drawn from the model. But, just as in Gardner and Ashby's work, the formal development of the problem is a general one, and thus applies to the wide range of contexts spelled out by these authors.

Specifically, consider a system with n variables (in an ecological application these are the populations of the n interacting species) which in general may obey some quite nonlinear set of first-order differential equations. The stability of the possible equilibrium or time-independent configurations of such a system may be studied by Taylor-expanding in the neighbourhood of the equilibrium point, so that the stability of the possible equilibrium is characterized by the equation

$$\mathrm{d}\mathbf{x}/\mathrm{d}t = \mathbf{A}\mathbf{x} \qquad (1)$$

Here in an ecological context $\mathbf{x}$ is the $n \times 1$ column vector of the disturbed populations x_j, and the $n \times n$ interaction matrix $\mathbf{A}$ has elements a_{jk}

which characterize the effect of species k on species j near equilibrium (Margalef 1968; May 1971). A diagram of the trophic web immediately determines which a_{jk} are zero (no web link), and the type of interaction determines the sign and magnitude of a_{jk}.

Following Gardner and Ashby, suppose that each of the n species would by itself have a density dependent or otherwise stabilized form, so that if disturbed from equilibrium it would return with some characteristic damping time. To set a timescale, these damping times are all chosen to be unity: $a_{jj} = -1$. Next the interactions are "switched on", and it is assumed that each such interaction element is equally likely to be positive or negative, having an absolute magnitude chosen from some statistical distribution. That is, each of these matrix elements is assigned from a distribution of random numbers, and this distribution has mean value zero and mean square value α. (For a fuller account of such a formulation, see Margalef 1968 and May 1971.) α may be thought of as expressing the average interaction "strength", which average is for simplicity common to all interactions. In short,

$$\mathbf{A} = \mathbf{B} - \mathbf{I} \qquad (2)$$

where $\mathbf{B}$ is a random matrix, and $\mathbf{I}$ the unit matrix. Thus we have an unbounded ensemble of models, one for each specific choice of the interaction matrix elements drawn individually from the random number distribution.

It is important to note that randomness only enters in the initial choice of the coefficients a_{jk}, which then define a particular model. Once the dice have been rolled to get a specific system, the subsequent analysis is purely deterministic.

The system (1) is stable if, and only if, all the eigenvalues of $\mathbf{A}$ have negative real parts. For a specified system size n and average interaction strength α, it may be asked what is the probability $P(n, \alpha)$ that a particular matrix drawn from the ensemble will correspond to a stable system. For large n, analytic techniques developed for treating large random matrices may be used to show[*] that such a matrix will be almost

May's approach builds on work by theoretical physicist Eugene Wigner on random matrix ensembles from 1959, as explained in his footnote. This is why May's stability criterion demonstrated in this paper and explained in more detail in his 1973 monograph is sometimes referred to as the May-Wigner theorem.

---

[*]From equation (2) it is obvious that the eigenvalues of $\mathbf{A}$ are $\lambda-1$, where λ are those of B. The "semi-circle law" distribution for the eigenvalues of a particular random matrix

certainly stable $(P \to 1)$ if

$$\alpha < (n)^{-1/2} \qquad (3)$$

and almost certainly unstable $(P \to 0)$ if

$$\alpha > (n)^{-1/2} \qquad (4)$$

The transition from stability to instability as α increases from the regime (3) into the regime (4) is very sharp for $n \gg 1$; indeed the relative width of the transition region scales as $n^{-2/3}$.

Such a precise answer for any model in the ensemble in the limit $n \gg 1$ is a consequence of the familiar statistical fact that, although individual matrix elements are liable to have any value, by the time one has an $n \times n$ matrix with n^2 such statistical elements, the total system has relatively well defined properties.

Next we introduce Gardner and Ashby's connectance, C, which expresses the probability that any pair of species will interact. It is measured as the percentage of non-zero elements in the matrix, or as the ratio of actual links to topologically possible links in the trophic web. The matrix elements in **B** now either, with probability C, are drawn from the previous random number distribution, or, with probability $1 - C$, are zero. Thus each member of the ensemble of matrices A corresponds to a system of individually stable parts, connected so that each part is affected directly by a fraction C of the other parts. For large n, $\alpha^2 C$ plays the role previously played by α^2, and we find the system (1) is almost certainly stable $(P(n, \alpha, C) \to 1)$ if

$$\alpha < (nC)^{-1/2} \qquad (5)$$

and almost certainly unstable $(P \to 0)$ if

$$\alpha > (nC)^{-1/2} \qquad (6)$$

---

ensemble was first obtained by Wigner[4], and subsequently generalized by him to a very wide class of random matrices whose elements all have the same mean square value[5]. Although the matrix **B** does not in general possess the hermiticity property required for most of these results to be directly applicable, the present results for the largest eigenvalue and its neighbourhood can be obtained by using Wigner's (1959) original style of argument on $(\mathbf{B})^{N} (\mathbf{B}^{\mathrm{T}})^{N}$ where N is very large. Indirectly relevant is Mehta (1967) and Ginibre (1965).

It is interesting to compare the analytical results with Gardner and Ashby's computer results for smallish n. (Their choice of A differs slightly from ours, but in essence they have the fixed value $\alpha^2 = 1/3$, and diagonal elements intrinsically -0.55 rather than -1.) Although our methods are based on the assumption that n is large, and are therefore only approximations when applied to $n = 4, 7, 10$, the two approaches in fact agree well when compared, being not more than 30% discrepant even for $n = 4$.

The central feature of the above results for large systems is the very sharp transition from stable to unstable behaviour as the complexity (as measured by the connectance and the average interaction strength) exceeds a critical value. This accords with Gardner and Ashby's conjecture.

Applied in an ecological context, this ensemble of very general mathematical models of multi-species communities, in which the population of each species would by itself be stable, displays the property that too rich a web connectance (too large a C) or too large an average interaction strength (too large an α) leads to instability. The larger the number of species, the more pronounced the effect.

Two corollaries are worth noting, although they should not be taken to have more than qualitative significance.

First, notice that two different systems of this kind, with average interaction strengths and connectances α_1, C_1 and α_2, C_2 respectively, have similar stability character if

$$\alpha_1^2 C_1 \simeq \alpha_2^2 C_2 \qquad (7)$$

Roughly speaking, this suggests that within a web species which interact with many others (large C) should do so weakly (small α), and conversely those which interact strongly should do so with but a few species. This is indeed a tendency in many natural ecosystems, as noted, for example, by Margalef (1968, p. 7): "From empirical evidence it seems that species that interact feebly with others do so with a great number of other species. Conversely, species with strong interactions are often part of a system with a small number of species. . . ."

A second feature of the models may be illustrated by using Gardner and Ashby's computations (which are for a particular α) to see, for

Whereas Gardner and Ashby conducted their primitive simulation analysis when the use of computer-based modeling by scientists was in its early stages, May provided an analytical framework that generalized their approach and results. Some ecologists came to understand the potential power, utility, and relevance of idealized mathematical approaches for ecology. May is now considered a pioneer of modern theoretical ecology, replacing the heuristic arguments of his predecessors with rigorous mathematical frameworks.

May's conclusion that instability results from connectance, average interaction strength, or number of species exceeding critical values threw a monkey wrench into the longstanding ecological paradigm that more complex, diverse ecosystems are more likely to be stable. It also inspired research that continues in various forms today. For example, people pointed out that his use of local asymptotic stability was not particularly relevant for ecosystems or other types of complex systems. Much effort thus went into exploring other, more relevant formulations of stability, such as robustness, persistence, resilience, and critical transitions.

In these final "corollaries" to his main stability criterion, May discusses two things that seem to follow. First, species with many interactions should do so weakly (low interaction strength), and those with high interaction strength should do so with few species. In more recent food web research, this has emerged as the notion that stability in "real" food webs results in part from the presence of long loops of interactions that are weak. Second, arranging interactions in blocks within a web will enhance stability. This is an aspect of non-random network structure that has been explored in a variety of ways, both empirically and via models, for myriad types of networks. These are the types of "devious strategies" that May had in mind for understanding the stability of complex systems, which led to areas of inquiry that continue to be important today.

example, that 12-species communities with 15% connectance have probability essentially zero of being stable, whereas if the interactions be organized into three separate 4×4 blocks of 4-species communities, each with a consequent 45% connectance, the "organized" 12-species models will be stable with probability 35%. That is, of the infinite ensemble of these particular 12-species models, essentially none of the general ones are stable, whereas 35% of those arranged into three "blocks" are stable. Such examples suggest that our model multi-species communities, for given average interaction strength and web connectance, will do better if the interactions tend to be arranged in "blocks"—again a feature observed in many natural ecosystems.

Acknowledgment

This work was sponsored by the US National Science Foundation.

REFERENCES

Gardner, M. R., and W. R. Ashby. 1970. "Connectance of Large Dynamic (Cybernetic) Systems: Critical Values for Stability." *Nature* 228:784.

Ginibre, J. 1965. "Reduced Density Matrices of Quantum Gases." *Journal of Mathematical Physics* 6 (2): 238–261.

Margalef, R. 1968. *Perspectives in Ecological Theory*. Chicago, IL: University of Chicago Press.

May, R. M. 1971. "Stability in Multispecies Community Models." *Mathematical Biosciences* 12 (1–2): 59–79.

Mehta, M. L. 1967. *Random Matrices*. New York, NY: Academic Press.

Wigner, E. P. 1959. "Statistical Properties of Real Symmetric Matrices with Many Dimensions." In *Proceedings of the Fourth Canadian Mathematical Congress, Banff, 1957*, 174–184. Toronto, Canada: University of Toronto Press.

BIRTH
1910
November 13, 1911
Vienna, Austria (then
Austria-Hungary)

1920

1924: The first meetings
of the Vienna Circle
take place as informal
discussion hours, by
1930 personal invitation
of Moritz Schlick.

1940

1949: When asked to edit
the sixth Macy Conference 1950
proceedings, von Foerster
agrees and suggests they
change the subject name
to "Cybernetics", after Norbert Wiener's 1948 book.

January 1, 1958: The
Biological Computer 1960
Laboratory is founded at
the University of Illinois
Urbana-Champaign.

VON FOERSTER 1972
University of Illinois
Urbana-Champaign

1970

1973: James Lighthill
publishes "Artificial
Intelligence: A General
Survey", also known as
the Lighthill Report, a
bleak report on the 1980
status of AI research and,
a factor contributing to
the first "AI Winter."

1990

DEATH
2000
October 2, 2002
Pescadero,
California,
congestive
heart failure

PHOTO ©1991 PAUL PANGARO

HE·I·NZ ·V·O·N· F·O·E·R·ST·E·R

[42]

THE DEEP CO-EVOLUTIONARY
ROOTS OF COMPLEXITY

Manfred D. Laubichler, Arizona State University
and Santa Fe Institute

For most of its history a founding principle of Western natural science has been the clear demarcation between the observer and the observed. We observed and measured natural phenomena as distinct from us and organized these observations into formal theories that allowed us to make predictions and ideally also provided a causal explanation of these phenomena. These epistemological values contributed to the remarkable successes of several scientific disciplines.

But this ideal of demarcation was questioned over the last century beginning with Einstein's theory of relativity, which challenged the immutable Cartesian coordinate system and introduced the vantage point of the observer and soon thereafter with the recognition of the fundamental limitation in our ability to determine all properties of particles, expressed by Heisenberg's uncertainty principle (Einstein 1924; Wilczek 2022).

These scientific breakthroughs led to an epistemological crisis first described in detail by the philosopher and polymath Ernst Cassirer (1922, 1950). Following Cassirer's initial diagnosis of epistemological uncertainty, we see several attempts to address these challenges by philosophers, mathematicians, psychologists, and biologists. Heinz von Foerster's contributions addressing this problem are among the deepest, but unfortunately still largely unknown, set of ideas.

Von Foerster's starting point is as simple as it is profound. Insofar as the observer is now a crucial part of any scientific account, we need a description of the observer to be part of any science. And, as the only observers we know are living beings (so far limited to our planet), we need a biologically sound theory of these observers and their ability to

H. von Foerster, "Notes on an Epistemology for Living Things," *BCL Report* #9.3 (1972), University of Illinois Urbana–Champaign. Reproduced in H. von Foerster, *Understanding Understanding: Essays on Cybernetics and Cognition*, New York, NY: Springer: 247–259 (2003).

Reprinted with permission of Springer.

make these observations and express them in a coherent form. In the paper "Notes of an epistemology for living things" he develops an initial formal account that aims to identify the properties of observers as living beings and their ability to develop a coherent system or word view. The goal of this exercise is very similar to the lifelong philosophical quest of his relative Ludwig Wittgenstein, namely, to identify what can be said clearly. And, also in line with Wittgenstein (1922, 1953), he saw both the need for and the limitations of strictly formal approaches.

The Viennese connection is crucial in contextualizing von Foerster's thinking, even though he did most of his groundbreaking work after he emigrated to the United States in 1949. His network of scientific collaborators is remarkable, as is his influence on many areas of science. From his base at the Biological Computer Laboratory at the University of Illinois Urbana–Champaign he contributed to computer science, artificial intelligence, biophysics, and epistemology. The founding father of second-order cybernetics, he inspired several attempts to develop a constructivist worldview by the likes of Humberto Maturana and Francisco Varela (1980; 1987), Gregory Bateson (1979), and Margaret Mead (1985).

How did the context of Vienna shape von Foerster's views? He was born in 1911 at the end of fin-de-siècle Vienna, but his formative years were in the 1920s and 1930s. A brilliant study by Richard Cockett (2023) details how numerous influential ideas in logic, philosophy, mathematics, psychology, economics, and management theory—not to speak of the arts—emerged during this short period. Many of these concepts came to full fruition in the United States and England as most of the key figures that made up this cultural and scientific ferment were Jewish and had to escape persecution by the Nazis and their allies. One theme that unites this diverse group of thinkers—which included Ludwig von Mises, Friedrich von Hayek, Joseph Schumpeter, Otto Neurath, Wittgenstein, Kurt Gödel, John von Neumann, Julius Tandler, and Paul Lazarsfeld, to name but a few—is a belief that they can use science to construct a better reality. All of von Foerster's work squarely fits within that tradition.

Are von Foerster's ideas still relevant today? His proposition-based approach, while worthwhile to work through, seems from a different era, one that was more focused on systematic and logical frameworks. There are some profound insights in these arguments, but, while these seem to address more directly philosophical arguments rather than current scientific problems, it would be a mistake to relegate von Foerster to the group of inspiring ancestors. His concerns about the "biology of the observer" and the implication for a constructivist worldview are today reflected in efforts to explore the consequences of niche construction for biological and cultural evolution.

The basic tenet of niche construction is that organisms do not passively experience environmental influences, but actively shape or construct their environments. This process leads to the introduction of emergent feedback loops into now fundamentally co-evolutionary processes. These co-evolutionary dynamics are still poorly understood and do not fit within the current framework of mathematical evolutionary biology. Von Foerster's approach can inspire the development of an adequate mathematical framework for these constructive elements of the co-evolutionary process (Laubichler and Renn 2015; Laland, Matthews, and Feldman 2016).

Going one step further, we can apply the same logic to the emergence of our cognitive abilities. Again, taking a co-evolutionary perspective, the process of how cognitive systems construct representations of the world would then be guided by filters of evolutionary success, meaning that the way these cognitive systems construct and represent the world is constrained by their ability to survive. This adds a biological view to any epistemological question— and not just any biological view, but one that highlights the continuous dynamics of cognitive niche construction whereby the representation of the world cannot be separated from the characteristics of the observer.

In the Anthropocene these acts of niche construction, material and cognitive, have reached an unprecedented scale. Human actions guided by our representations of world are now dramatically altering the whole planetary system. Focusing on the fundamental epistemological challenges of these "human in the loop" systems is therefore as topical as it ever was. ❧

REFERENCES

Bateson, G. 1979. *Mind and Nature: A Necessary Unity.* New York, NY: Dutton.

Cassirer, E. 1922. "Einstein's Theory of Relativity Considered from the Epistemological Standpoint." *The Monist* 32 (1): 89–134a. https://doi.org/10.5840/monist192232120.

———. 1950. *The Problem of Knowledge: Philosophy, Science, and History since Hegel.* New Haven, CT: Yale University Press.

Cockett, R. 2023. *Vienna: How the City of Ideas Created the Modern World.* New Haven, CT: Yale University Press.

Einstein, A. 1924. *Relativity: The Special and General Theory.* Translated by R. W. Lawson. London, UK: Methuen & Co. Ltd. https://libarch.nmu.org.ua/bitstream/handle/GenofondUA/16488/964ca726b8a24ca0a8c4814141014444.pdf?sequence=1.

Laland, K., B. Matthews, and M. W. Feldman. 2016. "An Introduction to Niche Construction Theory." *Evolutionary Ecology* 30:191–202. https://doi.org/10.1007/s10682-016-9821-z.

Laubichler, M. D., and J. Renn. 2015. "Extended Evolution: A Conceptual Framework for Integrating Regulatory Networks and Niche Construction." *Journal of Experimental Zoology Part B: Molecular and Developmental Evolution* 324 (7): 565–577. https://doi.org/10.1002/jez.b.22631.

Maturana, H. R., and F. J. Varela. 1980. *Autopoiesis and Cognition: The Realization of the Living.* Dordrecht, Netherlands: D. Reidel Publishing Co.

———. 1987. *The Tree of Knowledge: The Biological Roots of Human Understanding.* Boston, MA: New Science Library.

Mead, M., ed. 1985. *Cultural Patterns and Technical Change: A Manual.* Westport, CT: Greenwood Press.

Uexküll, J. v. 2014. *Umwelt und Innenwelt der Tiere.* Berlin, Germany: Springer Spektrum.

Uexküll, J. v., and D. L. Mackinnon. 1926. *Theoretical Biology.* New York, NY: Harcourt, Brace & Company, Inc.

Wilczek, F. 2022. *Fundamentals: Ten Keys to Reality.* New York, NY: Penguin.

Wittgenstein, L. 1922. *Tractatus Logico-Philosophicus.* New York, NY: Harcourt, Brace & Company.

———. 1953. *Philosophical Investigations.* Translated by G. E. Anscombe. New York, NY: Macmillan.

NOTES ON AN EPISTEMOLOGY
FOR LIVING THINGS

Heinz von Foerster

I

While in the first quarter of this century physicists and cosmologists were forced to revise the basic notions that govern the natural sciences, in the last quarter of this century biologists will force a revision of the basic notions that govern science itself. After that "first revolution" it was clear that the classical concept of an "ultimate science", that is an objective description of the world in which there are no subjects (a "subjectless universe"), contains contradictions.

To remove these one had to account for an "observer" (that is at least for one subject):

(i) Observations are not absolute but relative to an observer's point of view (i.e., his coordinate system: Einstein);

(ii) Observations affect the observed so as to obliterate the observer's hope for prediction (i.e., his uncertainty is absolute: Heisenberg).

After this, we are now in the possession of the truism that a description (of the universe) implies one who describes it (observes it). What we need now is the description of the "describer" or, in other words, we need a theory of the observer. Since to the best of available knowledge it is only living organisms which would qualify as being observers, it appears that this task falls to the biologist. But he himself is a living being, which means that in his theory he has not only to account for himself, but also for his writing this theory. This is a new state of affairs in scientific discourse for, in line with the traditional viewpoint which separates the observer from his observations, reference to this discourse was to be carefully avoided. This separation was done by no

This condenses the main epistemological shifts connected with the development of science in the late nineteenth and early twentieth centuries.

Here he makes two important arguments. First, that the observer needs to be part of any scientific description, and second, that the observer is a living organism.

means because of eccentricity or folly, for under certain circumstances inclusion of the observer in his descriptions may lead to paradoxes, to wit the utterance "I am a liar".

In the meantime, however, it has become abundantly clear that this narrow restriction not only creates the ethical problems associated with scientific activity, but also cripples the study of life in full context from molecular to social organizations. Life cannot be studied *in vitro*, one has to explore it *in vivo*.

The question before us "The Unity of Man: Biological Invariants and Cultural Universals" cannot be approached in the earlier, restricted frame of mind, should the answers we may come up with be testimony of our own awareness of our own biology and culture.

In contradistinction to the classical problem of scientific inquiry that postulates first a description-invariant "objective world" (as if there were such a thing) and then attempts to write its description, here we are challenged to develop a description-invariant "subjective world", that is a world which includes the observer. This is the problem.

This is the main challenge von Foerster poses in this article.

However, in accord with the classic tradition of scientific inquiry which perpetually asks "How?" rather than "What?", this task calls for an epistemology of "How do we know?" rather than "What do we know?"

The following notes on an epistemology of living things address themselves to the "How?" They may serve as a magnifying glass through which this problem becomes better visible.

II. Introduction

One clearly sees the influence of Wittgenstein in these propositions.

The twelve propositions labeled 1, 2, 3, ... 12, of the following 80 notes are intended to give a minimal framework for the context within which the various concepts that will be discussed are to acquire their meaning. Since Proposition Number 12 refers directly back to Number 1, Notes can be read in a circle. However, comments, justifications, and explanations, which apply to these propositions follow them with decimal labels (e.g., "5.423") the last digit ("3") referring to a proposition labeled with digits before the last digit ("5.42"), etc. (e.g., "5.42" refers to "5.4", etc.).

Although Notes may be entered at any place, and completed by going through the circle, it appeared advisable to cut the circle between propositions "11" and "1", and present the notes in linear sequence beginning with Proposition 1.

Since the formalism that will be used may for some appear to obscure more than it reveals, a preview of the twelve propositions (in somewhat modified form) with comments in prose may facilitate reading the notes.

1. *The environment is experienced as the residence of objects, stationary, in motion, or changing.*

Harmless as this proposition may look at first glance, on second thought one may wonder about the meaning of a "changing object". Do we mean the change of appearance of the same object as when a cube is rotated, or a person turns around, and we take it to be the same object (cube, person, etc.); or when we see a tree growing, or meet an old schoolmate after a decade or two, are they different, are they the same, or are they different in one way and the same in another? Or when Circe changes men into beasts, or when a friend suffers a severe stroke, in these metamorphoses, what is invariant, what does change? Who says that these were the same persons or objects?

From studies by Piaget[1] and others[2] we know that "object constancy" is one of many cognitive skills that are acquired in early childhood and hence are subject to linguistic and thus cultural bias.

The reference to Piaget and Maturana indicates that we need a cognitive, developmental and evolutionary account of the observer.

Consequently, in order to make sense of terms like "biological invariants", "cultural universals", etc., the logical properties of "invariance" and "change" have first to be established.

As the notes proceed it will become apparent that these properties are those of descriptions (representations) rather than those of objects. In fact, as will be seen, "objects" do owe their existence to the properties of representations.

To this end the next four propositions are developed.

2. *The logical properties of "invariance" and "change" are those of representations. If this is ignored, paradoxes arise.*

---

[1]Piaget, J.: *The Construction of Reality in the Child.* Basic Books, New York, (1954).

[2]Witz, K. and J. Easley: "Cognitive Deep Structure and Science Education" in *Final Report: Analysis of Cognitive Behavior in Children*; Curriculum Laboratory, University of Illinois, Urbana, (1972).

Two paradoxes that arise when the concepts "invariance" and "change" are defined in a contextual vacuum are cited, indicating the need for a formalization of representations.

3. *Formalize representations R, S, regarding two sets of variables x and t, tentatively called "entities" and "instants" respectively.*

Here the difficulty of beginning to talk about something which only later makes sense so that one can begin talking about it, is pre-empted by "tentatively", giving two sets of as yet undefined variables highly meaningful names, viz, "entities" and "instants", which only later will be justified.

This apparent deviation from rigor has been made as a concession to lucidity. Striking the meaningful labels from these variables does not change the argument.

Developed under this proposition are expressions for representations that can be compared. This circumvents the apparent difficulty to compare an apple with itself before and after it is peeled. However, little difficulties are encountered by comparing the peeled apple as it is *seen now* with the unpeeled apple as it is *remembered* to have been before.

With the concept "comparison", however an operation ("computation") on representations is introduced, which requires a more detailed analysis. This is done in the next proposition. From here on the term "computation" will be consistently applied to all operations (not necessarily numerical) that transform, modify, re-arrange, order, etc., either symbols (in the "abstract" sense) or their physical manifestations (in the "concrete" sense). This is done to enforce a feeling for the realizability of these operations in the structural and functional organization of either grown nervous tissue or else constructed machines.

4. *Contemplate relations, "Rel", between representations, R, and S.*

However, immediately a highly specific relation is considered, viz, an "Equivalence Relation" between two representations. Due to the structural properties of representations, the computations necessary to confirm or deny equivalence of representations are not trivial. In fact, by keeping track of the computational pathways for establishing equivalence, "objects" and "events" emerge as *consequences* of branches of computation which are identified as the processes of abstraction and memorization.

5. *Objects and events are not primitive experiences. Objects and events are representations of relations.*

Since "objects" and "events" are not primary experiences and thus cannot claim to have absolute (objective) status, their interrelations, the "environment", is a purely personal affair, whose constraints are anatomical or cultural factors. Moreover, the postulate of an "external (objective) reality" disappears to give way to a reality that is determined by modes of internal computations.[3]

6. *Operationally, the computation of a specific relation is a representation of this relation.*

Two steps of crucial importance to the whole argument forwarded in these notes are made here at the same time. One is to take a computation for a representation; the second is to introduce here for the first time "recursions". By recursion is meant that on one occasion or another a function is substituted for its own argument. In the above Proposition 6 this is provided for by taking the computation of a relation between *representations* again as a representation.

While taking a computation for a representation of a relation may not cause conceptual difficulties (the punched card of a computer program which controls the calculations of a desired relation may serve as an adequate metaphor), the adoption of recursive expressions appears to open the door for all kinds of logical mischief.

However, there are means to avoid such pitfalls. One is to devise a notation that keeps track of the order of representations, e.g., "the representation of a representation of a representation" may be considered as a third order representation, $R^{(3)}$. The same applies to relations of higher order, $n: Rel^{(n)}$.

The other is to distinguish in self-referring expressions between their extrinsic and intrinsic truth values. In general such expressions do not suffer from anomalies when in the affirmative. For instance, the sentence "This sentence is true" is affirmative recursive. Its extrinsic truth-value is "true", for the hypothesis that it is "false" is refuted by the sentence. Its intrinsic truth-value can be found by applying the sentence to itself, i.e., substituting for the part "This sentence ..." the whole

Another link to Wittgenstein—von Foerster references the *Tractatus*, but the *Philosophical Investigations* also factor in here.

---

[3] Castañeda, C.: *A Separate Reality.* Simon and Schuster, New York, (1971).

sentence. One obtains: "This sentence is true is true" which is true, for "true true" is "true".

The situation is different for a negative recursive expression, as, for instance, "This sentence is false". No extrinsic truth-value can now be established, for the hypothesis "false" would make the sentence true, in contradiction to its pronouncement. However, its intrinsic truth-value becomes stable after two substitutions. After the first we have "This sentence is false is false". But "false false" is "true", hence we obtain "This sentence is true". A second substitution operates on an affirmative recursive expression and thus yields forever "true".

While it is known that recursive, self-referring expressions can be constructed that will intrinsically never approach a stable form (transcendental recursive expressions), in this context they will not plague us, although they may provide important clues in a behavioral analysis which is beyond this elementary discussion.

After the concepts of higher order representation and relations have been introduced, their physical manifestations are defined. Since representation and relations are computations, their manifestations are "special purpose computers" called "representors" and "relators" respectively. The distinction of levels of computation is maintained by referring to such structures as n-th order representors (relators). With these concepts the possibility of introducing "organisms" is now open.

7. *A living organism is a third order relator which computes the relations that maintain the organism's integrity.*

The full force of recursive expressions is now applied to a recursive definition of living organisms first proposed by H. R. Maturana[4,5] and further developed by him and F. Varela in their concept of "autopoiesis".[6]

There are a number of related ideas connected to this proposition besides Maturana and Varela's concept of autopoiesis. One is the von Uexküll (1926, 2014) notion of *Umwelt* as an internal representation of the environment mediated by the sensory and cognitive capacities of an organism. Another dimension is that organisms are the product of a co-evolutionary dynamics between their internal states and the environment, which add an additional dynamics to these processes of "relating."

---

[4]Maturana, H.: "Neurophysiology of Cognition" in *Cognition: A Multiple View*, P. Garvin (ed.), Spartan Books, New York, pp. 3-23, (1970).

[5]Maturana, H.: *Biology of Cognition*, BCL Report No. 9.0, Biological Computer Laboratory, Department of Electrical Engineering, University of Illinois, Urbana, 95 pp.,(1970).

[6]Maturana, H. and F. Varela: *Autopoiesis*. Faculdad de Ciencias, Universidad de Chile, Santiago, (1972).

As a direct consequence of the formalism and the concepts which were developed in earlier propositions it is now possible to account for an interaction between the internal representation of an organism of himself with one of another organism. This gives rise to a theory of communication based on a purely connotative "language". The surprising property of such a theory is now described in the eighth proposition.

8. *A formalism necessary and sufficient for a theory of communication must not contain primary symbols representing communicabilia (e.g., symbols, words, messages, etc.).*

Outrageous as this proposition may look at first glance, on second thought however, it may appear obvious that a theory of communication is guilty of circular definitions if it assumes communicabilia in order to prove communication.

The calculus of recursive expressions circumvents this difficulty, and the power of such expressions is exemplified by the (indefinitely recursive) reflexive personal pronoun "I". Of course, the semantic magic of such infinite recursions has been known for some time, to wit the utterance "I am who I am".[7]

9. *Terminal representations (descriptions) made by an organism are manifest in its movements; consequently the logical structure of descriptions arises from the logical structure of movements.*

The two fundamental aspects of the logical structure of descriptions, namely their sense (affirmation or negation) and their truth value (true or false), are shown to reside in the logical structure of movement: approach and withdrawal regarding the former aspect, and functioning or dysfunctioning of the conditioned reflex regarding the latter.

It is now possible to develop an exact definition for the concept of "information" associated with an utterance. "Information" is a relative concept that assumes meaning only when related to the cognitive structure of the observer of this utterance (the "recipient").

10. *The information associated with a description depends on an observer's ability to draw inferences from this description.*

---

[7] Exodus, *3*, 14.

Classical logic distinguishes two forms of inference: deductive and inductive.[8] While it is in principle possible to make infallible deductive inferences ("necessity"), it is in principle impossible to make infallible inductive inferences ("chance"). Consequently, chance and necessity are concepts that do not apply to the world, but to our attempts to create (a description of) it.

11. *The environment contains no information; the environment is as it is.*

12. *Go back to Proposition Number 1.*

III. Notes

1. The environment is experienced as the residence of objects, stationary, in motion, or changing.

1.1 "Change" presupposes invariance, and "invariance" change.

2. The logical properties of "invariance" and "change" are those of representations. If this is ignored paradoxes arise.

2.1 The paradox of "invariance":

THE DISTINCT BEING THE SAME

But it makes no sense to write $x_1 = x_2$ (why the indices?). and $x + x$ says something about "$=$" but nothing about x.

2.2 The paradox of "change":

THE SAME BEING DISTINCT

But it makes no sense to write x $\neq$ x.

3 Formalize the representations $R, S, \ldots$ regarding two sets of variables x_i and t_j $(i, j = 1, 2, 3, \ldots)$ tentatively called "entities" and "instants" respectively.

---

[8]Aristotle: *Metaphysics*. Volume VIII of *The Works of Aristotle*, W. D. Ross (ed., tr.), The Clarendon Press, Oxford, (1908).

3.1 The representation R of an entity x regarding the instant t_1, is distinct from the representation of this entity regarding the instant t_2:

$$R\left(x\left(t_1\right)\right) \neq R\left(x\left(t_2\right)\right)$$

3.2. The representation S of an instant t regarding the entity x_1, is distinct from the representation of this instant regarding the entity x_2:

$$S\left(t\left(x_1\right)\right) \neq S\left(t\left(x_2\right)\right)$$

3.3. However, the comparative judgment ("distinct from") cannot be made without a mechanism that computes these distinctions.

3.4. Abbreviate the notation by

$$R\left(x_i\left(t_j\right)\right) \rightarrow R_{ij}$$
$$S\left(t_k\left(x_l\right)\right) \rightarrow S_{kl}$$

[where] $(i, j, k, l = 1, 2, 3, \ldots)$

4. Contemplate relations Rel_μ between the representations R and S:

$$\mathrm{Rel}_\mu\left(R_{ij}, S_{kl}\right)$$

[where] $(\mu = 1, 2, 3, \ldots)$

4.1. Call the relation which obliterates the distinction $x_i \neq x_l$ and $t_j \neq t_k$ (i.e., $i = l; j = k$) the "Equivalence Relation" and let it be represented by:

$$Equ\left(R_{ij}, S_{ji}\right)$$

4.11. This is a representation of a relation between two representations and reads:

"The representation R of an entity x_i regarding the instant t_j is equivalent to the representation S of an instant t_j regarding the entity x_i."

4.12. A possible linguistic metaphor for the above representation of the equivalence relation between two representations is the equivalence of "thing acting" (most Indo-European languages) with "act thinging' (some African languages) (cognitive duality). For instance:

"The horse gallops" $\leftrightarrow$ "The gallop horses"

4.2. The computation of the equivalence relation 4.1 has two branches: One computes equivalences for x only

$$Equ(R_{ij}, S_{ki}) = Obj(x_i)$$

4.211. The computations along this branch of equivalence relation are called "abstractions": *Abs*.

4.212. The results of this branch of computation are usually called "objects" (entities), and their invariance under various transformations $(t_j, t_k, \ldots)$ is indicated by giving each object a distinct but invariant label N_i ("Name"):

$$Obj(x_i) \rightarrow N_i$$

4.22. The other branch computes equivalences for t only:

$$Equ(R_{ij}, S_{jl}) \equiv Eve(t_j)$$

4.221. The computations along this branch of equivalence relation are called "memory": [illegible].

4.222. The results of this branch of computation are usually called "events" (instants), and their invariance under various transformations $(x_i, x_l, \ldots)$ is indicated by associating with each event a distinct but invariant label T_j ("Time"):

$$Eve(t_j) \rightarrow T_j$$

4.3. This shows that the concepts "object", "event", "name", "time", "abstraction", "memory", "invariance", "change", generate each other.

From this follows the next proposition:

5. Objects and events are not primitive experiences. "Objects" and "Events" are representations of relations.

5.1. A possible graphic metaphor for the complementarity of "object" and "event" is an orthogonal grid that is mutually supported by both (Fig. 1),

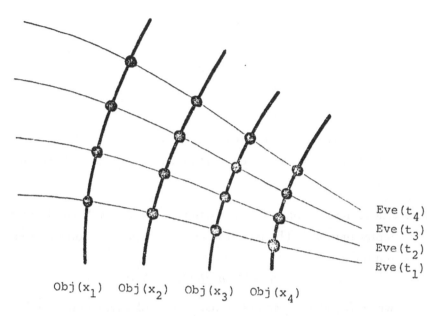

Eve(t_4)
Eve(t_3)
Eve(t_2)
Eve(t_1)

Obj(x_1) Obj(x_2) Obj(x_3) Obj(x_4)

Figure 1. "Objects" creating "Events" and vice versa.

5.2. "Environment" is the representation of relations between "objects" and "events"

$$Env(Obj, Eve)$$

5.3. Since the computation of equivalence relations is not unique, the results of these computations, namely, "objects" and "events" are likewise not unique.

5.31. This explains the possibility of an arbitrary number of different, but internally consistent (language determined) taxonomies.

5.32. This explains the possibility of an arbitrary number of different, but internally consistent (culturally determined) realities.

5.4. Since the computation of equivalence relations is performed on primitive experiences, an external environment is not a necessary prerequisite of the computation of a reality.

6. Operationally, the computation $Cmp(Rel)$ of a specific relation is a representation of this relation.

$$R = Cmp(Rel)$$

6.1. A possible mathematical metaphor for the equivalence of a computation with a representation is, for instance, Wallis' computational algorithm for the infinite product:

$$2 \times \frac{2}{1} \times \frac{2}{3} \times \frac{4}{3} \times \frac{4}{5} \times \frac{6}{5} \times \frac{6}{7} \times \cdots$$

Since this is one of many possible definitions of π $(3.14159\ldots)$ and π is a number, we may take π as a (numerical) representation of this computation.

6.2. Call representations of computations of relations "second order representations". This is clear when such a representation is written out fully:

$$R = Cmp\left(Rel\left(R_{ij}, S_{kl}\right)\right)$$

where R_{ij} and S_{kl} are, of course, "first order representations" as before (3.3).

6.21. From this notation it is clear that first order representations can be interpreted as zero-order relations (note the double indices on S and R).

6.22. From this notation it is also clear that higher order (n-th order) representations and relations can be formulated.

6.3. Call a physical mechanism that computes an n-th order representation (or an n-th order relation) an "n-th order representor" $RP^{(n)}$ (or an "n-th order relator" $RL^{(n)}$) respectively.

6.4. Call the externalized physical manifestation of the result of a computation a "terminal representation" or a "description".

6.5. One possible mechanical metaphor for relator, relation, objects, and descriptions, is a mechanical desk calculator (the relator) whose internal structure (the arrangement of wheels and pegs) is a representation of a relation commonly called "addition": Add(a,b). Given two objects, a = 5, b = 7, it computes a terminal representation (a description) of the relation between these two objects in digital, decadic form:

$$12 = Add(5, 7)$$

6.51. Of course, a machine with a different internal representation (structure) of the same relation Add(a,b), may have produced a different terminal representation (description), say, in the form of prime products, of this relation between the same objects:

$$2^2 \times 3^1 = \text{Add}(5, 7)$$

6.6. Another possible mechanical metaphor for taking a computation of a relation as a representation of this relation is an electronic computer and its program. The program stands for the particular relation, and it assembles the parts of the machine such that the terminal representation (print-out) of the problem under consideration complies with the desired form.

6.61. A program that computes programs is called a "meta-program". In this terminology a machine accepting meta-programs is a second-order relator.

6.7. These metaphors stress a point made earlier (5.3), namely, that the computations of representations of objects and events is not unique.

6.8. These metaphors also suggest that my nervous tissue which, for instance, computes a terminal representation in the form of the following utterance: "These are my grandmother's spectacles" neither resembles my grandmother nor her spectacles; nor is there a "trace" to be found of either (as little as there are traces of "12" in the wheels and pegs of a desk calculator, or of numbers in a program). Moreover, my utterance "These are my grandmother's spectacles" should neither be confused with my grandmother's spectacles, nor with the program that computes this utterance, nor with the representation (physical manifestation) of this program.

6.81. However, a relation between the utterance, the objects, and the algorithms computing both, is computable (see 9.4).

7. A living organism Ω is a third-order relator $\left(\Omega = RL^{(3)}\right)$ which computes the relations that maintain the organism's integrity:[9],[10]

$$\Omega\{Equ[R(\Omega(Obj)), S(Eve(\Omega))]\}$$

This expression is recursive in Ω.

7.1. An organism is its own ultimate object.

7.2. An organism that can compute a representation of this relation is self-conscious.

7.3. Amongst the internal representations of the computation of objects $Obj\,(x_i)$ within one organism Ω may be a representation $\mathrm{Obj}\,(\Omega^*)$ of another organism Ω^*. Conversely, we may have in Ω^* a representation $\mathrm{Obj}^*(\Omega)$ which computes Ω.

7.31. Both representations are recursive in Ω, Ω^* respectively. For instance, for Ω:

$$Obj^{(n)}\left(\Omega^{*(n-1)}\left(Obj^{*(n-1)}\left(\Omega^{(n-2)}\left(Obj^{(n-2)}\left(\ldots \Omega^*\right)\right)\right)\right)\right)$$

7.32. This expression is the nucleus of a theory of communication.

8. A formalism necessary and sufficient for a theory of communication must not contain primary symbols representing "communicabilia" (e.g., symbols, words, messages, etc.).

8.1. This is so, for if a "theory" of communication were to contain primary communicabilia, it would not be a theory but a technology of communication, taking communication for granted.

8.2. The nervous activity of one organism cannot be shared by another organism.

8.21. This suggests that indeed nothing is (can be) "communicated".

[9] Maturana, H.: "Neurophysiology of Cognition" in *Cognition: A Multiple View*, P. Garvin (ed.), Spartan Books, New York, pp. 3-23, (1970).

[10] Maturana, H.: Biology of Cognition, BCL Report No. 9.0, Biological Computer Laboratory, Department of Electrical Engineering, University of Illinois, Urbana, 95 pp., (1970).

8.3. Since the expression in 7.31 may become cyclic (when $Obj^{(k)} = Obj^{(k-2i)}$), it is suggestive to develop a teleological theory of communication in which the stipulated goal is to keep $Obj\,(\Omega^*)$ invariant under perturbations by Ω^*.

8.31. It is clear that in such a theory such questions as: "Do you see the color of this object as I see it?" become irrelevant.

8.4. Communication is an observer's interpretation of the interaction between two organisms Ω_1, Ω_2.

8.41. Let $Evs_1 \equiv Evs\,(\Omega_1)$, and $Evs_2 \equiv Evs\,(\Omega_2)$, be *sequences* of events $Eve\,(t_j)$, $(j = 1,2,3,\ldots)$ with regard to two organisms Ω_1 and Ω_2 respectively; and let Com be an observer's (internal) representation of a relation between these sequences of events:

$$OB\,(Com\,(Evs_1, Evs_2))$$

8.42. Since either Ω_1 or Ω_2 or both can be observers $(\Omega_1 = OB_1; \Omega_2 = OB_2)$ the above expression can become recursive in either Ω_1 or in Ω_2 or in both.

8.43. This shows that "communication" is an (internal) representation of a relation between (an internal representation of) oneself with somebody else.

$$R\left(\Omega^{(n+1)}, Com\left(\Omega^{(n)}, \Omega^*\right)\right)$$

8.44. Abbreviate this by

$$C\left(\Omega^{(n)}, \Omega^*\right)$$

8.45. In this formalism the reflexive personal pronoun "I" appears as the (indefinitely applied) recursive operator

$$Equ\left[\Omega^{(n+1)}C\left(\Omega^{(n)}, \Omega^{(n)}\right)\right]$$

or in words:

"I am the observed relation between myself and observing myself."

8.46. "I" is a relator (*and* representor) of infinite order.

9. Terminal representations (descriptions) made by an organism are manifest in its movements; consequently, the logical structure of descriptions arises from the logical structure of movements.

9.1. It is known that the presence of a perceptible agent of weak concentration may cause an organism to move toward it (approach). However, the presence of the same agent in strong concentration may cause this organism to move away from it (withdrawal).

9.11. That is "approach" and "withdrawal" are the precursors for "yes" or "no".

9.12. The two phases of elementary behavior, "approach" and "withdrawal", establish the operational origin of the two fundamental axioms of two-valued logic, namely, the "law of the excluded contradiction":

$$\overline{x \ \& \ \bar{x}}$$

in words: "not: x *and* not-x";

and the law of the excluded middle:

$$x \ v \ \bar{x}$$

in words: "x *or* not-x"; (see Fig. 2).

9.2. We have from Wittgenstein's *Tractatus*,[11] proposition 6.0621:

"... it is important that the signs "p" and "non-p" *can* say the same thing. For it shows that nothing in reality corresponds to the sign "non".

The occurrence of negation in a proposition is not enough to characterize its sense (non-non-p = p)."

9.21. Since nothing in the environment corresponds to negation, negation as well as all other "logical particles" (inclusion, alternation, implication, etc.) must arise within the organism itself.

---

[11]Wittgenstein, L.: *Tractatus Logico Philosophicus*, Humanities Press, New York, (1961).

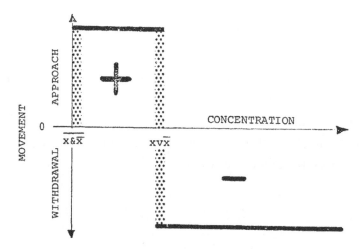

Figure 2. The laws of "excluded contradiction" $(\overline{x\&\bar{x}})$ and of "excluded middle" $(x \; v \; \bar{x})$ in the twilight zones between no motion $(M = 0)$ and approach $(+)$, and between approach $(+)$ and withdrawal $(-)$ as a function of the concentration (C) of a perceptible agent.

9.3. Beyond being logical affirmative or negative, descriptions can be true or false.

9.31. We have from Susan Langer, *Philosophy in a New Key*:[12]

"The use of signs is the very first manifestation of mind. It arises as early in biological history as the famous 'conditioned reflex', by which a concomitant of a stimulus takes over the stimulus-function. The concomitant becomes a *sign* of the condition to which the reaction is really appropriate. This is the real beginning of mentality, for here is the birthplace of *error*, and herewith of *truth*."

9.32. Thus, not only the sense (yes or no) of descriptions but also their truth values (true or false) are coupled to movement (behavior).

9.4. Let D* be the terminal representation made by an organism Ω^*, and let it be observed by an organism Ω; let Ω's internal representation of this description be $D(\Omega, D^*)$; and, finally let Ω's internal representation of his environment be $E(\Omega, E)$. Then we have:

---

[12]Langer, S.: *Philosophy in a New Key*, New American Library, New York, (1951).

The domain of relations between D and E which are computable by Ω represents the "information" gained by Ω from watching Ω^*:

$$Inf\,(\Omega, D^*) \equiv Domain\,\{Rel_\mu(D, E)\}\,(\mu = 1, 2, 3, \dots, m)$$

9.41. The logarithm (of base 2) of the number m of relations Rel_μ computable by Ω (or the negative mean value of the logarithmitic probabilities of their occurrence

$$< \log_2 p_i > = \sum_{i=1}^{m} p_i \log_2 p_i$$

is the "amount of information, H" of the description D^* with respect to Ω:

$$H\,(D^*, \Omega) = \log_2 m$$

(or $H(D^*, \Omega) = -\sum_{i=1}^{m} p_i \log_2 p_i$)

9.42. This shows that information is a relative concept. And so is H.

9.5. We have from a paper by Jerzy Konorski:[13]

"... It is not so, as we would be inclined to think according to our introspection, that the receipt of information and its utilization are two separate processes which can be combined one with the other in any way; on the contrary, information and its utilization are inseparable constituting, as a matter of fact, one single process."

10. The information associated with a description depends on an observer's ability to draw inferences from this description.

10.1. "Necessity" arises from the ability to make infallible deductions.

10.2. "Chance" arises from the inability to make infallible inductions.

11. The environment contains no information. The environment is as it is.

---

[13]Konorski, J.: "The Role of Central Factors in Differentiation" in *Information Processing in the Nervous System*, R. W. Gerard and J. W. Duyff (eds.), Excerpta Medica Foundation, Amsterdam, *3*, pp. 318-329, (1962).

12. The environment is experienced as the residence of objects, stationary, in motion, or changing (Proposition 1). ⯌

REFERENCES

Aristotle. 1908. *Metaphysics, Volume VIII of The Works of Aristotle.* Edited by W. D. Ross. Oxford, UK: Clarendon Press.

Castañeda, C. 1971. "A Separate Reality." (New York, NY).

Konorski, J. 1962. "The Role of Central Factors in Differentiation." In *Information Processing in the Nervous System,* 3:318–329. Amsterdam: Excerpta Medica Foundation.

Langer, S. 1951. "Philosophy in a New Key." (New York, NY).

Maturana, H. R. 1970a. *Biology of Cognition.* Technical report BCL Report No. 9.0. Biological Computer Laboratory, Department of Electrical Engineering, University of Illinois, Urbana.

———. 1970b. "Neurophysiology of Cognition." Edited by P. Garvin. (New York, NY), 3–23.

Maturana, H. R., and F. G. Varela. 1972. *Autopoiesis and Cognition (De Maquinas y Seres Vivos).* Santiago, Chile: Editorial Universitaria S. A. Faculdad de Ciencias, Universidad de Chile, Santiago.

Piaget, J. 1954. *The Construction of Reality in the Child.* New York, NY: Basic Books.

Wittgenstein, L. 1961. *Tractatus Logico-Philosophicus.* New York, NY: Humanities Press.

Witz, K., and J. Easley. 1972. *Cognitive Deep Structure and Science Education.* Technical report. Final Report: Analysis of Cognitive Behavior in Children. University of Illinois, Urbana.

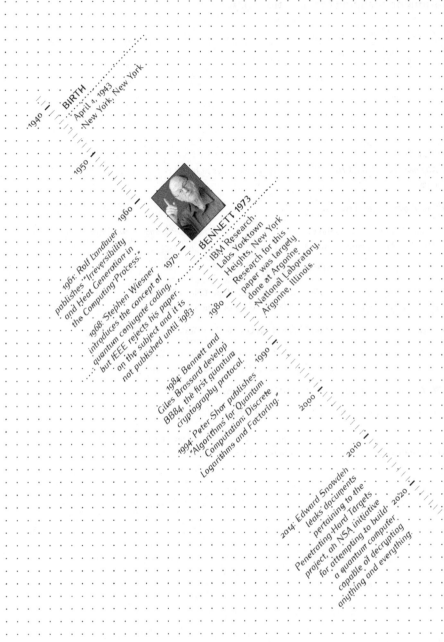

CHARLES·HENRY·BENNETT

[43]

THE ENERGY COST OF COMPUTING

*Jon Machta, University of Massachusetts Amherst
and Santa Fe Institute*

Brains and computers use lots of energy and dissipate that energy as heat into the environment. How much of this heat production is required by fundamental physical limits on computation and how much is the result of engineering or biological constraints and trade-offs?

Charles Bennett's "Logical Reversibility of Computation" is one of the seminal papers on the road to answering this question. It is a founding paper in several fields including the thermodynamics of computation, quantum computing, and biomolecular computing.

Bennett's paper shows that computation can be carried using only logically reversible processes. Before 1973, it was widely accepted that computation requires logical irreversibility.[1] What is logical reversibility and why might it appear to be a requirement for computing? Let's consider two logical operations–**NOT** and **AND**. The truth tables for these operations are shown in the figure.

C. H. Bennett, "Logical Reversibility of Computation," in *IBM Journal of Research and Development* 17 (6): 525–532 (1973).

Reprint courtesy of International Business Machines Corporation, © 1973 International Business Machines Corporation.

A	NOT A
T	F
F	T

A	B	A AND B
T	T	T
T	F	F
F	T	F
F	F	F

---

[1] See Landauer's foundational paper, chapter 17 of the previous volume.

Notice that the input of **NOT** can be uniquely determined from the output. On the other hand, the input of **AND** cannot always be determined from the inputs since there are three inputs, (T,F), (F,T), and (F,F), that all yield the same output, F. A logical operation is *logically reversible* if and only if its inputs are uniquely determined by its outputs. Mathematicians might prefer to say that **NOT** is an *invertible* function while **AND** is *not invertible*. It is clear just from counting that it is not possible for a Boolean function with two inputs and one output to be logically reversible. Thus the standard two input, one output logic gates that are among the elementary components of digital computers, such as **AND, OR, NAND**, and **NOR**, are all logically irreversible. The known models and physical realizations of computing before 1973 all involved logically irreversible operations, and it was widely believed that computing is necessarily logically irreversible.

Are there physical consequences of logical irreversibility? Logical irreversibility implies that information about the inputs is lost and, according to Landauer, the erasure of one bit of information requires the dissipation of heat into the environment of at least $kT \ln 2$, where k is Boltzmann's constant, T is the absolute temperature of the environment, and ln is the natural logarithm. Landauer's principle, taken together with the belief that computing is necessarily logically irreversible, implies that computation must dissipate heat for fundamental, unavoidable reasons.

Bennett refuted the belief that computing requires logical irreversibility and heat dissipation by showing explicitly that it is possible to design a general-purpose *logically reversible* computer. He did this in the context of Turing machines rather than the more familiar computers based on logic gates. Turing machines, like all computational devices, involve both memory and processing units. A Turing machine uses one or more linear memory "tapes" and a single processing unit. The processing unit or "head" is able to interact with one space of a tape at a time and can read to, write on and move a tape by one space left or right in a single step. The head has a finite number of internal states and a single step of the computation depends deterministically on the state of the head and what is written on the space(s) of the tapes currently examined by the head.

Turing machines are simple to describe and amenable to mathematical analysis, but they are not practical computing devices. Nonetheless, any computation that can be carried by a machine constructed of logic gates can be carried out by a Turing machine and vice versa; however, the Turing machine is more constrained and generally takes more steps to carry out a computation than a computer constructed with logic gates and random-access memory. Like computers built up of logically irreversible logic gates, the rules of standard Turing machines are logically irreversible, and it was believed that this was a requirement for Turing machines capable of general-purpose computation.

What Bennett showed by construction is that any computation that can be carried out by an irreversible one-tape Turing machine can also be carried out by a three-tape Turing machine that is logically reversible. Although the details are complicated, the basic idea in Bennett's construction of a reversible Turing machine is simple and elegant. First, Bennett shows how the rules of the original Turing machine can be replaced by an equivalent set of rules that are reversible. In general this requires extra internal states for the head and writing extra bits of information so that many-to-one rules of the original Turing machine become one-to-one rules for the new machine. The program or problem statement is entered as usual on the working tape (tape 1). The extra history produced by the reversible rules are written on tape 2. When the computation is complete, the result that appears on the working tape is written on tape 3. In the final step, the computation is run backwards so that tape 2 is restored to its original blank state, leaving the input on tape 1 and the output on tape 3.

Turing machines are very useful theoretical models, but practical digital computers are based on logic gates. Within a decade after Bennett's paper, a number of workers developed logically reversible gates and methods for connecting them so that arbitrary computations can be carried reversibly taking an input and, at the end of computation, leaving only the input and the output with no additional bits that need to be erased.

There are two broad classes of potential physical realizations of logically reversible computational devices. The first class, which Bennett describes in the discussion section of the paper, is a computer that is strongly coupled to a thermal environment. Standard silicon-based computers with irreversible logic gates are also in this class. Because existing technologies for implementing gates (whether logically reversible or not) dissipate far more than the Landauer bound, relatively little effort has been invested in engineering reversible hardware since there is more to be gained in engineering efforts to improve the efficiency of standard irreversible hardware without sacrificing speed and reliability. Indeed, logical reversibility can only be associated with dissipation less than kT per step if it is performed sufficiently slowly that all the components remain close to equilibrium with the environment. It is not possible to simultaneously optimize a computer of this type for both speed and dissipation so there are necessary trade-offs.

Biological micromachinery is also strongly coupled to the environment and, in some cases, does operate with only a few kT of dissipation per step. Some of this machinery is logically reversible or, at least, nearly so. It may well be that evolution has designed some of this machinery to be reversible for reasons of efficiency though, again, there is a necessary trade-off between speed, efficiency, accuracy, and robustness.

The other broad class of physical embodiments of computation consists of systems that are isolated from the environment and follow the laws of classical mechanics or quantum mechanics. Because both classical mechanics and quantum mechanics are time reversible, any implementation of computing that obeys these mechanical laws must be logically reversible. Before Bennett's paper, it was therefore believed that purely mechanical computers (without friction or other mechanism for breaking time reversibility) were not possible. Bennett's paper changed this thinking and within a decade both classical mechanical and quantum mechanical models of computation were developed. The models based on classical mechanics have not proved to be practical and it is not clear they are physically realizable because the non-linear interactions required for carrying out logical operations appear to be highly unstable and subject to chaos (Zurek 1984). Quantum mechanics, on the other hand, is a linear theory and not subject to chaos, at least as it is usually defined.

There is no mention of quantum mechanics in Bennett's paper, nonetheless, it is a founding work in the field of quantum computing and cited by the seminal papers in that field. The fundamental insight that computation can be logically reversible implies that quantum computing is at least possible and inspired research into what could be accomplished by a quantum computer. On a more technical level, Bennett's construction of a reversible Turing machine paved the way for constructing quantum Turing machines, which are necessarily logically reversible. Quantum Turing machines in turn facilitated the development of a rigorous theory of quantum computational complexity, which addresses the question of the extent that quantum computing is and is not more powerful than classical computing (see Bernstein and Vazirani 1997).

The impact of Bennett's paper on the theory of complex systems is profound. Complex adaptive systems process both information and energy and are strongly coupled to their environment with which they exchange both information and energy. The fundamental relationship between processing information and processing energy is subtle and has taken many decades to elucidate. Bennett's paper was a key step in developing this understanding. ⮐

REFERENCES

Bernstein, E., and U. Vazirani. 1997. "Quantum Complexity Theory." *SIAM Journal on Computing* 26 (5): 1411–1473. https://doi.org/10.1137/S009753979630092.

Hopfield, J. J. 1974. "Kinetic Proofreading: A New Mechanism for Reducing Errors in Biosynthetic Processes Requiring High Specificity." *Proceedings of the National Academy of Sciences* 71 (10): 4135–4139. https://doi.org/10.1073/pnas.71.10.4135.

Lecerf, Y. 1963. "Logique Mathématique : Machines de Turing Réversibles." *Comptes Rendus des Séances de l'académie des Sciences* 257:2597–2600.

Wolpert, D. H. 2019. "The Stochastic Thermodynamics of Computation." *Journal of Physics A: Mathematical and Theoretical* 52 (19): 193001. https://doi.org/10.1088/1751-8121/ab0850.

Zurek, W. H. 1984. "Reversibility and Stability of Information Processing Systems." *Physical Review Letters* 53 (4): 391–394. https://doi.org/10.1103/PhysRevLett.53.391.

LOGICAL REVERSIBILITY
OF COMPUTATION

C. H. Bennett, IBM Research

Abstract

The usual general-purpose computing automaton (e.g., a Turing machine) is logically irreversible—its transition function lacks a single-valued inverse. Here it is shown that such machines may be made logically reversible at every step, while retaining their simplicity and their ability to do general computations. This result is of great physical interest because it makes plausible the existence of thermodynamically reversible computers which could perform useful computations at useful speed while dissipating considerably less than kT of energy per logical step. In the first stage of its computation the logically reversible automaton parallels the corresponding irreversible automaton, except that it saves all intermediate results, thereby avoiding the irreversible operation of erasure. The second stage consists of printing out the desired output. The third stage then reversibly disposes of all the undesired intermediate results by retracing the steps of the first stage in backward order (a process which is only possible because the first stage has been carried out reversibly), thereby restoring the machine (except for the now-written output tape) to its original condition. The final machine configuration thus contains the desired output and a reconstructed copy of the input, but no other undesired data. The foregoing results are demonstrated explicitly using a type of three-tape Turing machine. The biosynthesis of messenger RNA is discussed as a physical example of reversible computation.[*][°]

Introduction

The usual digital computer program frequently performs operations that seem to throw away information about the computer's history, leaving the machine in a state whose immediate predecessor is ambiguous. Such operations include erasure or overwriting of data, and entry into a portion of the program addressed by several different transfer instructions. In other words, the typical computer is logically irreversible—its transition function (the partial function that maps

Erasure means physically resetting a random state of a memory element to a standard state, e.g., the state corresponding to "0." It is a many-to-one operation.

[°]Much of the work on physical reversibility reported in this paper was done under the auspices of the U.S. Atomic Energy Commission while the author was employed by the Argonne National Laboratory, Argonne, Illinois.

each whole-machine state onto its successor, if the state has a successor) lacks a single-valued inverse.

Landauer[1] has posed the question of whether logical irreversibility is an unavoidable feature of useful computers, arguing that it is, and has demonstrated the physical and philosophical importance of this question by showing that whenever a physical computer throws away information about its previous state it must generate a corresponding amount of entropy. Therefore, a computer must dissipate at least $kT \ln 2$ of energy (about 3×10^{-21} joule at room temperature) for each bit of information it erases or otherwise throws away.

An irreversible computer can always be made reversible by having it save all the information it would otherwise throw away. For example, the machine might be given an extra tape (initially blank) on which it could record each operation as it was being performed, in sufficient detail that the preceding state would be uniquely determined by the present state and the last record on the tape. However, as Landauer pointed out, this would merely postpone the problem of throwing away unwanted information, since the tape would have to be erased before it could be reused. It is therefore reasonable to demand of a useful reversible computer that, if it halts, it should have erased all its intermediate results, leaving behind only the desired output and the originally furnished input. (The machine must be allowed to save its input—otherwise it could not be reversible and still carry out computations in which the input was not uniquely determined by the output.) We will show that general-purpose reversible computers (Turing machines) satisfying these requirements indeed exist, and that they need not be much more complicated than the irreversible computers on which they are patterned. Computations on a reversible computer take about twice as many steps as on an ordinary one and may require a large amount of temporary storage. Before proceeding with the formal demonstration, the argument will be carried through at the present heuristic level.

The energy expended to erase information must be converted to heat. When one bit of information is erased, the entropy of the information-bearing degree of freedom decreases by $k \ln 2$. If the environment is at absolute temperature T, thermodynamics requires that at least $kT \ln 2$ heat is released into the environment. In principle the work done to erase a bit could be recovered during a subsequent re-randomization of the bit. In practice it is never recovered.

---

[1] R. Landauer, *IBM J. Res. Develop.* 3, 183 (1961). R. W. Keyes and R. Landauer, IBM J . Res. Develop. 14, 152 (1970), investigate a specific model computer whose energy dissipation per step is about kT.

The meaning and relationship of "random" and "mutual redundancy" is very subtle. One explanation is given in the foundational papers in this volume by Solomonoff (ch. 25), Chaitin (ch. 26), and Kolmogorov (ch. 30).

We begin with the reversible but untidy computer mentioned earlier, which has produced, and failed to erase, a long history of its activity. Now, a tape full of random data cannot be erased except by an irreversible process: however, the history tape is not random—there exists a subtle mutual redundancy between it and the machine that produced it, which may be exploited to erase it reversibly. For example, if at the end of the computation a new stage of computation were begun using the inverse of the original transition function, the machine would begin carrying out the entire computation backward, eventually returning the history tape to its original blank condition.[2] Since the forward computation was deterministic and reversible, the backward stage would be also. Unfortunately, the backward stage would transform the output back into the original input, rendering the overall computation completely useless. Destruction of the desired output can be prevented simply by making an extra copy of it on a separate tape, after the forward stage, but before the backward stage. During this copying operation (which can be done reversibly if the tape used for the copy is initially blank), the recording of the history tape is suspended. The backward stage will then destroy only the original and not the copy. At the end of the computation, the computer will contain the (reconstructed) original input plus the intact copy of the output; all other storage will have been restored to its original blank condition. Even though no history remains, the computation is reversible and deterministic, because each of its stages has been so.

One disadvantage of the reversible machine would appear to be the large amount of temporary storage needed for the history—for a ν-step first stage, ν records of history would have to be written. In a later section it will be argued that by performing a job in many stages rather than just three, the required amount of temporary storage can often be greatly reduced. The final section discusses the possibility of reversible physical computers, capable of dissipating less than kT of energy per step, using examples from the biochemical apparatus of the genetic code.

---

[2]R. W. Keyes [Science 168, 796 (1970)], in summarizing Landauer's argument, commented that a saved history might be used to reverse the steps of the original computation, but that this was not practical in a general purpose computer. He did not explicitly point out that a reversible machine can be made to erase its own history (an ability which, we have argued, allows it to be useful as a general purpose computer).

Logically Reversible Turing Machines

This section formalizes the argument of the preceding section by showing that, given an ordinary Turing machine **S**, one can construct a reversible three-tape Turing machine **R**, which emulates **S** on any standard input, and which leaves behind, at the end of its computation, only that input and the desired output. The **R** machine's computation proceeds by three stages as described above, the third stage serving to dispose of the history produced by the first. The remainder of this section may be skipped by those uninterested in the details of the proof.

The ordinary type of one-tape Turing machine[3] consists of a control unit, a read/write head, and an infinite tape divided into squares. Its behavior is governed by a finite set of transition formulas (commonly called quintuples) of the read-write-shift type. The quintuples have the form

$$AT \rightarrow T'\sigma A', \tag{1}$$

meaning that if the control unit is in state A and the head scans the tape symbol T, the head will first write T' in place of T; then it will shift left one square, right one square, or remain where it is, according to the value of σ ($-$, $+$, or 0, respectively); finally the control unit will revert to state A'. In the usual generalization to n-tape machines, T, T', and σ are all n-tuples within the quintuple.

Each quintuple defines a (partial) one-to-one mapping of the present whole-machine state (i.e., tape contents, head positions, and control state) onto its successor and, as such, is deterministic and reversible. Therefore a Turing machine will be deterministic if and only if its quintuples have non-overlapping domains, and will be reversible if and only if they have non-overlapping ranges. The former is customarily guaranteed by requiring that the portion to the left of the arrow be different for each quintuple. On the other hand, the usual Turing machine is not reversible.

In making a Turing machine reversible, we will need to add transitions that closely resemble the inverses of the transitions it already has. However, because the write and shift operations do not commute, the inverse of a read-write-shift quintuple, though it exists, is of a different type; namely,

The construction of a logically reversible Turing machine was anticipated by Lecerf (1963) in a formal mathematical paper, though the physical implications were not explored.

---

[3]For a good informal exposition of Turing machines see Chapter 6 of M. L. Minsky, *Computation: Finite and Infinite Machines*, Prentice-Hall, Inc., Englewood Cliffs, N. J., 1967.

shift-read-write. In constructing a reversible machine it is necessary to include quintuples of both types, or else to use a formalism in which transitions and their inverses have the same form. Here the latter approach is taken—the reversible machine will use a simpler type of transition formula in which, during a given transition, each tape is subjected to a read-write or to a shift operation but no tape is subjected to both.

Definition: A *quadruple* (for an n-tape Turing machine having one head per tape) is an expression of the form

$$A[t_1, t_2, \cdots, t_n] \to [t_1', t_2', \cdots, t_n']A', \qquad (2)$$

where A and A' are positive integers (denoting internal states of the control unit before and after the transition, respectively); each t_k may be either a positive integer denoting a symbol that must be read on the kth tape or a solidus (/), indicating that the kth tape is not read during the transition; each t_k' is either a positive integer denoting the symbol to be written on the kth tape or a member of the set $(-, 0, +)$ denoting a left, null, or right shift of the kth tape head. For each tape, $k, t_k' \in (-, 0, +)$ if and only if $t_k = /$. Thus the machine writes on a tape if and only if it has just read it, and shifts a tape only if it has not just read it.

Like quintuples, quadruples define mappings of the whole-machine state which are one-to-one. Any read-write-shift quintuple can be split into a read-write and a shift, both expressible as quadruples. For example, the quintuple (1) is equivalent to the pair of quadruples

$$AT \to T'A'' \qquad (3)$$

$$A''[// \cdots_1] \to \sigma A', \qquad (4)$$

where A'' is a new control-unit state different from A and A'. When several quintuples are so split, a different connecting state A'' must be used for each, to avoid introducing indeterminacy.

Quadruples have the following additional important properties, which can be verified by inspection. Let

$$\alpha \equiv A[t_1, \cdots, t_n] \to [t_1', \cdots, t_n']A' \qquad (5)$$

and

$$\beta \equiv A[u_1, \cdots, u_n] \to [u_1', \cdots, u_n']B' \qquad (6)$$

be two n-tape quadruples.

1) α and β are mutually inverse (define inverse mappings of the whole-machine state) if and only if $A = B'$ and $B = A'$ and, for every k, either $(t_k = u_k = /$ and $t_k' = -u_k')$ or $(t_k \neq /$ and $t_k' = u_k$, and $t_k = u_k')$. The inverse of a quadruple, in other words, is obtained by interchanging the initial control state with the final, the read tape symbols with the written, and changing the signs of all the shifts.

2) The domains of α and β overlap if and only if $A = B$ and, for every k, $(t_k = /$ or $u_k = /$ or $t_k = u_k)$. Nonoverlapping of the domains requires a differing initial control state or a differing scanned symbol on some tape read by both quadruples.

3) The ranges of α and β overlap if and only if $A' = B'$ and, for every k, $(t_k = /$ or $u_k = /$ or $t_k' = u_k')$. The property is analogous to the previous one, but depends on the final control state and the written tape symbols.

A *reversible, deterministic n-tape Turing machine* may now be defined as a finite set of n-tape quadruples, no two of which overlap either in domain or range. We now wish to show that such machines can be made to emulate ordinary (irreversible) Turing machines. It is convenient to impose on the machines to be emulated certain format-standardization requirements, which, however, do not significantly limit their computing power.[4]

Definition: An input or output is said to be *standard* when it is on otherwise blank tape and contains no embedded blanks, when the tape head scans the blank square immediately to the left of it, and when it includes only letters belonging to the tape alphabet of the machine scanning it.

---

[4]By the addition of a few extra tape symbols and quintuples, an arbitrary Turing machine can be made to obey these format requirements while computing essentially the same function as it did before. See M. Davis, *Computability and Unsolvability*, McGraw-Hill Book Co., Inc., New York, 1958, pp. 25–26.

Definition: *A standard Turing machine* is a finite set of one-tape quintuples

$$AT \rightarrow T'\sigma A' \tag{1}$$

satisfying the following requirements:

1. Determinism: No two quintuples agree in both A and T.

2. Format: If started in control state A_1 on any standard input, the machine, if it halts, will halt in control state A_f (f being the number of control states), leaving its output in standard format.

3. Special quintuples: The machine includes the following quintuples

$$A_1 b \rightarrow b + A_2 \tag{7}$$

$$A_{f-1} b \rightarrow b0A_f, \tag{8}$$

and control states A_1 and A_f appear in no other quintuple. These two are thus the first and last executed respectively in any terminating computation on a standard input. The letter b represents a blank.

The phrase "machine **M**, given standard input string I, computes standard output string P" will be abbreviated **M**: $I \rightarrow P$. For an n-tape machine this will become **M**: $(I_1; I_2; \cdots; I_n) \rightarrow (P_1; P_2; \cdots; P_n)$, where I_k and P_k are the standard input and the standard output on the kth tape. A blank tape will be abbreviated B.

The main theorem can now be stated:

Theorem: For every standard one-tape Turing machine **S**, there exists a three-tape reversible, deterministic Turing machine **R** such that if I and P are strings on the alphabet of **S**, containing no embedded blanks, then **S** halts on I if and only if **R** halts on $(I; B; B)$, and **S**: $I \rightarrow P$ if and only if **R**: $(I; B; B) \rightarrow (I; B; P)$.

Furthermore, if **S** has f control states, N quintuples and a tape alphabet of z letters, including the blank, **R** will have $2f + 2N + 4$ states, $4N + 2z + 3$ quadruples and tape alphabets of z, $N + 1$, and z letters, respectively. Finally, if in a particular computation **S** requires ν steps and uses s squares of tape, producing an output of length λ, then **R** will require $4\nu + 4\lambda + 5$ steps, and use s, $\nu + 1$, and $\lambda + 2$ squares on its three tapes, respectively. (It will later be argued that where $\nu \gg s$, the total space requirement can be reduced to less than $2\sqrt{\nu s}$.)

Proof: To construct the machine **R** we begin by arranging the N quintuples of **S** in some order with the standard quintuples first and last:

$$1) \qquad A_1 b \to b + A_2$$

$$\vdots$$

$$m) \qquad A_j T \to T' \sigma A_k \qquad\qquad (9)$$

$$\vdots$$

$$N) \qquad A_{f-1} b \to b0 A_f.$$

Each quintuple is now broken into a pair of quadruples as described earlier. The mth quintuple becomes

$$\begin{cases} A_j T \to T' A_m' \\ A_m' / \to \sigma A_k. \end{cases} \qquad (10)$$

The newly added states A_m' are different from the old states and from each other: each A' appears in only one pair of quadruples.

a The labels $1) \cdots m) \cdots N)$ are not part of the machine. They indicate correspondence to the quintuples of the original irreversible machine, which the reversible machine emulates.

b In the second stage the small braces indicate sets of quadruples, with one quadruple for each nonblank tape letter x.

Two extra tapes are then added, one for the history and one for the duplicate copy of the output. The ouput (third) tape is left blank and null-shifted for the present, but the history (second) tape is used to record the index m as each transition pair is executed.

The mth pair of quadruples now has the form

$$\begin{cases} A_j [T/b] \to [T' + b] A_m' \\ A_m' [/b/] \to [\sigma m 0] A_k. \end{cases} \qquad (11)$$

Notice that the history (second) tape is out of phase with the other two—it is written on while they are being shifted and vice versa. This phasing is necessary to assure reversibility—it serves to capture the information that would otherwise be thrown away when the specific

Stage		Quadruples	Contents of tape		
			Working tape	History tape	Output tape
			$\_$INPUT	$\_$	$\_$
	1)	$\begin{cases} A_1[b \mid b] \to [b+b]A_1' \\ A_1'[/ \ b \ /] \to [+ \ 1 \ 0]A_2 \end{cases}$			
Compute[a]	m)	$\begin{cases} A_j[T \mid b] \to [T' + b]A_m' \\ A_m'[/ \ b \ /] \to [\sigma \ m \ 0]A_k \end{cases}$			
	N)	$\begin{cases} A_{f-1}[b \mid b] \to [b+b]A_N' \\ A_N'[/ \ b \ /] \to [0 \ N \ 0]A_f \end{cases}$			
			$\_$OUTPUT	HISTOR$\underline{Y}$	$\_$
Copy output[b]		$A_f[b \ N \ b] \to [b \ N \ b]B_1'$			
		$B_1'[/ / /] \to [+ \ 0 \ +]B_1$			
	$x \neq b:$ {	$B_1[x \ N \ b] \to [x \ N \ x]B_1'$ }			
		$B_1[b \ N \ b] \to [b \ N \ b]B_2'$			
		$B_2'[/ / /] \to [- \ 0 \ -]B_2$			
	$x \neq b:$ {	$B_2[x \ N \ x] \to [x \ N \ x]B_2'$ }			
		$B_2[b \ N \ b] \to [b \ N \ b]C_f$			
			$\_$OUTPUT	HISTOR$\underline{Y}$	$\_$OUTPUT
	N)	$\begin{cases} C_f[/ \ N \ /] \to [0 \ b \ 0]C_N' \\ C_N'[b \mid b] \to [b-b]C_{f-1} \end{cases}$			
Retrace	m)	$\begin{cases} C_k[/ \ m \ /] \to [-\sigma \ b \ 0]C_m' \\ C_m'[T' \mid b] \to [T-b]C_j \end{cases}$			
	1)	$\begin{cases} C_2[/ \ 1 \ /] \to [- \ b \ 0]C_1' \\ C_1'[b \mid b] \to [b-b]C_1 \end{cases}$			
			$\_$INPUT	$\_$	$\_$OUTPUT

Table 1. Structure and operation of a three-tape reversible Turing machine. The computation proceeds in three stages using different sets of quadruples and control states, linkage occurring through states A_f and C_f. On the right the contents of the tapes are shown symbolically at the beginning and end of each stage. The underbar denotes the position of the head. The initial state is A_1 and, for a terminating computation, C_t is the final state.

control state $A_m{}'$ passes to the more general state A_k. The $+$ shifting of the history tape assures that a blank square will always be ready to receive the next m value. If the computation of **S** does not halt, neither will that of **R**, and the machine will continue printing on the history tape indefinitely. On the other hand, if (on a standard input) **S** halts, **R** will eventually execute the Nth pair of quadruples, finding itself in state A_f, with the output in standard format on tape 1. The history head will be scanning the number N which it has just written at the extreme right end of the history on tape 2. Control then passes to the second stage of computation, which copies the output onto tape 3 (see Table 1). The control states for this stage are denoted by B's and are distinct from all the A-type control states. Notice that the copying process can be done reversibly without writing anything more on the history tape. This shows that the generation (or erasure) of a duplicate copy of data requires no throwing away of information.

The third stage undoes the work of the first and consists of the inverses of all first-stage transitions with C's substituted for A's. In the final state C_1, the history tape is again blank and the other tapes contain the reconstructed input and the desired output.

As Table 1 shows, the total number of control states is $2N + 2f + 4$, the number of quadruples $4N + 2z + 3$, and the space and time requirements are as stated at the beginning of the proof. The non-overlapping of the domains and ranges of all the quadruples assures determinism and reversibility of the machine **R**. In the first stage, the upper transitions of each pair do not overlap in their domains because of the postulated determinacy of the original Turing machine **S**, whose quintuples also began $A_j T \rightarrow$. The ranges of the upper quadruples (as well as the domains of the lower) are kept from overlapping by the uniqueness of the states $A_m{}'$. Finally, the ranges of the lower quadruples are saved from overlapping by the unique output m on the history tape. The state A_f causes no trouble, even though it occurs in both stage 1 and stage 2, because by the definition of the machine **S** it does not occur on the left in stage 1; similarly for state C_f. The non-overlapping of the stage 2 quadruples can be verified by inspection, while the determinism and reversibility of stage 3 follow from those of stage 1.

Discussion

The argument developed above is not limited to three-tape Turing machines, but can be applied to any sort of deterministic automaton, finite or infinite, provided it has sufficient temporary storage to record the history. One-tape reversible machines exist, but their frequent shifting between the working and history regions on the tape necessitates as many as ν^2 steps to emulate a ν-step irreversible computation.

Most subsequent work on reversible computing, both quantum and classical, uses a model of computing built from reversible logical gates rather than Turing machines.

In the case that **S** is a universal Turing machine, **R** becomes a machine for executing any computer program reversibly. For such a general-purpose machine it seems highly unlikely that we can avoid having to include the input as part of the final output. However, there are many calculations in which the output uniquely determines the input, and for such a problem one might hope to build a specific reversible computer that would simply map inputs onto outputs, erasing everything else. This is indeed possible, provided we have access to an ordinary Turing machine which, given an output, computes the corresponding input. Let S_1 be the (irreversible) Turing machine that computes the output from the input and S_2 be the one that computes the input from the output. The reversible computation proceeds by seven stages as shown in Table 2, of which the first three employ a reversible form of the S_1 computer and, as in Table 1, serve to map the input onto the input and output. Stage four interchanges input and output. Stages five and seven use a reversible realization of the S_2 computer; stage five has the sole purpose of producing a history of the S_2 computation (i.e., of the input from the output) which, after the extra copy of the input has been erased in stage six, is used in stage seven to destroy itself and the remaining copy of the input, while producing only the desired output.

A particularly important example is factoring of large numbers since prime factorizations is invertible. Peter Shor showed that a quantum computer can indeed perform factorization reversibly, much more efficiently than a classical computer, and without needing to save the number to be factored or the history of the computation.

We shall now return to the more usual situation, in which the input must be saved because it is not a known, computable function of the output. Performing a computation reversibly entails only a modest increase in computing time and machine complexity; the main drawback of reversible computers appears thus to be the large amount of temporary storage they require for the history in any long, compute-bound job (i.e., one whose number of steps, ν, greatly exceeds the number of squares of memory used, s). Fortunately, the temporary storage requirement can be cut down by breaking the job into a sequence of n segments, each one

Stage	Action	Tape 1	Tape 2	Tape 3
		INPUT	–	–
1.	Forward S_1 computation			
		OUTPUT	HISTORY 1	–
2.	Copy output			
		OUTPUT	HISTORY 1	OUTPUT
3.	Retraced S_1 computation			
		INPUT	–	OUTPUT
4.	Interchange output with input			
		OUTPUT	–	INPUT
5.	Forward S_2 computation			
		INPUT	HISTORY 2	INPUT
6.	Reversible erasure of extra copy of input			
		INPUT	HISTORY 2	–
7.	Retraced S_2 computation			
		OUTPUT	–	–

Table 2. Reversible computer for a specific problem in which the input is a known, computable function of the output.

of which would be performed and retraced (and the history tape thereby erased and made ready for reuse) before proceeding to the next. Each segment would leave on the working tape (tape 1) a restart dump that would be used as the input of the next segment; but to preserve reversibility it would also have to leave (on tape 3, say) a copy of its own input, which would in most cases simply be the preceding restart dump. At the end of the computation we would have, in addition to the original input and desired output, all the $n - 1$ intermediate dumps (concatenated, e.g., on tape 3). These intermediate results, which would not have been produced had the job not been segmented, either can be accepted as permanent (but unwanted) output, in exchange for the n-fold reduction of the history tape, or can themselves be reversibly erased by first making an extra copy of the desired final output (putting it, say, on a previously unused part of tape 3), then *reversing the whole n-segment computation*. This reversal is possible because each segment has been performed reversibly. The sequence of restart dumps thus functions as a kind of higher-level history, and it is erased by a higher-level application of the same technique used to erase the primary histories. At the end of the computation, the machine will contain only the original input and the desired nth segment output, and every step of the original irreversible computation will have been performed twice forward and twice backward. For a job with ν steps and a restart dump of size s, the total temporary storage requirement (minimized by choosing

$n = \sqrt{\nu/s}$) is $2\sqrt{\nu s}$ squares, half on the history tape and half on the dump tape. A $(\frac{1}{2}\sqrt{\nu/s})$-fold reduction in space can thus be bought by a twofold increase in time (ignoring the time required to write and read restart dumps) without any unwanted output. By a systematic reversal of progressively larger nested sequences of segments one might hope to reach an absolute minimum temporary storage requirement growing only as $\log \nu$, for sufficiently large ν, with the time increasing perhaps as ν^2, because of the linearly increasing number of times each segment would have to be retraced.

It thus appears that every job of computation can be done in a logically reversible manner, without inordinate increases in machine complexity, number of steps, unwanted output, or temporary storage capacity.

Physical Reversibility

The existence of logically reversible automata suggests that physical computers might be made thermodynamically reversible, and hence capable of dissipating an arbitrarily small amount of energy per step if operated sufficiently slowly. A full treatment of physically reversible computers is beyond the scope of the present paper,[5] but it is worthwhile to give a brief and non-rigorous introduction to how they might work.

An obvious approach to the minimizing the energy dissipation is to design the computer so that it can operate near thermodynamic equilibrium. All moving parts would then, at any instant, have near-thermal velocity, and the desired logical transitions would necessarily be accomplished by spontaneous thermally activated motion over free energy barriers not much higher than kT. At first sight this might seem impossible—in existing electronic computers, for example, even when a component being switched is itself nondissipative (e.g., a magnetic core), the switching process depends on temporarily applying a strong external force to push the component irreversibly over a high free energy barrier. However, nature provides a beautiful example of a thermally activated "computer" in the biochemical apparatus responsible for the

These arguments have inspired much additional work showing that many elementary functions can be calculated using reversible logical gates without the need for many extra resources relative to the comparable resources for a reversible evaluation of the function.

The arguments in this section apply only to computers that are coupled to a thermal environment. Quantum computers are, ideally, decoupled from the environment and do not need to be operated slowly to be physically reversible.

---

[5]The author is currently preparing a paper on physically reversible model computers.

replication, transcription, and translation of the genetic code.[6] Each of these processes involves a long, deterministic sequence of manipulations of coded information, quite analogous to a computation, and yet, so far as is known, each is simply a sequence of coupled, thermally activated chemical reactions. In biochemical systems, enzymes play the essential role of selectively lowering the activation barriers for the desired transitions while leaving high barriers to obstruct all undesired transitions—those which in a computer would correspond to errors. Although the environment in which enzymes normally function is not at chemical equilibrium, many enzyme-catalyzed reactions are freely reversible, and one can find a set of equilibrium reactant concentrations at which both forward and reverse reactions occur equally rapidly, while competing uncatalyzed reactions have negligible rates. It is thus not unreasonable to postulate a thermally activated computer in which, at equilibrium, every logically allowed transition occurs equally often forward and backward, while illogical transitions hardly ever occur. In the following discussion chemical terminology will be used, without implying that thermally activated computers must be chemical systems.

The chemical realization of a logically reversible computation is a chain of reactions, each coupled only to the preceding one and the following one. It is helpful to think of the computing system as comprising a major reactant (analogous to DNA) that encodes the logical state, and minor reactants that react with the major one to change the logical state. Only one molecule of the major reactant is present, but the minor reactants are all present at definite concentrations, which may be manipulated to drive the computation forward or backward. If the minor reactants are in equilibrium, and the major reactant initially corresponds to the initial state of a ν-step computation, the system will begin a random walk through the chain of reactions, and after about ν^2 steps will briefly visit the final state. This does not deserve to be called a computation; it would be legitimate to insist that the system proceed through the chain of reactions with some positive drift velocity and, after sufficient time, have a high probability of being in the final state (if the computation has one). The former

---

[6]For a good introduction to this subject see James D. Watson, *Molecular Biology of the Gene* (2nd ed.), W. A. Benjamin, Inc., New York, 1970.

requirement can be met by adjusting the chemical potentials of the minor reactants so that each forward step dissipates a little energy ε; the latter can be met by dissipating a trivial extra amount during the last step. (If all steps had equal dissipation, $\varepsilon < kT$, the final state occupation probability would be only about ε/kT. By dissipating an extra $kT\ln(3kT/\varepsilon)$ of energy during the last step, this probability is increased to about 95%.) Given a uniform rate Γ for all forward reactions, an energy dissipation $\varepsilon < kT$ per step will buy a drift velocity (i.e., computation speed) of $\Gamma\varepsilon/kT$ steps per second. On the other hand, for $\varepsilon > kT$, backward steps will be effectively suppressed and the computation speed will approach the forward reaction rate Γ. The chemical system is thus a thermodynamically reversible computer of the type we have been seeking.

If we attempt to apply the preceding argument to a logically irreversible computer, we can see that here the reactions form a branching structure, with a main trunk corresponding to the desired computation path, and side branches corresponding to incorrect or "extraneous" reverse computations. The states on the side branches are valid predecessors of the final state but not valid successors of the initial state. A few such extraneous states would pose no problem—a small driving force would still suffice to push the system into the desired final state. Temporary backward excursions onto the side branches would occur, but would not lead to errors, contrary to what one might expect. Since no state of a deterministic computer can have more than one logical successor, the erroneously reversed operations would be corrected as soon as the computation proceeded forward again, and the desired path would be rejoined. The real problem comes from the enormous number of extraneous predecessors; typically they outnumber the states on the intended computation path by hundreds of orders of magnitude. This is because, in irreversibly programmed computations, one can usually proceed backward along an extraneous path for many steps, making further wrong choices along the way, before arriving at a state that has no predecessors.

If a thermally activated computer with many extraneous states is operated close to equilibrium, the system will spend only a minuscule fraction of its time on the desired path of computation, let alone in the desired final state. An acceptable computation rate requires 1) that finite (but time-consuming) backward excursions be largely suppressed, and 2) that infinite ones be completely suppressed. This in turn means (roughly speaking) that the dissipation per step must exceed $kT \ln m$, where m is the mean number of immediate predecessors 1) averaged over states near the intended path, or 2) averaged over all accessible states, whichever is greater. For a typical irreversible computer, which throws away about one bit per logical operation, m is approximately two, and thus $kT \ln 2$ is, as Landauer has argued, an approximate lower bound on the energy dissipation of such machines. For a logically reversible computer, however, m is exactly one by construction.

The biosynthesis and biodegradation of messenger RNA may be viewed as convenient examples of logically reversible and irreversible computation, respectively. Messenger RNA, a linear polymeric informational macromolecule like DNA, carries the genetic information from one or more genes of a DNA molecule, and serves to direct the synthesis of the proteins encoded by those genes. Messenger RNA is synthesized by the enzyme RNA polymerase in the presence of a double-stranded DNA molecule and a supply of RNA monomers (the four nucleotide pyrophosphates ATP, GTP, CTP, and UTP).[7] The enzyme attaches to a specific site on the DNA molecule and moves along, sequentially incorporating the RNA monomers into a single-stranded RNA molecule whose nucleotide sequence exactly matches that of the DNA. The pyrophosphate groups are released into the surrounding solution as free pyrophosphate molecules. The enzyme may thus be compared to a simple tape-copying Turing machine that manufactures its output tape rather than merely writing on it. Tape copying is a logically reversible operation, and RNA polymerase is both thermodynamically and logically reversible. In the cellular environment the reaction is driven in the intended forward direction of RNA synthesis by other reactions, which maintain a low concentration of free pyrophosphate, relative to the concentrations of nucleotide pyrophosphates.[8] A high pyrophosphate concentration would drive the reaction backward, and the enzyme would carry out a sequence-specific degradation of the RNA, comparing each nucleotide with the corresponding DNA nucleotide before splitting it off. This process, which may be termed logically reversible erasure of RNA, does not normally occur in

This informal analysis of the dissipation associated with irreversible computing is essentially correct but the formal theory of the thermodynamics of computing requires the use of stochastic thermodynamics, which was developed beginning in the late 1990s. A review of its application to computing can be found in Wolpert (2019).

RNA synthesis and several other logically reversible biochemical processes are not thermodynamically reversible. They dissipate energy to prevent copying errors using "kinetic proofreading" (Hopfield 1974).

---

[7] Ibid., p. 336 ff.

[8] Ibid., p. 155 ff.

biological systems—instead, RNA is degraded by other enzymes, such as polynucleotide phosphorylase,[9] in a logically irreversible manner (i.e., without checking its sequence against DNA). Polynucleotide phosphorylase catalyzes the reaction of RNA with free phosphate (maintained at high concentration) to form nucleotide phosphate monomers. Like the polymerase reaction, this reaction is thermodynamically reversible; however, because of its logical irreversibility, a fourfold greater phosphate concentration is needed to drive it forward than would be required for a logically reversible phosphorolytic degradation. The extra driving force is necessary to suppress the undesired synthesis of nonsense RNA by random polymerization.

In biological systems, apparently, the speed and flexibility of irreversible erasure outweigh its extra cost in free energy ($kT \ln 4$ per nucleotide in this case). Indeed, throughout the genetic apparatus, energy is dissipated at a rate of roughly 5 to 50 kT per step; while this is ten orders of magnitude lower than in an electronic computer, it is considerably higher than what would theoretically be possible if biochemical systems did not need to run at speeds close to the kinetic maximum—presumably to escape the harmful effects of radiation, uncatalyzed reactions, and competition from other organisms. ⸖

Acknowledgment

I thank Rolf Landauer for raising the question of reversibility of computation in the first place and for stimulating discussions of my models.

REFERENCES

Davis, M. 1958. *Computability and Unsolvability.* 25–26. New York, NY: McGraw-Hill Book Co., Inc.

Keyes, R. W. 1970. "Power Dissipation in Information Processing." *Science* 168 (3933): 796–801.

Keyes, R. W., and R. Landauer. 1970. "Minimal Energy Dissipation in Logic." *IBM Journal of Research and Development* 14 (2): 152–157.

---

[9]Ibid., p. 403.

Landauer, R. 1961. "Irreversibility and Heat Generation in the Computing Process." *IBM Journal of Research and Development* 5 (3): 183–191.

Minsky, M. 1967. *Computation: Finite and Infinite Machines.* Englewood Cliffs, NJ: Prentice-Hall, Inc.

Watson, J. D. 1970. *Molecular Biology of the Gene.* 2nd. New York, NY: W. A. Benjamin, Inc.

BIRTH
October 20, 1943

1947: Claude Lévi-Strauss publishes Les Structures Élémentaires de la Parenté.

1940

1950

1954: The term "social network" is first coined by sociologist John Barnes.

1960

GRANOVETTER 1973
Johns Hopkins University, Baltimore, Maryland

1970

1971: The Stanford Prison Experiment takes place.

1980

1985: Granovetter publishes "Economic Action and Social Structure: The Problem of Embeddedness."

1990

2000: Malcolm Gladwell publishes The Tipping Point. How Little Things Can Make a Difference.

2010

2020

MARK·SANFORD·GRANOVETTER·

[44]

WEAK TIES AND THE ORIGINS OF NETWORK SCIENCE

Duncan J. Watts, University of Pennsylvania

"The Strength of Weak Ties" is—I believe without exaggeration—*the* most cited paper ever published in a sociology journal, and one of the most influential papers ever written by a sociologist, especially among complexity scientists.

M. S. Granovetter, "The Strength of Weak Ties," in *American Journal of Sociology* 78 (6): 1360–1380 (1973).

Reprinted with permission of the American Journal of Sociology.

But what is it about? I suspect, although I cannot prove, that many people who cite the paper have not read it carefully. If they did, they might be surprised to learn that it is almost entirely qualitative in nature. No formulas, and only a handful of statistics, are presented to support the arguments. There are also only two figures: one, comically simple, showing a "forbidden triad" (a missing edge between two nodes, B and C, both of whom have strong ties to a third node A); and a hand-drawn schematic of a "local bridge" (an edge between two nodes, A and B, which, if deleted, would result in a shortest path length d(A,B) greater than two).

Perhaps most surprisingly, the "weak tie" itself—the core analytical concept on which the entire paper hinges—is defined almost in passing. Appealing to "intuition" and deferring "operational measures" to future studies, Mark Granovetter states only that "the strength of a tie is a (probably linear) combination of the amount of time, the emotional intensity, the intimacy (mutual confiding), and the reciprocal services which characterize the tie." Precisely what value of strength differentiates weak from strong is left entirely unaddressed except to note that "most of us can agree, on a rough intuitive basis, whether a given tie is strong, weak, or absent."

Interestingly, the analytical vagueness has an unexpected payoff. By refusing to pin himself down to any precise definition, Granovetter sidesteps any number of "whatabout" objections on his way to a major theoretical claim, which he builds up to via three more specific claims. The first is that "local bridges"—ties that connect nodes that would otherwise be more than two steps apart—are almost always weak. The second is that in shortening the distance between individuals in a network, these bridges increase access to novel information, which in turn can be useful for other purposes such as finding a job or adopting new innovations. The third, and most ambitious, claim is that bridges also serve the function of "knitting together" subgroups in the network, thereby facilitating larger-scale phenomena such as community organization.

Putting these three claims together, the true "strength" of weak ties is that they offer a solution to the "micro–macro problem": How does one go from the micro world of individuals and their interactions with one another to the macro world of groups, firms, cultures, and markets? As Granovetter himself notes, the micro–macro problem is fundamental to sociological theory. Indeed, it is not much of an exaggeration to say that it is the juxtaposition of the micro and the macro that makes social phenomena "social" in the first place. It is also essentially the same problem that arises in other fields, including in complexity science, where it goes by the label emergence. Given its pervasiveness and importance to sociology in particular, social science in general, and by extension to any field in which networks seem relevant, the importance of Granovetter's claims—if true—should be clear.

As it turns out, not everyone was persuaded. Before submitting his manuscript to the *American Journal of Sociology*, where it was eventually published, Granovetter (who was still finishing his PhD at time) submitted it to the *American Sociological Review*. Many years later, he still recalled the sting of the rejection letter he received: one reviewer called it "trivial" and "an addition in an endless series of thrusts beyond unsettled frontiers." The other criticized his "fuzzy conception" and "his failure to seriously ask just what his universe may be."

Part of the problem was that Granovetter had framed the initial draft in terms of "alienation," a term Karl Marx had coined to reflect the loss of self-determination that arose from class membership but which had since been used to describe almost any form of social isolation. The reviewers rightly pointed out that what Granovetter was talking about wasn't alienation as they understood it, but they missed the larger point. When Granovetter submitted it to AJS, he removed the references to alienation and, as he put it, "it obviously fared much better."[1]

Granovetter himself interpreted this experience as highlighting the importance of framing. Others have interpreted it as another example of academic journals' shortsightedness (see also: all those Nobel Prize-winning economics papers that were initially rejected). But reading the reviews more than fifty years on, I had a different impression. Indeed, the reviewers were distracted by the framing around alienation, but they also raised several quite legitimate issues. Granovetter *had* been vague about what he meant by weak ties and—in being so—had papered over many legitimate disagreements about "whether a given tie is strong, weak, or absent." Of equal importance, he had largely glossed over the causal mechanisms by which weak ties supposedly delivered their benefits. As a result, it was impossible to say what "is an optimum point in the balance of weak and strong ties for any given state of social being," as one reviewer put it. Finally, in focusing so much on tie strength, Granovetter had overlooked all the other ways in which ties might differ, and how these differences in "type" might also matter, potentially even more so than strength.

What I found interesting about these comments is, first, that I mostly agreed with them and, second, that the answers to them have now occupied several generations of network scientists. If we are honest with ourselves, we still do not have satisfactory answers, especially to the questions about mechanisms and optimality—if any such thing exists. Where we have made considerable progress is in formalizing the idea of local bridges—now called "shortcuts"—and showing in formal models of the sort to which Granovetter alluded how their presence contracts distances in large networks. We have also made a lot of progress in modeling various dynamical processes, especially diffusion processes, on networks of various types, and even conducting experiments—in both the lab and the field—that show causal effects of network ties on behavior.

---

[1] See https://scatter.wordpress.com/2014/10/13/granovetter-rejection for the original quote and a copy of the letter.

Considering the enormous volume of work that has devoted itself to answering the reviewers' questions,[2] their demand that Granovetter figure it out in one paper does seem preposterous. The true value of this paper—its strength if you will—is that it teed up the questions in such a clear and compelling way. Even today, with all that we have learned since 1973, it holds up remarkably well. It does so in part by elegantly summarizing and synthesizing many of the foundational studies of social network analysis, by Elizabeth Bott, Anatol Rapoport, Stanley Milgram, Paul Lazarsfeld, Elihu Katz, and others. And it does in part by anticipating the areas of conceptual and empirical difficulty, avoiding clumsy leaps to premature conclusions while remaining focused on its ambitious goal. No matter how much you know about network science, reading this paper will offer fresh perspectives and generate new ideas. If nothing else, it will make you fall in love with the problems, or—as in my case—remind you why you fell in love with them in the first place. ☙

REFERENCES

Adamic, L., and E. Adar. 2005. "How to Search a Social Network." *Social Networks* 27 (3): 187–203. https://doi.org/10.1016/j.socnet.2005.01.007.

Dodds, P. S., R. Muhamed, and D. J. Watts. 2003. "An Experimental Study of Search in Global Social Networks." *Science* 301 (5634): 827–829. https://doi.org/10.1126/science.1081058.

Easley, D., and J. Kleinberg. 2012. *Networks, Crowds, and Markets: Reasoning about a Highly Connected World.* Cambridge, UK: Cambridge University Press.

Eckles, D., E. Mossel, M. A. Rahimian, and S. Sen. 2019. *Long Ties Accelerate Noisy Threshold-Based Contagions.* Technical report. ArXiv:1810.03579 [cs.SI]. arXiv. https://doi.org/10.48550/arXiv.1810.03579.

Feld, S. L. 1981. "The Focused Organization of Social Ties." *American Journal of Sociology* 86 (5): 1015–1035. https://doi.org/10.1086/227352.

Jackson, M. O. 2008. *Social and Economic Networks.* Princeton, NJ: Princeton University Press.

Katz, E., and P. F. Lazarsfeld. 1955. *Personal Influence: The Part Played by People in the Flow of Mass Communications.* Glencoe, IL: Free Press.

Newman, M. 2018. *Networks: An Introduction.* Oxford, UK: Oxford University Press.

Newman, M. E. J., S. H. Strogatz, and D. J. Watts. 2001. "Random Graphs with Arbitrary Degree Distributions and Their Applications." *Physical Review E* 64 (2): 026118. https://doi.org/10.1103/PhysRevE.64.026118.

---

[2] See Newman (2018), Jackson (2008), and Easley and Kleinberg (2012) for excellent and comprehensive summaries.

Watts, D. J. 1999. "Networks, Dynamics, and the Small-World Phenomenon." *American Journal of Sociology* 105 (2): 493–527. https://doi.org/10.1086/210318.

Watts, D. J., and S. H. Strogatz. 1998. "Collective Dynamics of 'Small-World' Networks." *Nature* 393:440–442. https://doi.org/10.1038/30918.

THE STRENGTH OF WEAK TIES

Mark S. Granovetter, Johns Hopkins University

Abstract

Analysis of social networks is suggested as a tool for linking micro and macro levels of sociological theory. The procedure is illustrated by elaboration of the macro implications of one aspect of small-scale interaction: the strength of dyadic ties. It is argued that the degree of overlap of two individuals' friendship networks varies directly with the strength of their tie to one another. The impact of this principle on diffusion of influence and information, mobility opportunity, and community organization is explored. Stress is laid on the cohesive power of weak ties. Most network models deal, implicitly, with strong ties, thus confining their applicability to small, well-defined groups. Emphasis on weak ties lends itself to discussion of relations *between* groups and to analysis of segments of social structure not easily defined in terms of primary groups. [1]

This is still true today.

A fundamental weakness of current sociological theory is that it does not relate micro-level interactions to macro-level patterns in any convincing way. Large-scale statistical, as well as qualitative, studies offer a good deal of insight into such macro phenomena as social mobility, community organization, and political structure. At the micro level, a large and increasing body of data and theory offers useful and illuminating ideas about what transpires within the confines of the small group. But how interaction in small groups aggregates to form large-scale patterns eludes us in most cases.

I will argue, in this paper, that the analysis of processes in interpersonal networks provides the most fruitful micro-macro bridge. In one way or another, it is through these networks that small-scale interaction becomes translated into large-scale patterns, and that these, in turn, feed back into small groups.

In a nutshell, the central animating idea of network science. The key phrase is "in one way or another."

Sociometry, the precursor of network analysis, has always been curiously peripheral—invisible, really—in sociological theory. This is

---

[1] This paper originated in discussions with Harrison White, to whom I am indebted for many suggestions and ideas. Earlier drafts were read by Ivan Chase, James Davis, William Michelson, Nancy Lee, Peter Rossi, Charles Tilly, and an anonymous referee; their criticisms resulted in significant improvements.

partly because it has usually been studied and applied only as a branch of social psychology; it is also because of the inherent complexities of precise network analysis. We have had neither the theory nor the measurement and sampling techniques to move sociometry from the usual small-group level to that of larger structures. While a number of stimulating and suggestive studies have recently moved in this direction (Bott 1957; Mayer 1961; Milgram 1967; Boissevain 1968; Mitchell 1969), they do not treat structural issues in much theoretical detail. Studies which do so usually involve a level of technical complexity appropriate to such forbidding sources as the *Bulletin of Mathematical Biophysics*, where the original motivation for the study of networks was that of developing a theory of neural, rather than social, interaction (see the useful review of this literature by Coleman, 1960; also Rapoport, 1963).

This is one area in which we have made considerable progress.

The strategy of the present paper is to choose a rather limited aspect of small-scale interaction—the strength of interpersonal ties—and to show, in some detail, how the use of network analysis can relate this aspect to such varied macro phenomena as diffusion, social mobility, political organization, and social cohesion in general. While the analysis is essentially qualitative, a mathematically inclined reader will recognize the potential for models; mathematical arguments, leads, and references are suggested mostly in footnotes.

Not much happened here for the following twenty-five years, but see the foundational paper by Watts and Strogatz (1998) in Volume 4 for an early attempt at addressing this issue.

The Strength of Ties

Most intuitive notions of the "strength" of an interpersonal tie should be satisfied by the following definition: the strength of a tie is a (probably linear) combination of the amount of time, the emotional intensity, the intimacy (mutual confiding), and the reciprocal services which characterize the tie.[2] Each of these is somewhat independent of the other, though the set is obviously highly intracorrelated. Discussion of operational measures of and weights attaching to each of the four

The precise definition of tie strength is an ongoing debate, and far from settled.

---

[2] Ties discussed in this paper are assumed to be positive and symmetric; a comprehensive theory might require discussion of negative and/or asymmetric ties, but this would add unnecessary complexity to the present, exploratory comments.

To the contrary, in practice it can be very hard to draw these lines in a way that "most people" (or even one person) can agree. This analytical vagueness is very helpful to advance the argument, but it's still remarkable how quickly he sweeps over such a complex issue.

Key claim: that tie strength is related to embeddedness. Subsequent empirical work largely supports this claim: while weak ties can be present both in high and low embeddedness, strong ties are generally associated with high embeddedness.

elements is postponed to future empirical studies.[3] It is sufficient for the present purpose if most of us can agree, on a rough intuitive basis, whether a given tie is strong, weak, or absent.[4]

Consider, now, any two arbitrarily selected individuals—call them A and B—and the set, $S = C, D, E, \ldots$, of all persons with ties to either *or* both of them.[5] The hypothesis which enables us to relate dyadic ties to larger structures is: the stronger the tie between A and B, the larger the proportion of individuals in S to whom they will *both* be tied, that is, connected by a weak or strong tie. This overlap in their friendship circles is predicted to be least when their tie is absent, most when it is strong, and intermediate when it is weak.

The proposed relationship results, first, from the tendency (by definition) of stronger ties to involve larger time commitments. If A–B and A–C ties exist, then the amount of time C spends with B depends (in part) on the amount A spends with B and C, respectively. (If the events "A is with B" and "A is with C" were independent, then the event "C is with A and B" would have probability equal to the product of their probabilities. For example, if A and B are together 60% of the time, and A and C 40%, then C, A, and B would be together 24% of the time. Such independence would be less likely after than before B and C became acquainted.) If C and B have no relationship, common strong ties to A will probably bring them into interaction and generate one. Implicit here is Homans's idea that "the more frequently persons interact with one another, the stronger their sentiments of friendship for one another are apt to be" (1950, p. 133).

---

[3] Some anthropologists suggest "multiplexity," that is, multiple contents in a relationship, as indicating a strong tie (Kapferer 1969, p. 213). While this may be accurate in some circumstances, ties with only one content or with diffuse content may be strong as well (Simmel 1950, pp. 317–29). The present definition would show most multiplex ties to be strong but also allow for other possibilities.

[4] Included in "absent" are both the lack of any relationship and ties without substantial significance, such as a "nodding" relationship between people living on the same street, or the "tie" to the vendor from whom one customarily buys a morning newspaper. That two people "know" each other by name need not move their relation out of this category if their interaction is negligible. In some contexts, however (disasters, for example), such "negligible" ties might usefully be distinguished from the absence of one. This is an ambiguity caused by substitution, for convenience of exposition, of discrete values for an underlying continuous variable.

[5] In Barnes's terminology, the union of their respective primary stars (1969, p. 58).

The hypothesis is made plausible also by empirical evidence that the stronger the tie connecting two individuals, the more similar they are, in various ways (Berscheid and Walster 1969, pp. 69–91; Bramel 1969, pp. 9–16; Brown 1965, pp. 71–90; Laumann 1968; Newcomb 1961, chap. 5; Precker 1952). Thus, if strong ties connect A to B and A to C, both C and B, being similar to A, are probably similar to one another, increasing the likelihood of a friendship once they have met. Applied in reverse, these two factors—time and similarity—indicate why weaker A–B and A–C ties make a C–B tie less likely than strong ones: C and B are less likely to interact and less likely to be compatible if they do.

The theory of cognitive balance, as formulated by Heider (1958) and especially by Newcomb (1961, pp. 4–23), also predicts this result. If strong ties A–B and A–C exist, and if B and C are aware of one another, anything short of a positive tie would introduce a "psychological strain" into the situation since C will want his own feelings to be congruent with those of his good friend, A, and similarly, for B and *his* friend, A. Where the ties are weak, however, such consistency is psychologically less crucial. (On this point see also Homans [1950, p. 255] and Davis [1963, p. 448].)

Some direct evidence for the basic hypothesis exists (Kapferer 1969, p. 229 n.; Laumann and Schuman 1967; Rapoport and Horvath 1961; Rapoport 1963).[6] This evidence is less comprehensive than one might hope. In addition, however, certain inferences from the hypothesis have received empirical support. Description of these inferences will suggest some of the substantive implications of the above argument.

Here Granovetter relates tie strength to another important idea in social network theory: homophily, or the observed tendency of friends to be more similar (on a variety of dimensions) than strangers.

Granovetter relates tie strength to yet another important idea: structural balance.

---

[6] The models and experiments of Rapoport and his associates have been a major stimulus to this paper. In 1954 he commented on the "well-known fact that the likely contacts of two individuals who are closely acquainted tend to be more overlapping than those of two arbitrarily selected individuals" (p. 75). His and Horvath's 1961 hypothesis is even closer to mine: "one would expect the friendship relations, and therefore the overlap bias of the acquaintance circles, to become less tight with increasing numerical rank-order" (p. 290). (I.e., best friend, second-best friend, third-best, etc.) Their development of this hypothesis, however, is quite different, substantively and mathematically, from mine (Rapoport 1953a, 1953b, 1954, 1963; Rapoport and Horvath 1961).

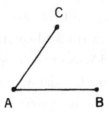

Figure 1. Forbidden triad

Weak Ties in Diffusion Processes

To derive implications for large networks of relations, it is necessary to frame the basic hypothesis more precisely. This can be done by investigating the possible triads consisting of strong, weak, or absent ties among A, B, and any arbitrarily chosen friend of either or both (i.e., some member of the set S, described above). A thorough mathematical model would do this in some detail, suggesting probabilities for various types. This analysis becomes rather involved, however, and it is sufficient for my purpose in this paper to say that the triad which is most *unlikely* to occur, under the hypothesis stated above, is that in which A and B are strongly linked, A has a strong tie to some friend C, but the tie between C and B is absent. This triad is shown in figure 1. To see the consequences of this assertion, I will exaggerate it in what follows by supposing that the triad shown *never* occurs—that is, that the B–C tie is always present (whether weak or strong), given the other two strong ties. Whatever results are inferred from this supposition should tend to occur in the degree that the triad in question tends to be absent.

Some evidence exists for this absence. Analyzing 651 sociograms, Davis (1970, p. 845) found that in 90% of them triads consisting of two mutual choices and one nonchoice occurred less than the expected random number of times. If we assume that mutual choice indicates a strong tie, this is strong evidence in the direction of my argument.[7]

---

[7] This assumption is suggested by one of Davis's models (1970, p. 846) and made explicitly by Mazur (1971). It is not obvious, however. In a free-choice sociometric test or a fixed-choice one with a large number of choices, most strong ties would probably result in mutual choice, but some weak ones might as well. With a small, fixed number of choices, most mutual choices should be strong ties, but some strong ties might show up as asymmetric. For a general discussion of the biases introduced by sociometric procedures, see Holland and Leinhardt (1971a).

Newcomb (1961, pp. 160–65) reports that in triads consisting of dyads expressing mutual "high attraction," the configuration of three strong ties became increasingly frequent as people knew one another longer and better; the frequency of the triad pictured in figure 1 is not analyzed, but it is implied that processes of cognitive balance tended to eliminate it.

The significance of this triad's absence can be shown by using the concept of a "bridge"; this is a line in a network which provides the *only* path between two points (Harary, Norman, and Cartwright 1965, p. 198). Since, in general, each person has a great many contacts, a bridge between A and B provides the only route along which information or influence can flow from any contact of A to any contact of B, and, consequently, from anyone connected *indirectly* to A to anyone connected indirectly to B. Thus, in the study of diffusion, we can expect bridges to assume an important role.

Now, if the stipulated triad is absent, it follows that, except under unlikely conditions, *no strong tie is a bridge.* Consider the strong tie A–B: if A has another strong tie to C, then forbidding the triad of figure 1 implies that a tie exists between C and B, so that the path A–C–B exists between A and B; hence, A–B is not a bridge. A strong tie can be a bridge, therefore, *only if* neither party to it has any *other* strong ties, unlikely in a social network of any size (though possible in a small group). Weak ties suffer no such restriction, though they are certainly not automatically bridges. What is important, rather, is that all bridges are weak ties.

In large networks it probably happens only rarely, in practice, that a specific tie provides the *only* path between two points. The bridging function may nevertheless be served *locally.* In figure 2a, for example, the tie A–B is not strictly a bridge, since one can construct the path A–E–I–B (and others). Yet, A–B *is* the shortest route to B for F, D, and C. This function is clearer in figure 2b. Here, A–B is, for C, D, and others, not only a local bridge to B, but, in most real instances of diffusion, a much more likely and efficient path. Harary et al. point out that "there may be a distance [length of path] beyond which it is not feasible for u to communicate with v because of costs or distortions entailed in each act of transmission. If v does not lie within this critical distance, then he will not receive messages originating with u" (1965, p.

Remarkably, this claim has largely withstood subsequent empirical scrutiny.

Again, a remarkably bold claim that, fifty years later, holds up pretty well.

Key observation that, once again, is largely correct.

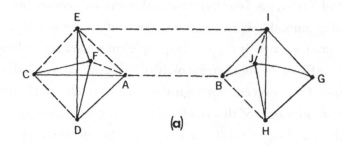

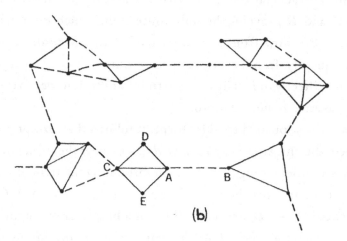

Figure 2. Local bridges. *a*, Degree 3; *b*, Degree 13. ——————— = strong tie; — — — — = weak tie.

Here Granovetter introduces the concept of "local bridge," anticipating Watts and Strogatz's notion of "shortcuts" by twenty-five years.

159). I will refer to a tie as a "local bridge of degree n" if n represents the shortest path between its two points (other than itself), and $n > 2$. In figure 2*a*, A–B is a local bridge of degree 3, in 2*b*, of degree 13. As with bridges in a highway system, a local bridge in a social network will be more significant as a connection between two sectors to the extent that it is the only alternative for many people—that is, as its degree increases. A bridge in the absolute sense is a local one of infinite degree. By the same logic used above, only weak ties may be local bridges.

Suppose, now, that we adopt Davis's suggestion that "in interpersonal flows of most any sort the probability that 'whatever it is' will flow from person i to person j is (a) directly proportional to the number of all-positive (friendship) paths connecting i and j; and (b) inversely proportional to the length of such paths" (1969, p. 549).[8] The significance of weak ties, then, would be that those which are local bridges create more, and shorter, paths. Any given tie may, hypothetically, be removed from a network; the number of paths broken and the changes in average path length resulting between arbitrary pairs of points (with some limitation on length of path considered) can then be computed. The contention here is that removal of the average weak tie would do more "damage" to transmission probabilities than would that of the average strong one.[9]

Intuitively speaking, this means that whatever is to be diffused can reach a larger number of people, and traverse greater social distance (i.e., path length),[10] when passed through weak ties rather than strong. If one tells a rumor to all his close friends, and they do likewise, many will hear the rumor a second and third time, since those linked by strong ties tend to share friends. If the motivation to spread the rumor is dampened a bit on each wave of retelling, then the rumor moving through strong ties is much more likely to be limited to a few cliques than that going via weak ones; bridges will not be crossed.[11]

Since sociologists and anthropologists have carried out many hundreds of diffusion studies—Rogers's 1962 review dealt with 506—one might suppose that the above claims could easily be put to test. But this is not so, for several reasons. To begin with, though most diffusion studies find that personal contacts are crucial, many undertake no sociometric investigation. (Rogers 1962, discusses this point.) When sociometric

Granovetter anticipates the idea of "contraction" of distances in a large network, which was key to Watts and Strogatz's (1998) "small-world" networks and explored more formally by Newman and Watts (2001).

This claim has generated a lot of debate in recent years. On the one hand, proponents of "complex" contagion argue that bridges are ineffective in transmitting contagions that require exposure to more than one "infected" individual. On the other hand, it remains unclear how much contagion is truly complex in this sense. Moreover, recent work (Eckles *et al.* 2019) has argued that bridges regain their utility even for complex contagion once a small amount of noise is introduced into the contagion rule. On balance, therefore, this claim still stands up pretty well.

Starting with Adamic and Adar (2005), empirical diffusion studies have increasingly leveraged network data. Unfortunately, these studies rarely have access to complete network data; thus, it remains difficult to identify which ties are bridges.

---

[8] Though this assumption seems plausible, it is by no means self-evident. Surprisingly little empirical evidence exists to support or refute it.

[9] In a more comprehensive treatment it would be useful to consider to what extent a *set* of weak ties may be considered to have bridging functions. This generalization requires a long, complex discussion and is not attempted here (see Harary et al. 1965, pp. 211–16).

[10] We may define the "social distance" between two individuals in a network as the number of lines in the shortest path from one to another. This is the same as the definition of "distance" between points in graph theory (see Harary et al. 1965, pp. 32–33, 138–41). The exact role of this quantity in diffusion and epidemic theory is discussed by Solomonoff and Rapoport (1951).

[11] If a damping effect is not specified, the whole population would hear the rumor after a sufficiently large number of retellings, since few real networks include totally self-contained cliques. The effective difference between using weak and strong ties, then, is one of people reached per unit of (ordinal) time. This could be called "velocity" of transmission. I am indebted to Scott Feld for this point.

techniques *are* used, they tend to discourage the naming of those weakly tied to the respondent by sharply limiting the numbers of choices allowed. Hence, the proposed importance of weak ties in diffusion is not measured. Even when more sociometric information is collected there is almost never an attempt to directly retrace the exact interpersonal paths traversed by an (idea, rumor, or) innovation. More commonly, the time when each individual adopted the innovation is recorded, as is the number of sociometric choices he received from others in the study. Those receiving many choices are characterized as "central," those with few as "marginal"; this variable is then correlated with time of adoption and inferences made about what paths were probably followed by the innovation.

One point of controversy in diffusion studies can be related to my argument. Some have indicated that early innovators are marginal, that they "underconform to norms to such a degree that they are perceived as highly deviant" (Rogers 1962, p. 197). Others (e.g., Coleman, Katz, and Menzel 1966, on the adoption of a new drug by doctors) find that those named more frequently adopt an innovation substantially earlier. Becker (1970) tries to resolve the question of whether early innovators are "central" or "marginal" by referring to the "perceived risks of adoption of a given innovation." His study of public health innovations shows that when a new program is thought relatively safe and uncontroversial (as with the drug of Coleman et al.), central figures lead in its adoption; otherwise, marginal ones do (p. 273). He explains the difference in terms of a greater desire of "central" figures to protect their professional reputation.

Kerckhoff, Back, and Miller (1965) reach a similar conclusion in a different type of study. A Southern textile plant had been swept by "hysterical contagion": a few, then more and more workers, claiming bites from a mysterious "insect," became nauseous, numb, and weak, leading to a plant shutdown. When the affected workers were asked to name their three best friends, many named one another, but the very *earliest* to be stricken were social isolates, receiving almost no choices. An explanation, compatible with Becker's, is offered: since the symptoms might be thought odd, early "adopters" were likely to be found among the marginal, those less subject to social pressures. Later, "it is increasingly likely that some persons who are socially integrated will be affected. . . . The contagion enters social networks and is disseminated with increasing rapidity" (p.

As with other controversies raised in the paper, this one remains unresolved.

13). This is consistent with Rogers's comment that while the *first* adopters of innovations are marginal, the next group, "early adopters," "are a more integrated part of the local social system than the innovators" (1962, p. 183).

"Central" and "marginal" individuals may well be motivated as claimed; but if the marginal are genuinely so, it is difficult to see how they can ever spread innovations successfully. We may surmise that since the resistance to a risky or deviant activity is greater than to a safe or normal one, a larger number of people will have to be exposed to it and adopt it, in the early stages, before it will spread in a chain reaction. Individuals with many weak ties are, by my arguments, best placed to diffuse such a difficult innovation, since some of those ties will be local bridges.[12] An initially unpopular innovation spread by those with *few* weak ties is more likely to be confined to a few cliques, thus being stillborn and never finding its way into a diffusion study.

That the "marginal" innovators of diffusion studies might actually be rich in *weak* ties is possible, given the usual sociometric technique, but in most cases this is purely speculative. Kerckhoff and Back, however, in a later more detailed analysis of the hysteria incident, indicate that besides asking about one's "three best friends," they also asked with whom workers ate, worked, shared car pools, etc. They report that five of the six workers earliest affected "are social isolates when friendship choices are used as the basis of analysis. Only 1 of the 6 is mentioned as a friend by *anyone* in our sample. This is made even more striking when we note that these 6 women are mentioned with considerable frequency when other bases for choice are used. In fact, they are chosen more frequently on a 'nonfriendship' basis than are the women in any of the other categories" (1968, p. 112).

---

[12] These individuals are what is often called, in organizational analysis, "liaison persons," though their role here is different from the one usually discussed. (Cf. the concept in graph theory of a "cut point"—one which, if removed from a graph, disconnects one part from another [Harary (1965)].) In general, a bridge has one liaison person on each side, but the existence of a liaison person does not imply that of a bridge. For local bridges, the concept of local liaisons could be developed. In a more microscopically oriented discussion I would devote more time to the liaison role. For now, I only point out that, under the present assumptions, one can be a liaison between two network sectors *only* if all his ties into one or both are weak.

Here Granovetter connects
weak ties to Milgram's
provocative "small-world"
experiments in the 1960s.
Subsequent work by Dodds
et al. (2003) found the
relationship was less clear-cut
but generally consistent.

This finding lends credence to the weak-tie argument, but is inconclusive. A somewhat different kind of diffusion study offers more direct support: the "small-world" investigations of Milgram and his associates. The name of these studies stems from the typical comment of newly introduced individuals who discover some common acquaintance; this situation is generalized in an attempt to measure, for arbitrarily chosen pairs of individuals in the United States, how long a path of personal contacts would be needed to connect them. A booklet is given to randomly designated senders who are asked to forward it toward some named target person, via someone the sender knows personally who would be more likely than himself to know the target. The new recipient then advances the booklet similarly; eventually it reaches the target or someone fails to send it on. The proportion of such chains completed has ranged from 12% to 33% in different studies, and the number of links in completed chains has ranged from two to 10, averaging between five and eight (Milgram 1967; Travers and Milgram 1969; Korte and Milgram 1970).

Each time someone forwards a booklet he also sends a postcard to the researchers, indicating, among other things, the relationship between himself and the next receiver. Two of the categories which can be chosen are "friend" and "acquaintance." I will assume that this corresponds to "strong" and "weak" ties. In one of the studies, white senders were asked to forward the booklet to a target who was Negro. In such chains, a crucial point was the *first* sending of the booklet from a white to a Negro. In 50% of the instances where the white described this Negro as an "acquaintance," the chain was ultimately completed; completion rate fell to 26%, however, when the white sent the booklet to a Negro "friend." (My computation, based on unpublished data kindly supplied by Charles Korte. See Korte (1967) and Korte and Milgram (1970).) Thus, weaker interracial ties can be seen to be more effective in bridging social distance.

Another relevant study, by Rapoport and Horvath (1961), is not exactly one of diffusion but is closely related in that it traces out paths along which diffusion *could* take place. They asked each individual in a Michigan junior high school ($N = 851$) to list his eight best friends in order of preference. Then, taking a number of random samples from the group (sample size, an arbitrary number, was nine), they traced out, for each sample, and averaged over all the samples, the total number of people reached by following along the network of first and second choices. That is, the first and second choices of each sample member were tabulated, then the first and second choices of *these* people were added in, etc., counting, at each remove, *only* names not previously chosen, and continuing until no new people were reached. The same procedure was followed using second and third choices, third and fourth, etc., up to seventh and eighth. (The theoretical connection of this tracing procedure to diffusion is discussed by Rapoport 1953a; 1953b, and especially, 1954.)

The smallest total number of people were reached through the networks generated by first and second choices—presumably the strongest ties—and the largest number through seventh and eighth choices. This corresponds to my assertion that more people can be reached through weak ties. A parameter in their mathematical model of the sociogram, designed to measure, approximately, the overlap of acquaintance circles, declined monotonically with increasing rank order of friends.[13]

Once again, Granovetter's intuition is remarkable.

Weak Ties in Egocentric Networks

In this section and the next, I want to discuss the general significance of the above findings and arguments at two levels: first that of individuals, then that of communities. These discussions make no pretense of being comprehensive; they are meant only to illustrate possible applications.

In recent years, a great deal of literature has appeared analyzing the impact on the behavior of individuals of the social networks in which they are imbedded. Some of the studies have emphasized the ways in which behavior is shaped and constrained by one's network (Bott 1957; Mayer 1961; Frankenberg 1965), others the ways in which individuals can manipulate these networks to achieve specific goals (Mayer 1966; Boissevain 1968; Kapferer 1969). Both facets are generally supposed to be affected by the structure of one's network. Bott argued that the crucial variable is that of whether one's friends tend to know one another

---

[13] This parameter, θ, measures such overlap in the following sense: it is zero in a random net—one in which individuals choose others at random—and is one in a net made up entirely of cliques disconnected each from every other. Intermediate values of θ, however, do not have a good intuitive interpretation in terms of individuals, but only with reference to the particular mathematical model defining the parameter; thus it does not correspond precisely to my arguments about friendship overlap.

("close-knit" network) or not ("loose-knit" network). Barnes makes this dichotomy into a continuous variable by counting the number of ties observed in the network formed by ego and his friends and dividing it by the ratio of possible ones; this then corresponds to what is often called network "density" (Barnes 1969; Tilly 1969).[14]

Epstein (1969) points out, however, that different parts of ego's network may have different density. He calls those with whom one "interacts most intensely and most regularly, and who are therefore also likely to come to know one another," the "effective network"; the "remainder constitute the extended network" (pp. 110-11). This is close to saying, in my terms, that one's strong ties form a dense network, one's weak ties a less dense one. I would add that one's weak ties which are not local bridges might as well be counted with the strong ties, to maximize separation of the dense from the less dense network sectors.

One point on which there is no general agreement is whether ego's network should be treated as composed only of those to whom he is tied directly, or should include the contacts of his contacts, and/or others. Analyses stressing encapsulation of an individual by his network tend to take the former position, those stressing manipulation of networks, the latter, since information or favors available through direct contacts may depend on who *their* contacts are. I would argue that by dividing ego's network into that part made up of strong and nonbridging weak ties on the one hand, and that of bridging weak ties on the other, both orientations can be dealt with. Ties in the former part should tend to be to people who not only know one another, but who also have few contacts not tied to ego as well. In the "weak" sector, however, not only will ego's contacts not be tied to one another, but they *will* be tied to individuals not tied to ego. Indirect contacts are thus typically reached through ties in this sector; such ties are then of importance not only in ego's manipulation of networks,

---

More or less identical to how Watts and Strogatz (1998) defined what they called "clustering."

[14]But if the crucial question is really whether ego's *friends* know each other, this measure should probably be computed after ego and his ties have been subtracted from the network; distortions caused by failure to do so will be especially great in small networks. It is important to note, also, that in *non*egocentric networks, there is no simple correspondence between density and any "average" measure of the extent to which the various egos have friends who know one another. "Density," as used here, should not be confused with the "axone density" of Rapoport's models—the number of choices issuing from each node of a network.

but also in that they are the channels through which ideas, influences, or information socially distant from ego may reach him. The fewer indirect contacts one has the more encapsulated he will be in terms of knowledge of the world beyond his own friendship circle; thus, bridging weak ties (and the consequent indirect contacts) are important in both ways.

I will develop this point empirically by citing some results from a labor-market study I have recently completed. Labor economists have long been aware that American blue-collar workers find out about new jobs more through personal contacts than by any other method. (Many studies are reviewed by Parnes 1954, chap. 5.) Recent studies suggest that this is also true for those in professional, technical, and managerial positions (Shapero, Howell, and Tombaugh 1965; Brown 1967; Granovetter 1970). My study of this question laid special emphasis on the nature of the tie between the job changer and the contact person who provided the necessary information.

In a random sample of recent professional, technical, and managerial job changers living in a Boston suburb, I asked those who found a new job through contacts how often they *saw* the contact around the time that he passed on job information to them. I will use this as a measure of tie strength.[15] A natural a priori idea is that those with whom one has strong ties are more motivated to help with job information. Opposed to this greater motivation are the structural arguments I have been making: those to whom we are weakly tied are more likely to move in circles different from our own and will thus have access to information different from that which we receive.

I have used the following categories for frequency of contact: often = at least twice a week; occasionally = more than once a year but less than twice a week; rarely = once a year or less. Of those finding a job through contacts, 16.7% reported that they saw their contact often at the time, 55.6% said occasionally, and 27.8% rarely ($N = 54$).[16] The skew is clearly

Remarkably, this is the first empirical result in the paper: evidence from Granovetter's fieldwork that information regarding jobs came mostly via weak ties.

---

[15] Although this corresponds only to the first of the four dimensions in my definition, supplementary anecdotal evidence from interviews makes it likely that, in this case, the entire definition is satisfied by this measure. At the time of research, it had not occurred to me that tie strength would be a useful variable.

[16] The numbers reported are small because they represent a random subsample of 100, who were interviewed personally, of the total sample of 282. The personal interview allowed more detailed questioning. Comparisons between the mail sample and the

to the weak end of the continuum, suggesting the primacy of structure over motivation.

In many cases, the contact was someone only marginally included in the current network of contacts, such as an old college friend or a former workmate or employer, with whom sporadic contact had been maintained (Granovetter 1970, pp. 76–80). Usually such ties had not even been very strong when first forged. For work-related ties, respondents almost invariably said that they never saw the person in a nonwork context.[17] Chance meetings or mutual friends operated to reactivate such ties. It is remarkable that people receive crucial information from individuals whose very existence they have forgotten.[18]

I also asked respondents where their contacts *got* the information they transmitted. In most cases, I traced the information to its initial source. I had expected that, as in the diffusion of rumors or diseases, long paths would be involved. But in 39.1% of the cases information came directly from the prospective employer, whom the respondent already knew; 45.3% said that there was one intermediary between himself and the employer; 12.5% reported two; and 3.1% more than two ($N = 64$). This suggests that for some important purposes it may be sufficient to discuss, as I have, the egocentric network made up of ego, his contacts, and *their* contacts. Had long information paths been involved, large numbers might have found out about any given job, and no particular tie would have been crucial. Such a model of job-information flow actually does

The only other empirical result: 85 percent of referrals came via paths of length one or two.

Here we see the importance of ethnographic work: a key motivating idea for the paper came from his subjects.

---

interview sample on the large number of items which were put to both show almost no significant differences; this suggests that results observed in the smaller sample on those items put to it alone would not be much different in the mail sample.

[17]Often when I asked respondents whether a friend had told them about their current job, they said, "Not a friend, an acquaintance." It was the frequency of this comment which suggested this section of the paper to me.

[18]Donald Light has suggested to me an alternative reason to expect predominance of weak ties in transfer of job information. He reasons that most of any given person's ties are weak, so that we should expect, on a "random" model, that most ties through which job information flows should be weak. Since baseline data on acquaintance networks are lacking, this objection remains inconclusive. Even if the premise were correct, however, one might still expect that greater motivation of close friends would overcome their being outnumbered. Different assumptions yield different "random" models; it is not clear which one should be accepted as a starting point. One plausible such model would expect information to flow through ties in proportion to the time expended in interaction; this model would predict much more information via strong ties than one which merely counted all ties equally.

correspond to the economists' model of a "perfect" labor market. But those few who did acquire information through paths with more than one intermediary tended to be young and under the threat of unemployment; influence was much less likely to have been exerted by their contact on their behalf. These respondents were, in fact, more similar to those using *formal* intermediaries (agencies, advertisements) than to those hearing through short paths: both of the former are badly placed and dissatisfied in the labor market, and both receive information without influence. Just as reading about a job in the newspaper affords one no recommendation in applying for it, neither does it to have heard about it fifth hand.

The usual dichotomy between "formal" or mass procedures and diffusion through personal contacts may thus be invalid in some cases where, instead, the former may be seen as a limiting case of long diffusion chains. This is especially likely where information of instrumental significance is involved. Such information is most valuable when earmarked for one person.

From the individual's point of view, then, weak ties are an important resource in making possible mobility opportunity. Seen from a more macroscopic vantage, weak ties play a role in effecting social cohesion. When a man changes jobs, he is not only moving from one network of ties to another, but also establishing a link between these. Such a link is often of the same kind which facilitated his own movement. Especially within professional and technical specialties which are well defined and limited in size, this mobility sets up elaborate structures of bridging weak ties between the more coherent clusters that constitute operative networks in particular locations. Information and ideas thus flow more easily through the specialty, giving it some "sense of community," activated at meetings and conventions. Maintenance of weak ties may well be the most important consequence of such meetings.

Interestingly, it was exactly this experience (in my case, moving from Australia to the US for my PhD) that motivated my own thinking about shortcuts many years later.

Weak Ties and Community Organization

These comments about sense of community may remind us that in many cases it is desirable to deal with a unit of analysis larger than a single individual. I would like to develop my argument further by analyzing, in this section, why some communities organize for common goals easily and effectively whereas others seem unable to mobilize resources, even against dire threats. The Italian community of Boston's West End, for example, was unable to even *form* an organization to fight against the "urban renewal" which ultimately destroyed it. This seems especially anomalous in view of Gans's description of West End social structure as cohesive (1962).

Variations in culture and personality are often cited to explain such anomalies. Gans contrasts "lower"-, "working"-, and "middle"-class subcultures, concluding that only the last provides sufficient trust in leaders and practice in working toward common goals to enable formation of an effective organization. Thus, the working-class West End could not resist urban renewal (pp. 229-304). Yet, numerous well-documented cases show that *some* working-class communities have mobilized quite successfully against comparable or lesser threats (Dahl 1961, pp. 192–99; Keyes 1969; Davies 1966, chap. 4).[19] I would suggest, as a sharper analytical tool, examination of the network of ties comprising a community to see whether aspects of its structure might facilitate or block organization.

Imagine, to begin with, a community completely partitioned into cliques, such that each person is tied to every other in his clique and to none outside. Community organization would be severely inhibited. Leafletting, radio announcements, or other methods could insure that everyone was *aware* of some nascent organization; but studies of diffusion and mass communication have shown that people rarely *act* on mass-media information unless it is also transmitted through personal ties (Katz and Lazarsfeld 1955; Rogers 1962); otherwise one has no particular reason to think that an advertised product or an organization should be taken seriously. Enthusiasm for an organization in one clique, then, would not spread to others but would have to develop independently in *each one* to insure success.

Here Granovetter invokes Katz and Lazarsfeld's (1955) foundational "two-step flow" of communication, which introduced the idea of "opinion leaders." Another fascinating connection with other important ideas that were floating around at the time.

The problem of trust is closely related. I would propose that whether a person trusts a given leader depends heavily on whether there exist intermediary personal contacts who can, from their own knowledge, assure him that the leader is trustworthy, and who can, if necessary, intercede with the leader or his lieutenants on his behalf. Trust in leaders is integrally related to the *capacity to predict and affect their behavior*. Leaders, for

---

[19] This point was brought to my attention by Richard Wolfe.

their part, have little motivation to be responsive or even trustworthy toward those to whom they have no direct or indirect connection. Thus, network fragmentation, by reducing drastically the number of paths from any leader to his potential followers, would inhibit trust in such leaders. This inhibition, furthermore, would not be entirely irrational.

Could the West End's social structure really have been of this kind? Note first that while the structure hypothesized is, by definition, extremely fragmented, this is evident only at a macroscopic level—from an "aerial view" of the network. The local phenomenon is cohesion. (Davis 1967, also noted this paradox, in a related context.) An analyst studying such a group by participant observation might never see the extent of fragmentation, especially if the cliques were not earmarked by ethnic, cultural, or other visible differences. In the nature of participant observation, one is likely to get caught up in a fairly restricted circle; a few useful contacts are acquired and relied on for introduction to others. The "problem of entry into West End society was particularly vexing," Gans writes. But eventually, he and his wife "were welcomed by one of our neighbors and became friends with them. As a result they invited us to many of their evening gatherings and introduced us to other neighbors, relatives and friends. . . . As time went on . . . other West Enders . . . introduced me to relatives and friends, although *most* of the social gatherings at which I participated were those of our *first* contact and their circle" (1962, pp. 340–41; emphasis supplied). Thus, his account of cohesive groups is not *inconsistent* with overall fragmentation.

Resembles the "connected caveman" model proposed in Watts (1999).

Now, suppose that all ties in the West End were either strong or absent, and that the triad of figure 1 did not occur. Then, for any ego, all his friends were friends of one another, and all their friends were ego's friends as well. Unless each person was strongly tied to *all* others in the community, network structure did indeed break down into the isolated cliques posited above. (In terms of Davis's mathematical treatment, the overall network was "clusterable," with unique clusters [1967, p. 186].) Since it is unlikely that anyone could sustain more than a few dozen strong ties, this would, in fact, have been the result.

Did strong ties take up enough of the West Enders' social time to make this analysis even approximately applicable? Gans reported that "sociability is a routinized gathering of a relatively unchanging peer group of family members and friends that takes place several times a week." Some "participate in informal cliques and in clubs made up of unrelated people.... In number, and in the amount of time devoted to them, however, these groups are much less important than the family circle" (1962, pp. 74, 80). Moreover, two common sources of weak ties, formal organizations and work settings, did not provide them for the West End; organization membership was almost nil (pp. 104-7) and few worked within the area itself, so that ties formed at work were not relevant to the community (p. 122).

Nevertheless, in a community marked by geographic immobility and lifelong friendships (p. 19) it strains credulity to suppose that each person would not have known a great many others, so that there would have been *some* weak ties. The question is whether such ties were bridges.[20] If *none* were, then the community would be fragmented in exactly the same way as described above, except that the cliques would then contain weak as well as strong ties. (This follows, again, from Davis's analysis of "clusterability," with strong and weak ties called "positive" and absent ones "negative" [1967].) Such a pattern is made plausible by the lack of ways in the West End to *develop* weak ties other than by meeting friends of friends (where "friend" includes relatives)— in which case the new tie is automatically not a bridge. It is suggested, then, that for a community to have many weak ties which bridge, there must be several distinct ways or contexts in which people may form them. The case of Charlestown, a working-class community which successfully organized against the urban renewal plan of the same city (Boston) against which the West End was powerless, is instructive in this respect: unlike the West End, it had a rich organizational life, and most male residents worked within the area (Keyes 1969, chap. 4).

Anticipates Feld's (1981) notion of "social foci" as generators of new ties.

In the absence of actual network data, all this is speculation. The hard information needed to show either that the West End was fragmented or that communities which organized successfully were not, and that both patterns were due to the strategic role of weak ties, is not at hand and would not have been simple to collect.

―――――――――――――――――

[20]See Jane Jacobs's excellent, intuitive, discussion of bridging ties ("hop-skip links") in community organization (1961, chap. 6).

Nor has comparable information been collected in *any* context. But a theoretical framework has, at least, been suggested, with which one could not only carry out analyses post hoc, but also *predict* differential capacity of communities to act toward common goals. A rough principle with which to begin such an investigation might be: the more local bridges (per person?) in a community and the greater their degree, the more cohesive the community and the more capable of acting in concert. Study of the origins and nature (strength and content, for example) of such bridging ties would then offer unusual insight into the social dynamics of the community.

Micro and Macro Network Models

Unlike most models of interpersonal networks, the one presented here is not meant primarily for application to small, face-to-face groups or to groups in confined institutional or organizational settings. Rather, it is meant for linkage of such small-scale levels with one another and with larger, more amorphous ones. This is why emphasis here has been placed more on weak ties than on strong. Weak ties are more likely to link members of *different* small groups than are strong ones, which tend to be concentrated within particular groups.

For this reason, my discussion does not lend itself to elucidation of the internal structure of small groups. This point can be made more clearly by contrasting the model of this paper to one with which it shares many similarities, that of James Davis, Paul Holland, and Samuel Leinhardt (hereafter, the DHL model) (Davis 1970; Davis and Leinhardt 1971; Holland and Leinhardt 1970, 1971a, 1971b; Davis, Holland, and Leinhardt 1971; Leinhardt 1972). The authors, inspired by certain propositions in George Homans's *The Human Group* (1950), argue that "the central proposition in structural sociometry is this: *Interpersonal choices tend to be transitive—if P chooses O and O chooses X, then P is likely to choose X*" (Davis et al. 1971, p. 309). When this is true without exception, a sociogram can be divided into cliques in which every individual chooses every other; any asymmetric choices or nonchoices are *between* such cliques, and asymmetry, if present, runs only in one direction. A partial ordering of cliques may thus be inferred.

Key point that anticipates the focus of modern network science on "large" ($N \gg 1$) networks.

If mutual choice implies equal, and asymmetric choice unequal, status, then this ordering reflects the stratification structure of the group (Holland and Leinhardt 1971b, pp. 107–14).

One immediate difference between this model and mine is that it is cast in terms of "choices" rather than ties. Most sociometric tests ask people whom they *like* best or would *prefer* to do something with, rather than with whom they actually spend time. If transitivity is built more into our cognitive than our social structure, this method might overstate its prevalence. But since the DHL model could recast in terms of ties, this is not a conclusive difference.

More significant is the difference in the application of my argument to transitivity. Let P choose O and O choose X (or equivalently, let X choose O and O choose P): then I assert that transitivity—P choosing X (or X, P)—is most likely when both ties—P–O and O–X—are strong, least likely when both are weak, and of intermediate probability if one is strong and one weak. Transitivity, then, is claimed to be a function of the strength of ties, rather than a general feature of social structure.

The justification of this assertion is, in part, identical with that offered earlier for the triad designated A–B–C. In addition, it is important to point out here that the DHL model was designed for small groups, and with increasing size of the group considered the rationale for transitivity weakens. If P chooses O and O chooses X, P should choose X out of consistency; but if P does not *know* or barely knows X, nonchoice implies no inconsistency. For the logic of transitivity to apply, a group must be small enough so that any person knows enough about every other person to be able to decide whether to "choose" him, and encounters him often enough that he feels the need for such a decision. Including weak ties in my model, then, lessens the expectation of transitivity and permits analysis of intergroup relationships and also of amorphous chunks of social structure which an analyst may ferret out as being of interest, but which are not easily defined in terms of face-to-face groups. Anthropologists have recently referred to such chunks as "quasi-groups" (Mayer 1966; Boissevain 1968).

Since, as I have argued above, weak ties are poorly represented in sociograms, there is little in the DHL empirical studies—which apply statistical tests to sociometric data—to confirm or disconfirm my argument on transitivity. One finding does lend itself to speculation, however. Leinhardt (1972) shows that the sociograms of schoolchildren conform more and more closely to the transitive model as they become older, sixth graders being the oldest tested. He interprets this as reflecting cognitive development—increasing capacity to make use of transitive logic. If my assertion is correct, an alternative possibility would be that children develop stronger ties with increasing age. This is consistent with some theories of child development (see especially Sullivan 1953, chap. 16) and would imply, on my argument, greater transitivity of structure. Some support for this explanation comes from Leinhardt's finding that proportion of choices which were mutual was positively correlated with both grade level and degree of transitivity. In these sociograms, with an average of only about four choices per child, it seems likely that most mutual choices reflected strong ties (see n. 7, above).

Conclusion

The major implication intended by this paper is that the personal experience of individuals is closely bound up with larger-scale aspects of social structure, well beyond the purview or control of particular individuals. Linkage of micro and macro levels is thus no luxury but of central importance to the development of sociological theory. Such linkage generates paradoxes: weak ties, often denounced as generative of alienation (Wirth 1938) are here seen as indispensable to individuals' opportunities and to their integration into communities; strong ties, breeding local cohesion, lead to overall fragmentation. Paradoxes are a welcome antidote to theories which explain everything all too neatly.

The model offered here is a very limited step in the linking of levels; it is a fragment of a theory. Treating only the *strength* of ties ignores, for instance, all the important issues involving their content. What is the relation between strength and degree of specialization of ties, or between strength and hierarchical structure? How can "negative" ties be handled? Should tie strength be developed as a continuous variable? What is the developmental sequence of network structure over time?

This is a profound remark that, regrettably, remains underappreciated fifty years on. The world would be a kinder place if humans were able to internalize the implications of this remark.

As such questions are resolved, others will arise. Demography, coalition structure, and mobility are just a few of the variables which would be of special importance in developing micro-macro linkage with the help of network analysis; how these are related to the present discussion needs specification. My contribution here is mainly, then, exploratory and programmatic, its primary purpose being to generate interest in the proposed program of theory and research. ❧

REFERENCES

Barnes, J. A. 1969. "Networks and Political Process." In *Social Networks in Urban Situations,* edited by J. C. Mitchell. Manchester, UK: Manchester University Press.

Becker, M. 1970. "Sociometric Location and Innovativeness." *American Sociological Review* 35:267–282.

Berscheid, E., and E. Walster. 1969. *Interpersonal Attraction.* Reading, MA: Addison-Wesley.

Boissevain, J. 1968. "The Place of Non-Groups in the Social Sciences." *Man* 3 (4): 542–556.

Bott, E. 1957. *Family and Social Network.* London, UK: Tavistock.

Bramel, D. 1969. "Interpersonal Attraction, Hostility, and Perception." In *Experimental Social Psychology,* edited by J. Mills. New York, NY: Macmillan.

Brown, D. 1967. *The Mobile Professors.* Washington, DC: American Council on Education.

Brown, R. 1965. *Social Psychology.* New York, NY: Free Press.

Coleman, J. S. 1960. "The Mathematical Study of Small Groups." In *Mathematical Thinking in the Measurement of Behavior,* edited by H. Solomon. Glencoe, IL: Free Press.

Coleman, J. S., E. Katz, and H. Menzel. 1966. *Medical Innovation: A Diffusion Study.* Indianapolis, IN: Bobbs-Merrill.

Dahl, R. 1961. *Who Governs?* New Haven, CT: Yale University Press.

Davies, J. C. 1966. *Neighborhood Groups and Urban Renewal.* New York, NY: Columbia University Press.

Davis, J. A. 1963. "Structural Balance, Mechanical Solidarity, Interpersonal Relations." *American Journal of Sociology* 68 (4): 444–462.

———. 1967. "Clustering and Structural Balance in Graphs." *Human Relations* 20 (2): 181–187.

———. 1969. "Social Structures and Cognitive Structures." In *Theories of Cognitive Consistency,* edited by R. P. et al. Abelson. Chicago, IL: Rand McNally.

———. 1970. "Clustering and Hierarchy in Interpersonal Relations." *American Sociological Review* 35 (5): 843–852.

Davis, J. A., P. Holland, and S. Leinhardt. 1971. "Comment." *American Sociological Review* 36:309–311.

Davis, J. A., and S. Leinhardt. 1971. "The Structure of Positive Interpersonal Relations in Small Groups." In *Sociological Theory in Progress*, edited by J. Berger, M. Zelditch, and B. Anderson, vol. 2. Boston, MA: Houghton-Mifflin.

Epstein, A. 1969. "The Nerwork and Urban Social Organization." In *Social Networks in Urban Situations*, edited by J. C. Mitchell. Manchester, UK: Manchester University Press.

Frankenberg, R. 1965. *Communities in Britain.* Baltimore, MD: Penguin.

Gans, H. 1962. *The Urban Villagers.* New York, NY: Free Press.

Granovetter, M. S. 1970. *Changing Jobs: Channels of Mobility Information in a Suburban Community.* Doctoral dissertation, Harvard University.

Harary, F. 1965. "Graph Theory and Group Structure." In *Readings in Mathematical Psychology,* edited by R. Luce, R. Bush, and E. Galanter, vol. 2. New York, NY: Wiley.

Harary, F., R. Norman, and D. Cartwright. 1965. *Structural Models.* New York, NY: Wiley.

Heider, F. 1958. *The Psychology of Interpersonal Relations.* New York, NY: Wiley.

Holland, P., and S. Leinhardt. 1970. "Detecting Structure in Sociometric Data." *American Journal of Sociology* 76 (3): 492–513.

———. 1971a. *Masking: The Structural Implications of Measurement Error in Sociometry.* Mimeographed. Pittsburgh, PA.

———. 1971b. "Transitivity in Structural Models of Small Groups." *Comparative Group Studies* 2 (2): 107–124.

Homans, G. 1950. *The Human Group.* New York, NY: Harcourt, Brace & World.

Jacobs, J. 1961. *The Death and Life of Great American Cities.* New York, NY: Random House.

Kapferer, B. 1969. "Norms and the Manipulation of Relationships in a Work Context." In *Social Networks in Urban Situations,* edited by J. C. Mitchell. Manchester, UK: Manchester University Press.

Katz, E., and P. Lazarsfeld. 1955. *Personal Influence.* New York, NY: Free Press.

Kerckhoff, A., and K. Back. 1968. *The June Bug: A Study of Hysterical Contagion.* New York, NY: Appleton-Century-Crofts.

Kerckhoff, A., K. Back, and N. Miller. 1965. "Sociometric Patterns in Hysterical Contagion." *Sociometry* 28 (1): 2–15.

Keyes, L. C. 1969. *The Rehabilitation Planning Game.* Cambridge, MA: MIT Press.

Korte, C. 1967. *Small-World Study (Los Angeles): Data Analysis.* Mimeographed. Poughkeepsie, NY.

Korte, C., and S. Milgram. 1970. "Acquaintance Networks between Racial Groups." *Journal of Personality and Social Psychology* 15:101–108.

Laumann, E. 1968. *Interlocking and Radial Friendship Networks: A Cross-Sectional Analysis.* Mimeographed. Ann Arbor, MI.

Laumann, E., and H. Schuman. 1967. *Open and Closed Structures.* Paper prepared for the 1967 ASA meeting. Mimeographed.

Leinhardt, S. 1972. "Developmental Change in the Sentiment Structure of Childrens' Groups." *American Sociological Review* 37:202–212.

Mayer, A. 1966. "The Significance of Quasi-Groups in the Study of Complex Societies." In *The Social Anthropology of Complex Societies*, edited by M. Banton. New York, NY: Praeger.

Mayer, P. 1961. *Townsmen or Tribesmen?* Cape Town, SA: Oxford University Press.

Mazur, B. 1971. "Comment." *American Sociological Review* 36:308–309.

Milgram, S. 1967. "The Small-World Problem." *Psychology Today* 1:62–67.

Mitchell, J. C. 1969. *Social Networks in Urban Situations.* Manchester, UK: Manchester University Press.

Newcomb, T. M. 1961. *The Acquaintance Process.* New York, NY: Holt, Rinehart & Winston.

Parnes, H. 1954. *Research on Labor Mobility.* New York, NY: Social Science Research Council.

Precker, J. 1952. "Similarity of Valuings as a Factor in Selection of Peers and Near-Authority Figures." Supplement, *Journal of Abnormal and Social Psychology* 47:406–414.

Rapoport, A. 1953a. "Spread of Information through a Population with Socio-Structural Bias. I. Assumption of Transitivity." *Bulletin of Mathematical Biophysics* 15:523–533.

———. 1953b. "Spread of Information through a Population with Socio-Structural Bias. II. Various Models with Partial Transitivity." *Bulletin of Mathematical Biophysics* 15:535–546.

———. 1954. "Spread of Information through a Population with Socio-Structural Bias. III. Suggested Experimental Procedures." *Bulletin of Mathematical Biophysics* 16:75–81.

———. 1963. "Mathematical Models of Social Interaction." In *Handbook of Mathematical Psychology*, edited by R. Luce, R. Bush, and E. Galanter, vol. 2. New York, NY: Wiley.

Rapoport, A., and W. Horvath. 1961. "A Study of a Large Sociogram." *Behavioral Science* 6:279–291.

Rogers, E. M. 1962. *Diffusion of Innovations.* New York, NY: Free Press.

Shapero, A., R. Howell, and J. Tombaugh. 1965. *The Structure and Dynamics of the Defense R & D Industry.* Menlo Park, CA: Stanford Research Institute.

Simmel, G. 1950. *The Sociology of Georg Simmel.* New York, NY: Free Press.

Solomonoff, R. J., and A. Rapoport. 1951. "Connectivity of Random Nets." *Bulletin of Mathematical Biophysics* 13:107–117.

Sullivan, H. S. 1953. *The Interpersonal Theory of Psychiatry.* New York, NY: Norton.

Tilly, C. 1969. *Community: City: Urbanization.* Mimeographed. Ann Arbor, MI.

Travers, J., and S. Milgram. 1969. "An Experimental Study of the 'Small-World' Problem." *Sociometry* 32:425–443.

Wirth, L. 1938. "Urbanism as a Way of Life." *American Journal of Sociology* 44 (1): 1–24.

BIOGRAPHICAL ODDITIES, VOLUME 2

HERBERT ALEXANDER SIMON | June 15, 1916–Feb. 9, 2001 | *c.f. Chapter 21*

In 1957, Simon predicted that a digital computer would be capable of becoming the World Chess Champion within the next ten years. In fact, his prediction came true forty years later in 1997, when IBM's Deep Blue beat World Chess Champion Garry Kasparov in a match under tournament conditions.

Simon was a great appreciator of Chinese history and culture. He would sign documents with the Chinese version of his name, *Si-ma Huh,* and liked knowing that, as a family name, *Si-ma* was connected to one of China's most famous historians, Si-ma Qian.

STANISŁAW MARCIN ULAM | April 13, 1909–May 13, 1984 | *c.f. Chapter 22*

On August 20, 1939, Ulam, at the insistence of his father, Józef, boarded a boat to America with his teenage brother, Adam, in tow. Two weeks later, Germany invaded Poland. Adam and Stanisław would be the only Ulam family members to survive the Holocaust.

Ulam was invited to join a secret project in 1943 in New Mexico. He borrowed a guide to New Mexico from the library at the University of Wisconsin, Madison and discovered the last four people to have checked it out were colleagues who had all but gone missing. That's how Ulam found out about the Manhattan Project, and it's what prompted him to accept the invitation.

EDWARD NORTON LORENZ | May 23, 1917–April 16, 2008 | *c.f. Chapter 23*

During World War II, Lorenz served as a meteorologist in the Army Air Corps as part of a joint MIT training program. His job, chiefly, was to forecast upper-level winds.

Lorenz was a singer and had excellent pitch. Even as a child, he could always tell when his mother was singing flat.

A lover of boardgames, card games, and jigsaw puzzles, Lorenz was also a talented chess player. While at MIT, Lorenz liked to play chess with faculty colleagues over lunch, including Norbert Wiener (who usually played multiple colleagues at once).

ALAN BELMONT COBHAM | Nov. 4, 1927–June 28, 2011 | *c.f. Chapter 24*

In the 1950s, Cobham served in the US Navy as part of the Operations Evaluation Group, begun as a civilian scientist corps to aid the Navy during World War II after a disastrous convoy escort mission to Canada prompted the Navy to reevaluate their technologies and maritime regulations.

Cobham did graduate work at multiple top-tier universities in the US, but he never completed a doctorate. Despite this, he went on to become a founding chair of Wesleyan University's Department of Mathematics and Computer Science.

RAYMOND J. SOLOMONOFF | July 25, 1926–Dec. 7, 2009 | *c.f. Chapter 25*

Solomonoff and his wife, Grace, once baked banana peels in their oven because a friend told them that consuming, or smoking, the baked peels would give them a psychedelic high. It did not work.

Solomonoff once gave Marvin Minsky what he described as a "hurry" clock; it was a regular clock that ran a little fast, which Solomonoff had labeled "HURRY."

While algorithmic complexity is commonly referred to as Kolmogorov complexity, Andrei Kolmogorov acknowledged that Solomonoff published on the idea first. Because of Chaitin's work in this vein, it is now also known as Solomonoff–Kolmogorov–Chaitin complexity.

Solomonoff loved to paint, designed and built his own house, and sometimes went twenty-four hours without sleeping.

GREGORY JOHN CHAITIN | June 25, 1947– | *c.f. Chapter 26*

Chaitin conceived of algorithmic complexity at age fifteen, independently of Solomonoff and Kolmogorov, as a result of an entrance-exam question for admission to a high school honors science program at Columbia University.

Chaitin's only degree is his high school diploma, and Chaitin believes in the power of individual study over traditional schooling.

In the early 1980s, Chaitin fulfilled a long-time goal of building his own telescope; he even ground the lens himself.

DAVID MALCOLM RAUP | April 24, 1933–July 9, 2015 | *c.f. Chapter 27*

The son of a botanist and an amateur lichen researcher, Raup spent his childhood summers traveling with his family on research trips, often to remote areas in the Canadian wilderness.

Raup, by his own admission, was not a very studious undergraduate. He almost did not graduate from the University of Chicago, where they passed him on the

condition that he would never return. Ironically, he would eventually return as head of the Department of Geophysical Sciences!

In his retirement, Raup enjoyed creating sculptures via multi-axis woodturning. He enjoyed coding and wrote code for a loom belonging to his wife, fiber artist Judy Yamamoto.

JOHN VON NEUMANN | Dec. 28, 1903–Feb. 8, 1957 | *c.f. Chapter 28*

Von Neumann once rode a mule to the bottom of the Grand Canyon and back while wearing a three-piece suit.

Von Neumann had an eidetic memory. He enjoyed memorizing the family trees and histories of European royalty for fun. He was such a quick and incomparable thinker that, on his visits to labs or military bases, it was not uncommon

to find scientists lined up to ask him to quickly correct their work on the spot.

A lover of cars, von Neumann was a reckless and speedy driver. Peers at the Institute of Advanced Studies dubbed a particular crossroads in Princeton "Von Neumann Corner" because he had been involved in so many car accidents there over the years.

BENOIT B. MANDELBROT | Nov. 20, 1924–Oct. 14, 2010 | *c.f. Chapter 29*

The initial "B." in Mandelbrot's name does not stand for anything.

Mandelbrot's family was Jewish and they fled Poland prior to its invasion, spending World War II in occupied France, constantly on the move. As a result, Mandelbrot did not have regular schooling during his childhood and he

was even apprenticed to a groom and to a toolmaker on separate occasions.

In his early childhood, prior to the war, Mandelbrot was educated at home by an uncle who taught him to play chess, read maps, and approach his schooling in an unorthodox fashion.

MOTOO KIMURA | Nov. 13, 1924–Nov. 13, 1994 | *c.f. Chapter 30*

During his childhood, Kimura suffered from an extreme case of food poisoning that required a long period of convalescence at home, during which he taught himself geometry to pass the time.

As an undergraduate, Kimura had hoped to study with geneticist Hitoshi Kihara

at Kyoto Imperial University. Kihara, however, encouraged Kimura to enter the botany program instead because it was part of the science faculty and its students were protected from being called up for military service, which enabled Kimura to avoid being drafted.

ANDREI NIKOLAEVICH KOLMOGOROV | April 25, 1903–Oct. 20, 1987 | *c.f. Chapter 31*

At age five, Kolmogorov published a paper in, and was the editor of, the mathematics section of his school's journal.

A lover of history, Kolmogorov published his first paper as an adult on land-holding practices in the Novgorod Republic in the fifteenth and sixteenth centuries.

In 1936, during the Great Purge, Kolmogorov was one of many scholars who testified against his mentor, Nikolai Luzin, in hearings accusing him of plagiarism, purposefully denying Kolmogorov and others rightful promotions, and of having anti-Soviet sympathies. While Luzin was convicted, he served no time.

MIKHAIL IVANOVICH BUDYKO | Jan. 20, 1920–Dec. 10, 2001 | *c.f. Chapter 32*

Budyko was part of the US–USSR Commission on the Protection of the Environment, which was established in 1972, and he co-chaired a climate working group within the commission.

Because of his predictions regarding the buildup of greenhouse gases in the atmosphere, Budyko was regarded by peers as a kind of climatology prophet, and he was often able to ascertain which

areas of climatology would produce the next innovative theory.

Having studied as a physicist, Budyko came to climatology and energetics by virtue of assignment; during World War II he finished his studies at the Main Geophysical Laboratory and did work in hydrology, related to the war effort, which altered his research focus for life.

STUART ALAN KAUFFMAN | Sept. 28, 1939– | *c.f. Chapter 33*

A physicist by training, Kauffman's interdisciplinary work extended beyond physics, biology, and complexity and into philosophy and, with a stint teaching at Harvard Divinity School, religion.

Kauffman wrote a story for children about the origins of life on Earth called

"The Surprising Story of Patrick S. 'The First', Rupert R., Sly. S., and Gus G. Protocells in Their Very Early Years" and narrated an animated segment featuring his protocell characters for *Science Animated* in 2020.

ROGER CHARLES CONANT | April 12, 1938–June 24, 2019 | *c.f. Chapter 34*

A singer and a lover of music, Conant was a member of the Purdue University glee club as an undergraduate, and in his retirement sang bass in a local choir. For eighteen years he hosted a monthly folk-singing event for local singers and musicians to get together and play.

Conant earned his PhD at the University of Illinois, and he never left. He spent his entire career at his alma mater and enjoyed lecturing and teaching as much as researching.

WILLIAM ROSS ASHBY | Sept. 6, 1903–Nov. 15, 1972 | *c.f. Chapter 34*

A lover of Shakespeare, Ashby kept a journal all of his adult life, and on the first page he introduced his informal memoir with "passing through nature . . ." a reference to *Hamlet*, Act I, scene II.

When Ashby was first offered a chair in the Department of Electrical Engineering at the University of Illinois, he and his wife, Rosebud, had spent the year painstakingly rehabbing an old schoolhouse in Gloucestershire, England, to live in. They spent the next decade living primarily in America until Ashby's retirement, when they could finally, permanently, stay in their country home.

Ashby was a talented woodworker, played the clarinet, painted watercolors, did photography, and even made inventions to help him out around his workshop, like makeshift zoom-lenses attached to glasses frames.

GEORGE ROBERT PRICE | Oct. 16, 1922–Jan. 6, 1975 | *c.f. Chapter 35*

In 1966, Price underwent surgery to for thyroid cancer, and the operation caused partial paralysis to his left shoulder and the left side of his face.

Price got his job at University College London after showing up at Galveston Lab one day and arguing his findings to all who would listen on what would become known as the Price equation. He was allegedly offered a job on the spot.

Price's work on altruism had a great effect on his life. Following a religious experience in 1970, he would give the actual clothes off his back to people in need, and he invited unsheltered people to stay in his home. Shortly before his suicide, he realized that this approach was only harming him, and he had made strides to begin working again.

OTTO EBERHARD RÖSSLER | May 20, 1940– | *c.f. Chapter 36*

Rössler is an honorary editor of the journal *Chaos, Solitons & Fractals*.

He has spent the majority of his academic career as a professor of chemistry at the University of Tübingen, despite long-standing disputes between Rössler, his wife, Reimara, and the university.

Rössler believes that when CERN's Large Hadron Collider was switched on, it caused catastrophic miniature black holes to develop that will eventually destroy the planet. His convictions were so strong that he was part of a lawsuit attempting to halt the experiment.

THOMAS CROMBIE SCHELLING | April 14, 1921–Dec. 13, 2016 | *c.f. Chapter 37*

Schelling consulted for the Stanley Kubrick film *Dr. Strangelove*, though he felt the film didn't make sense from a game theorist's standpoint; the "doomsday device" could not serve as a deterrent when the US had no idea it existed, and the use of B52 bombers for a preemptive strike would have been illogical in 1964, with ballistic missile technology already available.

During his tenure at the University of Maryland, he hosted movie nights on campus featuring the film.

Schelling's favorite sandwich was peanut butter and jelly on raisin bread.

He is the first known source of the phrase "collateral damage," used in his 1961 paper "Dispersal, Deterrence, and Damage."

EZRA B.W. ZUBROW | Jan. 14, 1945– | *c.f. Chapter 38*

In the late 1960s, as part of a survey project he had requested from the Air Force, Zubrow was given a tour of an air base in the Southwest where the U2 airplanes that had been used to gather photographs for Zubrow's research were housed. While on the tour, Zubrow accidentally caught a glimpse of plans for those same spy planes to make surveillance trips over Cuba, Vietnam, China, and areas in the Eastern Bloc.

Zubrow has achieved the highest-level professorship possible at State University of New York, Buffalo—Distinguished Service Professor—for a lifetime of climate-change activism and grassroots union organizing.

A cellist, Zubrow has played in the cello sections of several symphony orchestras in the Buffalo, New York area.

PHILIP WARREN ANDERSON | Dec. 13, 1923–March 29, 2020 | *c.f. Chapter 39*

Fellow SFI founder and Nobel laureate in physics Murray Gell-Mann often joked to Anderson that solid–state physics should have been renamed "squalid"-state physics.

Anderson had a lifelong passion for

Japanese culture and he was a first-Dan master of the Japanese strategy game Go. In 2007, the Japanese Go Association gave Anderson a lifetime achievement award for his love of, and dedication to, the game.

RICHARD MANNING KARP | Jan. 3, 1935– | *c.f. Chapter 40*

When he was in the tenth grade, Karp would pretend to be sick so that he could stay home and do geometry in his room instead.

As an undergraduate, Karp once took a mathematics course with a future Nobel laureate and a future Fields Medal winner. They were both so impressive that Karp felt he could not possibly hope to compete in the same field as the pair of them, and so he decided to turn his attention to the new field of computer science, and the rest is history.

Karp's father was a junior-high mathematics teacher, and Karp always admired his ability to draw a perfect circle, freehand.

When Eugene Lawler was arrested in 1969 for taking part in a Vietnam War protest, Karp bailed him out of jail.

ROBERT MCCREDIE MAY | Jan. 8, 1936–April 28, 2020 | *c.f. Chapter 41*

When May was made a life peer of the United Kingdom, he asked for the title of Baron May of Woollahra, Woollahra being a suburb of his hometown of Sydney. This was rejected, so he went with Oxford instead.

A major proponent of climate change action in the United Kingdom, May served as Chief Scientific Adviser to HM Government under Prime Ministers John Major and Tony Blair.

May was an avid hiker and runner and he organized group hiking trips with friends in Wales and England, and longer trips across Europe.

HEINZ VON FOERSTER | Nov. 13, 1911–Oct. 2, 2002 | *c.f. Chapter 42*

After World War II, upon returning to Vienna with his family, von Foerster worked two jobs to support them, one as a factory worker on an assembly line for a telephone company, and the other at the radio station in the American sector of Vienna, interviewing guests for arts and sciences programs.

At the sixth Macy Conference meeting, von Foerster was the youngest attendee, and it was he who suggested the subject of their meeting be dubbed "cybernetics" in honor of Norbert Wiener's book of the same title.

Von Foerster met Humberto Maturana at a conference when they both snuck out of the introductory session at the same time, noticed each other across the hall, and decided to spend the day visiting museums together.

CHARLES HENRY BENNETT | April 1, 1943– | *c.f. Chapter 43*

In 1960, when Bennett was seventeen, he competed in what was then called the Westinghouse Science Talent Search, a prestigious research competition for gifted high school students in math and science. Bennett came in fourth place, and he attended the awards banquet in a plaid suit and bow tie.

According to Bennett, it was Rolf Landauer who initially recruited him to join IBM.

A talented photographer, Bennett enjoys taking group photographs of fellow attendees at the conferences he attends.

MARK SANFORD GRANOVETTER | Oct. 20, 1943– | *c.f. Chapter 44*

A proponent of good technical writing in the social sciences, Granovetter is an admitted devotee of Strunk and White's classic *Elements of Style.*

For his PhD, Granovetter designed his own study, selected 100 candidates to interview, and wrote them all letters to that effect. How did he go about interviewing them? He showed up on their doorsteps, usually in the evening and after dark, and miraculously, none of them ever turned him away!

Despite more than 72,000 citations to date and a profound impact on the social sciences, this paper was initially rejected, and rather harshly. Granovetter still shows his rejection letter to his graduate students to encourage them never to give up.

EDITOR

DAVID C. KRAKAUER is the President and William H. Miller Professor of Complex Systems at the Santa Fe Institute. His research explores the evolution of intelligence and stupidity on Earth. This includes studying the evolution of genetic, neural, linguistic, social, and cultural mechanisms supporting memory and information processing, and exploring their shared properties. He served as the founding director of the Wisconsin Institutes for Discovery, codirector of the Center for Complexity and Collective Computation, and professor of mathematical genetics, all at the University of Wisconsin, Madison. He has been a visiting fellow at the Genomics Frontiers Institute at the University of Pennsylvania, a Sage Fellow at the Sage Center for the Study of the Mind at the University of California, Santa Barbara, a longterm fellow of the Institute for Advanced Study, and visiting professor of evolution at Princeton University. In 2012, he was included in the *Wired Magazine* Smart List: Fifty People Who Will Change the World. In 2016, he was included in *Entrepreneur Magazine*'s list of visionary leaders advancing global research and business.

Krakauer was previously chair of faculty and a resident professor and external professor at the Santa Fe Institute. A graduate of the University of London where he earned degrees in biology and computer science, he received his D.Phil. in evolutionary theory from Oxford University in 1995 and continued there as a postdoctoral fellow.

THE SANTA FE INSTITUTE PRESS

The SFI Press endeavors to communicate the best of complexity science and to capture a sense of the diversity, range, breadth, excitement, and ambition of research at the Santa Fe Institute; To provide a distillation of work at the frontiers of complex-systems science across a range of influential and nascent topics;

To change the way we think.

SEMINAR SERIES
New findings emerging from the Institute's ongoing working groups and research projects, for an audience of interdisciplinary scholars and practitioners.

ARCHIVE SERIES
Fresh editions of classic texts from the complexity canon, spanning SFI's four decades of advancing the field.

COMPASS SERIES
Provocative, exploratory volumes aiming to build complexity literacy in the humanities, industry, and the curious public.

SCHOLARS SERIES
Texts featuring foundational ideas, systems of knowledge, emerging methodologies, and areas of application in the complex-systems science world.

— ALSO FROM SFI PRESS —

Foundational Papers in Complexity Science, Volumes 1, 3 & 4
David C. Krakauer, ed.

The Complex World: An Introduction to the Foundations of Complexity Science
David C. Krakauer

For additional titles, inquiries, or news about the Press, visit us at
WWW.SFIPRESS.ORG.

EDITORIAL

David C. Krakauer
Publisher/Editor-in-Chief

Sienna Latham
Managing Editor

Zato Hebbert
Production Assistant

Laura Egley Taylor
Advisor/Designer

Ellis Wylie
Post-Production
Coordinator

Additional editorial support provided by Katie Mast, Bronwynn Woodsworth, and Shafaq Zia.

ABOUT THE SANTA FE INSTITUTE

The Santa Fe Institute is the world headquarters for complexity science, operated as an independent, nonprofit research and education center located in Santa Fe, New Mexico. Our researchers endeavor to understand and unify the underlying, shared patterns in complex physical, biological, social, cultural, technological, and even possible astrobiological worlds. Our global research network of scholars spans borders, departments, and disciplines, bringing together curious minds steeped in rigorous logical, mathematical, and computational reasoning. As we reveal the unseen mechanisms and processes that shape these evolving worlds, we seek to use this understanding to promote the well-being of humankind and of life on Earth.

COLOPHON

The body copy for this book was set in EB Garamond, a typeface designed by Georg Duffner after the Ebenolff-Berner type specimen of 1592. Headings are in Kurier, created by Janusz M. Nowacki, based on typefaces by the Polish typographer Małgorzata Budyta, and Cochin, a typeface produced in 1912 by Georges Peignot and based on the copperplate engravings of French 17th century artist Nicolas Cochin, for whom the typeface is named. For footnotes and captions, we have used CMU Bright, a sans serif variant of Computer Modern, created by Donald Knuth for use in TeX, the typesetting program he developed in 1978.

The SFI Press complexity glyphs used throughout this book were designed by Brian Crandall Williams.

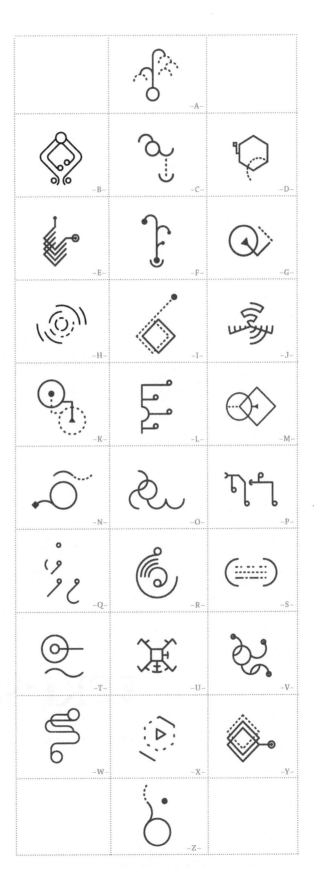

SANTA FE INSTITUTE
COMPLEXITY
GLYPHS

ZERO

ONE

TWO

THREE

FOUR

FIVE

SIX

SEVEN

EIGHT

NINE

-A-

-B- -C- -D-

-E- -F- -G-

-H- -I- -J-

-K- -L- -M-

-N- -O- -P-

-Q- -R- -S-

-T- -U- -V-

-W- -X- -Y-

-Z-

SCHOLARS SERIES

Made in the USA
Monee, IL
26 December 2024

75374947R00380